WORLD HEALTH ORGANIZATION
MONOGRAPH SERIES
No. 59

FLUORIDES AND HUMAN HEALTH

FLUORIDES

AND

HUMAN HEALTH

CONTRIBUTORS

P. ADLER – W. D. ARMSTRONG – Muriel E. BELL
B. R. BHUSSRY – W. BÜTTNER – H.-D. CREMER
V. DEMOLE – Y. ERICSSON – I. GEDALIA – H. C.
HODGE – G. N. JENKINS – S. S. JOLLY – E. J. LARGENT
N. C. LEONE – T. G. LUDWIG – A. E. MARTIN
G. MINOGUCHI – J. C. MUHLER – E. R. SCHLESINGER
A. H. SIDDIQUI – L. SINGER – A. SINGH – F. A. SMITH
G. K. STOOKEY – D. R. TAVES – P. VENKATESWARLU
J. C. WEATHERELL – S. M. WEIDMANN – I. ZIPKIN

Prepared in consultation with ninety-three dental and
medical specialists in various countries

WORLD HEALTH ORGANIZATION

GENEVA

1970

CONTENTS

REVIEWERS

Dr M. G. Allmark, Assistant Director-General, Drugs, Food and Drug Directorate, Department of National Health and Welfare, Ottawa, Ontario, Canada

Mr W. C. Allwright, Dental Surgeon, Dublin, Ireland

Dr K. Anastassov, Scientific Research Institute of Stomatology, Sofia, Bulgaria

Professor A. L. Bakry, *formerly* Vice-Dean, Dental Faculty, University of Cairo, Egypt, UAR

Professor L. J. Baume, Institute of Dental Medicine, University of Geneva, Switzerland

Dr D. S. Bernstein, Department of Nutrition, School of Public Health, Harvard University, Boston, Mass., USA

Dr N. N. Bery, Honorary Dental Adviser, Ministry of Health and Family Planning, Government of India, New Delhi, India

Professor C. Biörck, Serafimerlasarettet, Stockholm, Sweden

Dr P. E. Blackerby, jr, President, W. K. Kellogg Foundation, Battle Creek, Mich., USA

Dr J. Bojanini N., Chief, Department of Dental Health, Office of Public Health, Medellín, Colombia

Mr E. Brebner, Assistant Director, Division of Dental Health, Department of Health, Wellington, New Zealand

Professor F. A. Carranza, Faculty of Dentistry, University of Buenos Aires, Argentina

Professor Andrée Chaput, Faculty of Medicine of Paris, France

Dr R. Cova Rey, School of Public Health, Faculty of Medicine, Central University of Venezuela, Caracas, Venezuela

Professor W. J. Darby, Director, Division of Nutrition, Department of Medicine and Biochemistry, Vanderbilt University, Nashville, Tenn., USA

Professor A. I. Darling, Dental School, University of Bristol, England

Professor G. N. Davies, Dean, Dental College, University of Queensland, Brisbane, Australia

Professor M. Dechaume, Clinic of Stomatology, Faculty of Medicine of Paris, France

Professor J. Delibéros, Dental School of Paris, France

Dr L. Djoković, Faculty of Stomatology, University of Belgrade, Yugoslavia

Dr A. I. Dojnikov, Deputy Director, Moscow Medical Institute of Stomatology, Moscow, USSR

Professor R. D. Emslie, Department of Preventive Dentistry, Guy's Hospital, London, England

Dr K. Evang, Director-General, Health Services of Norway, Oslo, Norway

Professor G. Fanconi, *formerly* Director, Clinic of Paediatrics, University of Zurich, Switzerland

Dr F. A. L. Fernando, Surgeon in Charge, Dental Institute, Colombo, Ceylon

Professor E. Fernex, Institute of Dental Medicine, University of Geneva, Switzerland

Dr N. H. Fisek, Dean, School of Graduate Studies, Hacettepe University, Ankara, Turkey

Dr S. Forssman, National Institute of Occupational Health, Stockholm, Sweden

Professor J. W. Fox-Taylor, Department of Dental Surgery, University of Lagos Medical School, Lagos, Nigeria

Dr P. da Silva Freire, Chief, Dental Branch, Special Service of Public Health, Rio de Janeiro, Brazil

Dr D. J. Galagan, Dean, College of Dentistry, University of Iowa, Iowa City, USA

Dr J. W. Galloway, Chief Dental Officer, Scottish Home and Health Department, Edinburgh, Scotland

Dr R. M. Grainger, Clinic Director, Faculty of Dentistry, University of British Columbia, Vancouver, B. C., Canada

Dr G. Grappin, Faculty of Medicine and Pharmacy, University of Dakar, Senegal

Dr C. Gysel, President, Association des Licenciés et Dentistes universitaires de Belgique, Antwerp, Belgium

Professor J. H. de Haas, Netherlands Institute for Preventive Medicine, Leiden, Netherlands

Dr S. Halter, Director-General, Administration of Public Health, Ministry of Health, Brussels, Belgium

Dr R. Harris, Director, Institute of Dental Research, United Dental Hospital of Sydney, Australia

Professor A.-J. Held, Director, Institute of Dental Medicine, University of Geneva, Switzerland

Professor Emeritus C. Heymans, Institute of Pharmacology and Therapeutics, State University, Ghent, Belgium

Professor A. M. Horsnell, Department of Dental Science, University of Adelaide, Australia

Dr D. Hunter, Department of Medicine, Guy's Hospital, London, England

Dr A. Karim bin Nawab Din, Deputy Director of Medical Services (Dental), Ministry of Health, Kuala Lumpur, Malaysia

Dr D. P. Kennedy, Director-General of Health, Department of Health, Wellington, New Zealand

Dr W. Kessler, Marburg an der Lahn, Federal Republic of Germany

Dr J. W. Knutson, Professor of Preventive Dentistry and Public Health, School of Dentistry, University of California, Los Angeles, Calif., USA

Professor J. Kostlán, Director, Institute of Dental Research, Prague, Czechoslovakia

Dr S. MacNeill, Dental Adviser, Department of Health, Dublin, Ireland

Professor P. Macúch, Vice-Minister of Health, Prague, Czechoslovakia

Professor W. R. Mann, Dean, School of Dentistry, University of Michigan, Ann Arbor, Mich., USA

Professor N. D. Martin, Department of Preventive Dentistry, Faculty of Dentistry, University of Sydney, Australia

Professor J. N. Morris, Medical Research Council Social Medicine Research Unit, London School of Hygiene and Tropical Medicine, London, England

Dr R. E. Moyers, Professor of Orthodontics, School of Dentistry, University of Michigan, Ann Arbor, Mich., USA

Professor H. R. Mühlemann, Institute of Dentistry, University of Zurich, Switzerland

Dr T. Ockerse, Pretoria, South Africa

Professor K. Okamoto, Dean, School of Dentistry, Aichi-Gakuin University, Nagoya, Japan

Dr E. Onishi, Director, Department of Dental Research, National Institute of Health, Tokyo, Japan

Dr O. K. Osvald, Head, Dental Division, National Board of Health, Stockholm, Sweden

Miss Jean Oswald, Dental Officer, Ministry of Health, London, England

Dr J. Page, Lecturer, Child Dental Health, London Hospital Medical College Dental School, London, England

Dr V. N. Patwardhan, Assistant Director, Nutrition and Biochemistry, US Naval Medical Research Unit No. 3, Cairo, Egypt, UAR

Professor P. O. Pedersen, Dean, Royal Dental College, Copenhagen, Denmark

Dr S. Peterson, Dean, College of Dentistry, University of Tennessee, Memphis, Tenn., USA

Dr Vera Poncová, Chief, Division of Stomatology, Ministry of Health, Prague, Czechoslovakia

Professor A. Reis Viegas, Faculty of Hygiene and Public Health, University of São Paulo, Brazil

Dr J. D. Rodriguez, Dean, College of Dentistry, University of the Philippines, Manila, Philippines

Professor A. L. Russell, Dental Public Health, School of Public Health, University of Michigan, Ann Arbor, Mich., USA

Professor A. I. Rybakov, Director, Central Institute for Research on Stomatology, Ministry of Health of the USSR, Moscow, USSR

Dr A. Scheinin, Institute of Dentistry, University of Turku, Finland

Dr C. L. Sebelius, Chief, Division of Dental Health, Department of Public Health, Springfield, Ill., USA

Professor A. Seppilli, Director, Institute of Hygiene, University of Perugia, Italy

Professor H. R. Shah, Dean and Principal, de Montmorency College of Dentistry, University of Punjab, Lahore, Pakistan

Professor J. Shaw, School of Dental Medicine, Harvard University, Boston, Mass., USA

Dr K. L. Shourie, Dean, Government Dental College and Hospital, Bombay, India

Dr M. Rocha E Silva, Department of Pharmacology, Faculty of Medicine of Ribeirão Prêto, São Paulo, Brazil

Professor T. T. Školjar, Department of Therapeutic Stomatology, Kalinin State Medical Institute, USSR

Professor G. L. Slack, Dean of Dental Studies, London Hospital Medical College, University of London, England

Dr D. H. Small, Dental Specialist, Hong Kong Government Dental Service, Dental Headquarters, Wan Chai Polyclinic, Hong Kong

Professor R. G. S. Soemantri, Padjadjaran State University, Bandung, Indonesia

Professor F. J. Stare, Chairman, Department of Nutrition, School of Public Health, Harvard University, Boston, Mass., USA

Dr J. Stork, Secretary-Treasurer, Netherlands Dental Association, Utrecht, Netherlands

Dr C. J. Sundram, Principal, Dental Training School, Penang, Malaya, Malaysia

Professor J. Švejda, Director, Second Stomatological Clinic of the Medical Faculty, J. E. Purkyně University, Brno, Czechoslovakia

Professor T. Tandikul, Dean, School of Dentistry, University of Medical Sciences, Bangkok, Thailand

Professor R. Truhaut, Director, Toxicological Research Centre, Faculty of Pharmacology, University of Paris, France

Professor K. Ueda, Tokyo Dental College. Japan

Professor H. Urzua, Professor of Public Health Administration, University of Chile, Santiago, Chile

Professor B. Vahlquist, Department of Paediatrics, University Hospital, Uppsala, Sweden

Professor J. Waerhaug, Institute of Odontology, Oslo, Norway

Sir John P. Walsh, Dean, Faculty of Dentistry, University of Otago Dental School, Dunedin, New Zealand

Professor C. H. M. Williams, Professor of Periodontics, University of Toronto, Canada

Dr Wong Mook Qui, Assistant Director of Medical Services (Dental), Ministry of Health, Singapore

Dr Yim Khai Sun, Senior Dental Officer, Dental Clinic, Kuching, Sarawak, Malaysia

PREFACE

Since the late 1940's, the use of fluorides for the prevention of dental caries—especially the adjustment of the fluoride content of drinking water—has been a subject of considerable controversy. Public health authorities that have contemplated adopting measures of this kind have encountered strong opposition and have often had to undertake extensive reviews of the literature in order to reach a decision.

The World Health Organization has been concerned for many years about this situation and, in 1962, it received a specific request from the International Dental Federation "to convene a meeting with a view toward compiling an authoritative and up-to-date report on the metabolism of fluorine". This request was considered by the Organization but it was felt that such a task could not be properly accomplished at a meeting, in view of the vast amount of scientific material now available on fluorides and the difficulty of synthesizing it properly within the rigid time limits of a group discussion. It was decided instead to invite experts on questions relating to fluoridation and the effects of fluorides on human health to collaborate in the preparation of a monograph on the subject.

The objective of the monograph is to provide an impartial review of the scientific literature on the varied aspects of fluoridation and the many complex questions relating to the metabolism of fluorides and their utilization in medicine and public health. It is not intended to be a practical guide to the use of fluorides as a health measure, but rather a presentation of the facts to assist public health authorities and other interested persons to form an objective judgement.

To assist WHO in planning the monograph and in co-ordinating the various sections prepared by the 29 contributors, Professor Y. Ericsson was appointed as a special consultant and scientific editor. The valuable technical guidance that he provided at all stages in the production of the monograph is deeply appreciated.

In order to ensure that the monograph would be as representative as possible of dental and medical opinion throughout the world, the manuscript was circulated to 93 specialists, whose names are listed on pages 7-10, and to the six WHO Regional Offices. The comments of these reviewers were taken into account in preparing the final version. The World Health Organization expresses its sincere gratitude to all those who have collaborated in the production of this monograph.

CHAPTER 1

Introduction

Y. ERICSSON [1]

Fluorine, the most electronegative of all elements, has not only notable chemical qualities but also physiological properties of great interest and importance for human health and well-being. The chemical activity of the fluoride ion makes this ion physiologically more active than any other elemental ion. With low concentrations of the fluoride ion, enzymatic processes may be either inhibited or stimulated, and interactions with other organic or with inorganic body components may occur that are of great importance for human physiology.

Research into the biology of fluorides has been very extensive during the last decades, especially after it was demonstrated in the 1930s that fluorides in very small doses have remarkable influences on the dental system: on the one hand, a strong inhibition of dental caries; on the other, and with higher doses, a disturbance of enamel formation. In fact, the discovery of the connexion between excessive content of fluoride in water and endemic mottling of the enamel was one of the main starting-points of research into fluorides and hard-tissue physiology and pathology.

The ability of fluorides in very low doses to reduce the number of caries lesions by well over 50%, and to reduce the severity of the collective caries attack even more markedly, is naturally a finding which should be elaborated and utilized as extensively as possible in a situation where dental caries is by far the most widespread of all diseases and is, moreover, a disease that shows an increasing rate, especially in the developing countries, and against which the curative resources are insufficient even in the most developed countries.

Several other effects on the dental organ have been more or less established: influences on tooth form and appearance, on eruption time and alignment in the dental arches, and on the frequency and severity of periodontal disease. All these effects have been found to be advantageous except the mineralization disorder known as mottled enamel, which is caused by excessive fluoride ingestion during the period of tooth formation.

---

[1] Department of Cariology, Karolinska Institutet, Stockholm, Sweden

Fluorine is the most exclusive bone-seeking element existing, owing to its great affinity for calcium phosphate. It is therefore accumulated in every tissue showing calcification, be it physiological or pathological. However, neither the frequency nor the severity of pathological calcifications outside the skeletal system has ever been found to be aggravated by high fluoride ingestion.

In the bones, fluorine increases the size of the apatite crystals and reduces their solubility. This has naturally led to expectations of a positive role of fluorine as a skeletal stabilizer. Large doses of sodium fluoride have been tried as a therapeutic agent in the otherwise rather hopeless osteoporosis cases of Paget's disease, sometimes but not always with reported success. A somewhat spectacular report is that fluorine, which in the elemental form is used in missile propellants, has also, as sodium fluoride, been administered to the crew in manned space flights in order to counteract the loss of skeletal calcium that follows from weightlessness and physical inactivity.

During the work on this monograph, new, well-documented reports have appeared, giving further support to the theory that a certain degree of fluoride saturation, or possibly other fluoride influence on the skeleton, may provide a partial protection against senile osteoporosis. Since this condition is very widespread, particularly in aging women, and often leads to serious fractures and to invalidism, further knowledge of the role of fluorides in skeletal biology is urgently required. Increased research activity in this field can be foreseen, and it appears at present quite possible that the fluoride ingestion that is optimal from the point of view of skeletal function and stability will be found to be higher than that which is optimal for the formation of dental enamel.

Health surveys in districts with water supplies containing various concentrations of fluoride have also indicated a lower frequency of atherosclerotic calcification accompanying higher fluoride supply. This clinical material is rather limited, but animal studies seem to offer as a possible explanation fluorine-magnesium interactions and the role of magnesium deficiency in experimental atherosclerosis. The immense importance of atherosclerosis will probably also motivate greatly increased research along these intriguing lines.

The question "is fluorine an essential element?" has naturally been raised. It has not been possible to find a definite answer owing to the difficulty of producing a diet for animal experimentation that is fluorine-free but adequate in every other respect. However, there are indications that traces of fluorine are necessary for normal mineralization, and possibly also for normal reproduction. For the formation of a caries-resistant enamel, a certain fluoride supply is evidently essential.

It has often been expressly or tacitly assumed in the past that fluorine is absorbed and metabolized mainly as the simple fluoride ion. However, a number of reports indicate the considerable importance of several complex fluoride ions, e.g., CaF^+, MgF^+; and even more complex fluorine compounds may be formed and metabolized in the body. It is possible that further research will reveal physiologically important details in this field.

Although the controlled enrichment of drinking water with fluoride was taught us by nature and has the support of overwhelming evidence, public resistance to this measure, mainly on psychological grounds, has been remarkable. This has naturally led to efforts to utilize the powerful caries-preventive effect of fluorine in ways that would reduce total fluoride ingestion (local application) or make such ingestion non-compulsory (ingestion in vehicles other than piped water supplies). Such efforts have become increasingly important since water fluoridation is at present limited to waterworks of a certain technical standard and thus will leave out large population groups, particularly in developing countries, whence unanimous reports indicate a rapid, often alarming, rise of the caries rate. The need for automatic, inexpensive caries-preventive fluoride supply to large populations, using alternative vehicles, is therefore obvious and urgent. Vehicles such as salt and flour or other staple foods have been proposed and to some extent tested. However, before such methods can be introduced on a large scale, research on their effects as regards absorption and caries prevention, on the variations in different countries of the consumption of the proposed vehicles, and on the possibilities of avoiding overlapping with water supplies containing optimal or excessive amounts of fluoride must be carried out.

On the other hand, since fluoride doses only twice those which effectively prevent caries may cause slight disturbances of the calcification of enamel, and since doses about twenty times greater, when taken over a long period, are known to cause damage to the skeletal system, it is imperative that great competence and care should be exercised in the utilization of this powerful element.

Of the fears of harmful side-effects from controlled fluoride ingestion that have often been voiced, some can be regarded with the utmost scepticism on account of their unrealistic nature; for example, this is the case with the allegation of allergy to fluoride, which has never been described among the world's billions of consumers of the fluorine-rich beverage, tea. Others deserve serious consideration and are treated thoroughly in this book—for example, skeletal fluorosis and the possibility of interference with kidney or thyroid function.

Fluorine is an element of increasing interest in several other connexions also. Many fluorine compounds have been put to medical therapeutic use—for example, fluorine-containing corticosteroids, and organic fluorine compounds for narcosis, pneumothorax and cancer treatment; however, such compounds contain fluorine in strong covalent binding that has not been found to be broken biologically. Problems in industrial hygiene have arisen through the increasing use of fluorine compounds and often through a high fluorine content in dust and volatile waste products. Finally, fluorine-contaminated pasture and forage and fluorine-rich mineral salt fodder have caused problems for veterinary medicine in several countries.

Experience from human and animal cases of chronic fluoride poisoning has thus contributed to our knowledge of the role of fluorine in human physiology and pathology. Still more has the great volume of animal experimentation which has to supplement observations on man.

A word may be said here on a detail of terminology. Many of the contributors to this monograph have been anxious to use throughout the word "fluoride" to denote the ionized, physiologically available form of the element. The word "fluorine" has sometimes been thought to denote exclusively the gaseous form of the element. However, by analogy with iodine, fluorine may be used to denote collectively the element in all its forms —ionized, ionizable or non-ionizable. Where there is doubt as regards ionizability, e.g., in certain foods, fluorine is actually the better, more comprehensive word. For this reason, no effort has been made to change the word "fluorine", used by some contributors, where no confusion can be caused.

CHAPTER 2

The supply of fluorine to man

MURIEL E. BELL [1] — E. J. LARGENT [2] — T. G. LUDWIG [3]
— J. C. MUHLER [4] — G. K. STOOKEY [5]

1. INTRODUCTION (E. J. Largent)

The most electronegative of all chemical elements, fluorine, is so violently reactive chemically that it is rarely or never encountered in nature as elemental fluorine. Apart from the comparatively small amounts of manufactured gaseous fluorine, the element is largely found, in industry as in nature, in chemically combined form (the fluorides). Among the manufactured fluorides the inorganic materials constitute the larger volume, but organic fluorochemicals are increasing in volume and importance. In nature the rare organic fluorides are largely a curiosity and play virtually no role in the economy of man.

Combined chemically in the form of fluorides, fluorine is seventeenth in the order of abundance of elements in the earth's crust. This estimate, reported in 1953 by Fleischer, has not been changed by the results of more recent analyses of the elements in the earth's crust. Since its abundance is of this magnitude, it is not surprising that important amounts of fluoride are found in sea water, in numerous supplies of drinking water, in mineral deposits of fluorspar, cryolite and fluorapatite, and in surface dusts found close to a few of the mineral deposits. The principal sources of supply of fluoride available to the physiology of man are: (1) water; (2) some species of vegetation; (3) certain edible marine animals; (4) dusts in certain parts of the world; and (5) certain industrial processes.

The effects of fluorides on the health of man stem largely from dissolved fluoride present in many supplies of drinking water. However, particulate fluorides suspended in water may have a health importance that has largely been overlooked and given inadequate attention. Particulate fluoride could

[1] 56 Seaview Terrace, St Clair, Dunedin S.W.1, New Zealand.
[2] Richmond, Va., USA.
[3] Director, Dental Research Unit, Medical Research Council of New Zealand, Wellington, New Zealand.
[4] School of Dentistry, Indiana University, Indianapolis, Ind., USA.
[5] Assistant Professor of Basic Sciences, Indiana University, School of Dentistry, Indianapolis, Ind., USA.

become dispersed as a contaminant, not only in drinking water, but also in foods ingested by man and animals. These topics will be enlarged upon in succeeding sections of this chapter.

The biological history of fluoride-containing materials up to 1937 is recorded in the excellent monograph of Kaj Roholm. A monumental bibliography of the literature on fluorides has been compiled by Irene R. Campbell (Campbell & Widner, 1958) and another accompanies the excellent book by Hodge & Smith (1965), the most recent addition to the series *Fluorine Chemistry*, edited by Simons.

2. INGESTION FROM WATER (Muriel E. Bell & T. G. Ludwig)

In common with other forms of life man has a need for water as an essential nutrient. Water is required for a wide variety of functions including regulation of the body temperature, as a solvent, and as a vehicle in the transportation of other nutrients and of waste products through the vascular system and through the inter- and intra-cellular spaces. The requirement for water may vary from individual to individual; and in any one individual from time to time under the influence of internal or external stimuli. The need for water is, however, a continuing process and the body's stores must be maintained and replenished at appropriate intervals.

Of the waters available to man for personal needs it may be regarded as certain that none is pure in the strict sense of the word. All will contain a variety of substances, either in suspension or in solution, in greater or lesser amounts. Calcium, magnesium, sodium, potassium, manganese, strontium, barium, sulfate, chloride, and a wide variety of other substances may be found in most waters in varying concentrations. Fluoride will be found also in most, if not in all, potable waters. It is consequently almost universally available for ingestion by man from this source. It is therefore the purpose of this section to consider the origin and chemistry of fluoride in waters, to discuss the distribution and utilization of fluoride-bearing waters throughout the world, and to evaluate the amount of fluoride which man ingests in association with his water intake.

Origins of Fluoride in Waters

The seas

The bulk of the water normally available to man is involved in the hydrological cycle which may be regarded as being initiated in the seas. Seawater itself contains significant quantities of fluoride, levels having been variously recorded as 0.8-1.4 ppm (Wattenberg, 1943; Kappana et al., 1962). It is known that appreciable quantities of other halogens escape from the sea into the atmosphere and are eventually incorporated into rain or precipitation (Eriksson, 1952; Miller, 1961). This may be brought about either mechanically, droplets of sea-water being caught up by the wind as spray (Dean, 1963), or, as was suggested by Cauer (1938) in the case of iodine, chemically, the halogen ions being oxidized by ozone and liberated into the atmosphere in the form of a gas. Certainly, by the mechanical transfer of sea-spray, quantities of fluoride, as well as of the other halogens, from the seas should find their way into rain or precipitation, although the resultant concentrations would be of a low order.

The atmosphere

Additional fluorides are widely distributed in the atmosphere originating from the dusts of fluoride-containing soils (Williamson, 1953), from gaseous industrial wastes (MacIntire, Hardin & Hester, 1952), from the burning of coal fires in populated areas (Cholak, 1959), and from the gases emitted in areas of volcanic activity (Noguchi et al., 1963). All these sources may act to increase the fluoride level of rain or precipitation. In populated areas coal smoke is regarded as one of the chief contributors to atmospheric fluoride, concentrations of from 1 to 175 ppm fluoride having been found in 120 samples of coal from the British Commonwealth (Crossley, 1944) and of up to 295 ppm in Utah coals (Churchill, Rowley & Martin, 1948). The steam discharged from fumaroles of active volcanoes may also contain considerable quantities of fluoride, so that the fluoride levels of rain in areas of volcanic activity may also be substantially increased (Zies, 1929; Noguchi et al., 1963).

The earth's crust

The amount of fluoride entering water either directly from the seas or from atmospheric contamination is likely to be small, however, in comparison with the amounts derived from the solvent action of water on the rocks and soils of the earth's crust. Fluorides are widely distributed in nature and it has been estimated that the element fluorine, in the form of fluorides, constitutes about 0.032% of the earth's crust (Fleischer, 1953).

(a) *Rock-forming minerals.* In rocks and soils fluoride may occur in a wide variety of minerals, including fluorite, apatite, the micas, hornblende and a number of pegmatites such as topaz and tourmaline. Fluoride occurs most commonly as fluorite or fluorspar (CaF_2), which may contain up to 49% fluoride and can produce quite high values in rocks even when the mineral is present in only small quantities. Mineral apatite is widely distributed in all igneous rocks and has long been recognized as a fluoride carrier. Analyses of samples of apatites from igneous rocks (Kind, 1938) showed that they contained from 13 500 to 26 000 ppm fluoride. The micas may show fluoride values as high as 68 000 ppm, with biotite (970-35 000 ppm), phlogopite (3300-37 000 ppm) and lepidolite (19 000-68 000 ppm) generally showing higher values than muscovite (170-14 800 ppm) (Correns, 1956). The hornblendes may also contain fluoride, substituted for hydroxyl, in concentrations which may be of the same order as those found in the micas (Larsen & Draisin, 1950). Topaz is an independent fluoride mineral with the formula $Al_2F_2SiO_4$ and has a theoretical fluoride content of 21%. In practice the fluoride values found are generally somewhat lower.

(b) *Rocks*. The occurrence of fluoride in the various types of rocks composing the earth's crust have been extensively reviewed by Correns (1956). In plutonic rocks fluoride concentrations of from 20 to 4000 ppm have been reported. The highest values were reported by Seraphim (1951) for 16 syenites in the USA—concentrations ranging from 200 to 4000 ppm, with a mean of 1480 ppm. Seraphim also examined 26 granites from various localities in the USA and showed that their fluoride content ranged from 20 to 2300 ppm. Similar values for 13 German granites were recorded by Koritnig (1950), these having a mean fluoride content of 1330 ppm. In Finland the "rapakivi" granite was found to contain 1100-4700 ppm F (Sahama, 1945) and fluoride-rich waters have been associated with this granite.

Studies of the fluoride content of the volcanic and hypabyssal rocks were also reviewed by Correns (1956). In rocks of this type fluoride values ranging from 80 to 2500 ppm were reported. In this case the highest value, 2500 ppm, was recorded for a fluorite-bearing granite porphyry obtained from the Llano region of Texas (Goldich, 1941). Six andesites from Ägina were reported by Koritnig (1950) to have had a mean fluoride content of 620 ppm, while for 14 andesites from Méthana a value of 390 ppm was recorded. Many of the basalts are regarded by Correns as having a surprisingly high fluoride content. At Hoher Hagen and at Bramberg, Koritnig (1951) has reported basalts containing 270 ppm and 800 ppm respectively. Similar values for 16 basalts from the Columbia plateau were reported by Seraphim (*op. cit.*) while Shepherd (1940) reported the high value of 1060 ppm for a basalt from Mount Morrison, California.

In the sedimentary rocks Koritnig (1951) reported fluoride values of 80-450 ppm for a variety of sandstones, of 40-80 ppm for greywacke, and of 360 ppm for loess. Limestones are generally regarded as being poor in fluoride, although average values of 270 ppm for 16 German limestones were reported by von Englehardt (1936), while Shepherd (*op. cit.*) reported a value of 370 ppm fluoride in an argillaceous limestone.

Salt deposits of marine origin may also contain significant amounts of fluoride. In anhydrite from the Zechstein salt series, Koritnig found up to 890 ppm fluoride. Concentrations of 870 ppm have been reported in gypsum. The importance of fluoride in deposits of phosphate rock is well known. Its distribution in this form will be considered below.

(c) *Commercial ores.* Some mention should be made of the deposits of fluoride-containing minerals in which fluoride levels are sufficiently high for the deposits to represent ores of commercial value. The most important of these are fluorite or fluorspar, cryolite, and fluorapatite. Workable deposits of fluorspar occur in many places but the chief production areas are found in North America, especially in Illinois, Kentucky and Newfoundland, and in Russia, England, France and Germany. In Germany, the chief production areas are in Vogtland, Thuringia, Harz and the Upper Palatinate (Oberpfalz). In the USA alone it is estimated that deposits amount to at least 7 000 000 tons (Bredemann, 1956), much of which has a fluoride content exceeding 3.5%.

Cryolite, sodium aluminium fluoride, is preferred in industry because of its low melting-point and low decomposition temperature. The chief deposits of commercial interest are the cryolite-pegmatite deposits in Greenland.

Apatite is the main component in rock phosphates, the raw material for phosphatic fertilizers. Large deposits are found in the USA (in Tennessee, Florida and South Carolina), in the Soviet Union, in North Africa (Tunis, Algeria) and in the islands of the Pacific and the Caribbean archipelago. Nearly all raw phosphates in commerce have a high fluoride content. Gericke (1949) and Trömel (1953) have shown that the average fluoride content of most rock phosphates from the continents is about 3.5%, being as high as 4.2% in Moroccan phosphates. The island phosphates are geologically younger and consist in part of hydroxyapatite. The island phosphates therefore tend to have a lower fluoride content (Bredemann, 1956). Phosphates from Curaçao (Netherlands Antilles) have shown a fluoride content of 0.38-0.91%.

(d) *Soils.* Robinson & Edgington (1946) have determined the fluoride content in a large number of soils. In an analysis of 30 profiles they found in the majority a decrease in fluoride from below upwards; in one profile the reverse relationship was observed, and in eight profiles the fluoride content was nearly constant. Investigations of the fluoride content of soils in different countries were reviewed by Vinogradov (1954). In the USSR 46 analyses gave minimum and maximum fluoride contents of 30 and 320 ppm, with a mean of 200 ppm; 137 analyses in the USA gave minimum and maximum values of 10 and 7070 ppm, with a mean value of 290 ppm, while 23 analyses of New Zealand soils by Gemmel (1946) gave minimum and maximum values of 68 and 540 ppm, with an average of 200 ppm. The use of fluoride-containing phosphate fertilizers may increase the fluoride content of soils and of run-off from these soils, although these increases should normally be of a minor nature.

Chemistry of Fluoride in Water

The fluoride content of rain and precipitation will largely depend on the type and availability of atmospheric contaminants. The fluoride content of surface and underground waters, on the other hand, will be dependent on a wider variety of factors, chief of which will be the availability and solubility of the parent fluoride minerals with which these waters are in contact. The majority of fluoride-containing minerals are but sparingly soluble and their solubility may also be in part affected by that of the parent rock of which they form a constituent. In addition to the solubility and availability of the parent fluoride material, other factors will also play an important role in determining the concentrations of fluoride to be found in particular surface and underground waters. Amongst these will be the porosity of the rocks or soils through which the water passes and the speed with which the water flows; the temperature of the interaction between rock and water; the hydrogen ion concentration of the water; and the concentration of calcium ions present in the water. Fluoride levels will tend to be higher in alkaline waters and in the hotter waters that may be found, for example, in areas of volcanic activity. In many waters calcium ions will be present in excess and, under these conditions, the concentration-controlling mineral is likely to be calcium fluoride, which at normal temperatures has a solubility of about 15 ppm.

When a fluoride compound is dissolved in water, the element fluorine will be present mainly as fluoride ion, F^-. However, depending on the ionic concentration and on the pH of the solution, the fluoride will also be present in solution as HF_2^- and undissociated HF. In dilute solutions and at neutral pH, virtually all the fluoride will be present as fluoride ion, F^-. However, as the pH of the solution decreases, the proportion of F^- present decreases while the proportion of HF_2^- and undissociated HF increases (Borei, 1945).

This does not mean that different fluoride compounds will yield fluoride that in some way differs according to its source. This point is made because there are some who make a distinction between "natural" and "artificial" fluorides. If we assume that calcium fluoride is representative of natural fluorides while sodium fluoride is representative of artificial fluorides and dissolve these compounds in water under the equivalent conditions, it will be found that they ionize as shown in the equations below:

Calcium fluoride

$$CaF_2 \rightleftharpoons Ca^{++} + 2F^-$$

$$F^- + H^+ \rightleftharpoons HF$$

$$HF + F^- \rightleftharpoons HF_2^-$$

Sodium fluoride

$$NaF \quad \rightleftharpoons \quad Na^+ \quad + \quad F^-$$

$$F^- + H^+ \rightleftharpoons HF$$

$$HF + F^- \rightleftharpoons HF_2^-$$

In both instances fluoride is yielded in the forms F^-, HF and HF_2^-, and these will be chemically and physiologically identical (with their equivalents) irrespective of which of the two compounds they are derived from (cf. Chapter 3, section 2).

Distribution of Fluoride-bearing Waters

Because of the wide interest in the relationship of fluorides to human and stock health, an extensive literature is available on the distribution of fluoride-containing waters. Except in unusual circumstances, surface waters are generally low in fluoride, the levels being below 1 ppm. On the other hand, underground or subsoil waters may have a greater opportunity to contact fluoriferous material so that these waters may contain appreciable quantities of fluoride, depending on geological conditions (Cholak, 1959). The same considerations apply to mineral and hot spring waters as to other ground waters, and although these high mineral waters may not be extensively used as sources of drinking water, they may sometimes be used for medicinal purposes.

So voluminous is the literature dealing with the analytical data on fluoride in all types of natural waters that it would not be possible to deal fully with it here. For this reason it is intended to illustrate the ubiquitous occurrence of fluoride-bearing waters and to indicate the types of fluoride levels that can be expected by describing only representative studies from each of the six continental areas. Details of the distribution of fluoride-bearing waters in different countries are shown, however, in Table 1.

Africa

Investigations of the fluoride content of African waters have been reported by Ockerse (1946, 1949) from the Union of South Africa, by Williamson (1953) from Kenya, and by Wilson (1954) from Nigeria. These studies, especially those of Ockerse and of Williamson, are of special interest because they report unusually high fluoride levels in some waters which appear to be used, at least to a limited extent, by the indigenous peoples. Ockerse reported analyses of samples collected from more than 300 localities throughout the Union of South Africa. He has pointed out (Ockerse,

TABLE 1

FLUORIDE LEVELS IN NATURAL WATERS IN DIFFERENT COUNTRIES

Country	Range of fluoride levels (ppm)	References
Africa		
Ethiopia	0-0.9	US Interdepartmental Committee on Nutrition for National Defense (1960b)
Kenya	0-2800.0	Williamson (1953)
Nigeria	0-6.2	Wilson (1954)
South Africa	0-53.0	Kent (1949); Ockerse (1946, 1949)
Tanganyika	0-95.0	Tanganyika, Government Chemist (1955)
The Americas		
Argentina	0-1.6	Heer & Gómez Galissier (1950)
Brazil	0.0.6	Alvarenga Rossi & Dutra de Oliveira (1947); Gandra (1953); Spitzner (1947)
Canada	0-1.2	Box & Hodgins (1944)
Chile	0-1.5	Witkop, Barros & Hamilton (1962)
Cuba	0-0.4	Añorga & Melman (1951); Melman (1954)
Ecuador	0-1.5	Muñoz (1940); US Interdepartmental Committee on Nutrition for National Defense (1960a)
Peru	0-1.4	Maldonado & Guevara (1951); Pissani (1954); Zavala (1950)
USA	0-16.0	Abbott (1937); Akin & Jones (1952); Allen (1953); Babcock, Wisher & Durum (1952); Bacon (1948); Baker (1963); Barraclough & Marsh (1962); Bennett & Meyer (1952); Black & Brown (1951); Black & Stearns (1937); Boruff & Abbott (1933); Boswell (1963); Broadhurst, Sundstrom & Rowley (1950); Brown (1947); Carlston (1942); Carter & Herrick (1951); Cederstrom (1946); Christensen (1963); Clark & Mann (1938); Cohen & Everett (1963); Cooke, Martin & Meyer (1952); Crosthwaite & Scott (1956); DeBuchananne & Richardson (1956); DeWitt & Nichols (1937); Durfor & Becker (1962); Foster (1943); Hale (1955); Hale et al. (1947); Harris, Moore & West (1963); Jeup (1943); La Moreaux (1946); Lamar & Schroeder (1951); Larson (1963); LeGrand (1954); Leonard & Durum (1952); Maher (1941); Neisler (1963); North Dakota State Department of Health (1952); Ohio River Valley Water Sanitation Commission (1957); Page, Newcombe & Graeff (1963); Parks, Robinson & Law (1936); Pauszek (1949); Powell, Reade & Scott (1957); Prior, Schneider & Durum (1953); Schoff & Stovall (1943); Scott, Ey & Waring (1937); Searcy, Baker & Durum (1952); Sinclair (1963); Siple (1957); Smith et al. (1949); Storvick & Sullivan (1950); Sundstrom, Broadhurst & Dwyer (1949); Tait, Baker & Billingsley (1953); Taylor (1962); Thwaites (1956); US Department of Health, Education, and Welfare (1959); Walker (1953); Wisher & Durum (1952)
Asia		
China	0-13.0	Cheng (1939); Cheng & Chou (1939)
India	0-6.4	Marshal Day (1940); Raghavachari & Venkataramanan (1940); Ramamohana Rao & Bhaskaran (1964)
Iran	0-1.0	Joneidi (1955)
Israel	0.3-1.5	Gedalia (1953)
Japan	0-20.0	Kobayashi (1951, 1954); Kubota (1952); Okuno (1942)
Korea	0.8-10.0	Sugawa (1937)
Taiwan	0-1.5	US Interdepartmental Committee on Nutrition for National Defense (1961a)
Thailand	0-1.5	US Interdepartmental Committee on Nutrition for National Defense (1961b)
Australasia		
Australia	0-13.5	Jones (1949); Reid & Martin (1946); Ward (1954)
New Zealand	0-0.9	Chamberlain (1944); Denmead (1946); Hewat & Eastcott (1955)
Territory of Papua and New Guinea	0-0.6	Jones (1949)

TABLE 1 *(concluded)*

Country	Range of fluoride levels (ppm)	References
Europe		
Austria	0.4-0.8	Bredemann (1956); Koller (1950)
Belgium	0-1.7	Buydens (1956)
Cyprus	0-3.6	Bradwell (1950)
Czecho-slovakia	0-28.0	Bredemann (1956); Polák & Symon (1951)
Denmark	0-3.3	Møller (1965)
England	0-5.8	Heasman & Martin (1962)
Finland	0-5.0	Erkillä (1958); Wäre (1961)
France	0-7.0	Charonnat & Roche (1934)
Germany	0-4.9	Haack & Zimmerman (1952); Henkel (1961); Pohloudek-Fabini, Engst & Mörtzschky (1953); von Polheim & Dietrich (1955); Quentin (1952)
Hungary		Papp & Dippold (1950); Straub (1940, 1950)
Ireland	0-0.2	Drum (1949)
Italy and Sicily	0-7.1	Giardino & Police (1955); Pappalardo (1955); Talenti & Cardini (1953); Visintin & Monteriolo (1955)
Luxembourg	0-1.2	Nitschké (1953)
Netherlands	0-2.0	Stas, Kooijmans & van Ijssel (1937, 1941)
Norway	0-2.7	Natvig & Wilhelmsen (1963)
Poland	0-1.1	Geschwind & Jurkiewicz (1952); Wojciechowska & Kolaczkowski (1953)
Portugal	0-22.8	de Carvalho (1936)
Sardinia	0-5.0	Angellini & Demontis (1957)
Spain	0-6.3	Gómez Galissier & Heer (1950); Hoyos Ruiz (1953); Paraje (1950)
Sweden	0-10	Swedish National Board of Health (1966)
Switzerland	0-1.4	van Beuren & Leiser (1962); Demole & Held (1953)
USSR	0-7.0	Abuladze et al. (1959); Andreeva (1963); Gabovich (1949); Krainov & Korolskova (1964); Krepkogorskii & Bogusevich (1953); Moseshvili et al. (1962); Moshkina & Nikol'skaya (1964); Ostapenya, Gel'fer & Kagan (1961); Persits (1964); Rakityanskii (1963); Vinogradov, Danilova & Selivanov (1937)
Yugoslavia	0-4.2	Sibalić, Dordević & Perović (1960); Sibalić & Perović (1954); Tomic (1958, 1959)

1946) that most of South Africa is underlain by the Karroo sediments, which may contain up to 0.5% of fluoride. The levels of fluoride found in the different types of water tested are shown in Table 2. It will be seen that fluoride concentrations of up to 53 ppm are reported for certain boreholes and that these high levels are apparently associated with climatic influences,

TABLE 2

FLUORIDE LEVELS IN SOUTH AFRICAN WATERS [a]

Source	Fluoride concentration (ppm)
Springs (hot)	trace to 12.2
Springs (cold)	trace to 40.7
Wells	trace to 7.6
Boreholes	trace to 53.0
Ghorras [b]	trace to 6.3
Dams	trace to 8.9

[a] After Ockerse (1946).
[b] A ghorra is a shallow, isolated pool.

the levels increasing during hot dry weather and decreasing during periods of heavy rain.

Ockerse's (1949) data for the fluoride content of South African drinking water shows a fairly well defined geographical pattern, the fluoride levels being lowest (generally below 0.5 ppm) in the coastal areas of Cape Province and Natal and highest in the more arid areas of the interior.

Williamson (1953) has reported the results of 850 analyses of Kenyan waters. Of these, 339 contained fluoride at 0.1-0.9 ppm; 146 at 1.0-1.9 ppm; 148 at 2-3.9 ppm; 77 at 4-5.9 ppm; 72 at 6-9.9 ppm; 49 at 10-19.9 ppm; 6 at 20-29.9 ppm; and 12 at 30 ppm and over. The fluoride content of lakes ranged from 0.5 to 2800 ppm and of rivers and springs from 0.45 to 49 ppm. Many of the waters have high pH values, these sometimes being as high as pH 8 to pH 10. According to Williamson, the geological structure of Kenya is such that high fluoride levels in waters should be expected. Surface soils consist in many areas of a high percentage of volcanic ash and then pass through weathered trachyte tuffs or lavas to form a water table over the more compact and impervious phonolite or structures of the basement system. It would seem, however, that the other chemical characteristics of the waters—and possibly climatic conditions—play an important role in determining the very high fluoride levels to be found in some Kenyan waters.

The analyses of Nigerian waters undertaken by Wilson (1954) showed that spring waters from the central plateau contained 0.2-0.4 ppm. In the Niger and Benue villages levels of up to 3.3 ppm fluoride were recorded in some places.

The Americas

Probably more information is available regarding the distribution of fluoride-containing waters in the USA than in any other country. Analytical data for the whole of the USA have been compiled by the US Department of Health, Education, and Welfare (1959) and give information about fluoride levels in drinking-water sources in each of the States as well as in specific communities. The results show that at the beginning of 1957 there were 1903 communities in the USA with at least one source of drinking water with a natural fluoride content of 0.7 ppm or more. Of these communities, 52% are located in five States—Illinois, Iowa, Ohio, South Dakota and Texas. The States of Maine, Vermont, Massachusetts, Pennsylvania and Delaware reported no known communal water supplies with natural fluoride levels of 0.7 ppm or more. Fluoride levels averaging 0.7-1.1 ppm are present in 895 communities with about 4 256 000 residents; average fluoride levels of 1.2-1.4 ppm are found in 263 communities with 598 000 persons; and in 620 communities with about 1 400 000 people fluoride concentrations of 1.5 ppm or greater are present in drinking waters. The remaining 125 communities, with 698 000 persons, have average fluoride levels of less than 0.7 ppm, but either at least one source of water contains 0.7 ppm or more or the maximum fluoride level is 0.7 or greater. The average fluoride content of water supplies in the total communities enumerated ranges from below 0.7 ppm to as high as 7.7 ppm.

Discussing the use of high-fluoride waters in the USA, Cholak (1959) points out that in the State of New Mexico the fluoride content of 35 communities ranged from 1.1 to 12.0 ppm (Clark & Mann, 1938); in Kansas, one well contained fluoride in amounts ranging from 8 to 11 ppm (Smith et al., 1949), while the content in water from artesian wells in the sandstone region of North Dakota ranged from 2.8 to 7.5 ppm (Abbott, 1937). It is probable that the use of many of these high-fluoride waters has been discontinued or that they are now being treated for the removal of excess fluoride.

Analyses of waters in Ecuador have been reported by the US Interdepartmental Committee on Nutrition for National Defense (1960a). Fluoride concentrations were determined in samples of potable waters from 21 localities drawn from the five chief geographical areas of the country. At Latacunga and Ambato in the central sierra concentrations of 1.5 and 1.4 ppm fluoride were found respectively. In other parts of the country the levels ranged from 0 to 0.4 ppm fluoride, although they were generally in the vicinity of 0.1 ppm.

Witkop, Barros & Hamilton (1962) reported on the fluoride levels found in the drinking waters from eleven Chilean cities. Values in the northern area tended to be higher than those in the central or southern regions. Fluoride concentrations ranged from 0.8 to less than 0.1 ppm.

In Cuba analyses were undertaken by Melman (1954) of 209 samples of potable waters from wells, aqueducts and springs in six provinces. Fluoride concentrations ranged from 0 to 0.4 ppm.

Asia

Analytical data on the fluoride content of Asian waters are somewhat less extensive than those available from the other continental areas. There has been, however, long-standing interest in the fluoride concentrations to be found in the waters of the Indian subcontinent. Marshal Day (1940) undertook analyses of nine local waters in the vicinity of Lahore. In only one case did he find levels below 1 ppm fluoride; in five cases the levels were between 1.0 and 2.0 ppm, while the three remaining supplies contained 2.2 ppm, 4.2 ppm, and 6.4 ppm fluoride respectively. More recently Ramamohana Rao & Bhaskaran (1964) have reported on the distribution of fluoride-containing waters in the Kurnool district of Andhra Pradesh. From 44 localities 302 water samples were analysed. Samples were obtained from 178 draw wells, 82 step wells, 18 ore wells, 6 spring wells, 6 streams and a variety of other sources. The fluoride levels ranged from 0.1 to 6.0 ppm. Levels of 0.1-1.5 ppm were found in 77% of the samples, while 23% contained fluoride in concentrations exceeding 1.5 ppm.

Fluoride levels in water supplies in Thailand and in Taiwan have been reported by the US Interdepartmental Committee on Nutrition for National Defense (1961a, 1961b).   In Thailand 21 samples from 7 main geographical localities were analysed.   Fluoride concentrations ranged from less than 0.1 to 0.7 ppm, the highest value (0.7 ppm) being recorded at Sattaheep. In Taiwan, waters from 6 localities were analysed and the fluoride content was found to range from 0.1 to 1.1 ppm, the highest value (1.1 ppm) being recorded at Makung.

Australasia

Analyses of fluoride concentrations in Australian waters have been undertaken by Reid & Martin (1946) and by Jones (1949), who also undertook analyses of several waters in the Territory of Papua and New Guinea. Analyses of the fluoride content of New Zealand waters have been reported by Chamberlain (1944), Denmead (1946) and Hewat & Eastcott (1955). Jones (1949) analysed surface and underground waters obtained from 55 communities throughout the State of New South Wales, Australia.   Of these, samples from only three localities contained fluoride concentrations of 1.0 ppm or greater, while samples from 6 localities contained concentrations of 0.5-1.0 ppm.   The remaining samples contained less than 0.5 ppm fluoride.   Spring water samples collected from 5 villages in the Territory of Papua and New Guinea and analysed by Jones (*op. cit.*) contained from 0.2 to 0.5 ppm fluoride.

In New Zealand analyses of waters from 51 localities in the North Island were undertaken by Chamberlain (1944) and waters from 146 localities in the South Island were analysed by Denmead (1946).   Of the North Island waters all contained from 0 to 0.5 ppm fluoride, except one minor supply which contained 0.9 ppm and one hot mineral spring water which contained 4.5 ppm fluoride.   Of the South Island waters all contained less than 0.5 ppm fluoride except one minor supply which contained 0.9 ppm and two mineral spring waters which contained 5.0 ppm and 1.5 ppm respectively.   Similar results for the fluoride content of waters from 107 localities in New Zealand were reported by Hewat & Eastcott (1955), nearly all these waters containing less than 0.5 ppm fluoride.

Europe

Investigations of fluoride levels in European waters, especially in Germany and Scandinavia, have been extensively reviewed by Bredemann (1956).   As to Germany, an extensive series of analyses of waters in Thuringia has been undertaken by Henkel (1961).   Analyses of 3300 drinking-water samples from areas around Jena, Erfurt and the plain of the River Saale were carried out.   Waters from variegated sandstone formations averaged 0.2 ppm fluoride; in the Muschelkalk formation 0.3 ppm; from sandstone formation in an area of potassium mines and salt-water baths 0.4 ppm to 0.45 ppm; and from the plain of the Saale 0.1 ppm fluoride.

A survey of British waters during the decade 1950-59 showed that approximately a quarter of a million people were then consuming waters containing from 1.0 to 5.8 ppm fluoride (Heasman & Martin, 1962). Some of these sources have recently been superseded and in some other cases the water is now mixed with low-fluoride supplies.

In Denmark it was found (about 1955) that about 95 000 inhabitants used a drinking water containing 1.0 ppm or more fluoride (Møller, 1965).

In Finland, Wäre (1961) made 2764 water fluoride determinations and found a range of 0-5.0 ppm fluoride. About 6% of the rural population consumed water containing at least 1 ppm fluoride.

In Norway, Natvig & Wilhelmsen (1963) analysed 657 drinking waters, supplying about half the population, and found a range of 0-2.7 ppm fluoride, with only 13 waters above 0.5 ppm.

A recent Swedish mapping of the water fluoride content (Swedish National Board of Health, 1966) showed variations from near zero to about 10 ppm fluoride in piped waters, and one drilled well gave as much as 18 ppm. About half a million inhabitants consumed water containing 0.8 ppm or more fluoride.

Analyses of the fluoride content of more than 70 Croatian waters have been reported from Yugoslavia by Tomic (1958). From western Croatia, where the waters are generally soft, 39 samples averaged less than 0.1 ppm fluoride. A similar number of samples from north-eastern and central Croatia, where the waters tend to be harder, averaged 0.2 ppm fluoride, the highest levels being recorded at Ivanicgrad (0.8 ppm fluoride). Analyses of mineral and thermal waters from these areas gave results ranging from 0.4 to 1.2 ppm fluoride. Alkaline muriatic springs at Jamnica and Lasinja contained 2.2 ppm and 2.0 ppm fluoride, respectively, while a hot spring at Lipik contained 11 ppm fluoride.

From the Soviet Union, Andreeva (1963) has reported the results of analyses of 968 water samples from the Chuvash ASSR. Samples were taken from 5 surface waters, 887 shallow wells and 76 artesian wells. In 87% of the samples fluoride levels were below 0.5 ppm. Levels of 0.5-1 ppm fluoride were found in 11% of the shallow wells and in 25% of the artesian wells. Levels exceeding 1.5 ppm were found in two samples from shallow wells and in 11 samples from artesian wells. The highest levels recorded for the three types of source were 1.8 ppm, 2.2 ppm and 3.8 ppm respectively. The lowest levels (up to 0.3 ppm) tended to be found in northern and central Chuvash, while the highest levels (41% ranging from 0.5 to 1 ppm) were found in the district of Shemurshinsk.

Intake of Fluoride from Drinking Water

The amount of fluoride which is ingested with water will be dependent on the fluoride content of the water and on the amount of this water which is consumed daily. The fluoride content of the water can be determined fairly readily, but precise determination of the daily water intake of the individual is considerably more difficult. The early literature dealing with water intake has been considered by McClure (1939, 1943). Assessing the daily water requirement by the method of Adolph (1933), McClure (1943) estimated the daily fluoride intake of children aged 1-12 years from water containing 1 ppm fluoride. Adolph assessed the daily water requirement as equal to 1 ml per calorie of energy in the daily diet. Taking this as a basis and allowing for variations in drinking habits, McClure made two estimates of the amount of water drunk: (1) when drinking water was estimated to equal 25% of the daily requirement and (2) when it was estimated to equal 33% of the daily requirement. His results are shown in Table 3. The consumption of drinking water was estimated as ranging from 390-560 ml in children aged 1-3 years to 812-1166 ml in children aged 10-12 years. The intake of fluoride from water containing 1 ppm fluoride was therefore estimated at 0.390-0.560 mg daily for children aged 1-3 years, rising to 0.810-1.165 mg daily in children aged 10-12 years.

TABLE 3

ESTIMATED DAILY INTAKE OF FLUORINE FROM DRINKING WATER CONTAINING
1 PPM FLUORINE[a]

	1 to 3	4 to 6	7 to 9	10 to 12
Age (years)	1 to 3	4 to 6	7 to 9	10 to 12
Energy allowance (calories)	1 200	1 600	2 000	2 500
Water requirement (ml)	1 200	1 600	2 000	2 500
Drinking-water consumption:				
(1) When water drunk is equal to 25 % of the total daily water requirement and (a) 10 % and (b) 20 % of the total water content of the food is of drinking-water origin, the total daily consumption of drinking water would equal:				
(a)	390 ml	520 ml	650 ml	812 ml
(b)	480 ml	640 ml	800 ml	1 000 ml
(2) When water drunk is equal to 33 % of the total daily water requirement and (c) 10 % and (d) 20 % of the total water content of the food is of drinking-water origin, the total daily consumption of drinking water would equal:				
(c)	480 ml	640 ml	800 ml	1 000 ml
(d)	560 ml	746 ml	933 ml	1 166 ml
Total daily fluorine ingested from drinking water containing 1 ppm fluorine under the preceding conditions of water ingestion would equal:				
In water intake (a)	0.390 mg	0.520 mg	0.650 mg	0.810 mg
In water intake (b) and (c)	0.480 mg	0.640 mg	0.800 mg	1.000 mg
In water intake (d)	0.560 mg	0.745 mg	0.930 mg	1.165 mg

[a] After McClure (1943).

While these estimates have been of value in evaluating fluoride intake it has been considered that they do not adequately allow for fluctuations of water intake—and concomitantly of fluoride intake from water—under different climatic conditions. That climatic conditions may affect fluoride intake from water was indicated by the findings of Dean (1951), who reported that 0.5 and 0.7 ppm fluoride in the water of two towns in the southern State of Georgia—mean maximum temperature 68°F (20°C)—produced the same prevalence of dental fluorosis that would be produced in the mid-western States—mean maximum temperature 49°F (9.5°C)—by approximately 1 ppm fluoride.

The effect of climatic variation on water and fluoride intake, especially in warmer areas, has been extensively considered by Galagan (Galagan, 1953; Galagan & Lamson, 1953), who pointed out that intrinsically the amount of water required is influenced by body size and weight, by the kind of food eaten, by habit patterns and by physical activity. Externally, environmental factors will influence the water metabolism of the body and climatic factors especially may markedly affect water intake between different geographical localities. Of the climatic factors affecting water intake, mean annual temperature, excessive daytime temperatures, radiant heat gain, relative humidity, and wind movement are of the greatest importance. Galagan et al. (1957) conducted a survey of fluid intake over a one-year period by children aged 1-10 years living in two areas of California. They found that under normal living conditions the water intake increased directly with temperature increases, and they presented an equation which expressed the relationship between mean maximum temperature and water intake. This relationship was described by the estimation equation "ounces of water per pound of body weight $= -0.038 + 0.0062$ temperature". (Temperature here refers to the mean maximum temperature in degrees Fahrenheit (average of 5 consecutive years).) With this formula, water intake under differing climatic conditions can be calculated and, if the fluoride level of the drinking water is known, an assessment of fluoride intake from water can then be made. On this basis Galagan & Vermillion (1957) were able to derive a formula to estimate optimal fluoride levels in different climatic regions.

Recently, it has been considered that data on water intake, especially by young children in warmer climates, should be collected to test the suitability of calculated or recommended optimal water fluoride levels. Such studies have been made by Neumann (1957), Crosby & Shepherd (1957), Kruger (1960), Walker et al. (1963), and McPhail & Zacherl (1965). The results of these studies were generally in reasonable agreement and can be illustrated by those of Walker and associates, who showed that the direct water intake of children aged from 3-5 years to 8-12 years ranged from 349 ml to 493 ml, while the daily water intake (water drunk plus amount added to food) ranged from 926 ml in children 3-5 years old to 1209 ml in those 8-12 years old.　Somewhat higher values were recorded by Kruger (1960), who found the daily water intake (water drunk plus amount added to food) of children aged 6-8 years in three Queensland towns—mean maximum temperatures 87.6, 82.7 and 77.5°F (31, 28 and 25°C)—in summer averaged 1225, 1450 and 1089 ml respectively.　Although emphasizing the considerable extent of individual variability in water intake, Kruger considered that the intake of fluoride from water, the fluoride content of which had been adjusted according to estimates based on Galagan & Vermillion's calculations or on similar recommendations by the Australian National Health and Medical Research Council, should be satisfactory.　The above-mentioned formula of Galagan & Vermillion. relating optimal water fluoride level to climatic temperature, is discussed with special regard to tropical and subtropical, particularly Japanese, conditions in Chapter 8, section 4.

3. INGESTION FROM FOODS (J. C. Muhler)

Almost every known food and water supply contains traces of fluorides since fluorine is one of the more abundant elements in the earth's crust.

The amount of fluorides in foods is of utmost significance, since the combined ingestion of fluorine-containing water, fluoridated dentifrices, and high-fluoride foods may be either a useful or a harmful nutritional practice. Care needs to be exercised in avoiding the constant use of high-fluoride foods or the ingestion of fluoride from sources not proved important to dental health.

Comprehensive investigations of the fluoride content of specific items of food in various countries have been made by Machle, Scott & Treon (1939), Gabovich (1951), Reid (1936), Nömmik (1953), Clifford (1945), Matuura et al. (1954), and von Fellenberg (1948), while McClure (1949), Truhaut (1955), and Bredemann (1956) have assembled published data relative to the fluoride content of a large number of foods.

Table 4, taken from the work of McClure, indicates the fluoride content of a number of different foodstuffs.　The higher figures in this table are as a rule exceptional, and in some instances they are based on a single finding which may not be representative.　However, without doubt certain food materials contain relatively high concentrations of fluoride.　These include fish foods, teas and some wines.　As regards fluorine-rich tea, many analyses have been published.　The most recent, by Singer, Armstrong & Vatassery (1967), gives the figures 52-161 ppm F for the dry leaves of five different black teas and 336 ppm F for one green tea.　Infusion of 1.2-1.3 g of tea leaves in 125 ml of distilled water extracted 41-78% of the fluorine.

The combined intake of fluorine from food and fluoridated water has been studied by McClure.　Table 5 indicates children's daily intake of fluorine from both food and fluoridated drinking water according to age.

TABLE 4

FLUORINE CONTENT OF VARIOUS FOODSTUFFS [a]

Food	Fluorine content (ppm)
Animal tissue :	
Cow's liver, dry weight	5.20-5.80
Chicken liver, fresh weight	0.7-1.29
Calf liver, fresh weight	0.2
Cow's kidney, dry weight	6.9-10.1
Cow's heart muscle, dry weight	2.3-2.7
Meats :	
Chicken	1.40
Beef	2.00
Round steak	1.3
Pork	<0.2
Pork chops	1.0
Pork shoulder	1.2
Frankfurters	1.7
Lamb	1.2
Veal	0.9
Mutton	<0.2
Fish :	
Fish fillets	1.5
Mackerel	
boned	<0.2
with bones	3.9
fresh	26.89
dried	84.47
canned	12.10
Salmon	
canned	4.5
fresh	5.8
dried	19.3
Sardines	
canned	7.3
in olive oil	16.1
Shrimps	
canned	4.4
edible portion	0.9
Codfish	
fresh	7.0
salted	5.0
Oysters	
fresh	0.7
Crab meat, canned	2.0
Herring, smoked	3.5
Tuna fish flakes, canned	0.1
Eggs :	
Whole	1.2
White	1.5
Yolk	0.6
Whole milk :	0.07-0.22
Tea :	3.2-178.8
Average of ten samples	97.0
Citrus fruits :	
Grapefruit	0.36
edible portion	0.36
fresh	0.12
Lemon, fresh	0.028, 0.051, 0.174

[a] After McClure (1949).

TABLE 4 *(continued)*

Food	Fluorine content (ppm)	
Orange, edible portion	0.34	
Oranges, fruit, fresh	0.17-0.07	
Pomelo, fruit, fresh	0.10-0.16	
Non-citrus fruits :	*Fresh weight*	*Dry weight*
Apples	0.22-1.32	0.13-0.43
Apricot	0.06	0.24
Banana	0.23	0.65
Cherry	0.25	
Cherries, black	0.18	0.61
Currants	0.12	0.69
Fig	0.21	
Grapes	0.16	
Grape juice	0.093	
Gooseberries	0.11	0.72
Mango	0.18	
Pawpaw	0.15	
Pear	0.19	
Plum	0.22	0.10
Pineapple	0.14	
Pineapple, tinned	0.00	
Quince	0.06	0.37
Sweet melon	0.20	
Strawberry	0.18	
Watermelon	0.11	
Cereals and cereal products :	*Fresh weight*	*Dry weight*
Corn		
unspecified	0.62	0.70
canned	<0.20	
yellow	<0.10	
germ		8.0-11.0
meal, as purchased	0.22	
flakes		1.33
Ralston	0.58	
Wheat		
whole		0.53
unspecified	0.7	
bran	0.29	0.33
germ A, commercial	1.7	
germ B, commercial	4.0	
germ, pure	0.88	1.00
Cream of wheat		0.55
Flour		
wheat, white	0.35	
self-rising	0.45	
whole wheat		1.32
white	0.27	0.31
biscuit		0.0
baking	0.31	0.35
Bread, white		0.54
Rice		
unspecified	0.67	0.76
whole	<0.10	
middle	0.19	
Soybeans		4.00
Buckwheat		
unspecified		2.00
whole		1.70
bran		1.60
Oats		
unspecified		3.0
crushed	0.20	
mother's		0.92
fresh	0.25	0.29
Rye		
unspecified	0.61	0.69
black-eyed peas	0.23	

TABLE 4 (continued)

Food	Fluorine content (ppm)	
	Fresh weight	Dry weight
Rye (continued)		
cottonseed, meal	12.0	
hulls	12.0-14.0	
Spaghetti		
canned		1.15
dry		0.80
Macaroni, dry		0.82
Vegetables and tubers :	Fresh weight	Dry weight
Asparagus, canned		0.48
Beans		
string		0.64
string, canned		0.67
green	0.15	1.01
light green	0.11	0.73
lima, dry		4.51
lima, seeds		2.2
dry		1.04
dried		<0.20
navy, dry		1.70
Beets		
unspecified	0.2	
fresh		0.60
root		2.8
leaves, dry		3.80
tops		3.4
string	0.32	6.09
Cauliflower		
fresh		0.45
flower	0.12	0.86
leaves	0.08	0.83
unspecified	1.0	
Cabbage		
large		9.34
foreign		15.38
fresh		0.70
unspecified	0.13	
edible head		3.4
without leaves	0.8	9.5
Carrots		
unspecified	0.4	6.92
fresh		1.30
root		8.4
Celery		
unspecified	0.14	
edible stalks		8.5
Cress	0.24	4.38
Cucumber	0.20	
Endive	0.2	
Garlic		
green		17.72
Kale	0.16	
Lettuce		
loose, head		11.3
cabbage	0.30	4.45
prickly		5.18
fresh		0.42
Mustard		
greens	0.15	
leaves, salted, dried		3.0-4.8
Onions		
green		10.11
unspecified	0.60	
Parsley		
tops		11.3
unspecified	0.8	

TABLE 4 *(concluded)*

Food	Fluorine content (ppm)	
	Fresh weight	Dry weight
Parsnip, roots		5.5
unspecified	0.6	
green		6.69
fresh		0.60
Potatoes		
white		0.96
unspecified	0.20	
whole	6.4	22.0
peelings	0.07	0.35
Irish, tuber		1.4
sweet, unpeeled	0.13	
sweet	<0.20	
Pumpkin	0.10	
Radish	0.8	
Rhubarb	0.4	
Rutabaga (swede)		
tops		7.0
roots		2.9
Spinach		
fresh		1.11
unspecified	1.8	
winter	0.44	3.80
Squash, fresh		0.63
Tomatoes		
unspecified	0.24	2.40
fresh		0.53
Turnips		
greens	0.10	
tops		1.7
roots		2.6
Watercress	1.0	
Miscellaneous substances :	Fresh weight	Dry weight
Peanuts		
unspecified		1.36
tops		1.7
kernel		1.5
Almonds	0.90	0.90
Hazelnut	0.30	0.30
Chestnut		1.45
shell		0.24
Coconut, fresh	0.00	
Cocoa	0.5, 1.0	
Plain chocolate	0.50	
Milk chocolate	0.5, 1.0	
Molasses	0.00	
Sugar	0.32	
Honey	1.00	
Gelatin	0.00	
Glucose	0.50	
Malt	1.0, 1.5	
Powdered ginger	1.00	
Baking powder		
A	220.0	
B	19.0	
C	<0.1	
Coffee	0.2-1.6	
Butter	1.50	
Cheese	1.62	
Pork and beans, canned	1.40	
Wine and beer :		
Chinese, Shao-sing		
best grade	0.07	
second grade	0.05	
Port	0.24	
Beer	0.20	

TABLE 5

SUMMARY OF ESTIMATED DAILY INTAKE OF FLUORINE FROM FOOD
AND DRINKING WATER [a]

Age (years)	Body-weight (kg)	Daily fluorine intake			
		From drinking water [b] (mg)	From food [c] (mg)	Total (mg)	Total (mg per kg of body-weight)
1-3	8-16	0.390-0.560	0.027-0.265	0.417-0.825	0.026-0.103
4-6	13-24	0.520-0.745	0.036-0.360	0.556-1.105	0.023-0.085
7-9	16-35	0.650-0.930	0.045-0.450	0.695-1.380	0.020-0.068
10-12	25-54	0.810-1.165	0.056-0.560	0.866-1.725	0.016-0.069

[a] After McClure (1949).
[b] Containing 1 ppm fluorine.
[c] Dry substance containing 0.1-1 ppm fluorine.

Other calculations have been presented for adults in different countries and in different areas of the USA (Table 6).

The compiler of Table 6, Cholak (1959), makes the following comments:

"The values indicated opposite the listed American communities were obtained by the analysis of duplicates of the prepared meals of at least two persons in each of these communities, collected daily over periods of 40 to 160 days. It may be seen that the quantity of fluoride in the prepared food of the subjects in the several areas, with the exception of O'Donnell, Texas, increases with increase in the concentration of fluoride in the drinking water of the areas. Much of this increase is due, no doubt, to the water used in preparing the food. In the exceptional case of the subjects in O'Donnell, Texas, the relatively small amounts of fluoride in the prepared meals may be due to the fact that much of their food was shipped in and was of such type as to require little local water in its preparation.

TABLE 6

QUANTITIES OF FLUORIDE IN THE FOOD CONSUMED DAILY BY ADULTS
IN CERTAIN COUNTRIES [a]

Location [b]	Fluoride in food (mg)	
United States of America		
Cincinnati, Ohio (0.1)	0.34-0.80	Exclusive of F in drinking water
Galesburg, Ill. (2)	0.94-1.16	
Ennis, Tex. (5-6)	1.32-1.35	
Lake Preston, S. Dak. (6)	0.99-2.19	
Bartlett, Tex. (8)	2.33-3.13	
O'Donnell, Tex. (18)	1.41-1.49	
(Average general diet)	0.2+ -0.3+	
Norway	0.22-3.1	Inclusive of low-level F in drinking water
USSR	0.6-1.2	
Canada	0.18-0.3	
Switzerland	0.5	
England	0.6-1.8	

[a] After Cholak (1959).
[b] The figures in parentheses following the US cities represent the levels of concentration of fluoride, in mg per litre, in the drinking water.

"In the daily intake of fluoride, as represented opposite the names of individual countries, is included that derived from all beverages. The contribution made by tea may have constituted a significant proportion of the total fluoride."

One continues to hear the argument that since fluorides are found, to varying degrees of course, in almost all foods, and because of their wide distribution in the plant and animal kingdom, their mere presence must indicate some physiological importance to man.

Since fluorine is so universally distributed in the plant and animal kingdoms, the preparation of a diet totally free from fluorine is a real challenge. Moreover, the analytical difficulties encountered in accurately measuring such microquantities of fluorine as occur in many foods add to our vague interpretation of the element's position in nutrition and physiology. The criterion by which most studies have evaluated the utilization of fluoride in the diet is estimation of the retention of fluoride in the skeleton. Weight and reproduction studies have also been used, but have not contributed significantly to our knowledge of the subject, probably because the studies were not conducted for sufficiently long periods of time and because purified diets were used which in themselves adversely affect growth and reproduction. Also, since only trace amounts of the element are required by the organism and since almost every food, as well as air and water, contains some fluorine, animals and human beings are probably very seldom in acute need of it. It is also possible that our present state of knowledge concerning optimal levels and essential functions may be quite inadequate, and with additional investigations it might well be demonstrated that the microquantities normally present in most commonly eaten mixed diets and water supplies are not fully "adequate".

Sharpless & McCollum (1933) were the first workers who attempted to devise an adequate diet deficient only in fluorine, and to evaluate its essentiality in the rat. They stated only that "the diet was very low in fluorine but not quite free" and reported that the rats receiving the low-fluorine diet looked very healthy, were fat, and on the whole appeared normal in all respects. No differences could be noticed between the animals receiving the low-fluorine diet and the controls which were fed fluorine.

In 1944 McClendon reported on a diet stated to be fluorine-free and which was prepared from food grown in solution culture and chemically pure substances. Two rats were placed on the fluorine-free diet at 21 days of age. One of the rats died as a result of starvation in 48 days "because caries had destroyed the effective chewing surface of all the molar teeth". The other rat was temporarily saved from starvation by feeding it 10 ml of milk each day (to which was added 1 μg F). He concluded that fluorine "is necessary in a diet that has to be chewed".

The results of a larger scale experimental project based on growing dietary components in water culture have been described in a later publication by McClendon & Gershon-Cohen (1953). Rain water which was freed from fluoride by passing through Amberlite IR_4 was used for the nutrient solution medium.

Control rats received a diet whose constituents (containing 10% sucrose) were derived from field-grown crops plus fluorine in the drinking water at a fluorine concentration of 20 μg per ml.

The growth of the rats on the fluorine-free diet was significantly retarded: 19 receiving the fluorine-free diet gained an average of only 10.4 g in 46 days, as compared with 18 controls which gained 86.9 g in the same period (Table 7).

TABLE 7

EFFECT OF FLUORINE-FREE WATER-GROWN DIET ON WEIGHT
AND DENTAL CARIES IN RATS [a]

	No. of animals	Average weight (g)		No. of carious molars per rat
		at 22 days	at 88 days	
Control	18	41.2	128.1	0.5
Fluorine-free diet	19	40.8	51.2	10.2

[a] After McClendon & Gershon-Cohen (1953).

Reproduction was also reported to be impaired. A number of female rats fed the fluorine-free diet were mated to normal males, and no viable offspring were produced. From these data McClendon & Gershon-Cohen conclude that fluorine is "necessary in the diet of the rat".

The author of this section has also reported on the essentiality of fluorine in the rat (Muhler, 1954). The low-fluorine diet used in these studies was highly purified and consisted of casein, starch, butter, inorganic salts and vitamins. In all the diets fluorine was present as a constituent of the basal substances or as a contaminant, but no fluorine compounds were added to any of them. Essentiality of the element was studied by comparing animals receiving the low-fluorine diet with those ingesting the same diet with the fluorine retained, as regards weight increases, growth, reproduction, and fluoride retention in the skeleton.

Weight gain and reproduction in the animals receiving the highly purified low-fluorine diet were definitely affected. However, considerable caution must be exercised in relating this observation to the low fluorine content of the diet.

Maurer & Day (1957) also studied the importance of fluorine in nutrition in the rat, using a diet essentially the same as that described by Muhler, but claimed to be even more highly purified. The diet was estimated to contain "no more" than 0.007 ppm fluoride, although the authors stated that the exact fluorine content could not be determined. They concluded from these studies that fluorine was non-essential in nutrition, at least for the rat, and that "its value in the body is apparently limited to the promotion of resistance to dental caries".

Doberenz et al. (1964) developed a minimal fluoride diet by employing a hydroponic technique for the culture and production of sorghum and soybean of minimal fluoride content in special greenhouses equipped with microfilters, etc., to minimize exposure to fluoride.

Three groups of 9 Sprague-Dawley rats each (3 male, 6 female), 20 days old, housed in individual cages in a controlled dust-free environment, were fed the following diets for 10 weeks: (1) the minimal fluorine diet of green-house sorghum and soybean, containing 0.005 ppm fluoride; (2) the minimal fluorine diet with addition of 2.0 ppm F (as NaF); (3) a control diet of field-grown sorghum and soybean, containing 2.67 ppm F on a fresh-weight basis. All rats were sacrificed at 91 days of age. No impairment in heart, liver or kidney was caused by the low fluoride conditions imposed. The only significant differences in enzyme activities were seen in an increase in isocitric dehydrogenase levels in the serum (μmol α-ketoglutarate formed per ml per hour: 591, 384 and 404) and a decrease in liver homogenates (383, 436 and 436) in each of the above groups respectively.

Further study, with the use of diets lower in fluorine content than those reported here, concerning the essentiality of fluorine is needed, especially in regard to the effects on cellular enzyme systems, on normal and patho-logical calcification processes and on reproduction and initial growth responses.

4. INGESTION FROM DRUGS (G. K. Stookey)

Owing to the variety of preparations available commercially, the various fluoride-containing drugs discussed in this section have been divided into two arbitrary groups—those used as anticariogenic agents and those used for other purposes. With regard to fluoride metabolism, the first group is of greater importance since the agents are designed specifically for the metabolic utilization of the fluoride ion, whereas in the second group fluoride is commonly employed in a biologically inert form.

Drugs used as Anticariogenic Agents

Fluoride tablets, lozenges, and troches

In the past twenty years a considerable amount of attention has been given to the use of fluoride tablets, since their use could conceivably repre-sent a means whereby individuals might obtain optimal quantities of fluoride without having a communal fluoride water supply. Several clinical studies concerning the effectiveness of fluoride tablets have been reported and it is beyond the scope of this section to review these findings. Suffice it to say that the evidence from such a review (Stookey, 1966) suggests that, while the use of fluoride tablets may be partially effective in reducing the incidence of dental caries and warrants additional research, the procedure is fraught with several important limitations which severely restrict its role in preventive dentistry.

Although the metabolism of fluoride as ingested in drinking water has been thoroughly studied and numerous reports and reviews have appeared in the literature, only limited information is available concerning the metabolism of fluoride ingested in the form of a tablet. In general, fluoride tablets available commercially contain 0.25-1.00 mg of fluoride, commonly provided as sodium fluoride, an inert filler such as sodium chloride, and a small amount of disintegrant. Thus, a typical composition might consist of 2.21 mg NaF, 94.49 mg NaCl, and 0.05 mg disintegrant.

The results of studies (Stookey and associates, unpublished data) conducted to determine the rate of fluoride absorption and excretion following the daily ingestion of a single fluoride tablet containing 1.0 mg fluoride are partially summarized in Table 8 and Fig. 1. (Tables 8-12 are based on results

TABLE 8

FLUORIDE BALANCE DATA IN ADULTS FOLLOWING THE INGESTION
OF A FLUORIDE TABLET CONTAINING 1.0 mg FLUORIDE (as NaF)

Mean amount ingested (μg F/day)	Mean net amount excreted in urine (μg F/day)	Mean net amount excreted in faeces (μg F/day)	Total net amount excreted (μg F/day)	Estimated amount retained (μg F/day)
984.3 ± 9.8[a]	608.1 ± 35.4[a]	98.4 ± 11.9[a]	706.5	277.8
Percentage of ingested fluoride	61.7%	10.0%	71.7%	28.3%

[a] Standard error of the mean.

from our laboratory.) These studies were preceded by a control period in which no supplemental fluoride was ingested, in order that the appropriate "normal" values might be ascertained. The data in Table 8 indicate that the daily ingestion of a 1.0-mg fluoride tablet by young adults residing for at least three years in a communal fluoride area resulted in an excretion of only 10.0% of the ingested fluoride in the faeces, thus indicating that 90.0% of the ingested fluoride was absorbed from the gastrointestinal tract. Of this latter amount, 61.7% was subsequently excreted in the urine, leaving 28.3% remaining presumably in the skeleton, soft tissues, and circulating bodyfluids. Fig. 1 indicates that the maximum rate of urinary fluoride excretion occurred 2-4 hours after ingestion of the fluoride tablet, being preceded and followed by periods of rapid increase and decrease, respectively, in the rate.

FIG. 1

RATE OF URINARY EXCRETION OF FLUORIDE INGESTED AS 1.0-mg
FLUORIDE TABLET IN YOUNG ADULTS WITH 3 YEARS'
EXPOSURE TO FLUORIDATED DRINKING WATER

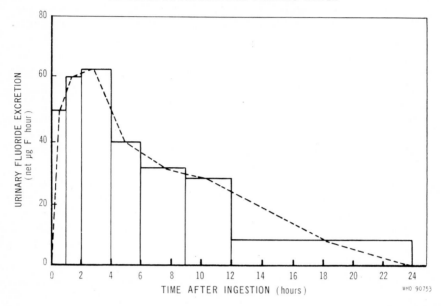

The results of a second study of similar design are shown in Table 9 and Fig. 2. Twelve young adult males, with more than five years' exposure to a fluoridated water supply, were selected for the study, which was conducted in the winter months with the tablets being ingested at 6 p.m. to reduce the possibility of elimination of fluoride through perspiration. It

TABLE 9

RATE OF URINARY EXCRETION OF FLUORIDE INGESTED AS A 1.0-mg FLUORIDE
TABLET IN YOUNG ADULTS WITH MORE THAN FIVE YEARS' EXPOSURE
TO A FLUORIDATED WATER SUPPLY

Time after ingestion (hours)	Mean amount excreted (net μg F/hour)	Percentage of urinary fluoride excreted during each time interval	Cumulative percentage of urinary fluoride excreted
0 - 1.5	84.7	13.1	13.1
1.5- 3	136.4	21.0	34.1
3 - 6	44.7	13.8	47.9
6 - 12	44.0	27.1	75.0
12 - 15	24.7	7.6	82.6
15 - 18	20.6	6.3	88.9
18 - 21	21.7	6.7	95.6
21 - 24	14.3	4.4	100.0

FIG. 2

RATE OF URINARY EXCRETION OF FLUORIDE INGESTED AS 1.0-mg FLUORIDE TABLET IN YOUNG ADULTS WITH 5 YEARS' EXPOSURE TO FLUORIDATED DRINKING WATER

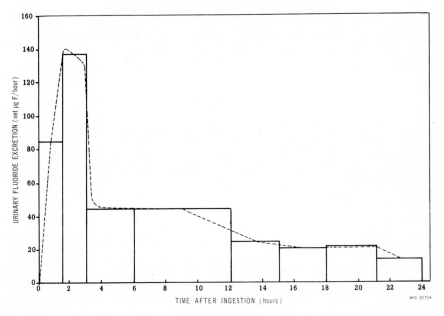

was found that 97.4% of the ingested fluoride was absorbed and subsequently excreted in the urine in the 24-hour period following the ingestion of the tablet. The data shown in Table 9 indicate that 34.1% of the fluoride ultimately excreted in the urine appeared within the first three hours following ingestion and that 47.9% and 75.0% had appeared after six and twelve hours, respectively. Fig. 2 indicates a rapid appearance of fluoride in the urine following ingestion of the tablet, with the maximum rate of excretion occurring 1.5-3.0 hours after ingestion. Again, a rapid decrease in the rate of excretion was noted, the fluoride content of the urine remaining only slightly above the normal control level during the last 12 hours of the study. These findings approximate to those reported by Zipkin & Leone (1957) in which the rate of urinary fluoride excretion in adults residing in an optimal fluoride area was studied after the ingestion of the fluoride-containing drinking water and the additional ingestion of 5.0 mg fluoride as sodium fluoride. Likewise, Hodge (1956) has cited the similar findings of Smith & Gardner (unpublished) following the ingestion of 1.5 mg of supplemental fluoride by adults residing in an optimal fluoride area.

The foregoing data thus indicate that the fluoride ingested in the form of a tablet containing 1.0 mg fluoride, provided as sodium fluoride, is at least 90% metabolically available in the human. Further, it is apparent that the fluoride is rapidly absorbed from the gastrointestinal tract and rapidly excreted in the urine, at least 75% of the fluoride ultimately destined for excretion in the urine appearing during the first twelve hours after ingestion.

The results of a study (Muhler et al., 1966) designed to compare the urinary excretion of fluoride ingested as sodium fluoride in aqueous solution and in commercially available fluoride tablets and carried out in subjects with no known previous exposure to fluoride who were permanent residents of a non-fluoride area ($<$ 0.1 ppm F) are summarized in Table 10 and Fig. 3.

TABLE 10

URINARY FLUORIDE DATA IN YOUNG ADULTS INGESTING NaF
IN AQUEOUS SOLUTION AND IN TABLETS

Regimen	Number of days	Urinary fluoride	
		Concentration (ppm F)	Total per day (mg)
Subject R. S.			
Pre-control.	11	0.213 ± 0.040[a]	0.259 ± 0.027[a]
2.0 mg F per day as aqueous NaF . . .	7	0.789 ± 0.063	1.403 ± 0.105
Mid-control	12	0.329 ± 0.051	0.434 ± 0.038
2.0 mg F per day as NaF tablets[b] . . .	16	0.822 ± 0.072	1.214 ± 0.083
Post-control	7	0.464 ± 0.049	0.546 ± 0.041
Subject R. R.			
Pre-control.	12	0.504 ± 0.037	0.524 ± 0.040
2.0 mg F per day as aqueous NaF . . .	14	1.286 ± 0.101	1.523 ± 0.114
Mid-control	8	0.470 ± 0.029	0.531 ± 0.038
2.0 mg F per day as NaF tablets[b] . . .	16	0.870 ± 0.097	0.932 ± 0.086
Post-control	8	0.516 ± 0.044	0.672 ± 0.045

[a] Standard error of the mean.
[b] Karidium tablets, Lorvic Corporation, Kansas City, Mo.

These data suggest that, after identical doses, less fluoride was excreted in the urine when it was ingested in tablet form than when it was ingested in the form of a solution. If one assumes logically that comparable amounts of the absorbed fluoride were retained by the skeletons of the subjects in question it appears that a higher amount of fluoride was absorbed from the gastrointestinal tract when the fluoride was ingested in aqueous solution. Data obtained in an unpublished study by Hennon, Stookey & Muhler which was comparable except in that the dietary regimen of the subjects was carefully controlled are summarized in part in Fig. 4 and indicate a rapid rate of appearance and excretion of fluoride in the urine as has been cited previously.

Studies concerning the metabolism of fluoride from fluoride tablets in children based upon the rate of excretion in the urine are somewhat less

FIG. 3

URINARY FLUORIDE LEVELS IN ADULTS INGESTING NaF IN AQUEOUS
SOLUTION OR IN TABLETS

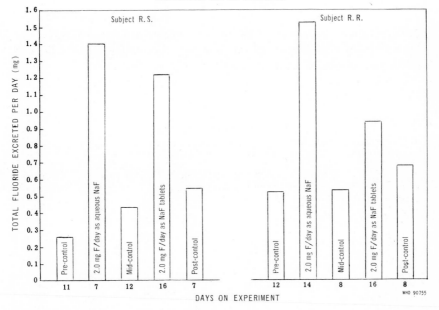

FIG. 4

CONCENTRATION OF FLUORIDE IN URINE AS A FUNCTION OF TIME AFTER
INGESTION OF 2.0 mg FLUORIDE (AS NaF) IN A TABLET [a]

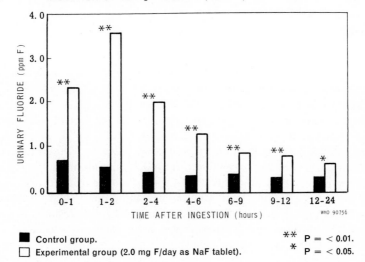

[a] The subjects were young adults with no previous exposure to fluoride and who received a
controlled low-fluoride diet throughout the study period.

indicative of the actual rate of absorption, since more of the fluoride absorbed from the gastrointestinal tract is retained in the various skeletal and dental hard tissues.

The results obtained in a clinical study (Hennon, Stookey & Muhler, 1967) involving children 3-6 years of age residing in a non-fluoride area (F<0.05 ppm) are summarized in Table 11. The children in Group 1 of

TABLE 11

URINARY FLUORIDE DATA IN CHILDREN RECEIVING EITHER A PLACEBO, A COMMERCIALLY AVAILABLE SODIUM FLUORIDE TABLET, OR A DELAYED-RELEASE-TYPE (DRT) CAPSULE

Time after initiation of study	Group 1 (Placebo)		Group 2 (NaF tablet)		Group 3 (DRT capsule)	
	ppm F	Total μg F[a]	ppm F	Total μg F[a]	ppm F	Total μg F[a]
Control	0.341	144	0.365	169	0.342	137
1 day	0.390	151	1.030	432	0.881	325
3 days	0.419	129	1.126	425	0.844	343
5 days	0.383	161	1.066	382	0.987	360
7 days	0.492	189	0.980	398	1.040	359
10 days	0.441	164	1.109	397	1.016	333
14 days	0.497	169	1.145	414	0.946	350
21 days	0.573	192	1.062	391	1.024	347
28 days	0.591	189	1.086	431	1.010	301
42 days	0.455	151	1.045	347	0.821	252
56 days	0.434	148	1.002	360	1.037	381
3 months . . .	0.414	150	0.834	345	0.881	307
4 months . . .	0.479	168	0.967	331	0.871	275
5 months . . .	0.522	199	1.093	354	0.845	277
6 months . . .	0.463	165	1.130	418	0.796	294
7 months . . .	0.482	158	0.914	330	0.795	298
8 months . . .	0.519	198	1.146	367	0.937	291
9 months . . .	0.426	136	1.097	425	0.982	369
10 months . . .	0.550	180	1.174	443	1.041	371
11 months . . .	0.593	189	1.083	536	1.095	420
12 months . . .	0.522	169	1.113	462	0.979	312

[a] Total amount of fluoride excreted during each respective 24-hour period.

this study were given a placebo, those in Group 2 a typical sodium fluoride tablet; while those in Group 3 were provided with a delayed-release-type capsule, designed on the basis of laboratory studies (Stookey & Muhler, 1966) to release fluoride at a slow rate into the gastrointestinal tract in order to approximate more closely to the ingestion of drinking water containing the optimal level of fluoride. The data in Table 11 indicate that, while the pre-experimental urine contained about 0.35 ppm fluoride, the ingestion of a typical fluoride tablet containing 1.0 mg fluoride resulted in a urinary fluoride concentration of about 1.0 ppm, beginning on the first experimental day, and the ingestion of the delayed-release-type capsule resulted in a comparable concentration of fluoride in the urine, but only after one week. These urinary fluoride concentrations showed no appreciable change throughout the first year of the study. If one considers the total amount of fluoride excreted in the urine by the children in the various groups, it is apparent that early in the study the children in the control group excreted about 150 μg fluoride daily and that the children receiving the 1.0-mg sodium fluoride tablet excreted about 400 μg fluoride daily. Assuming that about 90% of the ingested fluoride is absorbed from the gastrointestinal tract, these data would suggest that about 650 μg fluoride, or about 72% of the absorbed fluoride, is retained in the body. A similar comparison of the data obtained in the children who received the delayed-release-type capsule suggests that about 700 μg fluoride, or about 78% of the absorbed fluoride, is retained in the body—a value slightly greater than that observed with the typical fluoride tablet.

It thus appears that the daily ingestion of a fluoride tablet containing 1.0 mg fluoride in children may result in a greater amount of fluoride available for metabolic utilization than that derived from fluoridated water, since children ingest less than one litre of water daily and therefore receive a somewhat smaller total amount of metabolically available fluoride.

Fluoride-vitamin supplements

The use of fluoride supplements containing various vitamins has become of increased interest in recent years and at the present time a wide variety of preparations are commercially available. Perhaps the major contributing factor in this increased interest in vitamin-fluoride preparations as a means of supplemental fluoride therapy concerns the practical application of this concept. While it has been found (Hennon, Stookey & Muhler, 1967; Arnold, McClure & White, 1960) that persons ingesting fluoride tablets *per se* frequently lose interest in this form of therapy, Hennon, Stookey & Muhler (1966b) have suggested that interest is maintained by the patients when the supplemental fluoride is provided in a vitamin-fluoride preparation. This factor may be partially responsible for the clinical observations that a greater degree of protection against dental caries, approximating to that observed with fluoridated drinking water, appears to follow the ingestion of vitamin-fluoride preparations than the ingestion of non-vitamin-fluoride preparations (Stookey, 1966; Arnold, McClure & White, 1960).

Commercially available vitamin-fluoride preparations frequently contain, in addition to sodium fluoride, vitamins A, C, and D, and a few contain some members of the vitamin B complex as well. While it has been suggested that such preparations make it more difficult to regulate the dosage of fluoride prescribed, it should be noted that currently available products are designed with varying dosages of vitamins and fluoride so that one may prescribe the desired dosage of fluoride with ease.

Only limited information is available concerning the influence of various vitamins upon fluoride metabolism or *vice versa*. Hennon, Stookey & Muhler (1964) investigated the influence of four different vitamin-fluoride preparations upon fluoride retention in the rat and reported that preparations containing vitamins A, C, and D, in the presence and absence of thiamine, riboflavine, pyridoxine, calcium pantothenate, cyanocobalamin, and biotin, did not alter the metabolism of sodium fluoride. Showley et al. (1966) similarly noted that vitamin A, thiamine, riboflavine, pyridoxine, and pantothenic acid, all of which have established minimal daily requirements in the rat, did not markedly influence fluoride retention, although a greater retention of fluoride was noted when the level of vitamin supplementation fell short of the minimal daily requirements of each vitamin. Conversely, Harkins, Longenecker & Sarett (1963) have shown that relatively large dosages of sodium fluoride added to a vitamin supplement containing vitamin A, thiamine, riboflavine, pyridoxine, and pantothenic acid had no effect upon the growth rate or upon food and vitamin utilization in the rat.

With regard to the influence of individual vitamins upon fluoride metabolism, Muhler (1958) reported that elevated levels of ascorbic acid increased the retention of fluoride in the skeleton and soft tissues of guinea-pigs. Suttie & Phillips (1959) have reviewed the information available concerning vitamin supplementation and the incidence and severity of fluorosis in experimental animals and have suggested that elevated levels of vitamins A, C and D tend to mitigate the symptoms of fluorosis, ascorbic acid having the greatest effect. However, Lindemann (1966) has more recently reviewed the relationship between vitamin D supplementation and experimental fluorosis and suggested that the addition of this vitamin has no appreciable influence upon fluorosis. Collectively, these limited studies suggest that the levels and types of vitamin supplementation provided in commercially available vitamin-fluoride preparations have no appreciable influence upon fluoride metabolism in experimental animals, although additional studies are needed concerning these relationships.

No reports have appeared in the literature concerning the influence of vitamin supplementation upon the metabolism of fluoride in humans. Hennon and co-workers conducted a series of fluoride metabolic studies (Hennon, Stookey & Muhler, 1966a) in conjunction with a clinical study (Hennon, Stookey & Muhler, 1966b) in which the rate and amount of urinary fluoride excretion was determined in children 3-5 years of age who ingested a vitamin—sodium fluoride preparation continuously over a three-year period. The results indicate that during the first year of the study the subjects who received a non-fluoride-vitamin preparation excreted an average of 248.0 μg fluoride in the urine, whereas those who received the vitamin-fluoride preparation excreted an average of 409.9 μg fluoride, suggesting that about 82.0% of the ingested fluoride was absorbed from the gastrointestinal tract and subsequently retained in the body, primarily in the skeleton and developing dental structures. The latter value is about 14% greater than that observed previously with a non-vitamin-fluoride tablet. Similarly, the data obtained during the second and third year of the study indicate mean daily urinary fluoride excretion rates of 188.9 and 472.9 µg in the control and experimental subjects, respectively, suggesting that during this period about 68 % of the ingested fluoride was retained in the body.

The results of studies (Hennon, Stookey & Muhler, 1966a) designed to investigate the pattern of urinary fluoride excretion in children after ingestion of a vitamin-fluoride tablet are summarized in Fig. 5. The findings indicate that the excretion pattern after ingestion of a vitamin-fluoride tablet is comparable to that noted in an earlier study following the ingestion of a non-vitamin-fluoride tablet.

FIG. 5

AVERAGE RATE OF FLUORIDE EXCRETION BY CHILDREN AFTER INGESTION
OF EITHER A FLUORIDE OR A NON-FLUORIDE CHEWABLE VITAMIN TABLET

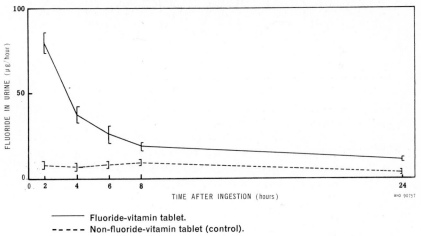

——— Fluoride-vitamin tablet.
– – – – Non-fluoride-vitamin tablet (control).

As part of their metabolic studies, Hennon and co-workers (1966a) investigated changes in the blood fluoride level following the ingestion of a vitamin-fluoride tablet and correlated these findings with the rate of urinary fluoride excretion. This study was conducted with closely controlled experimental conditions in young adults residing in a non-fluoride area and the results are summarized in Fig. 6. The urinary fluoride data indicate a rate of excretion comparable to that noted previously with both fluoride and vitamin-fluoride tablets with a maximum concentration occurring within the first two hours after ingestion of the tablet. Interestingly, the changes observed in the blood fluoride level closely parallelled the observations noted in the urine although the changes were of much lesser magnitude. In each instance the concentration of fluoride in the blood rose significantly within the first hour to a value about twice the normal or control level and returned to the control level within three hours after ingestion of the vitamin-

FIG. 6

AVERAGE FLUORIDE CONCENTRATION IN BLOOD AND URINE OF YOUNG ADULTS
INGESTING A CHEWABLE VITAMIN-FLUORIDE TABLET CONTAINING
1.0 mg FLUORIDE (AS NaF) EACH MORNING FOR THREE DAYS

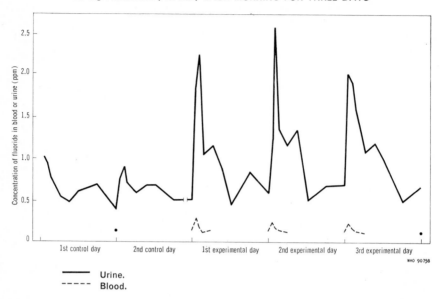

Urine.
Blood.

fluoride tablet. These data thus indicate that both in experimental animals and in humans the metabolism of fluoride ingested as a sodium fluoride tablet is not appreciably altered by the addition of vitamins to the tablet.

Fluoride-mineral supplements

Since the mechanism of action of systemic fluoride is thought to involve the conversion of hydroxyapatite to fluorapatite during tooth formation and since the deciduous dentition and a portion of the permanent dentition undergo calcification *in utero*, it has been suggested that fluoride must be provided prenatally in order to achieve maximal protection against dental caries, particularly in respect of the deciduous dentition. As a result a wide variety of vitamin-mineral-fluoride supplements, designed for prenatal ingestion, have been made available commercially. In addition, there are now several postnatal vitamin-mineral-fluoride preparations.

Unfortunately, there have been no reports in the literature directly concerned with the metabolism of fluoride provided as a vitamin-mineral-fluoride supplement. The results of a study conducted in our laboratories (Hennon, Burns & Muhler, unpublished data) in which equivalent amounts of fluoride were provided as sodium fluoride alone and as sodium fluoride in a typical commercially available vitamin-mineral prenatal supplement are summarized in Table 12. These data indicate that ingestion of the fluoride

TABLE 12

FLUORIDE CONTENT OF CARCASS AND FEMURS OF RATS GIVEN FLUORIDE EITHER ALONE OR IN A TYPICAL COMMERCIALLY AVAILABLE PRENATAL SUPPLEMENT

Regimen	No. of rats	Carcass			Femur			Net retention (%)
		Ash wt. (g)	Concentration (ppm F)	Total (µg F)	Ash wt. (mg)	Concentration (ppm F)	Total (µg F)	
				Group A				
Control diet	11	5.27 ± 0.38	261 ± 41	1 377 ± 246 [a]	363 ± 32	343 ± 32	125 ± 27 [a]	—
				Group B				
Control diet + fluoride	13	5.18 ± 0.37	3 558 ± 410	18 335 ± 1 931	376 ± 29	5 112 ± 552	1 919 ± 276	62.5
				Group C				
Prenatal supplement	12	5.32 ± 0.60	219 ± 76	1 177 ± 449	356 ± 41	284 ± 90	103 ± 37	—
				Group D				
Prenatal supplement + fluoride	13	5.27 ± 0.40	2 256 ± 424	11 827 ± 2 037	372 ± 39	2 788 ± 279	1 039 ± 125	38.6

[a] Standard error of the mean.

alone resulted in a skeletal retention of 62.5% whereas in the presence of the vitamin-mineral supplement only 38.6% of the ingested fluoride was retained. Thus the presence of the minerals, primarily calcium and iron, in the vitamin-mineral supplement reduced fluoride retention by about 40%.

These limited data, coupled with other information available in the literature, suggest that the metabolism of fluoride ingested in the form of a vitamin-mineral supplement may be significantly different from that observed when the fluoride is ingested alone. It is further apparent that additional studies concerning this aspect of fluoride metabolism are necessary before one can recommend the widespread use of vitamin-mineral-fluoride supplements.

Fluoride-containing dentifrices

The development of therapeutic dentifrices during the past twenty years has resulted in a significant portion of the population routinely using dentifrices containing fluoride, generally provided at a concentration of 1.0 mg fluoride per gram of dentifrice. The common usage and availability of these products, coupled with the design of the most effective products in such a manner that the fluoride is metabolically available through the proper

TABLE 13

SUMMARY OF UNSUPERVISED BRUSHING STUDIES CONCERNING THE METABOLISM OF FLUORIDE IN FLUORIDE-CONTAINING DENTIFRICES

Study	Experimental regimen	Fluoride content of drinking water (ppm F)	Mean age (years)	Urinary fluoride (ppm F)
Schweinsberger & Muhler (1956)	Non-fluoride dentifrice	0.10	11.4	0.24
	Stannous fluoride dentifrice	0.10	11.0	0.28
	Non-fluoride dentifrice	0.85	12.0	1.01
Schweinsberger & Muhler (1957)	Non-fluoride dentifrice			
	pre-control period	1.10	3.88	0.72
	experimental period			0.63
	post-control period			0.66
	Stannous fluoride dentifrice			
	pre-control period	1.10	4.67	0.91
	experimental period			0.82
	post-control period			0.80
	Non-fluoride dentifrice			
	pre-control period	0.10	3.17	0.30
	experimental period			0.29
	post-control period			0.32
	Stannous fluoride dentifrice			
	pre-control period	0.10	3.24	0.31
	experimental period			0.30
	post-control period			0.33
Büttner, Schülke & Soyka (1961)	Non-fluoride dentifrice	0.06	26	0.32
	Stannous fluoride dentifrice			0.34
	Non-fluoride dentifrice	0.06	32	0.37
	Amine fluoride dentifrice			0.42

choice of compatible cleaning and polishing agents and other ingredients, have resulted in several investigations concerning the systemic metabolism of the fluoride in these preparations.

The results of a series of studies conducted by Schweinsberger & Muhler (1956, 1957) and by Büttner, Schülke & Soyka (1961) are summarized in Table 13. The former investigators provided children residing in fluoride and in non-fluoride areas with either a stannous fluoride or a non-fluoride dentifrice for home use and determined the amount of fluoride excreted in the urine. The results of these studies indicated that in no instance was the urinary fluoride concentration significantly altered by the unsupervised use of the stannous fluoride dentifrice. Similar findings were reported by Büttner and co-workers (*op. cit.*) in two studies in adults in which the amount of urinary fluoride excretion was determined following the unsupervised use of fluoride and non-fluoride dentifrices.

TABLE 14

SUMMARY OF FLUORIDE BALANCE STUDIES IN HUMANS USING DENTIFRICES
CONTAINING VARIOUS FLUORIDE SALTS WITH SUPERVISED BRUSHING

Study	Age of subjects (years)	Source of fluoride	Fluoride concentration (ppm F)	Average retention (%)
Eichler, Appel & Burschel (1955) . .	4-18+	NaF	2 000	20
Winkler, Backer Dirks & Van Amerongen (1953)	11-15	NaF	700	30
Ericsson (1961)	Adults	NaF (^{18}F)	1 000	8
		SnF$_2$ (^{18}F)	1 000	12
		Na$_2$PO$_3$F (^{18}F)	1 000	6
Duckworth (1964) . . .	23-33	SnF$_2$ (^{18}F)	1 000	3

The results of four fluoride balance studies are summarized in Table 14. Eichler, Appel & Burschel (1955) noted that an average of about 20% of the fluoride in a single brushing with a dentifrice containing 2 mg fluoride per gram was retained by subjects ranging in age from 4 years to adulthood and suggested that with this particular product no more than about 0.4 mg fluoride would be retained from each brushing. Winkler, Backer Dirks & Van Amerongen (1953) found that, in teenaged children, a single brushing with a dentifrice containing 0.15% sodium fluoride resulted in a fluoride retention of about 60% of the soluble fluoride and about 30% of the total fluoride content of the dentifrice. Studies utilizing radioactive fluorine, ^{18}F, suggested considerably lower retention rates. Ericsson (1961) found that only 6-12% of the fluoride in three different types of fluoride-containing dentifrice was retained within the body following a single brushing with 0.4-0.6 g of the dentifrice. Duckworth (1964) suggested an even lesser retention—about 3% of the ^{18}F-labelled stannous fluoride contained in a dentifrice. The data obtained by the last-mentioned investigators suggest that the amount of fluoride retained in the body following a single brushing with a dentifrice containing 1000 ppm fluoride is of the order of 15-55 µg (0.015-0.055 mg).

In a metabolism study conducted in rats, Deshpande & Bester (1964) noted that only 30% of the fluoride ingested in the form of a stannous fluoride dentifrice was absorbed from the gastrointestinal tract and that about 81% of the absorbed fluoride was retained in the carcass of the animals.

Acute toxicity studies (Cooper, 1958) with fluoride-containing dentifrices have suggested that the toxicity is somewhat lower when the fluoride is ingested in a dentifrice than when it is ingested alone. It has been suggested (Büttner, Schülke & Soyka, 1961; Shaver & Smith, 1946) that this finding is due to the presence of interfering ions, such as calcium, which react with the fluoride in the gastrointestinal tract to prevent its subsequent absorption and therefore reduce the toxicity.

Fluoride-containing chewing-gum

The use of fluoride-containing chewing-gum as a method of providing the benefits of fluoride has been mentioned in the literature, but the work cited has been concerned primarily with the problems of compatibility associated with the compounding of such a vehicle, and with the uptake of the fluoride ion by the enamel rather than with the actual metabolic aspects of the fluoride ingested therefrom.

Clark (1962) in a series of compatibility studies indicated that 6.5-23.0% of the tin ions and 36-41% of the fluoride ions are removed from various tin fluoride solutions after reaction with the different components of a typical chewing-gum. These data would thus suggest that a significant proportion of the stannous fluoride added to the chewing-gum is in some manner, chemically or physically, bound within the gum and is thereby no longer available either for reaction with the oral hard tissues or for systemic utilization from the swallowing of the saliva. Emslie, Veall & Duckworth (1961) concluded, after a series of studies using ^{18}F, that 80-90% of the radioactive fluoride was released from the gum in 10 to 15 minutes, and that the uptake of the fluoride by a premolar tooth was about 20 µg after ten minutes' chewing of gum containing 100 µg of ^{18}F. Emslie and co-workers also state that the rate of release was not affected by the addition of 5.0% calcium carbonate, but that the addition of 2.0% citric acid greatly increased the retention of the fluoride by the chewing-gum. However, this increased retention within the gum was partially offset by an increased uptake of the ^{18}F by the teeth.

There are no references in the literature to the metabolic fate of fluorides incorporated in chewing-gum. However, it may be concluded that the metabolic fate is the same when the fluorine ion is supplied by chewing-gum as when it is supplied by any other vehicle, provided the fluoride is not in some manner "deactivated". For example, it has been shown previously that the presence of calcium significantly decreased the metabolic utilization of fluoride. It should be noted further that calcium carbonate and other calcium salts are common constituents of chewing-gums. Therefore, additional studies are needed to ascertain the metabolic fate of fluoride ingested with chewing-gum.

Fluoride-containing mouthwashes

The use of fluoride-containing mouthwashes has also been advocated as a method of deriving the dental benefits of fluoride. As has been mentioned previously, the metabolism of the fluoride ion is influenced by the same series of variables regardless of the vehicle used to administer the fluoride. However, the factors affecting metabolism, such as interfering ions which are present in other vehicles, i.e., dentifrices and vitamin-mineral supplements, are not normally present in mouthwashes. It may therefore be assumed that any fluoride which is swallowed after administration by mouthwash is probably rapidly absorbed and metabolized.

TABLE 15

SUMMARY OF FLUORIDE METABOLISM DATA FROM FLUORIDE-CONTAINING MOUTHWASHES

Study	Age of subjects	Source of fluoride	Concentration of fluoride	Mode of application (time, amount)	Average estimated retention in body (% of dosage)
Bossert & Dunning (1945)	Adults	NaF	0.1 %	2 min, 25 ml	3-9 %
	Adults	NaF	0.1 %	3 min, 25 ml	5-11 %
Hellstrom (1960)	Adults	NaF	0.1 %	1 min, 15 ml	30 %
	5-15 years	NaF	0.1 %	1 min, 10 ml	19 %

As shown in Table 15, Bossert & Dunning (1945) estimated the fluoride retention in adults following the use of a 0.1 % NaF mouthwash to be 3-9 % and 5-11 % of the total fluoride content of the mouthwash after single rinses of 2 and 3 minutes, respectively. These investigators suggested that as much as 6 % of the mouthwash may be swallowed and the fluoride thereby made available for gastrointestinal absorption. Hellstrom (1960), in an attempt to determine the metabolic fate of fluoride ingested from a mouthwash, reported that following the use of a 0.1 % NaF mouthwash, an average of 2.0 mg of fluoride in adults and of 0.85 mg in children was retained. This investigator reported that about 30 % and 19 % of the fluoride in 15-ml and

10-ml quantities of the mouthwash was retained by adults and children, respectively. These limited data thus suggest that additional studies are needed to determine the metabolic fate of fluoride provided in a mouthwash, particularly in children under unsupervised conditions.

Drugs used for Purposes other than as Anticariogenic Agents

Dentine obtundents

For more than twenty years various investigators have suggested the use of various fluorides as dentine obtundents to reduce hypersensitivity. Hoyt & Bibby (1943), for example, suggested the use of a fluoride-kaolin paste containing 33 % sodium fluoride as a means of reducing hypersensitivity of the dentine and indicated it to be effective. Comparable findings have been noted by numerous other investigators (Rieke, 1945; Clement, 1947; Rovelstad & St. John, 1949; Wetherill, 1956; Manning, 1961) using sodium fluoride in a paste or as an aqueous solution. More recent reports (Sieman, 1960; Lefkowitz, 1962; Lefkowitz, Burdick & Moore, 1963; Scott, 1962) have described the use of sodium fluoride applications by ionophoresis, while two studies (Collins, 1962; Jensen, 1964) have reported successful results using a stannous fluoride and a sodium fluoride dentifrice with ionophoresis. However, *in vitro* and *in vivo* tests have shown this procedure to be ineffective, probably because of the high electrical resistance of the enamel (Ericsson, 1958). The successful use of other fluorides such as sodium silicofluoride (Stout, 1955; Massler, 1955; Hunter, Barringer & Spooner, 1961) and an organic fluoride (Bandeltini, 1963) has been reported.

The metabolism of the fluoride provided in such treatment procedures *per se* has not been fully investigated. While it has been shown that the dentinal tubule allows passage of numerous elements, including fluoride, it has been suggested that only minute quantities of fluoride actually reach the pulp from such treatments. Owing to the high electronegativity of the fluoride ion and its pronounced affinity for cations, it would seem that most of the fluoride from such treatments would become chemically bound to the inorganic components of the dental hard tissues. Such fluoride would then be considered metabolically detoxified. The reported failure in all the studies cited previously of these fluoride treatments to elicit any untoward soft-tissue response in the pulp provides further evidence that very little fluoride actually reaches the dental pulp and is metabolically available for deposition in the calcified skeletal structures or for excretion.

Treatment of osteoporosis and related metabolic skeletal disorders

In the past few years several reports have appeared in the literature suggesting the use of large dosages of systemic fluoride in the treatment of various skeletal diseases involving a loss of the calcified component of bone.

Rich & Ensinck (1961) reported that daily administration of 60 mg fluoride, provided as sodium fluoride, to subjects afflicted with osteoporosis and Paget's disease resulted in the achievement of a positive calcium balance and that the subjects had an increased alkaline phosphatase activity in plasma. Subsequent studies by Rich and co-workers (Rich & Ensinck, 1962; Rich, Ensinck & Ivanovich, 1964; Rich & Ivanovich, 1965) and by others (Purves, 1962; Bernstein et al., 1963; Cohen & Gardner, 1966) confirm the earlier findings and suggest that dosages of fluoride of 0.5-1.0 mg per kg result in beneficial responses without untoward side-effects. Similarly, Shambaugh and co-workers (Shambaugh & Scott, 1964; Petrovic & Shambaugh, 1966) have suggested that comparable dosages of fluoride may be of significant value in arresting otosclerosis.

The metabolism of fluoride in the dosages prescribed for treatment of these conditions has been studied to a lesser degree. Rich, Ensinck & Ivanovich (1964) reported the fluoride balance in six subjects and their findings are summarized in Table 16. The data indicate that there is consid-

TABLE 16

METABOLISM OF FLUORIDE IN PATIENTS UNDER FLUORIDE TREATMENT
FOR METABOLIC SKELETAL DISORDERS [a]

Subject No.	1	1	2	2	3	4	4	5	6
Age of subject (years) . .	84	84	62	62	61	70	70	52	61
Dosage level (mgF/day) . .	50	50	50	40	50	85	50	75	60
Period of study (weeks) . .	1-7	32-36	30-34	72-75	1-9	1-5	28-32	31-35	40-45
Percentage in faeces . . .	48.80	66.60	17.32	9.12	14.62	8.54	19.04	34.22	32.88
Percentage in urine	26.20	32.08	50.02	70.10	57.28	43.05	29.50	36.45	19.35
Percentage retention . . .	24.00	1.32	32.66	20.78	28.10	48.41	51.46	29.33	47.77

[a] Data from Rich, Ensinck & Ivanovich (1964).

erable variation between subjects concerning the manner and amount of excretion of the fluoride. It may be seen that the amount of fluoride unaccounted for and presumed to be retained ranges from 1.32% to 51.46%. From these data it is readily apparent, however, that substantial amounts of fluoride are being retained by the subjects. These results are somewhat in contrast to those cited earlier, in which lesser dosages of fluoride were largely excreted by adults, and the findings are probably dependent upon the marked difference in the dosage levels.

It is of further interest to note that there is some suggestion that with increasing length of fluoride exposure the amount of fluoride retained within the body decreases. The data of Rich, Ensinck & Ivanovich (1964) indicate that in Subject 1 an initial retention of 24.00% was found while after four months of fluoride treatment only 1.32% of the ingested fluoride was retained. Similarly, Subject 2 had percentage retention values of 32.66 and 20.78 after 30 and 72 weeks of treatment. These findings closely parallel those obtained in our laboratories (Stookey, Epperson & Johnston, unpublished data).

Studies concerning the concentration of fluoride in the plasma of subjects receiving large dosages of fluoride indicate that significant increases in the plasma fluoride level are readily apparent following the therapy. Armstrong et al. (1964) have observed an increase generally of the magnitude of two to four times the pretreatment control level and these findings are again comparable to those noted in our studies (Stookey, Epperson & Johnston, unpublished data).

From these limited data it is readily apparent that additional studies are needed. For example, the minimal dosage level of fluoride required to obtain the desired beneficial response is not yet known, nor is it known how much fluoride need be absorbed and retained to produce these favourable skeletal responses. Many other metabolic aspects of this use of fluoride likewise merit further investigation.

Fluorinated corticosteroids

A considerable number of fluorine-containing analogues of adreno-corticosteroids have been prepared but only a few have been proved to have useful properties. Among these are 9αα-fluoro-17-hydroxycortico-sterone, 9α-fluorohydrocortisone, Δ′-9α-fluoro-16α-hydroxyhydrocortisone, and Δ′-9α-fluoro-16α-methylhydrocortisone. The pharmacological aspects of these compounds as well as those of many additional analogues have been adequately reviewed elsewhere (Hodge, Smith & Chen, 1963; Christy & Drucker, 1964; Smith & Hodge, 1959; Saunders, 1961) and no attempt will be made to discuss the voluminous findings here.

There is little to be said concerning the metabolism of the fluorine present in these compounds. The apparent physiological stability of the fluorine-carbon bond renders the fluorine metabolically unavailable and it is therefore not subject to the metabolic patterns observed with the free fluoride ion provided by inorganic fluorides.

Fluorine-containing anaesthetic agents

A wide variety of fluorinated organic compounds have been synthesized and studied for their potential use as general and topical anaesthetic agents owing to their generally low toxicity, high degree of stability, and relative non-flammability. Perhaps the most notable of these are trifluoroethylvinyl ether and 1,1,1-trifluoro-2,2-bromochloroethane. Hodge and co-workers (op. cit.) have adequately reviewed the toxicology and pharmacology of these compounds.

Since the fluorine present in these compounds is again bound to carbon and since this fluorine-carbon bond is not cleaved by biological processes, the fluoride is not metabolically available and does not enter the normal pathways of fluoride metabolism. The fluoride is therefore eliminated from the body along with the parent compound.

Miscellaneous fluorine-containing drugs

Many additional usages of organic fluorocompounds have been suggested and these compounds have received varying amounts of evaluation and application. Fluorine-containing α- and γ-substituted glycerol ether derivatives, such as 3-(2-trifluoromethyl-phenoxy)propane-1,2-diol and 3-(2-fluorophenoxy)propane-1,2-diol, have been suggested for use as muscle depressants. Fluorinated sympathomimetic amines have also been considered. Fluoride analogues of tyrosine and phenylalanine have been suggested as possible therapeutic agents in thyroid disorders. Fluorinated pyrimidines, fluoroacetate, fluorocholine, fluorinated dimethylazobenzene, and other organic fluorine compounds have been tried out with some success as chemotherapeutic agents in the treatment of cancer. Reports concerning numerous other applications—for example, as insecticides, bactericidal agents, antimalarial agents and the like—are abundant in the literature. The pharmacology of these compounds has also been reviewed recently by Hodge and co-workers (op. cit.). Owing to the chemical nature of these compounds, i.e., the presence of the carbon-fluorine bond, the fluorine present is metabolically inert.

Another class of fluorine-containing compounds of interest is the phosphofluoridates. Perhaps the best known of these compounds is diisopropyl-phosphofluoridate (DPF), which has been shown to be an extremely potent cholinesterase inhibitor and has had application as a nerve gas and as an insecticide. In these compounds the fluoride is bound to phosphorus, and within the body this bond is easily broken by protein interaction, releasing fluoride as free fluoride ions. It has been shown that within four hours after the ingestion of DPF essentially all the fluoride-phosphorus bonds have been broken. It is thus apparent that fluoride ingested as phosphofluoridate rapidly becomes metabolically available. However, it has been shown that the high general toxicity of these compounds is due to the phosphorylation of cholinesterase and not to the presence of fluoride. Owing to the high toxicity, relatively little information is available concerning the metabolism of the liberated fluoride; however, there is no reason to believe that this fluoride would be treated physiologically in a manner different from that derived from inorganic fluoride compounds. As such it should be rapidly eliminated from the circulating body-fluids by excretion in the urine and deposition in the skeleton.

5. INHALATION FROM DUST OR VAPOURS (E. J. Largent)

Inorganic fluorides enter man's environment only in a minor way as elemental fluorine, but considerable amounts may enter as (1) dusts, (2) gaseous compounds or vapours, (3) particulates suspended in gaseous fluorides, and perhaps (4) particulates dispersed in water.

Organic fluorocompounds do not mimic the physiological effects of inorganic fluorides.

Elemental Fluorine

Since elemental fluorine is rarely if ever found in nature, all of it comes from manufacturing processes, either in industry or in experimental laboratories. Most, if not all, is produced by the electrolytic decomposition of hydrogen fluoride (HF) in "fluorine cells". It has been used principally for effecting fluorine addition to chemical substances that are difficult to fluorinate. Conversion of uranium tetrafluoride to uranium hexafluoride is probably its most widespread use. Fluorine has been proposed as a fuel with hydrogen to produce thrust in the engines for rockets. The most recent—and at present very limited—use of elemental fluorine is to react it with noble gases, for example, xenon, to form fluoride compounds. Oxygen difluoride, chlorine trifluoride and nitrogen trifluoride are produced in small amounts, but at present no known important industrial processes use these compounds. Metal fluorides are also used sometimes as sources of fluorine —cobalt trifluoride, for example (Simons, 1954).

The acute effects of inhaling fluorine have been observed chiefly in experimental animals and were described by Stokinger in 1949. When fluorine contacts directly the skin of animals (or man), it reacts so violently that it produces a thermal type of burn. Inhalation of elemental fluorine at a level of 300 ppm was fatal to all animals exposed for 3 hours or longer. Longer periods of exposure at a level of 100 ppm produced an over-all mortality of 60%. Severe damage to the respiratory tract was the most frequently observed change among these animals.

Chronic changes induced by prolonged inhalation of fluorine (and perhaps oxygen fluoride, chlorine trifluoride and nitrogen trifluoride, see Green et al., 1961, and Torkelson et al., 1962) are more severe than those induced by other inorganic fluorides tested thus far. The results of exposure of animals to fluorine are recorded in Table 17 and can be compared with the results of similar exposure to HF, shown in Table 18. The lowest test level of exposure to fluorine, 0.5 ppm, produced little or no pulmonary

TABLE 17

RESULTS OF INHALATION OF GASEOUS FLUORINE [a]

Concentration of F_2	Duration		Effects on animals [b]
	days	hours	
5 ppm or more . .	18-29	95-160	Large numbers died (180 of 357)
2 ppm or less . .	31	176-178	Very few died (10 of 148)

[a] After Stokinger (1949).
[b] Rabbits, dogs, mice, rats, guinea-pigs, hamsters.

damage and little osseous or dental tissue alteration. A small increase in the fluoride content of bones was observed in exposed animals. In contrast, animals exposed to the lowest test level of fluoride as HF (8.6 ppm) showed a considerable increase in the fluoride content of bones, even though no damage to soft tissues was observed.

TABLE 18

RESULTS OF INHALATION OF GASEOUS HYDROGEN FLUORIDE [a]

Concentration of HF	Duration		Effects on animals
	days	hours	
33 ppm	26	166	All (47 of 47) rats and mice died; no (0 of 44) guinea-pigs, rabbits or dogs died
8.6 ppm	26	166	None (0 of 60) of the same 5 species died

[a] After Stokinger (1949).

No evidence has been reported of chronic changes of any type among workmen potentially exposed to elemental fluorine (Lyon, 1962).

Dusts

Fluorides dispersed in air have been potential health problems in areas where mineral deposits were located at or near the surface of the ground. Attention was focused on the "phosphate" areas of Algeria, Tunisia and Morocco prior to 1930, and for almost 10 years fluoride in drinking water was thought to be the cause of *darmous* and other adverse effects on animals raised in those areas. The assumption was made that fluoride leached from scattered deposits of fluorapatite resulted in such high levels of dissolved fluoride as to account for all the changes that were observed. Velu & Charnot in 1938, however, came to see very clearly that high-fluoride-containing dusts were the source of the adverse effects observed among animals. The severity of the changes in animals consistently diminished in the rainy season, a time when the vegetation was regularly washed free of dust. In this same connexion Spéder, in 1936, described dental fluorosis and fluoride-induced skeletal changes in man. His observations were made among residents in Algeria, Tunisia and Morocco and he mistakenly attributed the observed changes solely to the intake of fluoride in drinking water. Because he neglected to collect any duplicate samples of drinking water and of foods eaten by his subjects, he overlooked the potential contribution of dusts containing fluoride to the physiological changes which he reported.

The fluoride content of soils in part of Tennessee exceeds 7000 ppm and appears to be derived from outcroppings of phosphate rock (fluorapatite) in that area.   Dust from this soil can cause the vegetation in pastures to attain high levels of fluoride and this is thought to be the cause of fluoride-induced changes among some herds of livestock there.

The use of fluoride in some industrial processes may also generate fluoride-containing dusts.   One index of the dimensions of such a possibility may be the extent of the use of fluorspar (fluorite), a mineral which contains calcium fluoride and small amounts of impurities.   This mineral is used directly in steel making and as a raw material in the manufacture of other fluorides, including HF and synthetic cryolite (sodium aluminium fluoride).   The average world consumption of fluorspar for the years 1954 through 1959 was a little less than 2 million short tons.   Since that time consumption has been greater than 2 million tons per year (Ambrose, 1964).

Each year many millions of tons of phosphate rock and smaller amounts of cryolite are mined.   The industrial processing of these minerals may also be a source of fluoride-containing dusts.

Acute changes observed in animals and man have been caused by fluoride-containing dusts, but for the most part these changes relate more to ingestion than to inhalation of dust.   Dust inhaled and later swallowed may he of importance, but its importance is difficult to appraise.   Any serious bazard from dusts is likely to concern only the very readily soluble fluoride compounds such as sodium fluoride and potassium fluoride.   The acute toxicity of fluoride salts is discussed more completely in the introduction to Chapter 7.

Chronic changes induced by fluorides in dusts may include dental changes in animals, but are related to ingestion of dusts rather than to their inhalation.   Dust-induced dental changes in man also are related only to ingestion of the dust, either as a contaminant of food or suspended in drinking water. There have been no reports of any changes among workmen induced by highly insoluble dusts such as those from fluorspar or fluorapatite where there was no other type of fluoride (gaseous) present along with either of them.   Skeletal changes in man have been reported in relation to occupational exposure to other kinds of airborne dusts, and a description of·such changes is included in Roholm's classic monograph (1937).   The excellent work of Hodge & Smith (1965) includes a section by Dr Lent Johnson describing the newest concepts of the histopathological osseous changes induced by fluorides in animals.   It should be stressed, however, that the disabling effects of exposure to fluorides of the type described by Roholm have rarely or never been observed elsewhere in industry (Agate et al., 1949; Bishop, 1936; Collings et al., 1951, 1952).

According to Brailsford (1953), many cases of other types of bone changes have been incorrectly labelled "fluorosis".

A more complete discussion of the chronic effects of fluoride-containing dusts may be found in Chapter 8, section 6.

Gaseous Compounds

The most widely encountered fluoride-containing gaseous compound is probably HF. In the USA alone the production of HF has risen above 200 000 short tons per year. Certain industrial processes liberate silicon tetrafluoride which, when it reacts with water, also yields HF (as an aqueous solution in most instances, however). Boron trifluoride is also used in industry, though in lesser amounts. Sulfur hexafluoride is used electrically as it is a good dielectric, but it is a very inert material and does not possess any of the physiological properties common to most inorganic fluorides.

Acute changes from HF have been observed in animals and man. The adverse effects may be limited to the skin or to the eyes or may be very extensive, depending on the nature of the exposure, usually the result of some type of accident (Dieffenbacher & Thompson, 1962; Fleming et al., 1954). When the gas is inhaled by animals or man severe damage to the respiratory tract may occur, and the results can be fatal if the level of HF is much above 25-30 ppm and if the exposure is allowed to continue for too long a time (Machle et al., 1934, 1935; Stokinger, 1949). Some of the other gaseous fluorides are likely to be converted to HF and for this reason their adverse effects resemble those produced by HF. This, of course, does not apply to chemicals such as sulfur hexafluoride and many or all of the fluorine-containing organic compounds. Pyrolysis of organic fluorides can, however, generate HF among the decomposition products.

Chronic effects caused by fluoride-containing gases have been investigated in industry less extensively than is the case either with dusts or with mixtures of dusts and gases. Observations have been made on human experimental subjects exposed to HF (Largent, 1961). These experiments were too brief to permit any but the most trivial changes to have developed among the subjects. The levels of HF used, in the neighbourhood of 3 ppm, are thought to be safe for repeated exposure: 8 hours daily over periods of many years (American Conference of Governmental Industrial Hygienists, 1965).

A more complete discussion of the chronic effects of gaseous fluorides may be found in Chapter 8, section 6.

Gaseous and Particulate Fluorides Suspended Together

Among the various places where exposure to fluorides in air is encountered, there are relatively few that represent exposure exclusively to gaseous material or exclusively to particulate material. A mixture of these two types of material is most likely to be found in (1) the processing of fluorapatite to make phosphate fertilizers and (2) certain phases of manufacturing iron (Murray & Wilson, 1946), aluminium and fluoride chemicals generally, including HF. Fluorspar dust will likely be present around workmen who operate equipment for manufacturing HF and, hence, their potential exposure will be to both gaseous and particulate material. Near operations using aqueous solutions, both gaseous HF and droplets of the liquid may become dispersed into the air and the workmen may therefore be exposed to both types of material. Some of the particles (liquid aerosol or dust) may be trapped in the mouth, nose and throat of exposed persons and some or all of the material thus trapped may eventually be swallowed. In such a case, fluorides would be both inhaled and ingested. This combination of inhalation and ingestion of fluorides is unlikely to be of any importance in situations where the exposure to fluoride is completely overwhelming. However, the chronic effects of exposure to fluorides may be influenced by the fact that fluoride is swallowed as well as inhaled in certain circumstances; this topic is discussed further in Chapter 8, section 6.

Particulate Fluorides Dispersed in Water

The relative importance of particulate fluorides was missed in Algeria, Tunisia and Morocco for nearly 10 years. So far as is known, this aspect of exposure to fluorides has also been largely ignored in India (Shortt et al., 1937; Singh et al., 1963) and China (Kilborn, Outerbridge & Lei, 1950). At least there have been few or no balance studies to demonstrate how much more fluoride as a particulate substance is being ingested with food and water than is present solely as dissolved fluoride in liquids that are ingested there. In these areas the particulate fluorides may be of no importance as inhaled materials, but the particles may add a very important amount of fluoride as a contaminant in the food eaten or dispersed (undissolved) in the water ingested. It seems likely to the author of this section that fluoride as a particulate has played a much greater role than has fluoride dissolved in water in the cases of skeletal fluorosis reported in persons residing in Asia —especially, perhaps, those cited in the reports of A. Singh.

Acute effects of these particulates have not been observed. However, one fatal case of inhalation of an aqueous mist (derived from sodium fluoride in high concentration dissolved in water) has been reported (Hayhurst, 1943).

Generally, there have been no effects on the health of man from the inhalation of airborne inorganic fluorides within his place of residence. Any effects of any kind induced by airborne fluorides have concerned (1) the few instances reported where fluoride was present in the atmosphere within the area where men were at work or (2) where the fluorides became a contaminant which was ingested with food or water or both. Dusts have not been released into communities adjacent to industrial operations in amounts sufficient to influence the intake of fluoride by man. Contamination of the food and drinking water by dusts, when it has become a problem of any importance to the health of man, has been the result solely of the minerals deposited naturally in the soil.

Organic Fluorocompounds

The organic fluorocompounds now number in the thousands and their number has been increasing at a rapid rate. In general, the physiological effects of organic fluorocompounds bear no resemblance to those of inorganic fluorides. A discussion of some of the organic fluorine-containing compounds may be found in section 4 of this chapter.

The series *Fluorine Chemistry*, edited by Simons, is a rich source of information on organic fluorocompounds. Particularly praiseworthy is volume 3, prepared by Hodge and co-workers (1963), which contains the most extensive listing of the biological effects of such compounds that is at present available.

REFERENCES

Abbott, G. A. (1937) *Bull. N. Dak. geol. Surv.*, No. 9, p. 4

Abuladze, A. S., Pailodze, Y. B., Kutateladze, E. H., Anteleva, A. V. & Glonti, L. V. (1959) *Gig. i Sanit.*, **24**, No. 11, p. 71

Adams. D. F., Mayhew, D. J., Gnagy, R. M., Richey, E. P., Koppe, R. K. & Allen, I. W. (1952) *Industr. Engng Chem.*, **44**, 1356

Adolph, E. F. (1933) *Physiol. Rev.*, **13**, 336

Agate, J. N., Bell, G. H., Boddie, G. F., Bowler, R. G., Buckell, M., Cheeseman, E. A., Douglas, T. H. J., Druett, H. A., Garrad, J., Hunter, D., Perry, K. M. A., Richardson, J. D. & Weir, J. B. de V. (1949) *Industrial fluorosis. A study of the hazard to man and animals near Fort William, Scotland*, London, HMSO (Medical Research Council Memorandum No. 22)

Akin, P. D. & Jones, J. R. (1952) *Geology and ground-water resources of the Cloquet area, Carlton County, Minnesota* (Minnesota Department of Conservation, Division of Water Bulletin No. 6)

Allen, W. B. (1953) *The ground-water resources of Rhode Island : a reconnaissance* (Rhode Island Development Council Geology Bulletin No. 6)

Alvarenga Rossi, J. & Dutra de Oliveira, J. E. (1947) *Rev. bras. Med.*, **4**, 16

Ambrose, P. M. (1964) *Fluorspar and cryolite*, Washington, D.C., US Government Printing Office (Reprint from Bureau of Mines, *Minerals yearbook*, vol. 1, 1963)

American Conference of Governmental Industrial Hygienists (1965) *Threshold limit values adopted at the twenty-seventh annual meeting of the . . . in Houston, Texas, in May 1965*

Andreeva, V. S. (1963) *Gig. i Sanit.*, No. 28, p. 59

Angellini, B. & Demontis, G. (1957) *Igiene mod.*, **50**, 33

Añorga, C. J. & Melman, J. (1951) *Rev. cuba. Pediat.*, **23**, 346

Armstrong, W. D., Singer, L., Ensinck, J. & Rich, C. (1964) *J. clin. Invest.*, **43**, 555

Arnold, F. A., Jr, McClure, F. J. & White, C. L. (1960) *Dent. Progr.*, **1**, 8-12

Babcock, H. M., Wisher, F. N. & Durum, W. H. (1952) *Reconnaissance of the geology and ground-water resources of the Pumpkin Creek area, Morrill and Banner Counties, Nebraska* (US Geological Survey Circular No. 156)

Bacon, J. E. (1948) *Publ. Hlth News (Trenton N. J.)*, **29**, 7

Baker, G. K. (1963) *Water supply for the city of Claremont* (South Dakota State Geological Survey Special Report No. 25)

Bandeltini, M. (1963) *Dent. Abstr. (Chic.)*, **8**, 26

Barraclough, J. T. & Marsh, O. T. (1962) *Aquifers and quality of ground water along the gulf of western Florida* (State of Florida, Board of Conservation, Florida Geological Survey Report of Investigations No. 29)

Bennett, R. R. & Meyer, R. R. (1952) *Geology and ground-water resources of the Baltimore area* (Maryland Department of Geology, Mines, and Water Resources Bulletin No. 4)

Bernstein, D. S., Guri, C., Cohen, P., Collins, J. J. & Tamvakopoulos, S. (1963) *J. clin. Invest.*, **42**, 916

Beuren, G. van & Leiser, G. (1962) *Mitt. naturf. Ges. (Bern)*, **19**, 39

Bishop, P. A. (1936) *Amer. J. Roentgenol.*, **35**, 577

Black, A. P. & Brown, E. (1951) *Chemical character of Florida's waters 1951* (State of Florida, Board of Conservation, Division of Water Survey and Resources, Paper No. 6)

Black, A. P. & Stearns, T. W. (1937) *Fluorine in Florida waters.* In: *Proceedings of the 11th Annual Convention of the Florida Section of the American Water Works Association,* p. 5

Borei, H. (1945) *Ark. Kemi Miner. Geol.*, **20 A**, No. 8, pp. 1-215

Boruff, C. S. & Abbott, G. A. (1933) *Industr. Engng Chem., analyt. Ed.*, **5**, 236

Bossert, W. A. & Dunning, J. M. (1945) *J. dent. Res.*, **24**, 311

Boswell, E. H. (1963) *Cretaceous aquifers of northeastern Mississippi* (State of Mississippi, Board of Water Commissioners Bulletin 63-10, pp. 1-202)

Box, H. K. & Hodgins, H. J. (1944) *Engng Contract Rec.*, **57**, No. 22, pp. 10, 28; *Oral Hlth*, **34**, 284, 295

Bradwell, D. (1950) *Cyprus med. J.*, **3**, 449

Brailsford, J. F. (1953) *The radiology of bones and joints,* 5th ed., Baltimore, Williams and Wilkins

Bredemann, G. (1956) *Biochemie und Physiologie des Fluors, und der industriellen Fluor-Rauchschaden,* 2nd ed., Berlin, Akademie-Verlag

Broadhurst, W. L., Sundstrom, R. W. & Rowley, J. H. (1950) *Public water supplies in southern Texas* (US Geological Survey, Water Supply Paper No. 1070)

Brown, G. F. (1947) *Bull. Miss. St. geol. Surv.*, No. 65

Büttner, W., Schülke, S. & Soyka, S. (1961) *Toxicity of fluoride-containing dentifrices, in the present status of caries prevention by fluoride-containing dentifrices.* In: Mühlemann, H. R., & König, K. G., ed., *Caries Symposium, Zürich,* Berne & Stuttgart, Huber, pp. 92-99

Buydens, R. (1956) *Bull. Acad. roy. Méd. Belg.*, **21**, 132

Campbell, I. R. & Widner, E. W. (1958) *Annotated bibliography. The occurrence and biological effects of fluorine compounds. Vol. I : the inorganic compounds,* Cincinnati, Kettering Laboratory, University of Cincinnati, Ohio

Carlston, C. W. (1942) *Bull. geol. Surv. Ala.*, No. 52

Carter, R. W. & Herrick, S. M. (1951) *Water resources of the Atlanta Metropolitan Area* (US Geological Survey Circular No. 148)

Carvalho, A. H. de (1936) *Rev. Quím. pur. apl.*, **11**, 99

Cauer, H. (1938) *Mitt. Biochem.*, **299**, 89

Cederstrom, D. J. (1946) *Bull. Va geol. Surv.*, No. 68

Chamberlain, G. (1944) *N. Z. J. Sci. Technol., B,* **26**, 90

Charonnat, R. & Roche, S. (1934) *C. R. Acad. Sci. (Paris),* **199**, 1325

Cheng, F. S. (1939) *J. orient. Med.,* **30**, 649

Cheng, L. T. & Chou, T. P. (1939) *J. Chin. chem. Soc.,* **7**, 36

Cholak, J. (1959) *J. occup. Med.,* **1**, 501

Christensen, C. M. (1963) *Water supply for the city of Redfield* (South Dakota State Geological Survey Special Report No. 24)

Christy, N. P. & Drucker, W. D. (1964) *Corticosteroids.* In: *Pharmacotherapeutics of oral disease,* New York, McGraw-Hill, chapter 39

Churchill, H. V., Rowley, R. J. & Martin, L. V. (1948) *Analyt. Chem.,* **20**, 69

Clark, C. (1962) In: *International Association for Dental Research, 40th General Meeting, St. Louis, Missouri, March 1962 ; Abstracts,* Chicago, American Dental Association, Abstr. No. 152

Clark, J. D. & Mann, E. H. (1938) *Bull. Univ. New Mex. Chem. Ser.,* **2**, No. 5

Clement, A. J. (1947) *Brit. dent. J.,* **82**, 168

Clifford, P. A. (1945) *J. Ass. off. agric. Chem.,* **28**, 277

Cohen, P. & Everett, D. E. (1963) *A brief appraisal of the ground-water hydrology of the Dixie Fairview Valley area of Nevada* (Nevada Department of Conservation and Natural Resources. Groundwater Resources Reconnaissance Series Report No. 23)

Cohen, P. & Gardner, F. H. (1966) *J. Amer. med. Ass.,* **195**, 962

Collings, G. H., Jr et al. (1951) *A.M.A. Arch. industr. Hyg.,* **4**, 585-590

Collings, G. H., Jr et al. (1952) *A.M.A. Arch. industr. Hyg.,* **6**, 368

Collins, E. M. (1962) *Dent. Dig.,* **68**, 360

Cooke, C. W., Martin, R. O. R. & Meyer, G. (1952) *Geology and water resources of Prince Georges County* (Maryland Board of Natural Resources, Department of Geology, Mines, and Water Resources, Bulletin No. 10)

Cooper, S. L. (1958) *Proc. sci. Sect. Toilet Goods Ass.,* No. 29 (June)

Correns, C. W. (1956) *The geochemistry of the halogens.* In: Ahrens, L. H., Rankama, K. & Runcorn, S. K., ed., *Physics and chemistry of the earth,* London, Pergamon, vol. 1, pp. 181-233

Crosby, N. D. & Shepherd, P. A. (1957) *Med. J. Aust.,* **2**, 341-346

Crossley, H. E. (1944) *J. Soc. chem. Industr. (Lond.),* **63**, 289

Crosthwaite, E. G. & Scott, R. C. (1956) *Ground water in the North-Side Pumping Division. Minidoka Project, Minidoka County, Idaho* (US Geological Survey Circular No. 371),

Dean, G. A. (1963) *N.Z.J. Sci.,* **6**, 208

Dean, H. T. (1951) *J. Amer. Wat. Wks Ass.,* **43**, 17

De Buchananne, G. D. & Richardson, R. M. (1956) *Bull. Tenn. Div. Geol.,* No. 58, Part I

Demole, V. & Held, A.-J. (1953) *Bull. schweiz. akad. med. Wiss.,* **9**, 146

Denmead, C. F. (1946) *N. Z. J. Sci. Technol., B,* **28**, 158

Deshpande, S. S. & Bester, J. F. (1964) *J. pharm. Sci.,* **53**, 803

DeWitt, D. J. & Nichols, M. S. (1937) *J. Amer. Wat. Wks Ass.,* **29**, 980

Dieffenbacher, P. F. & Thompson, J. H. (1962) *J. occup. Med.,* **4**, 325

Doberenz, A. R., Kurnick, A. A., Kurtz, E. B., Kemmerer, A. R. & Reid, B. L. (1964) *Proc. Soc. exp. Biol. (N.Y.),* **117**, 689

Drum, J. A. (1949) *Sci. Proc. roy. Dublin Soc.,* **25**, 85

Duckworth, R. (1964) *Nature (Lond.),* 204, 489

Durfor, C. M. & Becker, E. (1962) *J. Amer. Wat. Wks Ass.*, **56**, 237

Eichler, O., Appel, I. & Burschel, R. (1955) *Dtsch. zahnärztl. Z.*, **10**, 1310

Emslie, R. D. Veall, N. & Duckworth, R. (1961) *Brit. dent. J.*, **110**, 121

Englehardt, W. von (1936) *Chemie Erde*, **10**, 187

Ericsson, Y. (1958) *Acta odont. scand.*, **16**, 127-141

Ericsson, Y. (1961) *Acta odont. scand.*, **19**, 41

Eriksson, E. (1952) *Tellus*, **4**, 280

Erkillä, S. (1958) *Suom. Lääk.-L.*, **13**, 1165

Fellenberg, T. von (1948) *Mitt. Lebensmitt. Hyg.*, **39**, 124

Fleischer, M. (1953) *Recent estimates of the abundance of the elements in the earth's crust*, Washington, D.C. (US Geological Survey Circular No. 285)

Fleming, A. J. et al., ed. (1954) *Modern occupational medicine*, Philadelphia, Lea and Febiger

Foster, W. C. (1943) *Catalyst (Easton, Pa)*, **28**, 84, 90, 110

Gabovich, R. D. (1949) *Gig. i Sanit.*, **14**, No. 7, p. 15

Gabovich, R. D. (1951) *Gig. i Sanit.*, **16**, No. 6, p. 31

Galagan, D. J. (1953) *J. Amer. dent. Ass.*, **47**, 159-170

Galagan, D. J. & Lamson, G. G., Jr (1953) *Publ. Hlth Rep. (Wash.)*, **68**, 497-508

Galagan, D. J. & Vermillion, J. R. (1957) *Publ. Hlth Rep. (Wash.)*, **72**, 491-493

Galagan, D. J., Vermillion, J. R., Nevitt, G. A., Stadt, Z. M. & Dart, R. E. (1957) *Publ. Hlth Rep. (Wash.)*, **72**, 484

Gandra, Y. R. (1953) *Rev. bras. Odont.*, **11**, 48

Gedalia, I. (1953) *Harefuah*, **44**, 231

Gemmel, G. D. (1946) *N. Z. J. Sci. Technol.*, *B*, **27**, 302

Gericke, S. (1949) *Z. Plf-Ernähr. Düng. Bodenk.*, **43**, 146

Geschwind, Z. & Jurkiewicz, J. (1952) *Gaz Woda Tech. sanit.*, **26**, 116

Giardino, G. & Police, P. (1955) *Clin. Odont.*, **10**, 229

Goldich, S. S. (1941) *J. Geol.*, **44**, 697

Gómez Galissier, B. J. & Heer, A. E. (1950) *An. Med. públ.*, **2**, 531

Green, E. A. et al. (1961) *The inhalation toxicity of perchlorylfluoride*, Washington, D.C. (US Government Research Reports, No. 35, p. 20)

Haack & Zimmerman (1952) *Zbl. Bakt.*, **158**, 304

Hale, H., Baker, R. C., Walling, I. W., Parrish, D. M & Billingsley, G. A. (1947) *Public water supplies of Arkansas* (University of Arkansas Bureau of Research Series No. 11)

Hale, W. E. (1955) *Geology and ground-water resources of Webster County, Iowa* (Iowa Geological Survey Water Supply Bulletin No. 4)

Harkins, R. W., Longenecker, J. B. & Sarett, H. P. (1963) *J. Nutr.*, **81**, 81

Harris, H. B., Moore, G. K. & West, L. R. (1963) *Geology and ground-water resources of Collett County, Alabama* (Geological Survey of Alabama, County Report No. 10)

Hayhurst, E. R. (1943) In: *Proceedings of the 8th annual meeting of the Industrial Hygiene Foundation of America* (Discussion of paper by E. J. Largent: "Fluorides as an industrial health problem")

Heasman, M. A. & Martin, A. E. (1962) *Mth. Bull. Minist. Hlth Lab. Serv.*, **21**, 150

Heer, A. E. & Gómez Galissier, B. J. (1950) *An. Med. públ.*, **2**, 291

Hellstrom, I. (1960) *Acta odont. scand.*, **18**, 263

Henkel, G. (1961) *Arch. oral Biol.*, **6**, 181 (Special Supplement: Proceedings of 8th ORCA Congress, London, July 1961)

Hennon, D. K., Stookey, G. K. & Muhler, J. C. (1964) *J. Pediat.*, **64**, 272

Hennon, D. K., Stookey, G. K. & Muhler, J. C. (1966a) In: *International Association for Dental Research, 44th Annual Meeting, Miami Beach, Fla., USA, March 1966; Abstracts,* Chicago, American Dental Association, Abstr. No. 459

Hennon, D. K., Stookey, G. K. & Muhler, J. C. (1966b) *J. Dent. Child.*, **33**, 3

Hennon, D. K., Stookey, G. K. & Muhler, J. C. (1967) *J. Dent. Child.*, **34**, 439

Hewat, R. E. T. & Eastcott, D. F. (1955) *Dental caries in New Zealand,* Christchurch, Baty (New Zealand Medical Research Council Report)

Hodge, H. C. (1956) *J. Amer. dent. Ass.*, **52**, 307

Hodge, H. C. & Smith, F. A. (1965) *Biological effects of inorganic fluorides.* In: Simons, J. H., ed., *Fluorine chemistry,* New York, Academic Press, vol. 4

Hodge, H. C., Smith, F. A. & Chen, P. S. (1963) *Biological effects of organic fluorides.* In: Simons, J. H., ed., *Fluorine chemistry,* New York, Academic Press, vol. 3

Hoyos Ruiz, E. C. H. A. (1953) *An. Bromat.*, **5**, 287

Hoyt, W. H. & Bibby, B. G. (1943) *J. Amer. dent. Ass.*, **30**, 1372

Hunter, G. C., Barringer, M. & Spooner, G. (1961) *J. Periodont.*, **32**, 333

Jensen, A. L. (1964) *J. Amer. dent. Ass.*, **68**, 216

Jeup, B. H. (1943) *Mth. Bull. Indiana Bd Hlth*, **47**, 171

Joneidi, M. J. (1955) *Rev. Fac. Méd. (Téhéran)*, **18**, No. 3, p. 16

Jones, P. B. (1949) *Dent. J. Aust.*, **21**, 231

Kappana, A. N., Gadre, G. T., Bhavnagary, H. M. & Joshi, J. M. (1962) *Curr. Sci.*, **31**, 273

Kent, L. E. (1949) *Trans. Proc. geol. Soc. S. Afr.*, **52**, 231

Kilborn, L. G., Outerbridge, T. S. & Lei, H. P. (1950) *Canad. med. Ass. J.*, **62**, 135-141

Kind, A. (1938) *Chemie Erde*, **12**, 50

Kobayashi, S. (1951) *Kagaku (Tokyo)*, **21**, 267

Kobayashi, S. (1954) *Bull. chem. Soc. Japan*, **27**, 314

Koller, S. (1950) *Öst. Z. Stomat.*, **47**, 505

Koritnig, S. (1950) *Z. analyt. Chem.*, **131**, 1

Koritnig, S. (1951) *Geochim. cosmochim. Acta.* **1**, 89

Krainov, S. R. & Korolskova, M. (1964) *Tr. vsesojuz. nauchno-isseled. Inst. Gidrogeol. inz. Geol.*, **9**, 72

Krepkogorskii, L. N. & Bogusevich, L. N. (1953) *Gidrokhim. Materialy*, **21**, 24

Kruger, B. J. (1960) *Pap. Dep. Dent. Univ. Qd.* **1**, 45

Kubota, K. (1952) *Folia pharmacol. jap.*, **48**, No. 1, Proc. 38

La Moreaux, P. E. (1946) *Geology and ground-water resources of the coastal plain of east central Georgia* (Georgia Department of Mines, Mining and Geology, Geological Survey Bulletin No. 52)

Lamar, W. L. & Schroeder, M. E. (1951) *Chemical character of Surface waters of Ohio, 1946-50* (Ohio Division of Water Bulletin No. 23)

Largent, E. J. (1961) *Fluorosis. The health aspects of fluorine compounds,* Colombus, Ohio State University Press

Larsen, E. S. & Draisin, W. M. (1950) *Composition of the minerals in the rocks of the southern Californian batholith.* In: *International Geological Congress, 18th session, 1948,* Stockport, Co-operative Wholesale Soc., vol. 2, p. 66

Larson, T. E. (1963) *Illinois St. Wat. Surv. Bull.*, No. 90

Lefkowitz, W. (1962) *J. prosth. Dent.*, **12**, 966

Lefkowitz, W., Burdick, H. C. & Moore, D. L. (1963) *J. prosth. Dent.*, **13**, 940

LeGrand, H. E. (1954) *Geology and ground-water in the Statesville area, North Carolina* (North Carolina Department of Conservation and Development, Division of Mineral Resources, Bulletin No. 68)

Leonard, A. R. & Durum, W. B. (1952) *Bull. Kans. St. geol. Surv.*, No. 98

Lindemann, G. (1965) *Acta odont. scand.*, **23**, 575

Lyon, J. S. (1962) *J. occup. Med.*, **4**, 199

McClendon, J. F. (1944) *Fed. Proc.*, **3**, 94

McClendon, J. F. & Gershon-Cohen, J. (1953) *J. Agric. Food Chem.*, **1**, 464

McClure, F. J. (1939) *Nat. Inst. Hlth Bull.*, No. 172, pp. 1-53

McClure, F. J. (1943) *Amer. J. Dis. Child.*, **66**, 362-369

McClure, F. J. (1949) *Publ. Hlth Rep. (Wash.)*, **64**, 1061

Machle, W., Scott, E. W. & Treon, J. (1939) *Amer. J. Hyg.*, **29**, No. 3, Sect. A, p. 139

Machle, W. F. et al. (1934) *J. industr. Hyg.*, **16**, 129

Machle, W. F. et al. (1935) *J. industr. Hyg.*, **17**, 223

MacIntire, W. H., Hardin, L. J. & Hester, W. (1952) *Industr. Engng Chem.*, **44**, 1365

McPhail, C. W. B. & Zacherl, W. (1965) *J. Canad. dent. Ass.*, **31**, 7

Maher, J. C. (1941) *Bull. geol. Surv. La,* No. 20

Maldonado, A. & Guevara, R. J. de D. (1951) *Bol. Soc. quím. Perú*, **17**, 211

Manning, M. A. (1961) *Dent. Surv.*, **37**, 731

Marshal Day, C. D. M. (1940) *Brit. dent. J.*, **68**, 409

Massler, M. (1955) *J. dent. Res.*, **34**, 761

Matuura, S., Kokubu, N., Wakimoto, S. & Tokimasa, M. (1954) *Kyushu J. med. Sci., C,* **2**, 37 (Abstract in *Chem. Abstr.*, 1956, **50**, Abstr. No. 17246)

Maurer, R. L. & Day, H. G. (1957) *J. Nutr.*, **62**, 561

Melman, J. (1954) *An. Acad. Cienc. méd. fís. natur. Habana*, **93**, 299

Miller, R. B. (1961) *N.Z.J.Sci.*, **4**, 844

Møller, I. J. (1965) *Dental fluorose og karies,* Copenhagen, Rhodos (Thesis)

Moseshvili, Y., Ugulava, M., Dzokhadze, G., Talakvadze, G., Khavtasi, D. & Gotsiridze, E. (1962) *Tr. tbilis. gos. Univ. Stalina*, **80**, 7

Moshkina, I. A. & Nikol'skaya, Y. P. (1964) *Geologija Geofiz. (Novosibirsk)*, **6**, 130

Muhler, J. C. (1954) *J. Nutr.*, **54**, 481

Muhler, J. C. (1958) *J. Amer. dent. Ass.*, **56**, 335

Muhler, J. C., Stookey, G. K., Spear, L. B. & Bixler, D. (1966) *J. oral Ther. Pharmacol.*, **2**, 241

Muñoz, A., J. E. (1940) *Geographical localization of fluoride waters (in Ecuador).* In: *Proceedings of the 8th American Scientific Congress,* vol. 7, p. 203

Murray, M. M. & Wilson, D. C. (1946) *Lancet*, **2**, 821

Natvig, H. & Wilhelmsen, L. H. (1963) *Fluorinnhold i norsk vannverksvann og bruken av fluortabletten i kariesprofylaksen,* Oslo

Neisler, H. (1963) *Hydrogeology of the carbonate rocks of the Lebanon valley, Pennsylvania* (Pennsylvania Topographic, Geological Survey, Ground Water Report W.18)

Neumann, H. H. (1957) *Arch. Pediat.*, **74**, 456

Nitschké, E. (1953) *Arch. Inst. G.-D. Luxemb. Sci. natur.*, **20**, 159

Noguchi, K., Ueno, S., Kamiya, H. & Nishiido, T. (1963) *Proc. Japan Acad.*, **39**, 364

Nömmik, H. (1953) *Fluorine in Swedish agricultural products, soil and drinking water*, Stockholm, Esselte

North Dakota State Department of Health (1952) *Off. Bull. N. Dak. Wat. Wks Conf.*, **19**, No. 10-12, pp. 4, 6

Ockerse, T. (1946) *Fluorine and dental caries in South Africa.* In: Moulton, F. R., ed., *Dental caries and fluorine*, Washington, D.C., American Association for the Advancement of Science

Ockerse, T. (1949) *Dental caries : clinical and experimental investigations*, Pretoria, Department of Public Health, Union of South Africa

Ohio River Valley Water Sanitation Commission (1957) *Water quality and flow variations in the Ohio river 1951-1955*, Cincinnati

Okuno, H. (1942) *J. chem. Soc. Japan*, **63**, 871

Ostapenya, P. V., Gel'fer, E. A. & Kagan, T. S. (1963) *Zdravoohr. Beloruss.*, **9**, 51

Page, L. V., Newcombe, R. & Graeff, G. D. (1963) *Water resources of Sabine Parish, Louisiana* (Louisiana Department of Conservation, Geological Survey of Public Works Water Resources Bulletin No. 3)

Papp, S. & Dippold, A. (1950) *Hidrol. Közl.*, **30**, 301

Pappalardo, G. (1955) *Boll. Soc. med.-chir. Catania*, **23**, 106

Paraje, R. (1950) *Rev. Asoc. bioquím. argent.*, **15**, 211

Parks, W. G., Robinson, M. & Law, M. (1936) *J. Amer. Wat. Wks Ass.*, **28**, 1064

Pauszek, F. H. (1949) *Public ground-water supplies in North Carolina* (US Geological Survey Progress Report No. 2)

Persits, M. M. (1964) *Stomatologija (Mosk.)*, **43**, 22

Petrovic, A. & Shambaugh, G. E. (1966) *Arch. Otolaryng.*, **83**, 104

Pissani, P. L. (1954) *An. Fac. Farm. (Lima)*, **5**, 506

Pohloudek-Fabini, R., Engst, R. & Mörtzschky, I. (1953) *Pharmazie*, **8**, 707

Polák, B. & Symon, K. (1951) *Čas. člék. es.*, **90**, 641

Polheim, P. von & Dietrich, H. (1955) *Landw. Forsch.*, **8**, 118

Powell, W. J., Reade, H. L. & Scott, J. C. (1957) *The geology and ground-water resources of Montgomery, Alabama, and vicinity* (Geological Survey of Alabama, Information Series No. 3)

Prior, C. H., Schneider, R. & Durum, W. H. (1953) *Water resources of the Minneapolis-St. Paul area, Minnesota* (US Geological Survey Circular No. 274)

Purves, M. J. (1962) *Lancet*, **2**, 1188-1189

Quentin, K.-E. (1952) *Münch. med. Wschr.*, **94**, 496

Raghavachari, T. N. S. & Venkataramanan, K. (1940) *Indian J. med. Res.*, **28**, 517-532

Rakityanskii, V. I. (1963) *Uchen. Zap. smolensk. gos. pedagog. Inst.*, **12**, 103

Ramamohana Rao, N. V. & Bhaskaran, C. S. (1964) *Indian J. med. Res.*, **52**, 180

Reid, E. (1936) *Chin. J. Physiol.*, **10**, 259

Reid, R. L. & Martin, N. D. (1946) *Med. J. Aust.*, **2**, 121

Rich, C. & Ensinck, J. (1961) *Nature (Lond.)*, **191**, 184

Rich, C. & Ensinck, J. (1962) *Clin. Res.*, **10**, 118

Rich, C. Ensinck, J. & Ivanovich, P. (1964) *J. clin. Invest.*, **43**, 545-556

Rich, C. & Ivanovich, P. (1965) *Ann. intern. Med.*, **63**, 1069

Rieke, H. W. (1945) *Dent. Surv.*, **21**, 1996

Robinson, W. O. & Edgingyon, G. (1946) *Soil. Sci.*, **61**, 341

Roholm, K. (1937) *Fluorine intoxication: a clinical-hygienic study, with a review of the literature and some experimental investigations*, London, Lewis

Rovelstad, G. H. & St. John, W. E. (1949) *J. Amer. dent. Ass.*, **39**, 670

Sahama, T. G. (1945) *Bull. Commn géol. Finl.*, **136**, 15-167

Saunders, B. C. (1961) *The physiological action of organic compounds containing fluorine.* In: *Advances in fluorine chemistry*, London, Butterworth, vol. 2

Scheinin, A. et al. (1964) *Acta odont. scand.*, **22**, 229-254

Schoff, S. L. & Stovall, J. W. (1943) *Bull. Okla. geol. Surv.*, No. 64

Schweinsberger, R. A. & Muhler, J. C. (1956) *J. dent. Res.*, **35**, 760

Schweinsberger, R. A. & Muhler, J. C. (1957) *J. Pediat.*, **51**, 634

Scott, H. M., Jr (1962) *J. Dent. Child.*, **29**, 225

Scott, R. D., Ey, L. F. & Waring, F. H. (1937) *J. Amer. Wat. Wks Ass.*, **29**, 9

Searcy, J. K., Baker, R. C. & Durum, W. H. (1952) *Water resources of the St. Louis area, Missouri and Illinois* (US Geological Survey Circular No. 216)

Seraphim, R. H. (1951) *Some aspects of the geochemistry of fluorine* (Thesis, Massachusetts Institute of Technology). Cited by Correns (1956)

Shambaugh, G. E. & Scott, A. (1964) *Arch. Otolaryng.*, **80**, 263

Sharpless, G. R. & McCollum, E. V. (1933) *J. Nutr.*, **6**, 163

Shaver, E. Q. & Smith, R. R. (1946) *J. dent. res.*, **5**, 121

Shepherd, E. S. (1940) *Amer. J. Sci.*, **238**, 117

Shortt, H. E., McRobert, G. R., Barnard, T. W. & Mannadi Nayar, A. S. (1937) *Indian J. med. Res.*, **25**, 553-568

Showley, J. E., Stookey, G. K., Hennon, D. K. & Muhler, J. C. (1966) *J. oral Ther. Pharmacol.*, **2**, 346

Sibalić, M., Dordević, M. & Perović, S. (1960) *Higijena*, **12**, 45

Sibalić, M. & Perović, S. (1954) *Glas. Hig. Inst.*, **3**, 64

Sieman, W. H. (1960) *J. Conn. St. dent. Ass.*, **34**, 5

Simons, J. H., ed. (1954) *Fluorine chemistry*, New York, Academic Press, vol. 2

Sinclair, W. C. (1963) *Ground-water appraisal of the Black Rock Desert area, north-western Nevada* (Nevada Department of Conservation and Natural Resources, Ground Water Resources Reconnaissance Series Report No. 20)

Singer, L., Armstrong, W. D. & Vatassery, G. T. (1967) *Econ. Bot.*, **21**, 285-287

Singh, A., Jolly, S. S., Bansal, B. C. & Mathur, O. C. (1963) *Medicine (Baltimore)*, **42**, 229-246

Siple, G. E. (1957) *J. Amer. Wat. Wks Ass.*, **49**, 283

Smith, F. A. & Hodge, H. C. (1959) *Fluoride toxicity.* In: Muhler, J. C. & Hine, M. K., ed., *Fluorine and dental health*, Bloomington, Indiana University Press

Smith, H. V., Caster, A. B., Fuller, V. H., Breazeale, E. L. & Draper, G. (1949) *Bull. Ariz. Univ.*, No. 225

Spéder, E. (1936) *Bull. Mém. Soc. Radiol. méd. Fr.*, **24**, 200

Spitzner, R. (1947) *Arch. Inst. biol. (Curitíba)*, **2**, 233

Stas, M. E., Kooijmans, L. H. L. & Ijssel, J. J. van (1937) *Water ('s-Gravenhage)*, **21**, No. 1-2, p. 1

Stas, M. E., Kooijmans, L. H. L. & Ijssel, J. J. van (1941) *Water ('s-Gravenhage)*, **25**, 181

Stokinger, H. E. (1949) *Toxicity following inhalation of fluorine and hydrogen fluoride.* In: Voegtlin, C. & Hodge, H. C., ed., *Pharmacology and toxicology of uranium compounds,* New York, McGraw-Hill

Stookey, G. K. (1966) *Fluoride therapy.* In: *Improving dental practice through preventive measures,* St. Louis, Mo., Mosby, chapter 5

Stookey, G. K. & Muhler, J. C. (1966) *J. Dent. Child.,* **33,** 90

Storvick, C. A. & Sullivan, J. H. (1950) *J. Amer. Wat. Wks Ass.,* **42,** 589

Stout, W. C. (1955) *J. Periodont.,* **26,** 208

Straub, J. (1940) *Orv. Hetil.,* **84,** 121

Straub, J. (1950) *Magy. allami földt. Intéz., Évk.,* **39,** No. 1

Sugawa, Y. (1937) *J. Chosen med. Ass.,* **27,** 1163

Sundstrom, R. W., Broadhurst, N. L. & Dwyer, B. C. (1949) *Public water supplies in central and north central Texas* (US Geological Survey, Water Supply Paper No. 1069)

Suttie, J. W. & Phillips, P. H. (1959) In: Muhler, J. C. & Hine, M. K., ed., *Fluorine and dental health,* Bloomington, Indiana University Press, pp. 70-77

Swedish National Board of Health (1966) *Fluoren i kariesprofylaxen,* Stockholm

Tait, D. B., Baker, R. C. & Billinglsley, G. A. (1953) *The ground water resources of Columbia County, Arkansas. A reconnaissance* (US Geological Survey Circular No. 241)

Talenti, M. & Cardini, C. (1953) *Nuovi Ann. Ig.,* **4,** 1

Tanganyika, Government Chemist (1955) *Annual report of the Government Chemist of Tanganyika,* 1954, Dar es Salaam, Government Printer (Abstract in *Wat. Pollut. Abstr.,* 1956, **29,** 267)

Taylor, F. B. (1962) *J. Amer. Wat. Wks Ass.,* **54,** 1257

Thwaites, F. T. (1956) *Rep. Wis. engng Exp. Sta.,* No. 8, p. 49

Tomic, D. (1958) *Gesundheits-Ing.,* **79,** 337

Tomic, D. (1959) *Acta pharm jugosl.,* **9,** 71

Torkelson, T. R. et al. (1962) *Toxicol. appl. Pharmacol.,* **4,** 770

Trömel, G. (1953) *Die chemischen und technischen Grundlagen der Herstellung von Phosphatdüngemitteln,* 2nd ed., Essen, Tellus-Verlag

Truhaut, R. (1955) *Ann. Falsif. Fraudes,* **48,** 237, 290

US Department of Health, Education, and Welfare (1959) *Natural fluoride content of communal water supplies in the United States,* Washington, D.C. (Public Health Service Publication No. 665)

US Interdepartmental Committee on Nutrition for National Defense (1960a) *Ecuador nutrition survey,* Washington, D.C., US Government Printing Office

US Interdepartmental Committee on Nutrition for National Defense (1960b) *Ethiopia nutrition survey,* Washington, D.C., US Government Printing Office

US Interdepartmental Committee on Nutrition for National Defense (1961a) *Republic of China. Nutrition survey of the Armed Forces,* Washington, D.C., US Government Printing Office

US Interdepartmental Committee on Nutrition for National Defense (1961b) *The Kingdom of Thailand. Nutrition survey (preliminary),* Washington, D.C., US Government Printing Office

Velu, H. & Charnot, A. (1938) *Maroc méd.,* No. 191

Vinogradov, A. P. (1954) *Geochemie seltener und nur in Spuren vorhandener chemischer Elemente im Boden,* Berlin, Akademie-Verlag

Vinogradov, A. P., Danilova, V. V. & Selivanov, L. S. (1937) *C.R. Acad. Sci. URSS,* **14,** 361

Visintin, B. & Monteriolo, S. (1955) [*Fluorine content of drinkable waters feeding important Italian towns*]. In: *Profilassi carie dental, 1° simposio internazionale,* p. 312

Walker, E. H. (1953) *Geology and ground-water resources of the Covington-Newport alluvial area, Kentucky* (US Geological Survey Circular No. 240)

Walker, J. S., Margolis, F. J., Luten Teate, H., Weil, M. L. & Wilson, H. L. (1963) *Science,* **140,** 890

Ward, L. K. (1954) *Fluorine in South Australian underground waters* (South Australia Department of Mines, Report of Investigations No. 1)

Wäre, M. (1961). Cited by Scheinin et al. (1964)

Wattenberg, H. (1943) *Z. anorg. allg. Chem.,* **251,** 86

Wetherill, C. E. (1956) *Dent. Surv.,* **32,** 767

Williamson, M. M. (1953) *E. Afr. med. J.,* **30,** 217

Wilson, D. C. (1954) *Nature (Lond.),* **173,** 305

Winkler, K. C., Backer Dirks, O. & Van Amerongen, J. (1953) *Brit. dent. J.,* **95,** 119

Wisher, F. N. & Durum, W. H. (1952) *Reconnaissance of the geology and ground-water resources of the Pass Creek Flats area, Carbon County, Wyoming, with a section on the chemical quality of the water* (US Geological Survey Circular No. 188)

Witkop, C. J., Barros, L. & Hamilton, P. A. (1962) *Publ. Hlth Rep. (Wash.),* **77,** 928

Wojciechowska, W. & Kolaczkowski, S. (1953) *Roczn. Zak. Hig. (Warsz.),* p. 239

Zavala, C. B. (1950) *An. Fac. Farm. (Lima)* **1,** 475

Zies, E. G. (1929) *The Valley of Ten Thousand Smokes. I. The acid gases contributing to the sea during volcanic activity* (National Geographic Society, Contributed Technical Papers 1, Katmai Series No. 4)

Zipkin, I. & Leone, N. C. (1957) *Amer. J. publ. Hlth,* **47,** 848-851

CHAPTER 3

Absorption of fluorides

H.-D. CREMER [1] & W. BÜTTNER [2]

1. INTRODUCTION

The present knowledge about fluoride absorption is based on numerous animal experiments and on observations and investigations in man. Adequate data with regard to the amount of ingested fluoride which will be absorbed can be obtained only by metabolic studies. Owing to the difficult nature of such studies, information on children is almost completely lacking. However, enough information is already available from metabolic investigations in adult humans for the main factors governing fluoride absorption to be known. It can safely be assumed that there are no differences in respect of mechanism and site of fluoride absorption between young and adult beings. Furthermore, certain conclusions with regard to absorption can be drawn from data on fluoride ingestion and subsequent fluoride retention in calcified tissues.

Before considering the absorption of fluoride after ingestion in water and other beverages, in food and in drugs, some general facts may be briefly summarized:

(1) Fluoride sources may be inorganic and organic;

(2) The inorganic fluoride compounds can be classified as soluble (e.g., NaF, HF, H_2SiF_6, Na_2SiF_6, Na_2PO_3F), insoluble (e.g., CaF_2, rock phosphate, cryolite) and inert (e.g., KBF_4).

From inorganic compounds, depending on their solubilities, fluoride ions are released and absorbed. With regard to fluoride effects, only the fluoride ion is of importance.

The absorption of fluoride ions from an ingested dose of soluble fluoride salts is rapid and nearly complete, whereas the absorption of fluoride from less soluble fluoride compounds is incomplete, depending on solubility,

[1] Director, Nutrition Institute, University of Giessen, Germany.
[2] Stomatology Clinic, University of Würzburg, Germany.

physical properties of crystals, particle size, mode of intake, etc. The stability of the inert fluoride compounds is so great that no fluoride ions are released or absorbed—KBF_4, for example, is completely excreted in the faeces and urine.

With organic fluorocompounds (e.g., fluoroacetates, fluorophosphates and fluorocarbons) the whole compounds are absorbed or inhaled and not the fluoride ions. The significance of these compounds for human health is discussed in Chapters 2 and 7.

2. MECHANISM AND SITE OF ABSORPTION

Mechanism

Fluoride absorption is passive in nature and no active transport mechanism is involved in the process. The rapidity of fluoride absorption has been shown in studies using the radioactive isotope [18]F. As early as 1941, Volker, Sognnaes & Bibby showed in the rat that, judging by the rapidity of ^{18}F-distribution in the body, absorption must be very rapid. Carlson, Armstrong & Singer (1960) demonstrated that 1 mg of fluoride labelled with ^{18}F and ingested by two adult humans was rapidly absorbed. A portable crystal scintillation counter was placed over the abdominal area and a few minutes after fluoride ingestion the counts showed a rapid decline due to fast absorption. The maximum plasma radiofluoride concentration was reached within 60 minutes. The short interval between intake of oral doses of soluble fluorides and excretion in the urine is also evidence of very rapid absorption. According to studies in humans by Hodge & Smith (1965), by Ericsson (1958) and by Carlson, Armstrong & Singer (op. cit.), between 20% and 33% of an ingested fluoride dose was found in the urine within 3 to 4 hours.

The results of numerous animal studies also show the rapidity of fluoride absorption. Only a few of these investigations will be mentioned. Wallace-Durbin introduced radioactive ^{18}F into the stomach of rats, and observed that within one hour 75% of the fluoride dose was absorbed (Wallace, 1953; Wallace-Durbin, 1954). Her observations were confirmed by Zipkin & Likins (1957), who found that 72% of a fluoride dose of 0.2 mg F^- as sodium fluoride solution, introduced into the stomach of unfed rats, was absorbed in one hour. The rates of fluoride absorption in unfed rats at various time intervals after ingestion are shown in Fig. 1. Absorption was found to be somewhat slower in unfed rats after administration by stomach-tube of higher amounts of fluoride (e.g., 1 mg F^- as NaF). The absorption rates from 1 to 24 hours reported by Stookey, Crane & Muhler (1964) are shown in Table 1. Between 80% and 90% were absorbed in 8 hours after administration, thus confirming the results obtained in the rat with radiofluoride

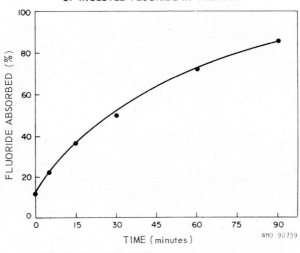

FIG. 1

GASTROINTESTINAL ABSORPTION OF 0.2 mg
OF INGESTED FLUORIDE IN THE RAT [a]

[a] After Zipkin & Likins (1957).

(^{18}F) by Ericsson (1958). Stookey, Crane & Muhler (*op. cit.*) also showed that two hours after fluoride administration the absorption rate is 32% less in fed rats than in unfed rats.

From the rapidity with which fluoride is absorbed, appears in blood and is distributed within the body, it can be concluded that no active transport system is involved in the absorption. It can be assumed that the mechanism for the removal of fluoride from the gastrointestinal tract is one of simple diffusion. This has been shown by *in vitro* studies on segments of the rat's

TABLE 1

RATE OF FLUORIDE ABSORPTION FROM GASTROINTESTINAL TRACT
OF UNFED RATS FOLLOWING ADMINISTRATION
OF 1.0 mg OF F$^-$ (AS NaF) [a]

Time after F$^-$ administration (hours)	Average F$^-$ absorbed (%)
0	—
1	29.1
2	58.1
3	68.5
4	73.4
6	81.3
8	86.4
12	89.5
16	90.8
24	94.9

[a] After Stookey, Crane & Muhler (1964).

gastrointestinal tract carried out by Stookey, Dellinger & Muhler (1964). Doses of 0.2 mg F^- diffused through rat intestines at a rate of 47.5% and through the stomach wall at a rate of 25.7% during 1 hour. The total diffusion rate from intestines and stomach thus accounted for 73.2%, confirming the *in vivo* fluoride absorption of 72% observed by Zipkin & Likins (*op. cit.*) after 1 hour in unfed rats receiving 0.2 mg F^- (see Fig. 1). In Table 2 are

TABLE 2

IN VITRO DIFFUSION OF 0.2 mg FLUORIDE FROM GASTROINTESTINAL SEGMENTS OF THE RAT [a]

Segment	No. of trials	Percentage of fluoride disappearing from lumen in		
		30 min	60 min	90 min
Intestine	7	23.7 ± 2.2	47.5 ± 2.5	59.4 ± 4.2
Stomach	6	14.8 ± 5.2	25.7 ± 3.6	35.4 ± 3.6
Total [b]		38.5	73.2	94.8

[a] After Stookey, Dellinger & Muhler (1964).
[b] Compare the figures with the data obtained by Zipkin & Likins (1957) *in vivo* (Fig. 1). The good agreement in percentage of fluoride absorption as a function of time is notable.

given the data for *in vitro* diffusion of fluoride from rat intestines and stomach (Stookey, Dellinger & Muhler, *op. cit.*). These investigators established (1) that there was a direct relationship between the rate of fluoride diffusion and the diffusion area of the intestinal wall, (2) that enzyme poisons—e.g., sodium cyanide, sodium iodoacetate or 2,4-dinitrophenol—did not alter the rate of fluoride diffusion from the inside to the outside of intestinal segments, and (3) that temperature variations from 20°C to 37°C did not influence the rate of fluoride diffusion from the intestine. These observations indicate that fluoride ions are absorbed by normal diffusion through the gastrointestinal wall.

Site

Observations with ^{18}F in man (Carlson, Armstrong & Singer, 1960) and in domestic animals (Perkinson et al., 1955) suggested that absorption of fluoride must occur from the stomach, in view of its rapid appearance in blood. The *in vitro* experiments of Foster & Rush (1961) have demonstrated that fluoride ions cross the gastric membranes. Similar *in vitro* studies by Stookey, Dellinger & Muhler (*op. cit.*), which demonstrated the diffusion of fluoride from the stomach as well as from the intestinal tract, have been described above.

Quantitative data on the absorption rate of fluoride *in vivo* by the gastric mucosa of the rat have been presented by Wagner (1962), who ligated the pylorus, injected a dose of 29.4 μg F⁻ (as NaF) directly into the stomach, ligated the gastro-oesophageal junction and determined the disappearance of fluoride from the stomach at various intervals up to 5 hours after injection. The residual fluoride which was found in the stomach is presented graphically in Fig. 2. For a brief period after injection little fluoride was absorbed from the stomach. After 15 minutes the residual fluoride began to decrease rapidly, and 1 hour after fluoride administration approximately

FIG. 2

DISAPPEARANCE OF FLUORIDE FROM THE LIGATED STOMACH OF THE RAT[a]

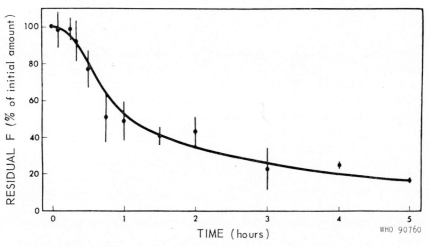

[a] After Wagner (1962).

An initial amount of 29.4 μg F⁻ as NaF was injected into the stomach after ligation of the pylorus. Each point is the mean value of data obtained from four rats with the standard error.

50% of the original dose had been absorbed by the gastric mucosa. The absorption continued, and after 5 hours only 16% of the initial fluoride dose was found in the stomach.

Stookey, Crane & Muhler (1962) determined the *in vivo* fluoride absorption rates in rats 30 minutes after injection of fluoride into various segments of the gastrointestinal tract. Some of their data are summarized in Table 3. The fluoride was injected into the segments, which were then completely ligated, at the top and the bottom, and analysed for residual fluoride 30 minutes later. Absorption from the stomach ranged from 26% to 36% depending on the age of the rats and on the fluoride dose (100-400 μg F⁻). From the first 5-cm segment of intestine, between 20% and 49% of an initial fluoride dose was absorbed; from the second and third 5-cm intestinal segments, between 36% and 49% was absorbed. It was shown that an appreciable amount of fluoride was absorbed from the stomach, though on the

TABLE 3

FLUORIDE ABSORPTION FROM SEGMENTS OF THE GASTROINTESTINAL
TRACT 30 MINUTES AFTER INJECTIONS OF 100 μg F⁻ (AS NaF) INTO
LIGATED SEGMENTS OF THE RAT [a]

Segment	No. of rats	Mean final weight (g)	Average F⁻ absorbed (%)
Stomach	6	120	35.3
Intestine:			
first 5 cm	3	120	49.3
third 5 cm	3	145	48.3

[a] After Stookey, Crane & Muhler (1962).

average the absorption was somewhat less from the stomach than from the intestine.

It was demonstrated in these animal experiments that the site of fluoride absorption is the entire gastrointestinal tract, and it can safely be assumed that the site of fluoride absorption in man is similar. Quantitative data on fluoride absorption in humans from specific segments of the gastrointestinal tract are, however, lacking.

Besides ingestion, absorption through the skin may also serve as a route in circumstances where hydrogen fluoride is being handled.

In occupational health, the absorption of inhaled fluoride as hydrogen fluoride, as fluoride vapours or as fluoride-containing dust plays an important role. Fluoride absorption from the lung is also rapid and nearly complete. Machle & Largent (1943) found an almost 100% absorption of inhaled hydrogen fluoride, and Collings, Fleming & May (1951) reported that the absorption was almost the same whether the fluoride was inhaled as fluoride-containing dust or as hydrogen fluoride. The lung as a site of fluoride absorption has been extensively studied by Largent, who discusses the subject in Chapter 2, section 5.

3.   ABSORPTION FROM BEVERAGES, FOOD AND FLUORIDE PREPARATIONS

Following the ingestion of fluoride in food, water and other beverages, as well as in fluoride-containing preparations, the ultimate amount of fluoride absorbed is what is of interest. The availability of fluoride for absorption is of importance if the ion is supplied for beneficial purposes, either in optimal amounts for dental caries prevention or in high amounts during short periods of time for the treatment of osteoporosis.

Ingestion with Drinking Water

Soluble fluorides in drinking water will be absorbed nearly completely (86-97 %), regardless of the level of fluoride in the water supply, which may vary from traces to 8 ppm F^- and more (McClure et al., 1945; Largent, 1960). Sometimes the question is raised as to the extent to which hard waters may interfere with fluoride absorption. Of the inorganic elements in drinking water, only calcium and magnesium are likely to be present in sufficient concentrations (1 ppm in very soft waters to as much as 100 ppm in very hard waters in areas of magnesium- or calcium-bearing rocks) to bind fluoride. Feldman, Morken & Hodge (1957) pointed out that in drinking water containing 1 ppm F^-, 0.03-2.8 % of the fluoride will be bound to calcium and 0.3-28 % to magnesium, depending on the hardness of the water (cf. Chapter 2, section 2). Nevertheless, fluoride up to the extent of 16 ppm F^- in any drinking-water supply with a pH of 5 or higher will be available as fluoride ions for nearly complete absorption. It has been shown by Largent & Heyroth (1949) that 96 % of the fluoride from a calcium fluoride solution was absorbed by the adult human. McClure et al. (*op. cit.*) reported a fluoride absorption of 83 % in the adult after daily ingestion of approximately 4 mg of fluoride (as calcium fluoride) in water. The fluorides that either occur naturally in water or are added to communal water supplies, e.g., NaF, Na_2SiF_6, H_2SiF_6, HF, $(NH_4)_2SiF_6$, to increase the fluoride level to 1 ppm F^- yield fluoride ions which are almost completely absorbed from the gastrointestinal tract. The reduced absorption in experimental animals of fluoride ingested in the form of CaF_2, or 25-100 ppm F in drinking water together with calcium-rich food, thus has no counterpart when fluoride at a level of about 1 ppm is ingested with even the hardest acceptable water.

Ingestion with Other Beverages

All beverages naturally contain fluoride ions derived from the waters used directly in their preparation. It is to be expected that fluoride absorption is as complete from them as from plain water. The absorption of fluoride from mineral waters and wines (F^- content up to 10 ppm and 6 ppm, respectively) is also not different from that from drinking water.

The fluoride absorption from milk and tea has been studied quite closely. Milk has been used as an alternative fluoride vehicle in one community of the USA and in another in Switzerland. Significant reductions in the caries rate among children were reported as a result of the intake of fluoridated milk (1 ppm F) supplied in the household and in school (Rusoff et al., 1962; Ziegler, 1964). The question was raised whether fluoride in milk is as readily available as it is in water. According to fluoride-retention studies in the rat, fluoride at concentrations of 5 and 10 ppm F^- was approximately equally available whether administered in water or in milk (Muhler & Weddle, 1955). Ericsson (1958), using ^{18}F, found that at concentrations of

1 and 4 ppm F⁻ the absorption of fluoride from milk was slower than that from water. However, the ultimate percentage absorbed was nearly the same whether the fluoride was supplied in milk or in water. Eight to ten hours after administration, 17-19 % of the fluoride in milk and 10-11 % of the fluoride in water remained unabsorbed. The author suggested that coagulation of milk in the stomach and incomplete diffusibility of fluoride may be factors causing some retardation in absorption.

Tea is a relatively rich natural source of fluoride. The fluoride content of various brands of tea ranges from 3.2 to 400 ppm on a fresh-weight basis. The average fluoride concentration of generally used tea is around 100 ppm. Approximately 90 % of the fluoride in tea leaves will be extracted after infusion and the fluoride concentration of the infusion itself is around 1 ppm F⁻ (Ham & Smith, 1950; Quentin, Souci & Indinger, 1960). Lawrenz & Mitchell (1941) demonstrated that fluoride in tea is somewhat less available than fluoride in water. In a fluoride balance study on three women aged 23 to 24 years, reported by Ham & Smith (1954), an average of 84 % fluoride absorption was found from a normal diet plus consumption of 1360-1815 ml of tea per day. With regard to skeletal storage of fluoride in an adult population, higher figures have been reported from England, where the tea consumption is high (Jackson & Weidmann, 1958), than from the USA (Zipkin et al., 1958).

Ingestion with Food

The absorption of fluoride from food depends on the solubility of the inorganic fluorides in the diet and on the calcium content of the diet. About 80 % of the fluoride normally occurring in the human diet is absorbed. If calcium (as calcium phosphates or as calcium carbonate) or aluminium compounds are added, the fluoride absorption is markedly reduced—to

TABLE 4

FLUORIDE ABSORPTION IN THE ADULT HUMAN [a]

Fluoride added	Period (weeks)	Daily intake of F⁻ (mg)	F⁻ absorbed (%)
NaF in water	14	6.47	97
NaF in water	2	12.40	97
NaF in water	2	19.40	96
CaF₂ in water	4	6.25	96
CaF₂ solid	3	6.43	62
Cryolite in water	5	25.40	93
Cryolite solid	4	6.41	62
Cryolite solid	3	6.61	77
Cryolite solid	3	12.40	67
Cryolite solid	6	18.40	70
Cryolite solid	3	36.40	65
Bone meal	5	6.31	37

[a] After Largent (1961).

about 50%. In such a case the fluoride is bound in a less soluble form and faecal excretion increases (Hodge & Smith, 1965).

Soluble fluoride compounds added to normal human diets are as readily absorbed as when they are added to water, whereas the absorption of less soluble fluorides included in food may be reduced by 20%. Data from balance studies on adult humans by Largent (1961) and by McClure et al. (1945) are shown in Tables 4 and 5.

TABLE 5

FLUORIDE ABSORPTION FROM FOOD AND WATER
BY FIVE YOUNG MEN [a]

Fluoride added	Daily intake of F⁻ (mg)	F⁻ absorbed (%)
Natural fluoride in water	3.77	89.7
NaF in water	3.69	86.5
NaF in food	4.76	83.3
CaF₂ in water	4.24	82.5
CaF₂ in food	5.34	68.9
Cryolite in food	5.34	68.2
Bone meal	4.18	53.6

[a] After McClure et al. (1945).

It has been demonstrated in studies on rats that the fluoride retention in bones and teeth is not significantly different following an intake of equal amounts of soluble fluoride (NaF) in drinking water and in food (McClure, 1939), thus indicating that NaF is absorbed to a similar extent from food and water.

Ingestion with Fluoride Preparations

Fluoride pills

Fluoride tablets or lozenges each usually contain 1 mg F^- as sodium fluoride to supply the optimal daily dose for partial caries prevention. The fluoride in NaF-containing pills is absorbed almost completely, depending on food composition, if ingested with meals; if ingested between meals, it is absorbed as completely as when ingested in water.

Some consideration has been paid to the possibility that 1 mg of fluoride ingested daily from one tablet may, owing to fast absorption and excretion, be less caries-protective than 1 mg of fluoride ingested daily in several small portions as in the case of fluoridated drinking water. In order to make the fluoride from tablets available over longer periods of time, the use of fluoride tablets containing a mixture of soluble and less soluble fluorides has been proposed. Twarock (1964) conducted fluoride-balance studies on children and adults who used either sodium fluoride tablets or tablets containing 1.3 mg F^- as a mixture of Na_3FeF_6, MgF_2, CaF_2, and NaF. According to the urinary fluoride excretion, the fluoride from sodium fluoride tablets was rapidly absorbed and almost completely excreted 8 hours after intake. The absorption of fluoride from tablets containing a mixture of fluoride salts was found to be retarded, elevated levels of fluoride being observed in the urine up to 16 hours after intake. However, no data are available to demonstrate that tablets of mixed fluorides are superior to NaF tablets with regard to the caries-protective effect.

Fluoridated salt

Since sodium fluoride in salt will be ingested with meals, the fluoride absorption will be slightly reduced, especially if the food is rich in calcium. Therefore, Ericsson, Santesson & Ullberg (1961) suggested that sodium monofluorophosphate (Na_2PO_3F) might be a more suitable compound than NaF for some types of ingestion because the fluoride absorption from Na_2PO_3F is more rapid and less influenced by calcium ions. These authors showed, in studies on rats using ^{18}F administered in milk, that the absorption of ^{18}F was more rapid, and significantly more complete 1 and 4 hours after intake, from sodium monofluorophosphate than from sodium fluoride. Na_2PO_3F was thus found to be a more stable source of fluoride than NaF in cases where the fluoride was administered simultaneously with food containing large or varying quantities of calcium. Recently Ericsson (1968) reported that, in rats, sodium fluoride ingested with 350 mmol NaCl reduced the skeletal fluoride uptake by about 20%, while ingestion with flour or similar viscous substances increased the utilization of fluoride by about the same amount. It was assumed that the opposite effects of the generally lower chloride concentrations and the viscous substances of ordinary salted foods would result in the utilization of fluoride in salt being similar to that of fluoride in water.

Bone meal

Finely ground bone meal, which has been proposed as a natural mineral supplement for humans, is a relatively poor source of fluoride. Only between 37% and 54% of fluoride from bone meal will be absorbed by the adult human, as has been shown in metabolic studies by Machle & Largent (1943) and by McClure et al. (1945). Fluoride from the fluoride-rich skeleton of marine fauna is also much less available than that from soluble fluorides. Hübner (1964) fed to rats equal amounts of F^- from NaF and from the finely ground teeth of the sperm whale (fluoride content: 1800 ppm, dry weight). In both cases, the fluoride was incorporated into the diet. Judging from the fluoride retention in the femora of these rats, the fluoride absorption from the whale-tooth powder was at least about 50% less than that from the sodium fluoride. The fluoride retention in the femora of the rats receiving the tooth powder amounted to only 40% of the fluoride retention in the femora of those receiving sodium fluoride.

4. FACTORS INFLUENCING ABSORPTION

The absorbability of the fluoride ion depends on numerous factors, including the solubility of the compound, the physical form of the ingested fluoride, the frequency of ingestion, the inorganic ion environment of the fluoride, and the organic constituents of the diet. Some of these factors have been mentioned in earlier chapters.

Influence of Organic Food Constituents

Observations in man, cattle and laboratory animals indicate that dietary nutrients can influence the development of fluorosis following the ingestion of elevated amounts of fluoride. Fluorosis is enhanced by generally poor diets, high fat intake, limited plane of nutrition, and calcium and vitamin deficiencies. On the other hand, some nutrients promote an increased tolerance to fluoride. Fresh green vegetables and ascorbic acid retard the development of fluorosis (Suttie & Phillips, 1959). It is not yet known if these effects are caused by differences in the absorbability of fluoride. Some fluoride retention data from rat studies suggest that fluoride absorption may be increased by elevated dietary fat.

Miller & Phillips (1955) and Büttner & Muhler (1958) found a significantly higher skeletal fluoride storage in rats when the dietary fat was increased from 5% to 20%. The fluoride retention data from these studies are shown in Table 6.

TABLE 6

EFFECT OF HIGH DIETARY FAT LEVELS ON FLUORIDE RETENTION IN THE RAT FEMUR

Type and concentration of dietary fat		Fluoride administration	F^- per femur (mg)	Reference
Cottonseed oil	5 % 10 % 20 % 5 % 10 % 20 %	0 0 0 } 0.1 % NaF in diet, 6 weeks	— 0.023 — 1.58 1.82 1.90	Miller & Phillips (1955)
Cottonseed oil Cottonseed oil Corn oil Crisco [a] Lard	5 % 20 % 20 % 20 % 20 %	} 2 mg F^-/day (as NaF) by stomach tube, 10 weeks	1.45 1.72 1.83 1.80 1.75	Büttner & Muhler (1958)

[a] Proprietary name of a hydrogenated vegetable oil used for culinary purposes.

Influence of Inorganic Elements

Inorganic ions in the water and food supply may interfere with fluoride absorption. In normally composed drinking water and food this interference is rather small and with regard to the caries-preventive effect of fluoride at the 1-ppm level in water can be ignored. Calcium, magnesium and aluminium are the ions that most effectively reduce fluoride absorption if present in high concentrations. This may be seen, for example, from the fluoride retention data in the rat reported by Weddle & Muhler (1954) and shown in Table 7. However, Wagner (1959) found that Ca^{++}, Mg^{++} and

TABLE 7

EFFECT OF Ca, Mg AND Al ON FLUORIDE RETENTION [a]
IN THE RAT [b]

Salt	Cation concentration	Total F stored (mg)	F retained (%)
CaCl₂	1.0	3.13	11
	0.1	5.92	21
	0.01	10.95	39
MgCl₂	1.0	5.88	21
	0.1	7.77	28
	0.01	11.43	41
AlCl₃	1.0	4.22	15
	0.1	8.49	30
	0.01	12.21	44
None	—	11.98	43

[a] 2 mg F⁻ (as NaF) administered daily by stomach tube. Total F⁻ ingested: 24 mg.
[b] After Weddle & Muhler (1954).

Fe^{++} in the lower concentrations likely to be present in water supplies did not affect fluoride absorption in the rat. He found no differences in fluoride absorption if Ca (0-200 ppm), Mg (0-160 ppm), Fe (0-20 ppm), or PO_4 (0-80 ppm) was added alone to the drinking water. It is interesting to note, however, that when Ca, Mg, Fe and PO_4 at levels of 200, 160, 20 and 80 ppm, respectively, were added in combination fluoride absorption in the rat was slightly reduced.

Several trace elements have also been tested with regard to their possible effect on fluoride absorption and fluoride retention. The results of experiments by Stookey, Crane & Muhler (1962) suggest that in older rats the absorption of fluoride may be increased by the presence of molybdenum. This effect was not observed in weanling rats. The effect of the trace elements molybdenum, manganese and vanadium on fluoride retention in the rat has been investigated by Büttner (1963). Some of the fluoride retention data obtained by this author are shown in Table 8. The results indicated that none of the trace elements in question influenced the absorption of fluoride, since no significant changes in fluoride retention were observed.

TABLE 8

EFFECT OF ADMINISTRATION OF Mo, Mn, V, and F IN DRINKING WATER
OF WEANLING RATS ON FLUORIDE RETENTION IN FEMORA [a]

Administration for 90 days in drinking water [b]	No. of rats	F in femur [c]	
		Concentration (ppm)	Total (μg)
Control	14	137 ± 4 [d]	44 ± 2 [d]
50 ppm Mo	13	130 ± 3	44 ± 1
50 ppm Mn	12	143 ± 3	47 ± 3
10 ppm V	17	138 ± 3	42 ± 2
50 ppm F	17	4 421 ± 77	1 451 ± 55
50 ppm Mo + 50 ppm F	15	4 335 ± 103	1 479 ± 73
50 ppm Mn + 50 ppm F	16	4 388 ± 86	1 401 ± 34
10 ppm V + 50 ppm F	16	4 250 ± 132	1 254 ± 59

[a] After Büttner (1963).
[b] Compounds used: $(NH_4)_6Mo_7O_{24}$, $4H_2O$; $MnCl_2$, $4H_2O$; NH_4VO_3; and NaF.
[c] Ash.
[d] Standard deviation.

Recently Ericsson (1966) confirmed the above-mentioned observations of Büttner. Using ^{99}Mo-labelled molybdate and ^{18}F-labelled fluoride, he found that molybdenum did not increase fluoride absorption or fluoride retention in the rat. The effect of various inorganic ions on fluoride absorption seems to be mainly of academic interest. In common human nutrition, the normal mineral concentrations will rarely be in the ranges at which the fluoride absorption may be affected significantly. In acute accidental fluoride poisoning, however, the immediate intake of calcium, magnesium or aluminium suspensions plays an important role by reducing the fluoride absorption. For instance, doses as high as 20-50 mg of sodium fluoride four times a day were tolerated without toxic symptoms by children of $3\frac{1}{2}$ to 6 years of age if the sodium fluoride was given orally together with a suspension of aluminium hydroxide (Black, Kleiner & Bolker, 1949).

As shown in studies on weanling rats by Cremer & Voelker (1953), the administration of 0.1% F^-, as NaF, in the diet caused death within 4 to 6 weeks. The animals survived and recovered, however, if from the fourth week onwards 3% calcium citrate had been added to the fluoride-containing diet.

5. ABSORPTION FROM FLUOROCOMPOUNDS AND FROM VAPOURS AND DUST

Inorganic Fluorides

The results of fluoride absorption studies in which several inorganic fluoride compounds (NaF, CaF_2 and cryolite) were ingested by human volunteers have already been given (see Tables 4 and 5). It has also been mentioned earlier that, according to the results of Ericsson, Santesson & Ullberg (1961), the fluoride absorption from Na_2PO_3F is more rapid and complete than that from sodium fluoride in the presence of larger amounts of calcium.

Zipkin & Likins (1957) studied the absorption of various fluoride compounds from the gastrointestinal tract of the rat. Each animal received by stomach tube 0.2 mg F^- in aqueous solutions of the various compounds. The percentage absorption from the entire gastrointestinal tract was determined 30 minutes after fluoride ingestion. The results are shown in Table 9. The fluoride from NaF, Na_2SiF_6, Na_2PO_3F and SnF_2 was

TABLE 9

ABSORPTION OF VARIOUS FLUORIDE COMPOUNDS FROM
THE GASTROINTESTINAL TRACT OF THE RAT [a]

Compound [b]	F^- absorbed 30 minutes after ingestion (%)
NaF	49.6 ± 4.3 [c]
Na_2SiF_6	50.9 ± 3.1
Na_2PO_3F . . .	43.2 ± 2.8
SnF_2	50.0 ± 1.7
KPF_6	77.2 ± 3.2
KBF_4	75.8 ± 2.7

[a] After Zipkin & Likins (1957).
[b] 0.2 mg F^- per rat, administered by stomach tube.
[c] Mean of 10 rats per compound ± SE.

absorbed to the same extent. KPF_6 and KBF_4, which are metabolically inert, had a significantly higher rate of absorption. The fluorine in these compounds is covalently held and hence has lost its identity as the fluoride ion. It is nevertheless of interest that the rate of absorption of the physiologically inert complex fluoride compounds exceeds that of the physiologically active simple fluorides.

Fluorine-containing Organic Compounds

Fluorine-containing organic compounds are not present in human diets or drinking water. The accidental absorption of organic fluorides as a problem of acute toxicity is discussed in Chapters 2 and 7.

Generally, three types of fluorine-containing organic compounds can be distinguished: (1) fluoroacetates, which are used as powerful rodenticides; (2) fluorophosphates, e.g., diisopropylphosphofluoridate (DPF); and (3) fluorocarbons. Fluoroacetates and fluorophosphates are readily absorbed and highly toxic in minute amounts, whereas fluorocarbons—e.g., Freons and Teflon—are characterized by their low toxicity or lack of toxic effects. However, highly toxic molecules are produced if Teflon is heated above

300°C. The thermal decomposition of Teflon yields highly toxic perfluoro-isobutylene (Largent, 1951; Hodge, 1964).

Vapours and Dust

Fluoride-containing gases, vapours or dust with fine particle size can be inhaled and absorbed. This problem of occupational health has been described and reviewed in detail by Largent (1961). High urinary fluoride concentrations have been frequently observed in factory workers handling cryolite, rock phosphate and hydrogen fluoride, and in welders. In many cases the urinary fluoride concentrations of such workmen exceeded 8 mg F^- per litre several-fold. It was expected that inhaled fluoride would be readily absorbed in the respiratory tract. Largent (1960) demonstrated in the adult human exposed to hydrogen fluoride, at concentrations of 1.42-4.74 ppm, that rapid absorption of inhaled fluoride occurred, causing fluoride excretions in the urine of between 3.5 and 20 mg F^- per day. In a study by Collings, Fleming & May (1951) the rates of fluoride absorption in industrial employees were found to be approximately the same whether the workers were inhaling particulate rock phosphate or gaseous fluoride in equivalent fluoride concentration in the air. Machle & Largent (1943) reported an almost 100% absorption of inhaled hydrogen fluoride.

6. SUMMARY

Fluoride ions from soluble inorganic fluoride compounds are rapidly absorbed. The absorption of fluoride present in the drinking-water supply and the absorption of soluble fluorides added to food is reasonably complete. Fluorides naturally present in normal human diets are absorbed to an extent of about 80%. Less soluble fluoride compounds—e.g., CaF_2, cryolite, rock phosphate and bone meal—are absorbed at a rate of approximately 60%. The mechanism of fluoride absorption seems to be one of simple diffusion through the gastrointestinal membranes. The fluoride ion is absorbed from the entire gastrointestinal tract. The presence of calcium, magnesium and aluminium in large amounts reduces the absorption of fluoride owing to the formation of less soluble complex fluorides. Inhaled fluorides derived from gases, vapours and dust are rapidly and nearly completely absorbed in the respiratory tract.

REFERENCES

Black, M. M., Kleiner, I. S. & Bolker, H. (1949) *N.Y. St. J. Med.*, **49**, 1187-1188

Büttner, W. (1963) *J. dent. Res.*, **42**, 453-460

Büttner, W. & Muhler, J. C. (1958) *J. Nutr.*, **65**, 259-266

Carlson, C. H., Armstrong, W. D. & Singer, L. (1960) *Proc. Soc. exp. Biol. (N.Y.)*, **104**, 235-239

Collings, H., Jr, Fleming, B. L. & May, R. (1951) *A.M.A. Arch. industr. Hyg.*, **4**, 585-590

Cremer, H. D. & Voelker, W. (1953) *Arzneimittel-Forsch.*, **3**, 411-412

Ericsson, Y. (1958) *Acta odont. scand.*, **16**, 51-77

Ericsson, Y. (1966) *Acta odont. scand.*, **24**, 405-417

Ericsson, Y. (1968) In: *International Association for Dental Research, 46th General Meeting, San Francisco, Calif., USA, March 1968 ; Abstracts*, Chicago, American Dental Association, Abstr. No. 283

Ericsson, Y., Santesson, G. & Ullberg, S. (1961) *Arch. oral Biol.*, **4**, 160-174 (Special Supplement: Proceedings of 7th ORCA Congress, Hamburg, June 1960)

Feldman, I., Morken, D. & Hodge, H. C. (1957) *J. Dent. Res.*, **36**, 192-202

Foster, W. C. & Rush, J. P. (1961) *Fed. Proc.*, **20**, 294-298

Ham, M. P. & Smith, M. D. (1950) *Canad. J. Res., F*, **28**, 227-233

Ham, M. P. & Smith, M. D. (1954) *J. Nutr.*, **53**, 225-232

Hodge, H. C. (1964) *Fluoride.* In: Comar, C. L. & Bronner, F., ed., *Mineral metabolism*, New York, Academic Press, vol. 2, part. A, pp. 591-594

Hodge, H. C. & Smith, F. A. (1965) *Biological effects of inorganic fluorides.* In: Simons, J. H., ed., *Fluorine chemistry*, New York, Academic Press, vol. 4, p. 137

Hübner, R. (1964) *Vergleichende Untersuchungen über die Wirkung von Knochenmehl, Pottwal-Zahnmehl und Natriumfluorid auf die Hartgewebe und den Kariesbefall der Albinoratte*, Giessen (Thesis)

Jackson, D. & Weidmann, S. M. (1958) *J. Path. Bact.*, **76**, 451-459

Largent, E. J. (1960) *A.M.A. Arch. industr. Hlth*, **21**, 318-323

Largent, E. J. (1961) *Fluorosis. The health aspects of fluorine compounds*, Columbus, Ohio State University Press, pp. 34-39

Largent, E. J. & Heyroth, F. F. (1949) *J. industr. Hyg.*, **31**, 134-138

Lawrenz, M. & Mitchell, H. H. (1941) *J. Nutr.*, **22**, 621-631

McClure, F. J. (1939) *Nat. Inst. Hlth Bull.*, No. 172, pp. 1-53

McClure, F. J., Mitchell, H. H., Hamilton, T. S. & Kinser, C. A. (1945) *J. industr. Hyg.*, **27**, 159-170

Machle, W. & Largent, E. J. (1943) *J. industr. Hyg.*, **25**, 112-123

Miller, R. F. & Phillips, P. H. (1955) *J. Nutr.*, **56**, 447-454

Muhler, J. C. & Weddle, D. A. (1955) *J. Nutr.*, **55**, 347-352

Perkinson, J. D., Jr, Whitney, I. B., Monroe, R. A., Lotz, W. E. & Comar, C. L. (1955) *Amer. J. Physiol.*, **182**, 383-389

Quentin, K.-E., Souci, S. W. & Indinger, J. (1960) *Z. Lebensmitt.-Untersuch.*, **111**, 173-179

Rusoff, L. L., Konikoff, B. S., Frye, J. B., Jr, Johnston, J. E. & Frey, W. W. (1962) *Amer. J. clin. Nutr.*, **11**, 94-101

Stookey, G. K., Crane, D. B. & Muhler, J. C. (1962) *Proc. Soc. exp. Biol. (N.Y.)*, **109**, 580-583

Stookey, G. K., Crane, D. B. & Muhler, J. C. (1964) *Proc. Soc. exp. Biol. (N.Y.)*, **115**, 295-298

Stookey, G. K., Dellinger, E. L. & Muhler, J. C. (1964) *Proc. Soc. exp. Biol. (N.Y.)*, **115**, 298-301

Suttie, J. W. & Phillips, P. H. (1959) In: Muhler, J. C. & Hine, M. K., ed., *Fluorine and dental health*, Bloomington, Indiana University Press, pp. 70-77

Twarock, H. (1964) *Zur Resorption von Fluorionen aus leichtlöslichen und schwerlöslichen Fluorsalzen,* Bonn (Thesis)

Volker, J. F., Sognnaes, R. F. & Bibby, B. G. (1941) *Amer. J. Physiol.,* **132,** 707-712

Wagner, M. J. (1959) In: Muhler, J. C. & Hine, M. K., ed., *Fluorine and dental health,* Bloomington, Indiana University Press, pp. 38-59

Wagner, M. J. (1962) *J. dent. Res.,* **41,** 667-671

Wallace, P. C. (1953) *The metabolism of F¹⁸ in normal and chronically fluorosed rats* (Thesis, University of California, Report No. UCRL-2196)

Wallace-Durbin, P. (1954) *J. dent. Res.,* **33,** 789-800

Weddle, D. A. & Muhler, J. C. (1954) *J. Nutr.,* **54,** 437-444

Ziegler, E. (1964) *Helv. paediat. Acta,* **19,** 343-354

Zipkin, I. & Likins, R. C. (1957) *Amer. J. Physiol.,* **191,** 549-550

Zipkin, I., McClure, F. J., Leone, N. C. & Lee, W. A. (1958) *Publ. Hlth Rep. (Wash.).* **73,** 732-740

CHAPTER 4

Distribution of fluorides

W. D. ARMSTRONG [1] — I. GEDALIA [2] — L. SINGER [1] — J. A. WEATHERELL [3]
— S. M. WEIDMANN [3]

1. INTRODUCTION (W. D. Armstrong)

Owing to the well-nigh universal presence of fluoride in foods and waters, intake of this element by way of the dietary is inevitable and has almost certainly taken place throughout the evolutionary development of man. This circumstance accounts for the constant occurrence of fluoride in body-fluids and tissues. Accurate fluoride analyses, particularly of soft tissues, pose difficult technical problems. However, dependable results obtained with significant numbers of a variety of mammalian tissues have become available during the last decade. These results now allow appraisals to be made of fluoride distribution in both soft and calcified tissues under conditions of normal and of augmented fluoride intakes. Also stemming from the same body of results is the discovery—and evaluation—of the physiological factors involved in the transport, deposition, and storage of fluoride in soft tissues and in the components of teeth and the skeleton.

One section of this chapter presents critical evaluations and interpretations of the results of fluoride analyses of blood, of soft tissues and of some secretions of the human, supplemented, where pertinent, by similar results from tissues of lower animals. Another section is devoted to a detailed and thorough presentation of the results of analyses for fluoride in dental hard tissues and in bone. These analyses have made possible the identification of important principles concerning the mutual interreactions of the calcified tissues, whose biological qualities are affected by fluoride, with fluoride. Finally, the role of the placenta in the delivery of fluoride

[1] University of Minnesota, Department of Biochemistry, Minneapolis, Minn., USA.

[2] Laboratory of Oral Chemistry and Fluoride Research, Hadassah School of Dental Medicine, Hebrew University, Jerusalem, Israel.

[3] Biological Research Unit, University of Leeds Dental School, Leeds, England. Dr Weidmann died in July 1969.

to the foetus has been elucidated by examination of the results of analysis for fluoride in the maternal blood, in the foetal blood and tissues, and in the placenta itself. An understanding of some of the aspects of fluoride transport and deposition that are treated in each of the sections of this chapter has been facilitated and supplemented by the use of radiofluoride.

2. DISTRIBUTION IN BODY-FLUIDS AND SOFT TISSUES
(W. D. Armstrong & L. Singer)

The presence of fluoride in "notable proportions" in the blood of humans, other mammals and numerous birds was reported by Nickles in 1856. In 1888 Tammann found fluoride in the white and yolk of hens' eggs, in the brain of a 30-day-old calf, and in the milk and blood of a cow. The first experimental study of fluoride deposition in soft tissues was reported in 1891 by Brandl & Tappeiner, who gave a dog daily food additives of 0.1-1.0 g of sodium fluoride for 21 months. Analyses of the tissues led to an estimate of the equivalent of 0.14, 1.84 and 0.51 g of sodium fluoride in the entire blood, muscle and liver, which corresponds to the incredibly high concentrations of 93, 690 and 161 ppm fluoride in the respective organs. While such studies have no present-day value as to the actual concentration of fluoride in tissues, they do indicate a keen awareness of the possibility of fluoride toxicity on the part of the early investigators. Gautier & Clausmann (1913) reported the fluoride content of a large number of animal tissues and found small amounts in blood, milk, bile and urine.

Fluoride in Blood Plasma

Blood plasma or serum is the most reliable fluid for sampling the fluoride content of body-fluids and is superior to whole blood for this purpose because of the unequal distribution of fluoride between red cells and plasma. On a volume basis, the erythrocytes have a fluoride content which is 40-50% that of plasma, and in normal blood about three-fourths of the total blood fluoride is in the plasma (Carlson, Armstrong & Singer, 1960a). Moreover, the results of analyses for fluoride in whole blood will be affected by marked variations of the haematocrit, while the plasma fluoride content remains constant. Also, the determination of fluoride in plasma is technically easier and is probably more reliable, because of the more simple composition of plasma, than is the analysis of whole blood for fluoride. For the above reasons, some of the studies in which the fluoride content of whole blood has been used to describe the fluoride status of the body should be interpreted with reservation. Undoubtedly much of the variability of the results and the high concentrations of fluoride found by earlier investigators, in whole blood and in soft tissues of animals and humans consuming normal amounts of fluoride, resulted from the use of inadequate and inexact analytical methods. Procedures of demonstrable reliability have, however, in recent years been described (Singer & Armstrong, 1959, 1965).

There is considerable evidence to indicate that regulatory mechanisms operate within the body to maintain the plasma fluoride content, and hence that of other body-fluids, within rather narrow limits (Singer & Armstrong, 1960, 1964; Smith, Gardner & Hodge, 1950). The mechanisms are effective under substantial variations of dietary fluoride intake, and in some abnormal metabolic conditions, with the result that the absorption of fluoride from the diet produces only a slight and transitory effect on plasma fluoride concentration (Carlson, Armstrong & Singer, 1960 b). The regulation of plasma fluoride concentration is due, in the first instance, to the large volume of extracellular body-fluids through which the absorbed fluoride is diluted. Also, an elevation of plasma fluoride content is further counteracted by sequestration of fluoride in the skeleton, by urinary excretion and, possibly, by perspiration loss when sweating is profuse.

The fluoride content of blood plasma of residents of five population centres in which the fluoride content of the communal waters varied from 0.15 to 5.4 ppm has been examined (Singer & Armstrong, 1960). In four of the centres, in which the water contained 0.15-2.5 ppm fluoride, the mean plasma fluoride values of the residents lay within the range 0.14-0.19 ppm and indicated that the human can maintain an effective fluoride homeostasis at these levels of intake. However, when the drinking water contained 5.4 ppm fluoride the regulatory mechanisms were not able to operate perfectly and a slight, but mathematically significant, increase in plasma fluoride, to a mean value of 0.26 ppm, was observed.

Effective regulation of plasma fluoride level in the human throughout the day has been demonstrated in three normal individuals consuming a normal diet and fluoridated water (Singer & Armstrong, 1960). The effectiveness of this regulation was further demonstrated by the results of radiofluoride (^{18}F) studies with two normal individuals given orally 1 mg of inert fluoride tagged with the isotope (Carlson, Armstrong & Singer, 1960b). The plasma fluoride concentrations were normal (0.17 and 0.13 ppm) in samples obtained at 40 minutes and the maximum radiofluoride concentration in the plasma occurred within 60 minutes after ingestion of the labelled fluoride. Based on the radiofluoride data, the fluoride content of the entire plasma volume could not have been increased, at any one time, by more than 8-10% of the ingested dose of 1.0 mg fluoride; this would have produced a maximum increase of about 0.03 ppm in the plasma fluoride content.

Results of recent work now make it evident that most, if not all, of the values cited for fluoride concentrations in plasma (and possibly also in other body-fluids) are for total fluoride and not for free and ionic fluoride. Taves (1966), using greatly modified diffusion techniques, found serum fluoride contents about 10 times lower than those obtained by the authors

(Singer & Armstrong, 1960) from analyses of ashed plasma samples. Later Taves (1968) found evidence that a large fraction of serum fluoride is associated with albumin and is revealed by ashing. More recent work by the authors (Singer & Armstrong, 1969; Armstrong, Venkateswarlu & Singer, unpublished data) bears out the view that plasma contains two forms of fluoride. One form is free and ionic, the other bound and non-ionic. It is the former kind of plasma fluoride that can be expected to participate in physiological reactions. An indication of the ionic fluoride concentration is given by the finding that about 15-20 % of the total fluoride of normal human plasma is absorbed by calcium phosphate.

Control of Plasma Fluoride Content

The plasma fluoride levels of patients with metabolic bone diseases treated by Rich, Ensinck & Ivanovich (1964) with large doses of sodium fluoride (50-100 mg fluoride per day) for 10-34 weeks did not rise above 1.8 ppm (Armstrong et al., 1964). The one patient whose plasma fluoride level reached 1.8 ppm on the 14th day of treatment, from the pretreatment level of 0.32 ppm, continued to receive 50 mg fluoride daily and, after 33 and 34 weeks of treatment, the plasma fluoride content had declined to 0.45 and 0.48 ppm. Other results from this laboratory (Armstrong & Singer, unpublished data), obtained in patients who also received sodium fluoride in the treatment of metabolic bone disease, indicate that there is a transitory rise in plasma fluoride content during the early weeks of treatment, with a later adjustment to a concentration near to that of the pretreatment value.

Factors such as the previous fluoride exposure, the dose rate, the skeletal fluoride load, and the normality of the skeleton may influence the over-all ability of the homeostatic mechanisms to regulate plasma fluoride content, and these mechanisms can be overextended in the human, as already mentioned, and in the rat by very large fluoride intakes.

The possibility of a net movement of fluoride from bone to blood in cases of demineralizing bone disease, thus elevating the plasma fluoride content, was investigated in rats raised on high fluoride intakes and then treated with parathyroid hormone (Singer & Armstrong, 1964). Although an elevation of blood calcium from 9.7 to 11.6 mg per 100 ml was observed, there was no alteration in plasma fluoride content (0.26 ppm) as a result of bone mobilization. Presumably the fluoride mobilized from the bones which underwent resorption was redeposited at other skeletal sites or was excreted in the urine. Starvation of animals for periods of up to 7 days did not produce significant differences in serum fluoride levels, the concentrations being approximately the same in animals sacrificed at zero, 3 and 7 days of the starvation period (Singer & Armstrong, 1964). It thus appears that the fluoride content of the body-fluids can be supported by the skeletal pool when the intake of fluoride is markedly reduced. These observations, and the relative constancy of the plasma and soft-tissue fluoride contents in rats provided with substantial variations in dietary fluoride intake (Armstrong, Vogel & Singer, unpublished data), suggest that the kidney may operate to conserve, or to excrete, fluoride when the intake is markedly reduced or is moderately excessive.

To obtain further information on the fluoride regulatory mechanisms, groups of rats were raised on a diet containing either 0.5 or 100 ppm fluoride and distilled water. Some animals were used as controls and others were either sham-operated or bilaterally nephrectomized (Singer, Armstrong & Vogel, 1965). The intact animals of the low-fluoride-intake group had a mean plasma fluoride content of 0.17 ppm. The high-fluoride diet (100 ppm) appeared to have caused the normal capacity of the body to regulate body fluoride content to be exceeded, since elevated mean plasma fluoride contents (about 0.5 ppm) were obtained with all high-fluoride-intake animals whether from the control, the sham-operated or the nephrectomized group. The results obtained with the nephrectomized rats indicate that there is an effective body-fluid fluoride regulatory mechanism residing in the skeletal tissues even when renal function is completely eliminated.

Other animals, raised on diets sufficiently different in fluoride concentration to produce threefold differences in skeletal fluoride content, exhibited similar plasma fluoride contents (0.26 ppm) (Singer & Armstrong, 1964). Also, there is evidence that rats raised on commercial rodent food containing 60-80 ppm fluoride can tolerate 75 ppm fluoride in the water without significant alteration of plasma fluoride content; but it appears that this is near the critical intake above which there is a slight rise in plasma fluoride concentration (Armstrong, Vogel & Singer, unpublished data). Although the plasma fluoride levels of rats may be elevated by feeding high concentrations of fluoride, the muscle fluoride content remains normal (0.21 ppm) when the plasma fluoride is elevated to approximately 0.50 ppm (Singer, Armstrong & Vogel, 1965). The unpublished data of Armstrong, Vogel & Singer indicate that when the plasma fluoride is elevated to 0.8 ppm a slight rise in muscle fluoride content occurs.

Fluoride in Whole Blood

Smith, Gardner & Hodge (1950) reported that the whole blood fluoride level exhibited only a threefold variation in two populations supplied with water with a 23-fold difference in fluoride content. In the population group using water containing 1.0 ppm fluoride, the most frequently found blood fluoride content was 0.1 ppm.

Fluoride estimations by Singh & Jolly (1961) on the whole blood of patients in India exhibiting skeletal fluorosis indicated an average of 1.5 ppm fluoride, with a range of 0.5-6.1 ppm. These values are quite variable and some of the high blood fluoride contents are difficult to accept as correct

since they would, on the basis of our experience with rats (Armstrong &
Singer, unpublished data), probably not be compatible with life. In a subsequent publication, Singh et al. (1962) reported the whole blood fluoride
contents of fluorosis patients with and without neurological complications
to be 2.0 ± 1.88 (SD) and 4.8 ± 3.83 (SD) ppm, respectively. One
patient was found to have had a blood fluoride concentration of
14.5 ppm. Other results of analyses for fluoride in the blood and urine of
fluorosis patients obtained by Singh, Jolly & Bansal (1961) are given in
Table 1.

TABLE 1

WHOLE BLOOD AND URINE FLUORIDE LEVELS OF PATIENTS
WITH ENDEMIC FLUOROSIS (ppm) [a]

Non-neurological patients		Neurological patients	
Blood	Urine	Blood	Urine
1.3	10.4	4.6	4.8
1.1	8.3	5.6	18.0
0.8	5.7	1.8	6.6
3.2	4.2	0.5	3.5
1.8	3.2	0.6	4.5
1.1	4.2	1.7	6.7
1.2		0.6	5.6
		2.0	1.8
		0.6	2.3
			7.4
			25.5
			5.8
Mean 1.50	Mean 6.00	Mean 2.00	Mean 7.71
SD ± 0.748	SD ± 2.55	SD ± 1.76	SD ± 6.67

[a] After Singh, Jolly & Bansal (1961).

Srikantia & Siddiqui (1965) reported a study of the blood fluoride levels
in 31 male adults between 18 and 40 years of age who had consumed well
waters with fluoride contents of between 6.8 and 8.2 ppm and who exhibited
various degrees of skeletal fluorosis. The mean blood fluoride content was
29 ± 1.9 ppm (SE), with a range of 9-75 ppm. These blood fluoride concentrations would undoubtedly be incompatible with life and are, therefore,
believed to be incorrect. A personal communication to us from the senior
author of the report indicates that a mistake in publication erroneously
reported these results at 10 times their actual value. The corrected values
are in agreement with those of Singh and his colleagues (Singh & Jolly,
1961; Singh, Jolly & Bansal, 1961; Singh et al., 1962).

The detailed studies of Shupe et al. (1963) demonstrated the ability of
cattle to regulate the fluoride level of the blood even when the dietary intakes
of fluoride were such that various degrees of fluorosis were present (Table 2).
The urinary excretion of fluoride by the animals was vastly different among

TABLE 2

FLUORIDE CONTENT OF BOVINE BODY FLUIDS (ppm) [a]

Fluid	Normal animals [b]	Fluorosed animals [b]		
		Borderline	Moderate	Severe
Milk	up to 0.12	0.08-0.15	0.15-0.25	0.15 and above
Blood	up to 0.30	0.15-0.40	0.30-0.50	0.50 and above
Urine	2.27-6.30	8.0 -14.8	10.5-21.0	14.7-30.1

[a] After Shupe et al. (1963).
[b] The animals were 2-6 years of age. The dry soft tissues of the animals in all groups contained up to 1.2 ppm fluoride. This result is equivalent to values of up to 0.4 ppm of the fresh weight.

the groups, whereas the fluoride contents of milk and blood showed only small variations. Small increases in the fluoride level of cattle blood with increments of fluoride intake were also reported by Greenwood et al. (1964). Cattle fed approximately 10, 28, 50 or 100 ppm fluoride in the dry ration for periods up to 7.3 years had levels of 0.07, 0.11, 0.21 and 0.45 ppm fluoride, respectively, in their blood.

Fluoride in Soft Tissues

Herman, Mason & Light (1958) examined the fluoride content of human tissues from 38 cases of urolithiasis and concluded that "none of the tissues revealed fluoride contents elevated significantly above the normal values in the literature". They found no evidence that fluoride in the amounts ingested by these patients was toxic to the kidneys. Gettler & Ellerbrook (1939) concluded, from a survey of the literature and their own investigation, that there seemed to be no appreciable accumulation of fluorine under normal

TABLE 3

FLUORIDE CONTENT OF DOG TISSUES (ppm FRESH WEIGHT) [a]

Tissue	Normal	Chronic fluorosis [b]	Acute poisoning [c]
Blood	0.27 (2) [d]	0.28 (2) [d]	7.4 (2) [d]
Brain	0.31 (1)	0.33 (2)	2.5 (5)
Lung	0.40 (1)	0.22 (1)	8.9 (5)
Heart	0.44 (1)	0.46 (2)	6.7 (5)
Spleen	0.41 (1)	0.21 (1)	7.5 (4)
Liver	0.36 (2)	0.37 (2)	9.0 (5)
Kidney	0.42 (1)	0.40 (1)	8.7 (5)
Pancreas . . .	0.27 (1)	0.31 (2)	4.4 (3)
Muscle	0.30 (1)	0.33 (1)	5.7 (3)

[a] After Gettler & Ellerbrook (1939).
[b] 18-32 mg of sodium fluoride per kg of body-weight daily for 2 weeks.
[c] Lethal amounts of sodium fluoride or sodium fluosilicate administered by stomach tube or in food.
[d] The parentheses indicate the number of dogs.

circumstances in any of the vital organs of the human or dog. These investigators believed that their analyses of dog and human tissues (Tables 3 and 6) proved the normal presence of fluoride in tissues and, further, that the high values and wide variations for fluoride in tissues that had been reported by earlier authors were due to insensitive and inaccurate analytical methods. This conclusion is correct in the opinion of the present writers and this is why much of the earlier literature has not been reviewed in detail here.

TABLE 4

FLUORIDE CONTENT OF RAT TISSUES [a]

Tissue	Fluoride (ppm fresh weight)
Plasma	0.30 ± 0.027 [b] (14) [c]
Liver	0.15 ± 0.010 (37)
Muscle	0.22 ± 0.024 (40)
Tendon	0.66 ± 0.055 (14)

[a] Armstrong & Singer, unpublished data.
[b] SE.
[c] The parentheses indicate the number of samples.

Table 4 presents a compilation of our analyses for fluoride in tissues and in the plasma of rats fed a commercial rodent food (Armstrong & Singer, unpublished data). The report of Smith et al. (1960) furnishes data on the fluoride content of desiccated human tissues (Table 5). Unfortunately the

TABLE 5

CONCENTRATION OF FLUORIDE IN HUMAN SOFT TISSUES
(ppm DRY WEIGHT) [a]

Tissue	Content of F in water	
	0-1.0 ppm	1.0-4.0 ppm
Heart	2.29 ± 0.796 [b]	2.78 ± 1.364 [b]
Liver	2.34 ± 0.972	2.27 ± 1.109
Lung	5.12 ± 3.104	6.18 ± 3.106
Kidney	3.26 ± 0.968	8.49 ± 6.63
Spleen	4.91 ± 4.143	3.58 ± 1.324
Aorta	41.0 ± 50.27	25.1 ± 19.54

[a] After Smith et al. (1960).
[b] SD.

results are not given on a fresh-tissue basis and, for this reason, cannot be directly compared with those of Gettler & Ellerbrook (1939). If the desiccated tissues are assumed to have been derived from organs which contained 65% water, the values of Smith et al. can be converted to the fresh-tissue basis. The results are then in fair agreement with those of Gettler & Eller-brook, and indicate, with the exception of the aorta, a fluoride content of 0.5-1.0 ppm in normal fresh human tissues.

Call et al. (1965) used some of the soft tissues obtained at autopsy from 127 subjects for fluoride determinations and related the results to the duration of fluoride exposure of the subjects. One group was constituted of persons who were older than 15 years and who had resided for at least 10 years (mean 40.1 years) in an industrial area (Utah, USA) in which fluoride had been liberated into the air in an elevated concentration. The second group was comprised of persons who were younger than 15 years of age or who had lived for a period of less than 10 years (mean 2.32 years) in the same area. The results, given in Table 6, showed no differences in the

TABLE 6

FLUORIDE CONTENT OF HUMAN TISSUES (ppm FRESH WEIGHT)

Tissue	Normal [a]	Fluoride-poisoning fatalities [a]	Exposure to high atmospheric fluoride concentration [b]	
			Long term	Short term
Blood	0.27 (4) [c]	9.2 (5) [c]	—	—
Brain	0.53 (4)	2.5 (2)	1.8	1.5
Lung	0.27 (3)	14.0 (2)	3.9	3.5
Heart	0.45 (3)	10.6 (1)	2.5	1.9
Spleen	0.28 (2)	11.8 (1)	1.7	1.8
Liver	0.54 (3)	9.3 (5)	1.6	1.4
Kidney	0.68 (2)	9.0 (3)	2.9	2.9
Thyroid			5.2	4.0
Aorta.			29.4	28.2
Pancreas			1.8	1.7

[a] Data from Gettler & Ellerbrook (1939).
[b] Data from Call et al. (1965).
[c] The parentheses indicate the number of subjects.

fluoride contents of the specimens from the two groups and indicate that fluoride is not stored in significantly increased amounts in soft tissues when the period of exposure is increased. The results of Smith et al. (1960) in Table 5 also fail to demonstrate a difference in the fluoride content of human soft tissues as a consequence of an enhanced fluoride intake, in this case from water. The fluoride content of the aorta has been found by two groups of workers (Call et al., 1965; Smith et al., 1960) to be higher than that of other soft tissues and was correlated by Call and co-workers with the degree of arteriosclerosis and calcification. The fluoride present in calcified plaques in blood vessels is, like that of skeletal tissues and urinary calculi (Herman, Mason & Light, 1958), secondary to the calcification.

The fluoride contents of fresh tissues from normal dogs and from dogs in which chronic fluorosis or acute fluoride poisoning had been induced are given in Table 3 (Gettler & Ellerbrook, 1939). There is a remarkable similarity between the concentrations of fluoride in the tissues of normal dogs and humans and, also, between those of acutely poisoned dogs and humans (Tables 3 and 6). The results of analyses of the tissues of chronically fluorosed dogs also indicate that the fluoride contents of the soft tissues were not different from those of the normal animal (Table 3). These data, like those obtained from the human (Table 5), point to the remarkable ability of the body to prevent large and sustained rises in body-fluid fluoride content.

The fluoride contents of the soft tissues of cattle, on a dry-weight basis, have also been reported (Shupe et al., 1963) and are shown in Table 7. The

TABLE 7

FLUORIDE IN SOFT TISSUES
OF DAIRY CATTLE (DRY WEIGHT) [a]

Tissue	ppm F
Kidney	21.4
Lung	14.5
Spleen	0.86
Heart	0.80
Liver	0.71
Skeletal muscle	0.67

[a] After Shupe et al. (1963).

fluoride contents of the spleen, heart, liver and muscle, when related to a fresh-weight basis, are similar to those found in the corresponding tissues of the human, dog and rat. The fluoride concentration in the lungs of these cattle should not be considered to be typical of soft tissues since the animals had been, like the humans referred to in Table 5, exposed to an atmosphere with a high fluoride content from industrial sources. The feeding habits of cattle probably result in inhalation of particulate forms of fluoride present on the vegetation. As indicated in Table 5, the kidney is frequently found to have a higher fluoride content than other organs owing to the urine, which has a much higher fluoride content than plasma, retained in the renal tubules and collecting ducts.

The distribution of injected radiofluoride (^{18}F) in the tissues of animals has shown, independently of chemical analytical techniques, that there is a rapidly attained and ubiquitous occurrence of fluoride in animal tissues (Armstrong & Singer, 1965; Carlson, Singer & Armstrong, 1960; Ericsson, 1958; Ericsson & Hammarström, 1965; Ericsson & Ullberg, 1958; Hein et al., 1956; Perkinson et al., 1955; Wallace-Durbin, 1954; Wills, 1940). Carlson, Singer & Armstrong (1960), by comparing the $^{18}F/Cl$ ratio in animal tissues, demonstrated that ^{18}F readily penetrates the cells of skeletal muscle, liver and skin and cardiac muscle. From radioactive and analytical data the following mean values ($\pm$ SD) for chloride and fluoride in tissue fluid spaces, in terms of ml per kg, were calculated: chloride, 264 ± 22 (liver) and 118 ± 13 (muscle); fluoride, 540 ± 55 (liver) and 330 ± 18 (muscle) (Armstrong & Singer, 1965). Since the ratios of concentration in tissue water to concentration in plasma water were less than 1.0, it is inferred that intracellular fluid has a lower concentration of ionic fluoride than plasma. Comparison with the concentration in brain tissue indicates either a barrier to fluoride or the presence of a slowly exchangeable fluoride pool. However, analytical data indicate a concentration of fluoride in brain tissue similar to that in other tissues when expressed on a fresh-weight basis (Herman, Mason & Light, 1958; Smith et al., 1960).

Fluoride in Maternal and Foetal Blood

The literature does not satisfactorily define the relative concentrations of fluoride in maternal and in foetal plasma or the response of either to an increased fluoride intake. Zipkin & Babeaux (1965) recently summarized the literature relating to placental transfer of fluoride. In contrast to the findings pertaining to the regulation of plasma fluoride in population groups drinking communal water with different fluoride concentrations (0.15-2.5 ppm) (Singer & Armstrong, 1960), it has been reported that the blood fluoride of pregnant women may rise slightly in circumstances of increased fluoride intake. There are indications that, as the fluoride exposure was increased through drinking water (Gedalia et al., 1961, 1964b), by ingestion of fluoride tablets (Gedalia et al., 1964b), or from fluoride added to tea (Held, 1954; Ziegler, 1956), there was an increase in maternal whole blood fluoride from about 0.1 to about 0.3 ppm and a corresponding increase in the fluoride content of foetal blood. Held (1954) reported that the fluoride concentrations in 16 samples each of maternal and foetal blood were similar. He also found that fluoride intakes of 1.5-2.5 mg daily, for periods of up to 45 days, increased the whole blood fluoride concentration of pregnant women above their individual pretreatment levels. However, the mean fluoride content of samples of maternal whole blood prior to initiation of the fluoride treatment was 0.22 (range 0.17-0.30) ppm, while that after the period of increased fluoride intake, at the time of parturition, was little different —namely, 0.24 (range 0.21-0.30) ppm fluoride. The mean foetal blood fluoride was 0.24 (range 0.20-0.29) ppm. Blood fluoride studies by Gedalia and co-workers are reported in Chapter 4, section 4.

Fluoride in Milk, Saliva and Spinal Fluid

Zipkin & Babeaux (1965) also summarized much of the literature relating to the concentration of fluoride in human and animal milk. In this book, reference can be made to Chapter 5, section 2.

Fluoride in saliva is a field covered in the same section.

New information has recently been presented (Ericsson, 1969) on the fluoride content of human saliva and milk. Using a slight modification of the Bäumler-Glinz method for determination of fluoride by diffusion from perchloric acid (Bäumler & Glinz, 1964), the fasting fluoride concentrations of human saliva and milk were found to be below 0.05 ppm, somewhat lower than the figures reported by earlier authors. Ingestion of 0.3 mg fluoride in 300 ml water produced a slight elevation of fluoride content in the saliva of some subjects; when 1.65 mg fluoride was given under the same conditions, the salivary fluoride content of all subjects was higher than the fasting concentration after 30 minutes. The fluoride concentration of milk was not affected by these intakes of fluoride.

The spinal fluid of 29 patients admitted for diagnostic myelogram examinations was found (Singer, Lavender & Armstrong, unpublished data) to have a mean fluoride content of 0.10 ± 0.008 (SD) ppm. The concentration of fluoride in this fluid is considerably lower than that in the plasma, 0.23 ± 0.070 (SD) ppm, of the same patients.

3. DISTRIBUTION IN HARD TISSUES

(S. M. Weidmann & J. A. Weatherell)

The use of fluoride in caries prophylaxis has given the element a special, recent significance. Adding fluoride to communal water supplies will inevitably expose large sections of the population to higher levels of the element than they have hitherto been accustomed. Assessments must, therefore, be made not only of its effectiveness as a weapon against dental decay, but also of possible hazards of increased fluoride ingestion and absorption. A thorough knowledge of the manner of uptake, concentration and distribution of fluoride in the body tissue is, therefore, essential.

Fluoride has a marked affinity for hard tissues and has been detected in every specimen of bone or tooth analysed. The reason for this is that there is probably no fluoride-free diet and most naturally occurring waters contain at least traces of the element. However small the amounts of fluoride ingested, a good proportion, up to about half, is incorporated and retained by the hard tissues, the remainder being rapidly excreted. The extent of fluoride uptake in different parts of the skeleton and dentition depends upon the amounts ingested and absorbed by the organism, the duration of fluoride exposure and the type, region and metabolic activity of the tissue concerned. There is, thus, a great disparity in fluoride levels, both between different individuals and between different types of mineralized structures. Even within tissues which appear to be structurally homogeneous, concentrations may vary markedly over distances of only a few microns.

This section describes the distribution of fluoride in skeletal and dental tissues and gives an account of the factors thought to influence its absorption and retention.

Ingestion, Absorption and Excretion of Fluoride

The amount of fluoride ingested by different individuals varies appreciably. In the majority of instances the levels depend almost entirely upon the diet and water supply, though occasionally some fluoride may find its way into the organism by inhalation, for example, of fluoride-containing gases or dust.

Among the many possible fluoride-containing items of diet, citrus fruits probably contain least fluoride and bone meal, because of the capacity of bone to accumulate the element, is at the top of the scale. Tea and beer probably constitute supplementary sources that could be of significance to the national level of fluoride ingestion. An excessive consumption of fish, with its relatively high fluoride content derived from sea water, may similarly impose a regional bias upon the amount ingested (Hadjimarkos, 1962a), and the use of salt prepared from sea water can increase the dietary fluoride level (Hadjimarkos, 1962b).

Concentrations of fluoride in the public water supplies of different parts of the world vary enormously (see Chapter 2, section 2). It has been alleged that in particular regions of India the indigenous people may ingest amounts as great as 20 mg fluoride per day from their drinking water (Pandit et al., 1940). A considerable proportion of this, however, is presumably not dissolved fluoride but arises from suspended fluoride-containing rock dust accumulated in the shallow wells from which the water is drawn. Further disparities in the quantities of fluoride ingested are, of course, imposed by climatic variations, which markedly affect the volume of water consumed.

The quantity of fluoride absorbed by the skeleton is usually more closely related to the amount present in the drinking water than to that contained in the diet. Zipkin et al. (1958) showed a linear relationship between the fluoride level of the water supply and the average fluoride concentration of human bone (Fig. 1). The amount of fluoride absorbed from the diet depends not only upon the absolute quantity of the element present, but also upon the influence of associated dietary constituents. In general, any substance able to complex or combine with fluoride and render it insoluble hinders fluoride absorption from the gastrointestinal tract. Calcium affects absorption in this way, reducing the uptake of fluoride by bone and increasing faecal excretion of the element (Ericsson, 1958; Weddle & Muhler, 1957). Magnesium also reduces gastrointestinal absorption, while other substances such as PO_4, Fe, SO_4 and Mo, may enhance it (Stookey, Crane & Muhler, 1964).

FIG. 1

RELATION OF FLUORIDE CONCENTRATION IN HUMAN BONES TO
FLUORIDE CONCENTRATION IN DRINKING WATER[a]

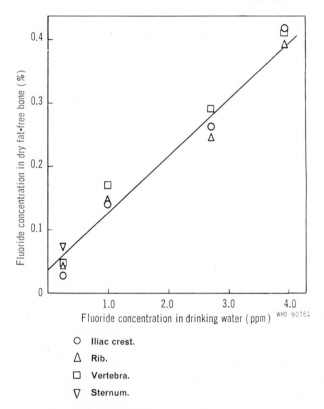

O   Iliac crest.

△   Rib.

▢   Vertebra.

▽   Sternum.

[a] After Zipkin et al. (1958).

At levels of intake between 1 and 20 ppm, up to half of the ingested fluoride appears to be retained by the skeleton. Most of the remainder is rapidly excreted *via* the urine, and about 5-10% is excreted *via* the faeces (Largent, 1961). None remains for any length of time in the blood or the soft tissues, though a little may be found in pockets of ectopic calcification. The fluoride retained by the body seems to be exclusively combined with mineralized tissue.

Incorporation of Fluoride into Bone and Tooth Mineral

Chemical analyses of fluoride-rich hard tissues have shown that the incorporation of fluoride slightly alters the chemical composition of bone and tooth mineral (Table 8). The carbonate and citrate contents are lowered

TABLE 8

EFFECT OF FLUORIDE ON THE CHEMICAL COMPOSITION OF BONES AND TEETH [a]

Reference	Species	Tissue	F (ppm in ash)	Ca/P	Ca/CO$_2$	Ca/Mg	Ca/citrate
Kick et al. (1935)	Pig	Femur	653 19 140	2.20 2.18	8.5 9.5	49 34	— —
McCann & Bullock (1957)	Rat	Femur	{ 200 { 12 100	1.99 2.02	8.8 9.4	41 33	— —
		Incisor dentine	{ 500 { 6 400	1.74 1.81	14.0 14.2	18 14	— —
		Incisor enamel	{ 21 { 2 030	1.99 1.97	— —	139 50	— —
Weidmann, Weatherell & Whitehead (1959)	Ox	Femur cortical exos- totic	6 850 11 100	2.17 2.18	8.4 9.5	57 52	— —
Zipkin, McClure & Lee (1960)	Man	Iliac crest	800 2 200 4 000 6 900	2.22 2.15 2.24 2.17	6.7 6.7 7.5 7.4	78 73 66 67	17.4 19.4 21.8 24.6

[a] P, CO$_2$, Mg, and citrate percentages are related to Ca.

and the magnesium level increased; the Ca/P ratio, however, remains unchanged.

Several workers have inferred from these observations that fluoride can replace carbonate or bicarbonate groups situated within or at the surface of the crystallites. This impression has been supported by experiments in which the uptake of fluoride into suspended bone powder was studied *in vitro*. Addition of bicarbonate to the incubating medium inhibited fluoride incorporation, presumably by competing for sites at the surface of the crystal lattice (Neuman et al., 1950). Fluoride uptake was similarly reduced by raising the pH of the incubation medium, which suggested an analogous competition between fluoride and hydroxyl ions. Several investigators have demonstrated a corresponding uptake of fluoride by enamel powder, and Scheinin (1954) found the uptake to be greatly dependent on the fluoride concentration and pH of the solution as well as on the duration of application. These findings leave little doubt that fluoride can enter the mineralized tissues by replacing certain ions and groups normally associated with hydroxyapatite crystallites.

Neuman & Neuman (1958) proposed a three-stage mechanism to describe the entry of ions into the apatite crystal lattice. The crystallite was considered to be surrounded by a hydration shell and the incorporation of fluoride into the crystal lattice prefaced by its exchange with one of the ions or polarized molecules present in this loosely integrated sheath. The second stage involved the exchange of fluoride in the hydration shell with an ion or group at the surface of the apatite crystal. Such entry of fluoride into the apatite crystal surface could be accomplished not only by hetero-ionic exchange with hydroxyl or bicarbonate groups, but also by iso-ionic exchange with fluoride already present in the crystal. Iso-ionic exchange was demonstrated by Brudevold et al. (1957) when they found that the uptake of ^{18}F into enamel was enhanced by an appreciable concentration of fluoride in the tooth surface. Finally, ions present in the crystal surface might migrate slowly into vacant spaces in the crystal interior during recrystallization.

Fluoride incorporation does not appear to alter the Ca/P ratio of the mineral salt. This observation, together with the supporting evidence that alterations in the Ca/P ratio of the incubating medium did not alter the uptake of fluoride *in vitro* (Neuman et al., 1950), upholds the contention that the element does not replace phosphate groups of hydroxyapatite to any great extent. The only deviation from this general picture arises during the topical application of concentrated fluoride solutions (1 %) to enamel surfaces (Brudevold, 1962). In this case a double decomposition will occur, CaF_2 being precipitated and phosphate released according to the equation:

$$Ca_{10}(PO_4)_6(OH)_2 + 20NaF \rightarrow 10CaF_2 + 6Na_3PO_4 + 2NaOH$$

This displacement of phosphate only occurs, however, when apatite reacts with fluoride solutions at least a hundred times as concentrated as those encountered during ingestion of normal diets. In the context of the present discussion, fluoride seems to be incorporated almost exclusively by a simple substitution which involves no severe disruption of the apatitic structure.

Other chemical changes in fluoride-rich tissues are not so readily explained. The biggest change in the composition of fluoride-rich bone concerns the citrate content; reductions of up to 40% were observed by Zipkin et al. (1963) in the bones of growing rats. At first these authors explained the decrease by a substitution of citrate with fluoride, analogous to the exchange of fluoride with bicarbonate and hydroxyl (Zipkin, McClure & Lee, 1960). The dissimilarity of fluoride and citrate in valency and size, however, made this explanation somewhat tenuous, and other interpretations have since been proposed. The possibility has been considered that fluoride limits the uptake of citrate by increasing the crystallinity of the apatite lattice, thereby reducing its reactivity (Zipkin et al., 1963). Whether increased crystallinity could account for the loss of almost half the binding sites of citrate is a point worthy of consideration. Perhaps the lowered citrate content is not directly connected with the mechanism of fluoride incorporation at all, but relates to an effect of the element upon bone metabolism. Much of the citrate produced in bone is undoubtedly retained in the tissue as calcium citrate. Any alteration of citrate metabolism due to enzymatic inhibition by fluoride might, therefore, affect the citrate levels in bone.

The increase of magnesium in fluoridated bone is not easily accounted for. Although it is tempting to suggest that magnesium precipitates in some complex form when fluoride ion is present in the extracellular environment, there is no evidence for this. Whereas fluoride undoubtedly increases the magnesium content of bone, too few values are available to establish a proportionate correlation between the two elements. Nor is there any magnesium fluorocompound known with a sufficiently low solubility product. At present no cogent suggestion can be made why fluoride enhances bone magnesium levels.

Most workers seemed to disregard precipitation reactions as an important mechanism by which fluoride is incorporated into skeletal tissues. At the high levels of ingestion associated with fluorosis, however, the presence of CaF_2 has been suspected by several workers. Schour & Smith (1934), for instance, found a slightly increased Ca/P ratio in fluorotic teeth of rats that they took to indicate CaF_2 deposition. Bauer (1945) noticed very irregular calcification in bones of fluorotic dogs, together with granules which he regarded as CaF_2. Bélanger et al. (1958) also observed an accumulation of larger less-well-oriented crystals resembling CaF_2. A further possible precipitation mechanism was implied by Kuyper & Kutnerian (1962), who suggested from *in vitro* data that fluorapatite may deposit from tissue containing 3 ppm fluoride.

The consensus of opinion is, however, that the main reaction by which fluoride is incorporated into hard tissues is that of ionic substitution.

Effect of Growth, Remodelling and Metabolic Activity on Fluoride Uptake

Fluoride may also enter the mineral by its incorporation during the phase of crystal growth. Substitution of fluoride for ions in the crystal surface is usually termed "exchange", whereas incorporation into the apatite lattice during crystal formation or growth may be designated "uptake by accretion". The relative importance of the two processes in fluoride incorporation has not been established.

The extent to which exchange and accretion contribute to the incorporation of any bone-seeking element is of general interest. The problem has been studied extensively in relation to radioactive tracers such as ^{32}P and ^{45}Ca (e.g., Bauer, Carlsson & Lindquist, 1955), but despite several attempts the situation is still not clarified. It can be said, however, that uptake by accretion will be maximal during the phase of bone growth or tooth development when a large proportion of the crystallites are still forming. Exchange reactions will also be maximal at this stage, since the crystallites are then predominantly small in size, large in number and offer an extensive surface area to exchanging ions. In addition to this, the greater hydration of young mineralized tissue ensures a high permeability which provides better access of tissue fluids to crystal surfaces.

Bones

The predictably high uptake of fluoride by the skeleton during growth is borne out by considerable experimental data. The rapidly growing bones of young animals absorb fluoride more readily than those of older individuals (Table 9). Zipkin & McClure (1952) fed 20 mg fluoride to rats of different ages and showed that the younger the animal, the more fluoride accumulated in its skeleton. Suttie & Phillips (1959) also demonstrated this when they compared fluoride uptake by the femora of weanling, half-grown and

TABLE 9

RETENTION OF FLUORIDE BY BONES OF GROWING AND MATURE ANIMALS

Reference	Species	Tissue	Age	Dose	Duration (days)	F (ppm in ash)
Zipkin & McClure (1952)	Rat	Femur	30 days 90 days 150 days 210 days 330 days	10 ppm F in water until a total of 20 mg F ingested	136 139 132 116 107	1 240 1 140 800 720 470
Suttie & Phillips (1959)	Rat	Femur	Weanlings Young Mature	500 ppm F in food *ad lib.*	3	2 333 1 038 771
Weidmann & Weatherell (1959)	Rabbit	Long bones (dia-physis)	1-2 months 3-4 months Mature	500 ppm F in water *ad lib.*	22	6 180 4 100 1 555

mature rats. Weidmann & Weatherell (1959) found that under conditions of *ad libitum* ingestion, the over-all uptake of fluoride into the bones of young, half-grown and mature rabbits likewise decreased with advancing age. There are few comparable data about the rates of fluoride incorporation into young human bones of different ages.

At all ages some regions of bone are more active than others. This is clearly demonstrated by regional differences in radioisotope uptake. Within individual bones the distribution of fluoride corresponds closely to the pattern of biological activity established by such tracer studies. Cancellous structures, for instance, invariably contain more fluoride than the less active compacta, and the biologically active surfaces of bone take up fluoride more readily than interior regions. This can be seen histologically in auto-radiographs taken from the bones of ^{18}F-injected animals (Perkinson et al., 1955) and from results obtained by chemical analysis (Table 10).

Table 10 shows that the distinctions between the fluoride uptake of different regions of the same bone and of different types of bone are more pronounced in adult than in young animals, presumably because in the latter biological activity is high throughout all areas of bone.

TABLE 10

RETENTION OF FLUORIDE BY DIFFERENT REGIONS AND TYPES OF BONE

Reference	Spe-cies	Age	Bone type and region	Dose	Duration	F (ppm in ash)
Gardner et al. (1959)	Dog	Adult	Diaphysis, compacta Epiphysis, cancellum Diaphysis, subperiosteal Diaphysis, interior	13 ppm in diet ad lib.	Life-long	2 285 3 132 3 257 2 160
		Young	Diaphysis, compacta Epiphysis, cancellum Diaphysis, subperiosteal Diaphysis, interior			— 415 345 315
Weidmann & Weatherell (1959)	Rabbit	Adult	Diaphysis, compacta Metaphysis, cancellum Diaphysis, subperiosteal Diaphysis, average	500 ppm in water ad lib.	22 days	1 585 9 220 6 640 1 585
		3-4 months	Diaphysis, compacta Metaphysis, cancellum Diaphysis, subperiosteal Diaphysis, average			4 070 9 070 5 680 4 070
		1-2 months	Diaphysis, compacta Metaphysis, cancellum Diaphysis, subperiosteal Metaphysis, average			5 860 9 470 7 860 5 860
Weatherell (unpublished data)	Man	33 years	Diaphysis, compacta Metaphysis, cancellum Diaphysis, subperiosteal Diaphysis, interior Rib, compacta Rib, cancellum	< 0.1 ppm F in water ad lib.	Life-long	703 885 1 250 679 1 685 3 500

Teeth

The factors which govern the incorporation of fluoride into dental structures are essentially similar to those pertinent to bone. Fluoride is again taken up most rapidly during the phases of growth and development. Dental tissues differ from bones, however, in that once formed there is no remodelling and, in the enamel, no cellular activity. Also, the much lower permeability of mature dentine and especially of enamel imposes a restriction of ionic mobility not encountered in osseous systems.

In the early stages of odontogenesis, the lowly calcified tissues will present relatively little hindrance to the transport of ions. The over-all uptake of fluoride in dentine and enamel is, therefore, maximal during their periods of formation and calcification.

The overriding influence of growth and development upon fluoride uptake in teeth was soon realized. Wallace-Durbin (1954) found that the incisors of mature rats took up much more ^{18}F than the molars, presumably because in the mature animal the molars had ceased to grow whereas the incisors grew continuously. There was, on the other hand, no difference between the ^{18}F autoradiographs of incisors and molars of young rats, in which both types of teeth were growing. Similarly, Weidmann (1962) found no differences between the fluoride uptake of incisors from young and adult rabbits, owing no doubt to the fact that rabbit incisors grow throughout life. Compared with teeth of limited growth, e.g., those of the cat, the continuously growing teeth of rats and rabbits incorporate several times more fluoride.

Even after growth is terminated, the uptake of fluoride is for a time appreciable. This is presumably due to the still considerable incorporation of mineral into the incompletely calcified teeth. Weidmann (1962) showed this in the permanent teeth of half-grown cats which took up more fluoride than those of adult specimens. Apparently, the state of mineralization *per se* affected fluoride uptake, for the difference in fluoride content between half-grown and adult cat teeth could only be attributed to the incompletely calcified state of the half-grown animals' dentition. Jenkins (1955) also implied this when he suggested that full benefit of fluoride in caries prevention depended on the fluoride's being ingested during the calcification period. The same consideration is probably implicit in Weaver's earlier (1944) statement that the optimal prophylactic effect of fluoride was achieved during the pre-eruptive and immediately post-eruptive phases of the tooth.

Three phases of dental fluoride uptake can be visualized: that occurring in the phase of formation, that occurring during the subsequent period of mineralization and that occurring after mineralization is complete. In the first phase, the element is probably taken up uniformly throughout the tissue; in the second, uptake will be largest in areas where mineralization occurs; in the third, when the teeth have fully formed and achieved complete mineralization, uptake will be almost entirely limited to the marginal regions of both enamel and dentine.

Enamel has a very low average concentration of fluoride and in the tissue interior the levels are particularly small. It appears that relatively low concentrations of fluoride are achieved during the brief period of formation. When enamel has attained a minimal degree of calcification, the increasing difficulty of ionic penetration quickly produces a concentration gradient from surface to interior regions. This preferential accumulation of fluoride in the surface regions of enamel occurs at some stage prior to eruption of the teeth, probably shortly after the enamel has been formed but before its calcification is complete. Incorporation of fluoride into the enamel of permanent teeth continues at a relatively high rate as long as the tissue's mineralization is incomplete. In the fully calcified permanent tooth the rate of uptake is slow, and surveys of enamel fluoride concentrations in human teeth (Jackson & Weidmann, 1959) show how the over-all accumulation of fluoride by enamel gradually decreases with age.

With advancing age fluoride is largely concentrated in the outer regions of enamel. Analyses of layers of enamel, successively removed from the surface towards the amelo-dentinal junction, reveal very high levels of fluo-

FIG. 2

PATTERN OF FLUORIDE DISTRIBUTION IN HUMAN ENAMEL IN
THE LABIAL ASPECT OF A PERMANENT UPPER INCISOR

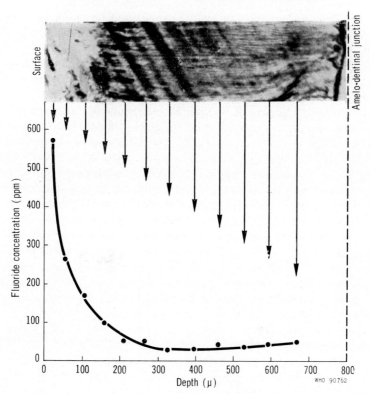

ride in the outer regions (Weatherell & Hargreaves, 1965). The characteristic pattern of distribution, shown in Fig. 2, is seen even before eruption.
After a tooth has erupted, fluoride continues to enter the enamel from the
oral fluids, being trapped in the first 100-200 μ of the enamel subsurface.
Almost all the fluoride present in this superficial zone will be acquired by
hetero-ionic exchange. Only in the early period of a tooth's history, before
the enamel has attained full mineralization, will accretion by crystal growth
play some part.

The average concentration of fluoride in dentine is two or three times
that of enamel and, as in enamel, growth and mineralization significantly
affect uptake of the element. In the continuously growing molars of the
rabbit, Weidmann (1962) found a much greater uptake of administered
fluoride in root dentine, i.e., where the tissue is formed, than in the dentine
of the crown. Fluoride uptake is, similarly, very much greater in the dentine
of continuously growing teeth, as in those of the rabbit, than in the permanent teeth of the cat. Like enamel, dentine has an enhanced capacity for

fluoride absorption during the process of mineralization as well as during growth. Weidmann demonstrated this by showing a significant increase in the fluoride level of dentine in half-grown cats after 46 days of fluoride administration; dentine from teeth of mature cats showed no significant increase. The difference seemed due to the fact that the dentine of the half-grown cats was not fully mineralized.

Dentinal fluoride is not homogeneously distributed throughout the rissue. As in bone and enamel, the element tends to accumulate in surface tegions. This will be due not only to the impermeability of the tissue, but also to chemical trapping of fluoride by ionic exchange at the pulpal surface. The highest concentration is, therefore, found closest to the pulp chamber (Yoon et al., 1960), where the systemic blood supply of fluoride is maximal, and the level falls from the pulpal border to the amelo-dentinal junction. Another factor leading to a high concentration of fluoride in pulpal dentine is the formation of secondary dentine within the pulpal cavity of permanent and deciduous teeth. In secondary dentine, fluoride concentration is higher than that of primary dentine (Jenkins & Speirs, 1954) probably because its period of formation and, therefore, its exposure to the pulpal supply of fluoride are more protracted. An interesting exception to this concentration gradient is found in deciduous teeth, the pulpal surface of which in their later stages is gradually removed by resorption. This phenomenon and its effect on fluoride levels are discussed later in this section.

Cementum has been the least studied dental hard tissue, presumably because of sampling difficulties. Histologically, it is more akin to bone than to dentine or enamel and the little information available suggests that its fluoride content is considerably higher. Yoon et al. (1960) put the level of cemental fluoride higher even than that at the pulpo-dentinal surface, and Singer & Armstrong (1962) found that cementum contains more fluoride than any other skeletal tissue. This may be partly ascribed to the small amount of remodelling taking place in this unusual structure.

Effect of Vascularity and Blood Flow on Fluoride Uptake

Apart from the intrinsic capacity of hard tissues to take up fluoride, greater in forming than in biologically static areas, there is the question of fluoride availability, i.e., the extent to which vascularity and blood flow govern fluoride uptake. The problems of fluoride transport to different areas of bone have received considerable attention. It has been suggested by a number of authors that the preferential uptake of a bone-seeking element at tissue surfaces is due to a better blood supply relative to that of the interior. Volker, Sognnaes & Bibby (1941) felt that the higher ^{18}F activity in the maxilla than in the femur was due to the greater intra-osseous blood circulation in flat bones than in tubular bones. Wallace-Durbin (1954), who examined ^{18}F incorporation into various hard tissues of the fully grown rat, showed that uptake decreased in the order mandibles → epiphyses → diaphyses. She supposed that the large uptake in actively calcifying areas could be explained by the relatively great vascularity of newly forming tissue. Perkinson et al. (1955) found heavy deposits in the primary spongiosa below the epiphyseal plate and a generalized spotty distribution of tracer in the trabecular regions. Believing that fluoride entered skeletal tissues by ionic exchange rather than by incorporation into newly forming bone, these authors concluded that vascularity, blood supply and crystal size governed the rate of reaction.

Whereas gross anatomical features, such as vascularity, might to some extent regulate the access of tissue fluid to bone mineral, the availability of crystal surfaces to ions contained in tissue fluids almost certainly depends chiefly upon variations in crystal growth, hydration, and size. In biologically active regions the extensive and accessible surface area offered by many small hydrated crystallites apparently far outweighs any dissimilarity in anatomical structure. *In vitro*, when the entire bone surface has uniform and free access to bone-seeking tracers, only the incompletely calcified recently formed regions are appreciably labelled by exchange. *In vivo*, such discrimination between forming and non-forming areas will be even greater, since in the living animal there is the additional factor of mineral accretion during the process of crystal formation and growth. The formative activity of a region is, therefore, the overriding factor governing the extent of fluoride uptake.

Whereas most of the observed variations of fluoride distribution can be accounted for by differences in crystal growth, size, vascularity and blood flow, a few observations are not so readily explained. Wallace-Durbin (1954), for instance, observed faster ^{18}F uptake in the rat's mandibles than in its epiphyses, and a preferential ^{18}F uptake in the periosteal region of long bones of the mature animals. Weidmann & Weatherell (1959) found a similar preferential accumulation of fluoride in the periosteal region of long bones and in the mandibular cortex of mature rabbits given high levels of fluoride in their drinking water. The mandibular compacta and the periosteal region of long bones are not thought to be particularly active in the mature animal and so the crystallites are unlikely to be small or the tissue undermineralized. Neither is it considered that the vascularity is very high or the blood supply exceptionally efficient in these regions. It could be argued that since the periosteal surfaces of long bones and mandibles are prone to fluorotic exostoses, the high level of fluoride found in these areas by Weidmann & Weatherell (1959) was directly due to the commencement of exostotic growth; fluorotic exostoses are known to contain considerable amounts of fluoride. It seems possible, however, to assume that for exostoses to form a comparatively high prior concentration of fluoride is necessary. The clarification of this phenomenon must await further information.

Effect of Level of Fluoride Ingestion on Fluoride Uptake

In all hard tissues at all stages of development, the level of fluoride is related to ingestion.

Bones

Zipkin et al. (1958) showed that the relationship between the fluoride concentrations in different bones from the same individual is maintained at varying levels of fluoride ingestion. Reports from many animal experiments also agree that there is a fairly consistent pattern of fluoride distribution between the different types and regions of bone at various levels of fluoride administration (see Table 10).

Such consistent relationships are maintained so long as the intake of fluoride is not so high, or of such duration, as to cause the skeletal changes associated with skeletal fluorosis. The most obvious symptom of this condition is the pathological growth of exostoses, the sites and forms of which are many and various. In man, these may occur after long periods of fluoride ingestion at levels of 4-8 ppm or above in water. Wherever such exostoses arise, the uptake of fluoride increases. Analyses of exostotic bone and adjacent normal bone from fluorotic animals clearly demonstrated the enhanced fluoride uptake in the rapidly forming exostotic bone (Weidmann & Weatherell, 1959).

Teeth

In teeth, as in bone, the concentration of fluoride relates closely to the quantity ingested. Fluoride levels of both dentine and enamel correlate well with the concentration of fluoride in the drinking water (Table 11). Although the absolute levels may rise or fall, depending on fluoride intake, the differential between dentine and enamel is maintained throughout the life of the tooth (Jackson & Weidmann, 1959).

The figures given in Table 11 suggest a linear relationship between the level of fluoride in the drinking water and the concentration of the element in the enamel surface. Such remarkable correlation, however, is to some extent fortuitous, because the variations between different individual age-groups will be appreciable and the thickness of the surface layer analysed by the different workers extremely variable.

During the period of tooth formation, the ingestion of amounts of water-borne fluoride as low as 1 ppm may produce slight white spots in the enamel surfaces in a few cases. These may be due to the effect of fluoride upon the ameloblast during tooth formation. They are not aesthetically displeasing and resemble other imperfections in enamel commonly seen in teeth from districts where the fluoride content of the drinking water seems low

TABLE 11

FLUORIDE CONCENTRATION (EXPRESSED AS PPM IN ASH) IN DENTINE AND ENAMEL AT
DIFFERENT LEVELS OF FLUORIDE INGESTION

Reference	Species	Age	Dose (ppm F in water)	Duration	Enamel			Dentine whole
					surface	interior	whole	
McClure & Likins (1951)	Man	Adult	0.1	Life-long	—	—	86	332
			7.6	Life-long	—	—	658	1 968
Jackson & Weidmann (1959)	Man	20-49 years	<0.5	Life-long	—	—	108	508
		20-35 years	1.2	Life-long	—	—	180	922
		20-35 years	1.9	Life-long	—	—	320	1 290
Jenkins & Speirs (1953)	Man	Adult	<0.25	Life-long	590	80	—	—
			1.4	Life-long	960	110	—	—
			2.0	Life-long	1 310	270	—	—
Brudevold, Steadman & Smith (1960)	Man	20-29 years	0.1	Life-long	571	48	—	—
			1.0	Life-long	889	129	—	—
			3.0	Life-long	1 930	152	—	—
			5.0	Life-long	3 370	570	—	—

enough to preclude the possibility of fluorosis. Higher levels of fluoride ingested during amelogenesis increase both the incidence and the severity of the fluorotic lesions.

Influence of Fluoride Saturation

Fluoride is taken up at crystallite surfaces and it has been debated whether after long periods of exposure, or at relatively high levels of incorporation, saturation of the available sites might occur and subsequent uptake be reduced.

Bones

Several workers have noticed that the rate of uptake by bones of experimental animals gradually decreased as the periods of fluoride exposure were prolonged. This observation could imply saturation, but might also be partly due to a gradual fall in bone activity or growth rate as the animal aged during the period of fluoride administration. Suttie & Phillips (1959) found, however, that both young and old rats tended to take up fluoride less rapidly when they had been subjected to prior doses of the element. A diet containing 500 ppm fluoride had been supplied to the rats in question, and it seems feasible that at such high dosage some saturation of available bone surfaces might occur. At much lower levels of ingestion, such as those usually encountered by man, it is extremely unlikely that any saturation could arise. The normal processes of bone activity, i.e., exchange, recrystallization and remodelling, would ensure a constant renewal of bone mineral, either by removing fluoride from the crystal surfaces by back-exchange and recrystallization, or by replacement of fluorotic bone with new bone during the normal process of remodelling.

Teeth

In dentine and cementum the situation appears somewhat analogous to bone; at low rates of ingestion the continued formation of tissue will tend to offset fluoride saturation.

Enamel presents a somewhat different picture. Once enamel has been formed, cellular activity ceases and the incorporation of fluoride depends solely upon ion-exchange mechanisms. Penetration of fluoride into the interior regions of enamel is obstructed by the chemical trapping of ions in the outer regions and, presumably, by the low permeability of this highly calcified structure. This results in the precipitous fall of fluoride concentration from external to internal regions shown in Fig. 2.

The concentration of fluoride at any point within the enamel appears to fall exponentially from surface to interior. Saturation might occur in the surfaces of the outermost crystallites, but this remains a matter of conjecture. Perhaps the slight wear to which tooth surfaces are subjected is sufficient to prevent it. Whether saturation does occur in the outermost layer is difficult to assess. Chemical analysis gives only an average value and can never reveal variations in the fluoride content of crystal surfaces. In shark teeth, and probably in those of some other fish continually exposed to the high fluoride content of a marine environment, almost complete deposition of tooth mineral as fluorapatite (i.e., 3.8 % F) has been demonstrated (Büttner, 1966). The surface layers of enamel from human teeth rarely contain even a third of this amount.

Removal of Fluoride from Hard Tissues

The discussion so far has not taken into account the circumstances by which fluoride might be removed from skeletal and dental systems. Several authors have noticed that, once present, fluoride is lost with difficulty from hard tissues. Savchuck & Armstrong (1951) observed that after withdrawal of fluoride approximately 10-15 % was eliminated from the rat skeleton in 40 days; the remainder appeared to be more firmly fixed and after 40 days the level changed little. McCann & Bullock (1957) also found that after long periods of fluoride exposure *in vivo* or *in vitro* skeletal fluoride was removed with difficulty. They suggested that, although fluoride incorporated by surface exchange may be removable, that which is more deeply incorporated into the crystal is removed by an extremely slow reaction.

Bones

Fluoride is certainly not irrevocably deposited in skeletal tissues. Experiments with rats of various ages have shown that there is an initial rapid decrease in the skeletally bound fluoride, followed by a more gradual removal (Savchuck & Armstrong, 1951). Hodge (1952) pointed to a similar phenomenon in man. He offered the explanation that the escape of fluoride from mineral to tissue fluids by back-exchange with ions in the hydration shell could account for the relatively rapid loss of fluoride in the period immediately following incorporation.

Whereas there are good reasons to believe that the element will be removed relatively quickly as long as it is situated at the surfaces of crystallites, there is no direct experimental evidence in support of Hodge's hypothesis. It is not possible to say, therefore, to what extent exchange or osteoclastic activity is responsible for the initial removal of fluoride from the skeleton. According to Hodge, the remodelling of bone by osteoblastic and osteoclastic activity was responsible for the more gradual, later phase of fluoride removal, accounting for a slower but considerable loss of the element. There is no doubt that some of the incorporated fluoride will eventually be buried deeply by crystal growth and subsequent apposition of new tissue. In this state, although fluoride could not escape from the mineral crystallites by exchange, it could still be released by osteoclastic resorption.

Measurements of fluoride levels in bone or urine give no direct indication of the extent of fluoride mobilization, for some of the fluoride released may be reincorporated. Likins et al. (1959) found that, although some of the fluoride present in the proximal metaphysis of the growing rat tibia had been lost during bone growth, there was considerable uptake in the adjacent developing bone segment. They came to the conclusion that fluoride, released during remodelling, did not necessarily enter the general circulation but redeposited in nearby sites of growth. It does indeed seem likely that some fluoride released into tissue fluid by resorption or exchange will redeposit rapidly in adjacent areas of active formation.

The evidence of fluoride removal from the human skeleton rests entirely upon measurements of urinary excretion rates. There is no way of directly detecting skeletal fluoride loss in man. Largent (1961) examined the urinary excretion of stored fluoride in persons who had ingested large amounts for long periods. For some time after discontinuation of fluoride administration, urinary excretion remained in excess of ingestion. The levels of excretion fell according to an exponential equation and were still in excess of intake in the 96th week after discontinuation of high-level absorption. Largent estimated that the decline of excess urinary fluoride reached its midpoint in 75 to 80 weeks and that a state of balance was reached in 200 to 225 weeks. He assumed that eventually the urinary fluoride concentration would reach a level similar to that in the drinking water. This assumption is supported by the evidence of McClure & Kinser (1944), who found that the concentration of fluoride in human urine bore a linear relationship to the fluoride content of the domestic drinking-water supply.

According to Largent (1961), the total amount of fluoride deposited in bones relates to the level of fluoride ingestion. So long as the level of ingestion remains unchanged, any further storage will eventually be offset by the mobilization of some previously stored fluoride. A balance appeared to be maintained between absorption and storage, on the one hand, and mobilization and excretion on the other. In the case of ten human subjects, he found that intake and output of fluoride were nearly equal. Two residents from each of five cities were examined, the fluoride of the water supplies in these cities ranging from 2 to 20 ppm. The findings suggested that in each of the five cities the residents stored enough fluoride to reach a state of equilibrium. This appears to support the view expressed by several workers that the fluoride concentration of bones increases with age for a time but that eventually a steady state is reached, after which there is no further rise in skeletal fluoride concentration. More will be said about this later.

Teeth

Direct evidence of fluoride removal from dentine emerged from a study of deciduous teeth. Hargreaves & Weatherell (1965) showed that the fluoride concentration of dentine from the crowns of deciduous teeth rose with age to a maximum and then dropped steeply when the process of resorption, which precedes the exfoliation of deciduous teeth, began (Fig. 3). The fall in fluoride level appeared to be due entirely to the osteoclastic removal of high-fluoride dentine from the pulpal surface.

There is little information about the lability of enamel-bound fluoride. No doubt the incorporated fluoride of the interior regions is firmly fixed, but that present in the tooth surface may be less permanently bound. Some surface fluoride may escape by exchange with the ions present in saliva and some may be lost by wear due to attrition or abrasion during mastication (Hallsworth & Weatherell, 1969). In the continuously growing teeth of rodents, fluoride is lost as teeth grow and are continually worn away. Weidmann (1962) demonstrated this type of fluoride loss in the case of rat incisors; in the permanent dentition of the cat such loss was not observed. It seems likely that the wear sustained by enamel during the long life-span of human teeth might result in the removal of a few microns of tissue from the enamel surface, together with its associated fluoride. This could explain the low levels of fluoride found in the labial surfaces of some incisors from persons over the age of 50 (Weatherell & Hargreaves, 1966).

In conclusion, three mechanisms have been considered for the removal of fluoride from hard tissues: back-exchange with ions contained in tissue

FIG. 3

VARIATIONS WITH AGE IN THE FLUORIDE CONTENT OF DECIDUOUS DENTINE
IN SECOND MOLAR TEETH FROM CHILDREN LIVING IN AREAS SUPPLIED WITH
DRINKING WATER CONTAINING < 0.5 ppm F (STANDARD DEVIATION SHOWN
FOR EACH AGE-GROUP) [a]

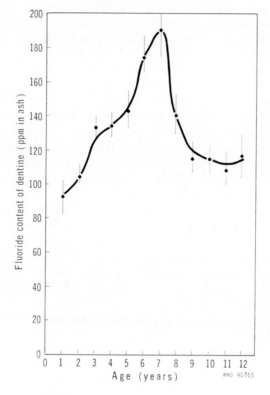

[a] After Hargreaves & Weatherell (1965).

fluids; resorption of tissue; and mechanical abrasion. A major loss of
fluoride by back-exchange is difficult to visualize since it would act against
surface accumulation, which is a well-established fact. In contrast, resorption has been proved to remove demonstrable amounts of fluoride. Whether
it is the sole agent or not will have to await further information about bone
activity.

Effect of Age on Accumulation of Fluoride

Estimations of fluoride levels show that both bones and teeth tend to
accumulate fluoride with age. Provided that the level of ingestion does not
decrease, the balance between fluoride uptake and removal is clearly in
favour of uptake.

Bones

The concentration of fluoride in bone undoubtedly increases with time and a number of surveys have been carried out to establish the extent to which the element accumulates throughout life. The first investigation into human bone of different ages was that of Glock, Lowater & Murray (1941), who estimated the fluoride content of ground samples from 14 whole ribs taken *post mortem* from persons in two London hospitals. A rise in fluoride content with age was clearly demonstrated, but the rate of accumulation could not be established because of the large scatter of values. Such scatter is inevitable when samples are taken indiscriminately from a bone with so variable a structure as rib. The wide disparity between the fluoride levels of tissue surfaces compared to interior regions and between compact and cancellous bone has been stressed earlier. Reliable sampling techniques are, therefore, crucial, since comparisons between the fluoride content of speci-mens from different individuals can only be made when they are carefully chosen from similar anatomical sites and structures. To avoid errors aris-ing from injudicious faulty sampling, Smith, Gardner & Hodge (1953) compared specimens of rib cortex and Jackson & Weidmann (1958) res-tricted their analyses to rib cancellum. Both groups of workers demonstrated that the fluoride content of bone rose with age. But whereas the results of Smith and co-workers (*op. cit.*) seemed to indicate a linear increase in fluoride concentration with age, Jackson & Weidmann (1958) found that fluoride tended to accumulate less readily in older specimens and that a plateau level of fluoride concentration was reached at the age of about 55. Blayney, Bowers & Zimmerman (1962) made a survey of iliac crest specimens and came to conclusions similar to those of Jackson & Weidmann. It is doubtful, however, whether either of these two studies presented conclusive evidence that a plateau was reached, because the scatter of results was very large and the number of observations relatively small. Zipkin et al. (1958) presented data from analyses of iliac crest, rib and vertebrae from persons who lived in areas with 0.1-4 ppm fluoride in the drinking water. No levelling with age was observed in these predominantly cancellous structures in either low (0.1 ppm) or high (2.6 ppm) fluoride groups, although the years of residence varied between 10 and 90 years. Recent analyses (Fig. 4) of compact bone from the femora of persons living in an area containing 0.1 ppm fluoride in the drinking water do not suggest that the rate of fluoride accumulation in this tissue declines with age (Weatherell, 1966). More work is required before any categoric statement about reaching a plateau level can be made.

It is difficult to predict from the knowledge of bone activity what the true situation might be. Assuming that the rate of bone formation decreases as the skeleton ages, it would seem reasonable to expect that less fluoride is taken up by older bone. There is, on the other hand, less remodelling in the older skeleton as well as less growth and, therefore, a larger fraction of

FIG. 4

FLUORIDE CONTENT OF FEMORAL COMPACTA FROM HUMANS OF DIFFERENT
AGES LIVING IN DISTRICTS SUPPLIED WITH DRINKING WATER CONTAINING
< 0.5 ppm F [a]

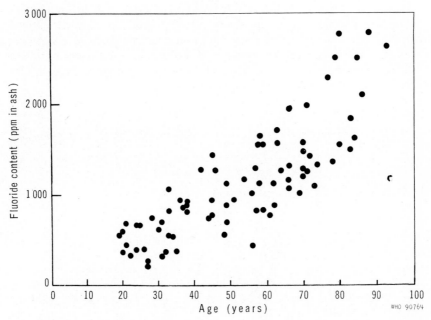

[a] After Weatherell (1966).

"static" bone in which fluoride might gradually accumulate by ionic exchange. It should also be considered what differences could exist in these respects between cancellous and cortical structures. Only further data can resolve these questions.

It can be visualized that less fluoride leaves the bones than enters them by exchange. This would imply that the fluoride ion present in tissue fluid exchanges more readily with groups of the apatite crystallite than *vice versa*. Such a tendency is quite feasible in view of the greater stability and insolubility of fluorapatite in comparison with hydroxy- or carbonato-apatites. This view is empirically supported by the fact that hard tissues, e.g., the surface of enamel, or archaeological specimens of bones and teeth buried for long periods, absorb and accumulate fluoride by exchange even when the fluoride concentration in the surrounding environment is low. Thus, fluoride might accumulate by exchange not only in new bone, when the apatite crystallites are small and well hydrated, but also in the mature, less available crystal surfaces of biologically static regions, uninvolved in the processes of remodelling. In older persons small areas of bone very likely persist for many years in such a static state, during which time they might well accumulate comparatively high levels of fluoride by exchange. If the level of fluoride ingestion remains low, areas of newly formed bone might therefore have considerably lower levels of the element than older inactive regions. The distribution of fluoride across the cortex of an adult human femur can occasionally reveal a very complex situation in which extreme differences in fluoride concentration are found in contiguous layers of bone (Fig. 5). The most likely explanation of this phenomenon seems to be that the regions of bone containing relatively low levels of fluoride were of more recent origin than those corresponding to the peak values.

FIG. 5

FLUORIDE DISTRIBUTION ACROSS THE FEMORAL CORTEX OF AN ADULT HUMAN

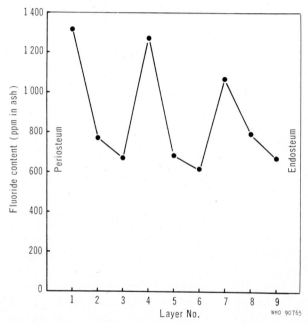

The over-all accumulation of fluoride with age, however, might not only result from an increase of fluoride in static regions, but also be due to a progressive rise in the fluoride content of the more labile areas. If, as Likins et al. (1959) suggested, some of the fluoride mobilized by bone resorption is re-incorporated into adjacent areas of formation, the tendency in labile regions would be towards a fluoride increase. In adult individuals the amount of bone resorbed is balanced by the amount formed. Should the newly laid down bone always contain some of the fluoride mobilized from nearby areas of resorption, however, there will be a small but continuous gain of fluoride.

The process of bone removal itself could lead to an enhancement of the bone fluoride levels. While it is debatable whether the osteoclast can discriminate between fluoridated and non-fluoridated bone, resorption usually affects anatomically specific areas of tissue, e.g., the endosteal region of long bones from which in old persons a considerable proportion of bone may be removed. Such resorption would increase the fluoride concentration of the tissue if the region removed had relatively low levels of fluoride, leaving behind areas of bone which fortuitously contained higher concentrations of the element. An alteration in fluoride concentration by this means was described earlier (see page 121); in the case cited, the preferential removal of high-fluoride dentine from the pulpal surfaces of deciduous teeth led to a lowered fluoride concentration. In the human femur, the rise in fluoride concentration after the age of 50 (Fig. 4) may partly be due to the preferential removal of low-fluoride endosteal bone as the cortex thins with age.

Finally, the purely speculative point might be mentioned as to whether a preferential dissolution of bone mineral might occur, leaving behind an increased concentration of fluorapatite. Such a possibility has been mooted (Neuman & Neuman, 1958; Jenkins, 1962) but there is no experimental evidence that osteoclasts are influenced by fluoride concentration.

The question of skeletal fluoride accumulation is clearly a complicated one. It is still a matter of conjecture whether predominance of exchange over back-exchange, reabsorption of mobilized fluoride into areas of bone formation, or the relative insolubility of fluorapatite is the most important factor contributing to accumulation of the element in the skeleton.

Teeth

Cementum, like bone, appears to absorb high levels of fluoride, but no information is available about its change in fluoride concentration with age.

The levels of fluoride in dentine and enamel are considerably lower than those in bone from the same individual. A relatively rapid increase in the average fluoride concentration is found during the early years of a tooth's life, but this rate of accumulation gradually declines as the tooth ages. Jackson & Weidmann (1959) demonstrated this pattern in both dentine and enamel of teeth from districts where different concentrations of fluoride were present in the water supply. The trends with age are shown in Fig. 6 and 7. The general pattern has been confirmed by Armstrong & Singer (1963).

The non-uniform distribution of fluoride in both dentine and enamel greatly reduces the value of results obtained by analysis of average samples. After the tooth has fully formed, fluoride is chiefly incorporated at tissue surfaces. There is no information about the way the fluoride level in the

FIG. 6

RELATIONSHIP BETWEEN AGE AND DENTINAL FLUORIDE
IN HUMAN PREMOLARS[a]

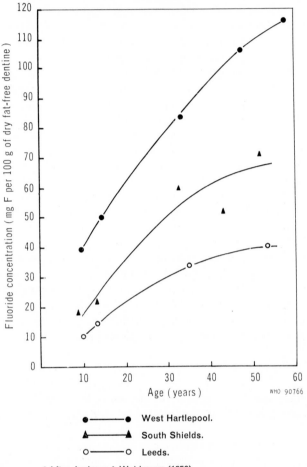

WHO 90766

●————● West Hartlepool.

▲————▲ South Shields.

○————○ Leeds.

[a] After Jackson & Weidmann (1959).

pulpal surface of permanent dentine changes with age. Since fluoride seems
to be taken up more readily by secondary than by primary dentine, alterations in its concentration at the pulpal surface will probably to some extent
depend upon the rate and amount of secondary dentine formation.

Fluoride in the outer regions of enamel might be expected to increase in
concentration both with the level of ingestion and with age. The former
relationship has been clearly established both in permanent (Brudevold,
Gardner & Smith, 1956) and in deciduous teeth (Weatherell & Hargreaves,
1966). Both the level of fluoride in the enamel surface and the penetration

of the element into subsurface regions and concentration in the tissue interior relate to the fluoride content of the drinking water.   The change in concentration in the enamel surface with age is not clearly established.   In deciduous teeth from regions with low and with high fluoride in the drinking water, no correlation between age and the fluoride content of enamel surfaces was seen (Weatherell & Hargreaves, 1966).   The situation in respect of the surface enamel of permanent teeth is also uncertain.   Brudevold, Gardner & Smith (1956) suggested that there was some increase with age in the fluoride content of the outer layer of enamel.   Recent studies of the labial surfaces of permanent incisors from a low-fluoride district revealed, however, that some teeth from individuals in their fifties or sixties contained surprisingly little fluoride.   This suggested the possibility that a few microns of the tooth surface, with its associated high level of fluoride, might have been lost for one reason or another during the long period of the teeth in the mouth.   Recent work (Hallsworth & Weatherell, 1969) showed that when a tooth surface had been worn away in the mouth, the high concentration of fluoride in the outer region of enamel was not restored, even in

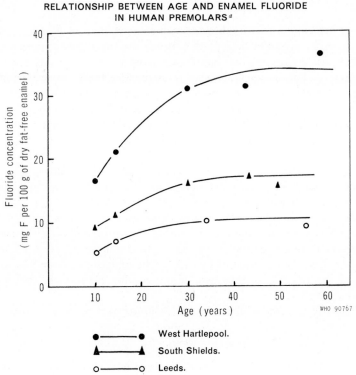

FIG. 7

RELATIONSHIP BETWEEN AGE AND ENAMEL FLUORIDE
IN HUMAN PREMOLARS[a]

WHO 90767

● ——— ●   West Hartlepool.

▲ ——— ▲   South Shields.

○ ——— ○   Leeds.

[a] After Jackson & Weidmann (1959).

West Hartlepool (England) where the fluoride concentration in drinking water was 2 ppm.

The extent to which fluoride accumulates in both bones and teeth with age, and the factors which govern it, are not clearly established. Such information might be important from several points of view. Observations about the life-long absorption and retention of fluoride will provide information to supplement and support knowledge about the skeletal incorporation and accumulation of other bone-seeking elements. Studies of fluoride levels in the surfaces of teeth relate directly to the many investigations into the role of fluoride in caries prophylaxis, and evidence about the loss of surface fluoride might at the same time provide information about the resistance of enamel surfaces to wear and erosion. Until recently, various technical problems have made many studies difficult. With the greatly improved methods for fluoride estimation and tissue sampling now available, there is every hope that the work of the next few years will resolve many of the uncertainties which at present obscure the picture of fluoride distribution and incorporation in the hard tissues.

4. DISTRIBUTION IN PLACENTA AND FOETUS (I. Gedalia)*

The placenta is the organ across which exchanges of gaseous, nutritive and excretory products take place between the foetal and maternal tissues, i.e., between their respective bloodstreams which histologically are in close proximity. The placental tissue is permeable even to high-molecular compounds like gamma-globulins, but generally an inverse relation exists between the molecular weight of substances and their ability to pass through the placenta (Villee, 1960). It has not been ascertained which mechanism is responsible for placental transfer—the ultrafilter theory, according to which the placenta acts as an inert, semipermeable membrane, or the vital function theory, according to which a preformed mechanism regulates a secretory process. The physiological characteristics of the placenta are not the same for all species of animals.

Studies on the placental transfer of fluoride have been induced by the demonstration of the influence of fluoride on the mineralization of teeth and on their resistance to dental caries. Of particular interest is the knowledge of the absorption and storage of fluoride in the human foetus and its relationship to the fluoride metabolism of the mother (Brzezinski, Bercovici & Gedalia, 1960).

Placental transfer of fluoride was demonstrated to occur under certain physiological conditions in the mouse (Ericsson & Ullberg, 1958; Ericsson, Ullberg & Appelgren, 1960), the rat (Lehman & Muhler, 1954;

* Since 1961, the author's studies have been aided by USPHS research grants D-1323-01-04 from the Institute of Dental Research, National Institutes of Health, Bethesda, Md. Some of the work quoted here was supported by the Mead Johnson Research Center.

Büttner & Muhler, 1958; Brzezinski et al., 1961), the dog (Knouff et al., 1936), the rabbit (Maplesden et al., 1960; Ericsson & Malmnäs, 1962), sheep (Bawden, Wolkoff & Flowers, 1964), and humans (Gardner et al., 1952; Held, 1954; Feltman & Kosel, 1955; Ziegler, 1956; Gedalia et al., 1961, 1964b; Ericsson & Malmnäs, 1962). In pregnant animals a certain amount of fluoride had to be present in the diet or drinking water before an appreciable amount of fluoride could be detected in the newborn (Lehman & Muhler, 1954; Büttner & Muhler, 1958; Brzezinski et al., 1961). Ericsson and co-workers (Ericsson & Ullberg, 1958; Ericsson, Ullberg & Appelgren, 1960), using an ^{18}F autoradiographic technique in pregnant mice, located the highest concentration of fluoride in the skeleton; the soft tissues were extremely low in fluoride, with the exception of the kidney and placenta.

Evidence with regard to the extent of placental transfer in humans has been conflicting (Gardner et al., 1952; Held, 1954; Feltman & Kosel, 1955; Ziegler, 1956). Past studies have established certain relationships between the daily fluoride intake by pregnant women and the fluoride content of the maternal blood, placental tissue and foetal blood at birth. Higher fluoride values were found in the maternal blood and placental tissue of pregnant women living in an area where the drinking water contained 1 ppm fluoride than in those living in a fluoride-free area (Gardner et al., 1952). The comparison of fluoride concentrations in foetal blood and placental tissue of women drinking practically fluoride-free water with those of women given fluoridated water or fluoride tablets has shown that in both groups the full-term placental tissue contained much more fluoride than the foetal blood (Feltman & Kosel, 1955). Ziegler (1956) compared the fluoride values in placental tissue, maternal blood and foetal blood of women drinking almost fluoride-free water with those of women given additional fluoride in milk. In the latter group there was a marked increase of fluoride concentration in the maternal blood and placental tissue, but in the foetal blood the fluoride value increased only slightly. All these studies indicated that fluoride accumulates in placental tissue, which may act as a partial barrier, protecting the foetus from toxic amounts (Gardner et al., 1952; Feltman & Kosel, 1955; Ziegler, 1956). However, Held (1954) reported about the same concentration of fluoride in maternal and foetal blood, as well as a similar increase in maternal and foetal blood fluoride levels after supplemental fluoride had been given, which he considered to imply that the placenta passively permits fluoride transfer to the foetus. In view of challenging reports on the importance of fluoride ingestion to pregnant women for the protection of the child's teeth, the fluoride relationships in placental tissues, maternal blood and foetal blood were re-investigated (Gedalia et al., 1961, 1964b; Ericsson & Malmnäs, 1962).

Table 12 shows that when the fluoride intake was low (drinking water containing about 0.1 ppm F), the fluoride content of the placental tissue was lower than that of the maternal or of the foetal blood, thus indicating little

TABLE 12

FLUORIDE CONCENTRATION IN PLACENTAL TISSUE, FOETAL BLOOD,
AND MATERNAL BLOOD AT LOW AND AT ELEVATED FLUORIDE INTAKE [a]

Material	Low fluoride intake		Elevated fluoride intake	
	Mean fluoride value (ppm)	SD	Mean fluoride value (ppm)	SD
Placenta	0.121	0.06	0.228	0.09
Foetal blood	0.165	0.07	0.175	0.05
Maternal blood	0.150	0.06	0.234	0.10

[a] After Gedalia et al. (1964b).

obstruction to the passage of fluoride from the maternal to the foetal blood stream. On the other hand, when the fluoride intake was elevated, either from drinking water containing about 1 ppm F or through fluoride-tablet supplementation, the fluoride content of the placental tissue and of the maternal blood was higher than that of the foetal blood (Gedalia et al., 1964b). The limited permeability of the placenta to increased concentration of fluoride ions suggests that the placenta plays a role in the transfer of fluoride from mother to foetus (Gedalia et al., 1961, 1964b). However, all figures given for blood and placental fluoride content should be judged against the background of the micro-analytical difficulties and the degenerative changes taking place in the placenta towards the end of pregnancy. According to the ^{18}F auto-radiographic studies in pregnant mice (Ericsson & Ullberg, 1958; Ericsson, Ullberg & Appelgren, 1960), the full-term placenta contains areas of calcification which take up fluoride thus reducing the amount which enters the foetus. Such areas of calcification are probably responsible for the high fluoride content in the human placenta at the time of delivery.

The relatively high permissible body dose of [18]F (Armstrong, Singer & Carlson, 1958) made it possible to study the fluoride transfer across the placenta of patients undergoing late therapeutic abortions in connexion with sterilization. Such investigations, supplemented by experiments on rabbits whose placentas are of the same type as those of humans, were carried out by Ericsson & Malmnäs (1962). In both humans and rabbits, the ^{18}F content of the foetal blood was found to be very low 5-30 minutes after intravenous injection, always less than one-third of the simultaneous ^{18}F concentration in the maternal blood. The ^{18}F concentration of the placenta was between that of the maternal and that of the foetal blood (Fig. 8).

Recently the placental transfer of ^{18}F was analysed autoradiographically and quantitatively in the late pregnancy of mice (1-2 days before expected parturition) (Ericsson & Hammarström, 1964). The foetal skeleton accumulated much less ^{18}F than the maternal skeleton of these animals, owing to the slow diffusion of fluoride through the placenta and to the great homeostatic

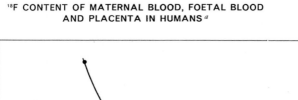

FIG. 8
^{18}F CONTENT OF MATERNAL BLOOD, FOETAL BLOOD
AND PLACENTA IN HUMANS[a]

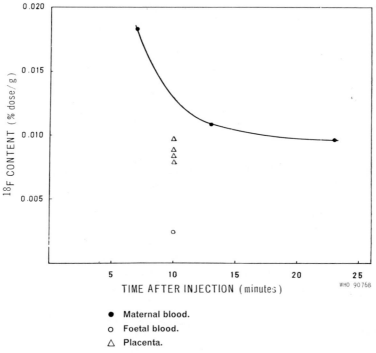

● Maternal blood.
○ Foetal blood.
△ Placenta.

[a] After Ericsson & Malmnäs (1962).

capacity for fluoride of the mammalian body (Carlson, Armstrong & Singer, 1960b). A sudden increase in maternal blood fluoride, such as that induced by the intake of fluoride tablets or by injection of ^{18}F in pregnancy, should therefore not produce any great rise in the fluoride concentration of the foetal blood.

Once fluoride enters the foetal circulation it is incorporated into foetal bones and teeth undergoing calcification. The fluoride is probably deposited as fluorapatite. In 1948, Martin published findings on the fluoride content of the femur, the pooled mandible and maxilla and the tooth buds from eight foetuses obtained from an area in Chicago which had a water supply low in fluoride at that time.

The results (Table 13) did not reveal any clear relationship between the amount of fluoride and the weight of the foetus. This finding agrees with more recent fluoride analyses of femurs, mandibles and teeth in 6-9 months old human foetuses from low-fluoride areas (Gedalia et al., 1964a)

TABLE 13

FLUORIDE CONTENT OF DRY FOETAL BONES AND
TEETH FROM A LOW-FLUORIDE AREA (CHICAGO, 1946-47) [a]

Foetus No.	Tissue analysed	Weight (g)	Fluoride (ppm)
1	Femur	4 790	29.0
	Mandible and maxilla		27.0
	Tooth buds		17.0
2	Femur	1 950	20.0
	Mandible and maxilla		19.0
	Tooth buds		13.0
3	Femur	1 125	16.0
	Mandible and maxilla		15.0
	Tooth buds		8.7
4	Femur	1 435	27.0
	Mandible and maxilla		24.0
	Tooth buds		13.4
5	Femur	1 300	24.0
	Mandible and maxilla		24.0
	Tooth buds		15.0
6	Femur	3 180	23.5
	Mandible and maxilla		20.0
	Tooth buds		15.0
7	Femur	4 660	14.0
	Mandible and maxilla		15.0
	Tooth buds		9.0
8	Femur	1 000	10.6
	Mandible and maxilla		9.3
	Tooth buds		8.0

[a] After Martin (1948).

which do not indicate an appreciable increase in fluoride content of the
calcified tissues with age of the foetus (Table 14).

TABLE 14

FLUORIDE CONTENT OF ASHED FOETAL BONES AND TEETH
FROM A LOW-FLUORIDE AREA
(ABOUT 0.1 ppm F, TEL-AVIV, 1961-63) [a]

Foetal age (months)	Number of cases	Mean fluoride value (ppm)		
		Femur	Mandible	Teeth
6	21	39.7	42.3	30.9
7	24	40.7	39.0	34.0
8	13	42.3	38.5	31.7
9	27	43.8	46.9	40.8

[a] After Gedalia et al. (1964a).

In medium (Table 15) and elevated (Tables 16 and 17) fluoridated-
drinking-water areas (Gedalia et al., 1964a; Blayney & Hill, 1964; Gedalia,
Zukerman & Leventhal, 1965), the fluoride content of bones and teeth
generally increased with advancing age of the foetus as a result of the

prolonged effects of the fluoride exchange and incorporation processes (Hodge, 1952).

The difference in the fluoride content of the foetal skeletal tissues from low (Tables 13 and 14), medium (Table 15) and elevated (Tables 16 and 17) fluoride areas is probably due to the different fluoride concentrations in the foetal blood from which the newly formed mineral crystals

TABLE 15

FLUORIDE CONTENT OF ASHED FOETAL BONES AND TEETH FROM
A MEDIUM-FLUORIDE AREA (ABOUT 0.55 ppm F, JERUSALEM, 1961-63) [a]

Foetal age (months)	Number of cases	Mean fluoride value (ppm)		
		Femur	Mandible	Teeth
6	31	59.0	47.0	32.6
7	20	71.6	53.5	43.0
8	7	79.4	66.0	57.9
9	34	92.5	78.8	69.7

[a] After Gedalia et al. (1964a).

TABLE 16

FLUORIDE CONTENT OF ASHED FOETAL BONES AND TEETH FROM
AN ELEVATED-FLUORIDE AREA
(ABOUT 1 ppm F, NEGEV, SOUTHERN ISRAEL, 1961-64) [a]

Foetal age (months)	Number of cases	Mean fluoride value (ppm)		
		Femur	Mandible	Teeth
6	20	55.2	57.2	44.0
7	6	63.0	65.7	47.0
8	13	79.9	70.3	52.0
9	25	85.2	85.0	53.8

[a] After Gedalia, Zukerman & Leventhal (1965).

TABLE 17

FLUORIDE CONTENT OF ASHED FOETAL BONES AND TEETH FROM
A FLUORIDATED-DRINKING-WATER AREA
(ABOUT 1 ppm F, EVANSTON, ILLINOIS, 1953) [a]

Foetus No.	Period of gestation (weeks)	Weight of baby (g)	Results of analysis (ppm)			
			Femur	Mandible	Maxilla	Tooth buds
1	28	880	78.9	155.6	125.5	
2	35	2 126	95.1	92.7	82.0	45.8
3	21	950	89.2	78.4	82.5	
4	36	2 416	121.6	120.1	111.8	89.2

[a] After Blayney & Hill (1964).

incorporate fluoride (Gedalia et al., 1964a; Gedalia, Zukerman & Leventhal, 1965). The similar foetal blood fluoride levels (Table 12) observed at low, medium and elevated fluoride intake (Gedalia et al., 1964b) may be the result of a rapid clearance of fluoride from foetal blood during the mineralization period of the foetal skeleton (Bawden, Wolkoff & Flowers, 1964). In adults living in places with different fluoride concentrations in the drinking-water supply (0.1-2.5 ppm), the plasma fluoride concentrations, too, were reported to show but small variations (Armstrong & Singer, 1959). The fluoride contents of the bones and teeth of foetuses from medium (Table 15) and elevated, either naturally (Table 16) or artificially (Table 17), fluoride areas of corresponding diets were not very different, thus confirming the limited permeability of the placenta in humans and rodents at increased fluoride intake (Gedalia et al., 1964b; Ericsson & Hammarström, 1964). Additional evidence of limited permeability is the inability to find mottled enamel, even in areas of severe endemic dental fluorosis, in any of the deciduous incisors (McClure, 1962) which are known to be almost completely calcified prenatally (Schour & Massler, 1940).

As to the fluoride content of the different foetal hard tissues, that of the femur is generally higher than that of the mandible or teeth at corresponding ages. Differences in the distribution of fluoride in various skeletal compounds in experimental animals have been attributed to their vascularity and rate of growth (Volker, Sognnaes & Bibby, 1941) which may perhaps account for the pattern of fluoride deposition in human foetal bones and teeth.

5. SUMMARY (W. D. Armstrong)

Application of adequate analytical procedures always reveals fluoride to be present in mammalian body-fluids and tissues, and further, that particularly large amounts occur in calcified tissues. Blood plasma is the most convenient and reliable indicator of the concentration of fluoride in body-fluids. Results have been presented which show that the mean plasma fluoride of normal humans is in the range 0.14-0.19 ppm and that the mean equilibrium plasma fluoride content is not elevated above this range in persons using water containing up to 2.5 ppm fluoride. Undoubtedly the plasma fluoride content of individuals rises slightly for brief periods of time following ingestion of fluoride in food and water, as has been demonstrated in animals and humans in studies with radiofluoride, but the degree of plasma fluoride elevation under these conditions, as deduced from the same studies, is so small as to be difficult to define by chemical analytical procedures. Even in patients who have been treated daily with amounts of fluoride which are fiftyfold larger than those which could be obtained from properly fluoridated water, the elevation of plasma fluoride content is limited in degree.

The fluoride content of soft tissues, with the exception of tendon, appears to be of the same order of magnitude as that of plasma, and there is evidence, derived from chemical analyses and distribution of radiofluoride in tissues, that intracellular fluids have a lower ionic fluoride content than extracellular fluid. As is the case with plasma, the soft tissues are markedly unresponsive in reflecting an increase of fluoride intake by an elevation of fluoride content. Fluoride intakes which produce acute intoxication will, however, result in clearly demonstrable elevations in the fluoride content of most soft tissues.

The fluoride contents of calcified tissues usually stand in the following descending order: cementum, bone, dentine and enamel. Calcified tissues, whether normal or ectopic, have a propensity for fixing fluoride, and a linear relationship between the fluoride content of the skeleton of humans and that of the drinking water has been demonstrated. This relationship exists because water is the most variable agent of fluoride intake and is frequently the most important quantitative source of fluoride in the dietary.

Fluoride is incorporated into lattice of the mineral of bones and teeth, and possibly also at crystal surface locations. Incorporation of fluoride occurs at the time of deposition of the mineral and by hetero-ionic exchange after the crystal has formed. The degree to which the latter process occurs varies with the anatomical structure and physiological state of the calcified tissue. There is a good positive correlation between the rate of turnover of a calcified tissue and the fluoride content of that tissue. The circumstances of variations of degree of acquisition of fluoride by hetero-ionic exchange, and the influence of remodelling of a calcified tissue on its behaviour towards fluoride, account for the variations in fluoride content at different sites in the same bone or tooth. Thus, subperiosteal and cancellous bone have higher fluoride contents than the compact part of the diaphysis. In enamel, the fluoride concentration decreases in an exponential fashion from the outer surface towards the amelo-dentinal junction; and, in dentine, the highest fluoride content is found in the pulpal surface, the amounts decreasing as the enamel is approached. The higher amounts of fluoride in the nearer-the-surface layers of enamel and dentine are due to the continued acquisition of fluoride by the mineral of these layers, probably by hetero-ionic exchange, after the near maturation of each apposititional layer. The outer 100-200 μ of enamel continues to acquire fluoride from the oral fluids after eruption of the tooth and certainly, in this case, hetero-ionic exchange is the predominant process by which the fluoride is deposited in the superficial enamel layer.

While there is clear evidence that the fluoride content of the bones of humans tends to increase with age and with fluoride intake, it is not yet certain whether the bones reach, or approach, an upper limit in their fluoride concentration except, possibly, under most unusual circumstances of fluoride intake which produce frank osteofluorosis. A considerable fraction of the fluoride in bones with markedly elevated fluoride contents is retained for a very long time after withdrawal of a high-fluoride-containing dietary. However, the apparent prolonged retention of fluoride in the skeleton could be due to resorption and redeposition in the same bony structure.

The placenta allows fluoride to reach the foetal circulation to some extent, and the same factors involved in fluoride deposition in bones during extra-uterine life operate in the foetal bones.

REFERENCES

Armstrong, W. D. & Singer, L. (1959) *J. dent. Res.*, **38**, 673

Armstrong, W. D. & Singer, L. (1963) *J. dent. Res.*, **42**, 133-136

Armstrong, W. D. & Singer, L. (1965) In: *International Association for Dental Research, 43rd General Meeting, Toronto, Canada, July 1965 ; Abstracts*, Chicago, American Dental Association, p. 46, Abstr. No. 38

Armstrong, W. D., Singer, L. & Carlson, C. (1958) *J. dent. Res.*, **37**, 69

Armstrong, W. D., Singer, L., Ensinck, J. & Rich, C. (1964) *J. clin. Invest.*, **43**, 555

Bauer, G. C. H., Carlsson, A. & Lindquist, B. (1955) *Kungl. fysiogr. Sällsk. Lund Förh.*, **25**, 1

Bauer, W. H. (1945) *Amer. J. Orthodont.*, **31**, 700

Bäumler, J. & Glinz, E. (1964) *Mitt. Lebensmitt. Hyg.*, **55**, 250

Bawden, J. W., Wolkoff, A. S. & Flowers, C. E., Jr (1964) *J. dent. Res.*, **43**, 678-683

Bélanger, L. F., Visek, W. J., Lotz, W. E. & Comar, C. L. (1958) *Amer. J. Path.*, **34**, 25

Blayney, J. R., Bowers, R. C. & Zimmerman, M. (1962) *J. dent. Res.*, **41**, 133

Blayney, J. R. & Hill, I. N. (1964) *J. Amer. dent. Ass.*, **69**, 291-294

Brandl, J. & Tappeiner, H. (1891) *Z. Biol.*, **28**, 518

Brudevold, F. (1962) *Chemical composition of the teeth in relation to caries.* In: Sognnaes, R. F., ed., *Chemistry and prevention of dental caries*, Springfield, Ill., Thomas, pp. 32-88

Brudevold, F., Gardner, D. E. & Smith, F. A. (1956) *J. dent. Res.*, **35**, 420-429

Brudevold, F., Hein, J. W., Bonner, J. F., Nevin, R. B., Bibby, B. J. & Hodge, H. C. (1957) *J. dent. Res.*, **36**, 771

Brudevold, F., Steadman, L. T. & Smith, F. A. (1960) *Ann. N.Y. Acad. Sci.*, **85**, 110

Brzezinski, A., Bercovici, B. & Gedalia, I. (1960) *Obstet. and Gynec.*, **15**, 329-331

Brzezinski, A., Gedalia, I., Danon, A. & Sulman, F. G. (1961) *Proc. Soc. exp. Biol. (N.Y.)*, **108**, 342-345

Büttner, W. (1966) In: *Advances in fluorine research and dental caries prevention*, Oxford, Pergamon, vol. 4, p. 193 (Proceedings of 12th ORCA Congress, Utrecht, Netherlands, June 1965)

Büttner, W. & Muhler, J. C. (1958) *J. dent. Res.*, **37**, 326-329

Call, R. A., Greenwood, D. A., Le Cheminant, W. H., Shupe, J. L., Nielsen, H. M., Olson, L. E., Lamborn, R. E., Mangelson, F. L. & Davis, R. V. (1965) *Publ. Hlth Rep. (Wash.)*, **80**, 529-538

Carlson, C. H., Armstrong, W. D. & Singer, L. (1960a) *Amer. J. Physiol.*, **199**, 187

Carlson, C. H., Armstrong, W. D. & Singer, L. (1960b) *Proc. Soc. exp. Biol. (N.Y.)* **104**, 235-239

Carlson, C. H., Singer, L. & Armstrong, W. D. (1960) *Proc. Soc. exp. Biol. (N.Y.),* **103**, 418-420

Ericsson, Y. (1958) *Acta odont. scand.,* **16**, 51-77

Ericsson, Y, (1969) *Caries Res.,* **3**, 159

Ericsson, Y. & Hammarström, L. (1964) *Acta odont. scand.,* **22**, 523-538

Ericsson, Y. & Hammarström, L. (1965) *Acta physiol. scand.,* **65**, 126

Ericsson, Y. & Malmnäs, C. (1962) *Acta obstet. gynec. scand.,* **41**, 144-158

Ericsson, Y. & Ullberg, S. (1958) *Acta odont. scand.,* **16**, 363-374

Ericsson, Y., Ullberg, S. & Appelgren, L. E. (1960) *Acta odont. scand.,* **18**, 253-261

Feltman, R. & Kosel, J. (1955) *Science,* **122**, 560-561

Gardner, D. E., Smith, F. A., Hodge, H. C., Brudevold, F. & Eldridge, D. M. (1959) *J. appl. Physiol.,* **14**, 427

Gardner, D. E., Smith F. A., Hodge, H. C., Overton, D. E. & Feltman, R. (1952) *Science,* **115**, 208-209

Gautier, A. & Clausmann, P. (1913) *Bull. Soc. Chim. biol. (Paris),* s. 4, **13**, 909

Gedalia, I., Brzezinski, A. Bercovici, B. & Lazarov, E. (1961) *Proc. Soc. exp. Biol. (N.Y.),* **106**, 147-149

Gedalia, I., Brzezinski, A., Portuguese, N. & Bercovici, B. (1964a) *Arch. oral Biol.,* **9**, 331-340

Gedalia, I., Brzezinski, A., Zukerman, H. & Mayersdorf, A. (1964b) *J. dent. Res.,* **43**, 669-671

Gedalia, I., Zukerman, H. & Leventhal, H. (1965) *J. Amer. dent. Ass.,* **71**, 1121-1123

Gettler, A. O. & Ellerbrook, L. (1939) *Amer. J. med. Sci.,* **197**, 625

Glock, G. E., Lowater, F. & Murray, M. M. (1941) *Biochem. J.,* **35**, 1235

Hadjimarkos, D. M. (1962a) *Arch. oral Biol.* **7**, 651

Hadjimarkos, D. M. (1962b) *Nature (Lond.),* **195**, 392

Hallsworth, A. S. & Weatherell, J. A. (1969) *Caries Res.,* **3**, 109-118

Hargreaves, J. A. & Weatherell, J. A. (1965) In: *Advances in fluorine research and dental caries prevention,* Oxford, Pergamon, vol. 3, p. 247 (Proceedings of 11th ORCA Congress, Sandefjord, Norway, July 1964)

Hein, J. W., Bonner, J. F., Brudevold, F., Smith, F. A. & Hodge, H. C. (1956) *Nature (Lond.),* **178**, 1295

Held, H. R. (1954) *Schweiz. med. Wschr.,* **84**, 251-254

Herman, J. R., Mason, B. & Light, I. (1958) *J. Urol. (Baltimore),* **80**, 263

Hodge, H. C. (1952) In: *Transactions of the Fourth Conference on Metabolic Interrelations,* New York, Josiah Macy Jr. Foundation, p. 250

Jackson, D. & Weidmann, S. M. (1958) *J. Path. Bact.,* **76**, 461

Jackson, D. & Weidmann, S. M. (1959) *Brit. dent. J.,* **107**, 303

Jenkins, G. N. (1955) *Brit. dent. J.,* **99**, 249

Jenkins, G. N. (1962) *Int. dent. J.,* **12**, 208

Jenkins, G. N. & Speirs, R. L. (1953) *J. Physiol., (Lond.),* **121**, 21P

Jenkins, G. N. & Speirs, R. L. (1954) *J. dent. Res.,* **33**, 734

Kick, C. H., Bathke, R. M., Edgington, B. H., Wilder, O. H. M., Record, P. R., Wilder, W., Hill, T. J. & Chase, S. W. (1935) *Bull. Ohio agric. Exp. Sta.,* No. 558

Knouff, R. A., Edwards, L. F., Preston, D. W. & Kitchin, P. C. (1936) *J. dent. Res.*, **15**, 291-294

Kuyper, A. C. & Kutnerian, K. (1962) *J. dent. Res.*, **41**, 345

Largent, E. J. (1961) *Fluorosis. The health aspects of fluorine compounds*, Columbus, Ohio State University Press, p. 22

Lehman, D. & Muhler, J. C. (1954) *J. dent. Res.*, **33**, 669

Likins, R. C., Scow, R. O., Zipkin, I. & Steere, A. C. (1959) *Amer. J. Physiol.*, **197**, 75

McCann, H. G. & Bullock, F. A. (1957) *J. dent. Res.*, **36**, 391

McClure, F. J. (1962) *Fluoridation of drinking water and control of dental caries*, Bethesda, Md., National Institute of Dental Research, p. 197

McClure, F. J. & Kinser, C. A. (1944) *Publ. Hlth Rep. (Wash.)*, **59**, 1575-1591

McClure, F. J. & Likins, R. C. (1951) *J. dent. Res.*, **30**, 172

Maplesden, D. C., Motzok, I., Oliver, W. T. & Branion, H. D. (1960) *J. Nutr.*, **71**, 70-76

Martin, D. J. (1948) *J. dent. Res.*, **27**, 27-33

Neuman, W. F. & Neuman, M. W. (1958) *The chemical dynamics of bone mineral*, Chicago, University of Chicago Press

Neuman, W. F., Neuman, M. W., Main, E. R., O'Leary, J. & Smith, F. A. (1950) *J. biol. Chem.*, **187**, 655-661

Nickles, J. (1856) *C. R. Acad. Sci. (Paris)*, **43**, 885

Pandit, C. G., Raghavachari, T. N. S., Rao, D. S. & Krishnamurti, V. (1940) *Indian J. med. Res.*, **28**, 533-558

Perkinson, J. D., Jr, Whitney, I. B., Monroe, R. A., Lotz, W. E. & Comar, C. L. (1955) *Amer. J. Physiol.*, **182**, 383-389

Rich, C., Ensinck, J. & Ivanovich, P. (1964) *J. clin. Invest.*, **43**, 545-556

Savchuck, W. B. & Armstrong, W. D. (1951) *J. Biol. Chem.*, **193**, 575

Scheinin, A. (1954) *Suom. Hammaslääk Seur. Toim.*, **50**, Suppl. 2, pp. 53-64

Schour, I. & Massler, M. (1940) *J. Amer. dent. Ass.*, **27**, 1918-1931

Schour, I. & Smith, M. C. (1934) *Bull. Ariz. agric. Exp. Sta.*, No. 52, p. 69-91

Shupe, J. L., Miner, M. L., Greenwood, D. A., Harris, L. E. & Stoddard, G. E. (1963) *Amer. J. vet. Res.*, **24**, 964-979

Singer, L. & Armstrong, W. D. (1959) *Analyt. Chem.*, **31**, 105

Singer, L. & Armstrong, W. D. (1960) *J. appl. Physiol.*, **15**, 508-510

Singer, L. & Armstrong, W. D. (1962) *J. dent. Res.*, **41**, 154

Singer, L. & Armstrong, W. D. (1964) *Proc. Soc. exp. Biol. (N.Y.)*, **117**, 686

Singer, L. & Armstrong, W. D. (1965) *Analyt. Biochem.* **10**, 495

Singer, L. & Armstrong, W. D. (1969) *Arch. oral Biol.*, **14** (in press)

Singer, L., Armstrong, W. D. & Vogel, J. J. (1965) In: *International Association for Dental Research, 43rd Annual Meeting, Toronto, Canada, July 1965 ; Abstracts*, Chicago, American Dental Association, p. 46, Abstr. No. 38

Singh, A. & Jolly, S. S. (1961) *Quart. J. Med.*, **30**, 357-372

Singh, A., Jolly, S. S. & Bansal, B. C. (1961) *Lancet*, **1**, 197-199

Singh, A., Jolly, S. S., Devi, P., Bansal, B. C. & Singh, S. S. (1962) *Indian J. med. Res.*, **50**, 387-398

Smith, F. A., Gardner, D. E. & Hodge, H. C. (1950) *J. dent. Res.*, **29**, 596-600

Smith, F. A., Gardner, D. E. & Hodge, H. C. (1953) *Fed. Proc.*, **12**, 368

Smith, F. A., Gardner, D. E., Leone, N. C. & Hodge, H. C. (1960) *A.M.A. Arch. industr. Hlth,* **21**, 330-332

Srikantia, S. G. & Siddiqui, A. H. (1965) *Clin. Sci.,* **28**, 477

Stookey, G. K., Crane, D. B. & Muhler, J. C. (1964) *Proc. Soc. exp. Biol. (N.Y.),* **115**, 295-298

Suttie, J. W. & Phillips, P. H. (1959) *Arch. Biochem.,* **83**, 355

Tammann, G. (1888) *Hoppe-Seylers Z. physiol. Chem.,* **12**, 322

Taves, D. R. (1966) *Nature (Lond.),* **211**, 192

Taves, D. R. (1968) *Nature (Lond.),* **217**, 1050

Villee, C. A. (1960) *Placenta and fetal membranes,* Baltimore, Williams and Wilkins, p. 29

Volker, J. F., Sognnaes, R. F. & Bibby, B. G. (1941) *Amer. J. Physiol.,* **132**, 707-712

Wallace-Durbin, P. (1954) *J. dent. Res.,* **33**, 789-800

Weatherell, J. A. (1966) *Handb. exp. Pharmak.,* **20**, 141

Weatherell, J. A. & Hargreaves, J. A. (1965) *Arch. oral Biol.,* **10**, 139

Weatherell, J. A. & Hargreaves, J. A. (1966) In: *Advances in fluorine research and dental caries prevention,* Oxford, Pergamon, vol. 4, p. 181 (Proceedings of 12th ORCA Congress, Utrecht, Netherlands, June 1965)

Weaver, R. (1944) *Brit. dent. J.,* **77**, 185

Weddle, D. A. & Muhler, J. C. (1957) *J. dent. Res.,* **36**, 386

Weidmann, S. M. (1962) *Arch. oral Biol.,* **7**, 63

Weidmann, S. M. & Weatherell, J. A. (1959) *J. Path. Bact.,* **78**, 243

Weidmann, S. M., Weatherell, J. A. & Whitehead, R. G. (1959) *J. Path. Bact.,* **78**, 435

Wills, J. H. (1940) *J. dent. Res.,* **19**, 585

Yoon, S. H., Brudevold, F., Gardner, D. E. & Smith, F. A. (1960) *J. dent. Res.,* **39**, 845

Ziegler, E. (1956) *Mitt. naturw. Ges. Winterthur,* **28**, 1-63

Zipkin, I. & Babeaux, W. L. (1965) *J. oral Ther. Pharmacol.,* **1**, 652-665

Zipkin, I. & McClure, F. J. (1952) *J. Nutr.,* **47**, 611

Zipkin, I., McClure, F. J. & Lee, W. A. (1960) *Arch. oral Biol.,* **2**, 190-195

Zipkin, I., McClure, F. J., Leone, N. C. & Lee, W. A. (1958) *Publ. Hlth Rep. (Wash.),* **73**, 732-740

Zipkin, I., Schraer, R., Schraer, H. & Lee, W. A. (1963) *Arch. oral Biol.,* **8**, 119

CHAPTER 5

Excretion of fluorides *

H. C. HODGE [1], F. A. SMITH [2] & I. GEDALIA [3]

1. INTRODUCTION

Fluoride, a prototype bone-seeker, in its skeletal deposition also serves as an excellent example of a cumulative element.   Because excessive, prolonged fluoride exposure leads not only to high skeletal concentrations but also to characteristic ill-effects, e.g., crippling fluorosis, more than ordinary significance is attached to evidence concerning F elimination.

Fluoride is excreted in the urine, deposited in the skin which is shed, lost through the sweat, and excreted in the faeces.   Fluoride occurs in traces in milk, in saliva, in hair and, presumably, in tears.   Fluoride is probably not exhaled in the breath, although definitive data are lacking.

The principal route of fluoride excretion is *via* the urine.   With astonishing rapidity, quantities of F appear, generally reflecting the daily intake but governed by other factors, several of which are known, such as (*a*) the total intake, (*b*) the form in which the fluoride is taken into the body, (*c*) whether the individual is relatively unexposed or regularly exposed to fluoride, and (*d*) the health status of the individual, especially with regard to advanced kidney disease.   These factors, as well as the urinary excretion of fluoride in pregnancy and during the process of mobilization of fluoride from skeletal stores, are discussed in some detail in this chapter.

Efforts have been made to include all human data by direct citation or by reference.   Animal data are included to substantiate human experience or to furnish evidence in the absence of human data.

* Part of the work reported here was supported by the US Atomic Energy Commission at the University of Rochester Atomic Energy Project (Report No. UR-49-1163), and part by the US Public Health Service (Grant GM-15 190).

[1] Professor of Pharmacology and Toxicology, School of Medicine and Dentistry, University of Rochester, N.Y., USA.

[2] Department of Pharmacology and Toxicology, University of Rochester, N.Y., USA.

[3] Laboratory of Oral Chemistry and Fluoride Research, Hadassah School of Dental Medicine, Hebrew University, Jerusalem, Israel.

2. EXCRETION ROUTES OTHER THAN URINARY

Faecal Excretion

About 10% of the total daily fluoride excretion can usually be accounted for in the faeces.

An individual ingesting an average diet in the USA and not drinking fluoridated water usually excretes less than 0.2 mg in the faeces (range 0.01-0.5 mg) per day. When diets contain relatively insoluble fluoride compounds, e.g., bone meal, cryolite, insoluble calcium salts, or fluoride precipitants such as aluminium or calcium compounds, larger amounts of fluoride pass through the gastrointestinal tract and are excreted in the faeces. Under such circumstances the percentage excreted of the total fluoride ingested may be considerably larger, as much as 30% or more (Largent, 1961; Rich, Ensinck & Ivanovich, 1964). Animal studies confirm this principle (Lawrenz & Mitchell, 1941; Lawrenz, Mitchell & Ruth, 1939; Messner, Weinreb & Gedalia, 1965).

Part of the fluoride in the faeces is almost certainly undissolved, un-absorbed fluoride. With insoluble fluorides, the smallness of the ingested particles enhances absorption; for instance, fluoride in rock-phosphate powder, which is known to have a low solubility, ingested in a finely dispersed form as may happen in fertilizer plants, was recovered in the faeces only to the extent of 13-19% of the total intake. Part of the faecal fluoride probably represents fluoride that has been absorbed and re-excreted *via* the gastric and intestinal juices. Soluble fluorides given intravenously appear in the intestinal contents, as has been shown by the animal studies of Wallace-Durbin (1954) using radiofluoride and also by the faecal analyses carried out after oral administration of soluble fluorides by Wagner & Muhler (1957). Re-excretion into the gut presumably accounts for the extra faecal fluoride observed after inhalation of HF (Largent, 1959). In subjects who inhaled 1 to nearly 5 ppm HF in air, the faecal fluoride level was increased 3- to nearly 10-fold. Urinary fluoride analyses for these same individuals showed that 4 to over 9 mg were excreted per day during the period of HF exposure. It therefore seems reasonable to assume that the total fluoride taken into the body by these subjects ranged perhaps from 8 to 18 mg per day, of which 0.2 to 0.7 mg per day appeared in the faeces (see p. 148).

Several investigators have reported on fluoride concentrations in human faecal samples taken under a variety of conditions of fluoride intake. For example, when the F intake was 0.4-0.5 mg, faecal excretion ranged from 0.03 to 0.12 mg F daily; when the intake was 4-19 mg (as NaF or CaF_2 solution), faecal excretion increased to 0.19-0.33 mg (Largent, 1961; Machle, Scott & Largent, 1942; McClure et al., 1945). Ham & Smith (1954b) reported human faecal values ranging from 0.09 to 0.15 mg per day on a normal diet. Selected data from Largent's study show that faecal excretion

TABLE 1

FLUORIDE BALANCE IN HUMANS [a]

F in water supply (ppm)	Age (years)	Length of residence (years)	Time of observation (days)	F ingested daily (mg)			F excreted daily (mg)			Balance (mg/day)
				Fluid	Food	Total	Faeces	Urine	Total	
2	35	10	96	2.4	1.2	3.6	0.4	2.9	3.3	+0.3
5.5	55	29	60	3.8	1.3	5.1	0.6	4.5	5.1	0
6.1	57	34	133	6.7	1.0	7.7	0.4	8.1	8.5	− 0.8
8	57	19	140	11.3	2.5	13.8	1.4	10.4	11.8	+2.0
20	30	8	45	20.8	1.5	22.3	1.4	12.3	13.7	+8.6

[a] Selected data from Largent (1961).

was 0.6 mg per day or less when the water contained up to 6 ppm, but was greater when the water contained 8 or 20 ppm (Table 1).

Excretion in Sweat

Some fluoride is lost from the body in sweat; during excessive perspiring appreciable amounts may be excreted in this way.

Individuals living in a comfortable environment probably lose a little fluoride from the body daily in the sweat; the amount is unknown. When subjects were maintained at an ambient temperature of 84-85°F (about 29.5°C) and a relative humidity of about 50%, about 25% of the fluoride excreted per day appeared in the sweat, although in the investigation in question sweat was collected during only 8 hours out of the 24 (McClure et al., 1945).

Under hot, moist conditions McClure et al. (*op. cit.*) found up to 46% of the ingested fluoride in the sweat. Perspiration samples collected during one or two hours from the same subject ingesting 0.4-0.5 mg F daily contained 0.02-0.06 mg of F. Largent (1961) found that excretion rates of fluoride in the sweat sometimes nearly equalled those in the urine. Crosby & Shepherd (1957) found that under conditions of profuse sweating "up to 50% of the total fluoride excreted appeared in the sweat". Individual variability may be considerable. In Largent's two subjects one "appeared to excrete only extremely small amounts of fluoride through the skin" (Largent, 1961); during fluoride-ingestion periods sweat contained 0.3-1.8 ppm F, and the subjects responded differently to an increase in the fluoride intake level (see also McClure et al., 1945). Crosby & Shepherd (1957) observed that within one hour after ingestion of a fluoride dose, higher levels occurred in sweat, probably because of the temporarily increased fluoride level of the blood. The concentrations in sweat may be higher than those in plasma, although no investigation has deliberately compared plasma and sweat concentrations in a single experiment. In two individuals ingesting normal amounts of fluoride, the sweat concentrations ranged from 0.3 to 0.7 ppm in one and from 0.5 to 0.9 ppm in the other (Crosby & Shepherd, *op. cit.*), values higher than the normal plasma levels of 0.1-0.2 ppm (Singer & Armstrong, 1960).

Although there is some evidence that the concentration in sweat is higher when additional fluoride is ingested, the significance of sweat as a route of excretion has not been established. To a limited extent sweating can be considered to provide an autoregulation of the fluoride balance when fluctuating climatic conditions considerably vary the intake of fluoride from drinking water.

Excretion in Milk

Fluoride is a natural constituent of human milk. Negligibly small fractions of the daily fluoride intake are excreted in milk.

FIG. 1

CONCENTRATION OF ^{18}F IN THE BLOOD AND MILK OF A COW AFTER INGESTION OF RADIOACTIVE SODIUM FLUORIDE [a]

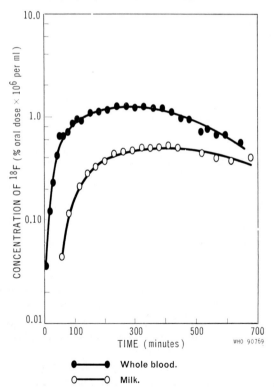

[a] After Perkinson et al. (1955).

The concentrations in human milk range from less than 0.1 to about 0.2 ppm. This range is so nearly that of blood plasma that it is tempting to describe the concentration of fluoride in milk as being similar to that in blood. Perkinson et al. (1955) showed that radiofluoride given orally to a dairy cow was excreted thereafter in the milk in concentrations similar to but lower than those in the blood (Fig 1). No such data are available on humans. Elevated fluoride concentrations in the drinking water or supplemental fluoride intake may increase somewhat the fluoride content of milk in lactating women (Held, 1955). Held reported that the F content of human milk was increased by about 15-40% by daily supplements of 5 mg F. Just as human or animal plasma fluoride levels show little increase when drinking water concentrations are elevated, so fluoride concentrations in cow's milk increased only slightly when fluoride concentrations in the feed were raised. Suttie, Miller & Phillips (1957) showed that cattle receiving feed normally containing 3-5 ppm F excreted milk containing 0.1 ppm F, and as the level in the feed increased to 50 ppm F the milk concentration increased to about 0.4 ppm F, thus being still within safe limits for human consumption.

Trace quantities of fluoride in milk are bound to fat and to the albumin-globulin fraction, whereas casein contains about one-fourth of the total fluoride in the whole milk (Ericsson, 1958a). Fluoride in milk is not completely diffusible.

Fluoride administered in milk to rats or humans was absorbed slightly more slowly than when given in water, but ultimately as completely. These facts should not prevent milk from being used as a fluoride vehicle when drinking water cannot be fluoridated; however, long-term clinical experiments should be continued. It is a matter of conjecture whether the small amounts of fluoride in the mother's milk are of importance to tooth and bone development of the newborn. Analyses of human milk have been reported by Bercovici, Gedalia & Brzezinski (1960) and by Büttner (1962). Fluoride concentrations in normal cow's milk and in the milk of several species of animals absorbing unusual amounts of fluoride have been summarized by Hodge & Smith (1965, pp. 149, 150).

Excretion in Saliva

Only a negligible fraction of the total fluoride intake can be accounted for in the saliva.

Less than 1% of the activity of ingested radiofluoride was recovered from human saliva samples (Carlson, Armstrong & Singer, 1960). The normal concentrations (McClure, 1941) are presumably very similar to those in blood. Only fragmentary information is available on salivary flow rates and fluoride contents in man. A subject who took 8 mg of fluoride showed detectable fluoride in the saliva only after 2 hours (Büttner & Muhler, 1962). In normal young adults whose drinking water contained

1 ppm F, no correlation was found between the paraffin-stimulated flow rates of parotid saliva and the F contents (Busch & Shklair, 1965). Radio-fluoride given intravenously to a cat appeared in the submaxillary saliva within a minute (Wills, 1940).

Fluoride excretion in stimulated saliva did not differ appreciably from that in unstimulated in spite of much higher flow rates (Hattyasy, 1957). Salivary F concentrations range between 0.04 and 0.5 ppm (mean values of 0.1-0.2 ppm) (Dvir, Gedalia & Sulitzeanu, 1962; Gedalia, Yardeni & Gershon, 1963; Martin & Hill, 1950; McClure, 1941) irrespective of drink-ing-water concentrations up to 1.8 ppm F (McClure, 1941). Dvir and asso-ciates (*op. cit.*) and Martin & Hill (1950) examined the fluoride content of pooled and individual saliva samples from children drinking artificially and naturally fluoridated water. Human saliva from the parotid duct contained slightly lower ^{18}F concentrations than plasma at various times after inges-tion of ^{18}F (Carlson, Armstrong & Singer, 1960). The secretion rate and buffer capacity of human saliva increased very slightly after ingestion of 5-10 mg F (Ericsson, 1959).

The distribution and reactions of the fluoride ion in enamel-saliva environment have been followed in radioactive studies with ^{18}F (Ericsson, 1958b). Fluoride is practically completely diffusible in saliva; no appreciable binding to organic components or precipitation occurs.

The trace amounts of fluoride in saliva seem to play a minor role in the accumulation of surface-enamel fluoride; however, the long-term bathing effects on the surface enamel by the continuous saliva flow should not be dismissed (Brudevold, Gardner & Smith, 1956).

It has been postulated that fluoride from the saliva may be incorporated into dental calculus during precipitation of the latter (Gedalia, Yardeni & Gershon, 1963). The mean fluoride contents of saliva samples from calculus-bearing and calculus-free groups were similar, 0.18 and 0.16 ppm, respec-tively. No tendency to dental calculus deposition could be detected in persons with an increased fluoride content in the saliva.

Analyses of human saliva have been tabulated by Hodge & Smith (1965, p. 146).

3. URINARY EXCRETION

Relation to Circumstances of Fluoride Intake

The urinary fluoride level is widely regarded as one of the best indices of fluoride intake. In discussing the significance of urinary fluoride concen-trations, however, at least two groups of individuals, with differing circum-stances of intake, should be recognized.

1. Individuals whose normal intake is fairly constant. In such individuals, urinary fluoride concentrations may fluctuate because variable amounts are consumed in the usual mixed diet or because different amounts of water are

Largent, E. J. (1961) *Fluorosis. The health aspects of fluorine compounds*, Columbus, Ohio State University Press

Lawrenz, M. & Mitchell, H. H. (1941) *J. Nutr.*, **22**, 91-101

Lawrenz, M., Mitchell, H. H. & Ruth, W. A. (1939) *J. Nutr.*, **18**, 127-141

Lerman, D., Gedalia, I., Rosenzweig, K. A. & Brzezinski, A. (1962) In: *Proceedings of the 6th Congress of the European Organization for Research on Fluorine and Dental Caries Prevention, Padua, 1959*, Edition de la Clinique dentaire de l'Université de Pavia, pp. 237-241

Likins, R. C., McClure, F. J. & Steere, A. C. (1956) *Publ. Hlth Rep. (Wash.)*, **71**, 217-220

Linsman, J. F. & McMurray, C. A. (1943) *Radiology*, **40**, 474-483

Longwell, J. (1957) *Roy. Soc. Hlth J.*, **77**, 120-129

McClure, F. J. (1941) *Amer. J. Dis. Child.*, **62**, 512-515

McClure, F. J. & Kinser, C. A. (1944) *Publ. Hlth Rep. (Wash.)*, **59**, 1575-1591

McClure, F. J., Mitchell, H. H., Hamilton, T. S. & Kinser, C. A. (1945) *J. industr. Hyg.*, **27**, 159-170

Machle, W. & Largent, E. J. (1943) *J. industr. Hyg.*, **25**, 112-123

Machle, W., Scott, E. W. & Largent, E. J. (1942) *J. industr. Hyg.* **24**, 199-204

Maes, J., Dufaux, J. & Vandenbroucke, J. (1960) *Acta clin. belg.*, **15**, 65-80

Martin, D. J. & Hill, I. N. (1950) *J. dent. Res.*, **29**, 291-297

Messner, Z., Weinreb, M. M. & Gedalia, I. (1965) *Alpha Omegan.* **58**, 140-147

Perkinson, J. D., Jr, Whitney, I. B., Monroe, R. A., Lotz, W. E. & Comar, C. L. (1955) *Amer. J. Physiol.*, **182**, 383-389

Rich, C., Ensinck, J. & Ivanovich, P. (1964) *J. clin. Invest.*, **43**, 545-556

Roholm, K. (1937) *Fluorine intoxication : a clinical-hygienic study, with a review of the literature and some experimental investigations*, London, Lewis

Shupe, J. L., Harris, L. E., Greenwood, D. A., Butcher, J. E. & Nielsen, H. M. (1963) *Amer. J. vet. Res.*, **24**, 300-306

Singer, L. & Armstrong, W. D. (1960) *J. appl. Physiol.*, **15**, 508-510

Sircovitch, O., Gedalia, I. & Zukerman, H. (1964) *Harefuah*, **67**, 123-127

Smith, F. A., Gardner, D. E. & Hodge, H. C. (1955) *A.M.A. Arch. industr. Hlth*, **11**, 2 10

Suttie, J. W., Miller, R. F. & Phillips, P. H. (1957) *J. Nutr.*, **63**, 211-224

Wagner, M. J. & Muhler, J. C. (1957) *J. dent. Res.*, **36**, 552-558

Wallace-Durbin, P. (1954) *J. dent. Res.*, **33**, 789-800

Wills, J. H. (1940) *J. dent. Res.*, **19**, 585-590

Yudkin, E. P., Czerniejewski, J. & Blayney, J. R. (1954) *J. dent. Res.*, **33**, 691-692

Zipkin, I., Lee, W. A. & Leone, N. C. (1957) *Amer. J. publ. Hlth*, **47**, 848-851

Zipkin, I., Likins, R. C., McClure, F. J. & Steere, A. C. (1956) *Publ. Hlth Rep. (Wash.)*, **71**, 767-772

CHAPTER 6

Physiological effects of small doses
of fluoride

G. N. JENKINS [1] — P. VENKATESWARLU [2] — I. ZIPKIN [3]

1. INTRODUCTION (I. Zipkin)

Primary interest in this chapter is centred on present-day knowledge of how the body handles fluoride at different doses up to about 4 ppm in the water supply for extended periods of time. Three areas of discussion are pursued.

First, Professor Venkateswarlu reviews our present knowledge of the concentration of fluoride in body-fluids and in soft tissues, as well as the relationship of fluoride to intermediary carbohydrate, lipid and protein metabolism. The effect of fluoride on hormones, vitamins and enzymes is also discussed. Secondly, the author of this introduction discusses the effects of fluoride on the chemical and physical structure of bone, and the mechanisms affecting the deposition and mobilization of skeletal fluoride. Finally, Professor Jenkins collates the information available on the effect of fluoride on the chemistry and morphology of teeth, and on suggested mechanisms to explain the cariostatic effect of fluoride.

Wherever possible the human is the subject of relevance. Where fluoride data for man are unavailable, corollary studies on experimental animals are presented.

2. EFFECTS ON BODY-FLUIDS AND SOFT TISSUES
(P. Venkateswarlu)

Fluoride accumulates to easily measurable levels in calcified tissues and it is also present in soft tissues, but in only minute traces which are difficult

[1] The Sutherland Dental School, University of Newcastle upon Tyne, England.
[2] Department of Biochemistry, University of Minnesota, Minneapolis, Minn., USA.
[3] Professor of Biochemistry, Division of Periodontology, School of Dentistry, University of California, San Francisco, Calif., USA.

to determine. For this reason the bulk of the earlier work on fluoride meta-bolism was confined to the hard tissues. More recently, the development of fairly dependable micromethods for fluoride determination and the avail-ability of radiofluoride (^{18}F) have given impetus to the study of fluoride metabolism in the soft tissues and body-fluids.

For want of space this review is restricted to the metabolism of inorganic fluorides. An excellent review of the biological effects of organic fluorides has been published by Hodge, Smith & Chen (1963).

In the following text, F denotes the fluoride ion.

Mechanisms of Transport and Homeostasis of Fluoride

Gastrointestinal absorption of fluoride

The process of gastrointestinal absorption of F appears to be governed by an interplay of anatomical, physiological and biochemical factors. From different groups the following findings have been reported. F absorption in the ruminants was observed to be confined mostly to the rumen (Perkinson et al., 1955). The greater gastrointestinal absorption of F in the rabbit than in the rat was attributed to the longer gastrointestinal tract of the rabbit (Largent, 1948). F transport was not found to vary with the anatomical site of the small intestine (Venkateswarlu, 1962). Wagner (1962a) observed that 80% of the administered F was absorbed through the rat gastric mucosa in 15-20 minutes when the pyloric sphincter was ligated. Curiously, molybdenum was reported to depress gastric absorption and increase intestinal absorption of F in the adult rat, while it diminished intes-tinal absorption in the young rat (Stookey, Crane & Muhler, 1962). These findings need confirmation.

Soluble fluorides are fairly well absorbed in contrast to insoluble fluorides. Nevertheless, at low concentrations the less soluble fluorides can be very nearly as effective sources of F as the more soluble fluorides. Al^{+++}, Ca^{++} and Mg^{++} which can form insoluble complexes with F decrease absorption of F. Citrate and other substances which can complex Ca^{++} and thereby counteract the influence of Ca^{++} present in the gastrointestinal juices facilitate F absorption. Absorption of physiologically inert and covalently bound F compounds (KPF_6, $(C_2H_5)_4 NPF_6$, KBF_4) is greater than that of the physiolo-gically active simple fluorides (NaF, Na_2SiF_6, SnF_2) (Zipkin & Likins, 1957). A possible explanation of this finding is that while a fraction of ionic fluorides can be complexed by intestinal Ca and phosphate ions by precipitation as CaF_2 or adsorption on insoluble calcium phosphate and thus rendered unavailable for absorption, covalent fluorides cannot be so complexed and seem to be wholly available for (passive) absorption. The PO_3F ion in, for example, Na_2PO_3F is only gradually split by enzymes in the digestive tract and while its F content is metabolically available its absorption is much less influenced by calcium salts (Ericsson, 1967).

Intestinal transport of F seems to be passive (Stookey, Dellinger & Muhler, 1964), in contrast to that of chloride (Armstrong, Venkateswarlu & Singer, 1961), and regulated by plasma F level. A low plasma F level, such as might be expected in an actively growing young animal with relatively little prior exposure to F (Savchuck & Armstrong, 1951; Zipkin & McClure, 1952) or in starvation (F depletion) (Stookey, Crane & Muhler, 1964), may facilitate F absorption, whereas an elevated plasma F level, such as could occur in continuous ingestion of F (Lawrenz, Mitchell & Ruth, 1940) or in renal failure (bilateral nephrectomy) (Stookey, Crane & Muhler, 1963), may decelerate the intestinal absorption of F. However, these probabilities remain to be substantiated by actual determination of plasma F levels in the different situations.

The active transport of F from the serosal to the mucosal side of everted intestinal sacs of rats has been reported (Parkins, 1966).

Distribution of fluoride in blood

At the normal pH of 7.4, the erythrocyte: plasma ratio of ^{18}F is 0.66 : 1 in the dog; the ratio decreases with increase in pH and *vice versa*. This pH-dependent migration of ^{18}F is similar to the chloride shift, although there are some quantitative differences in the migration of fluoride and chloride ions (Carlson, Armstrong & Singer, 1960a).

Less than 5% of plasma ^{18}F is non-diffusible. In fluoridated serum, F migrates to a large extent with the serum albumin, and only a small proportion migrates freely towards the anode, whereas F is completely absent from the serum globulin fractions (Sforzolini, Cusma & Mastrantonio, 1964). Ca has been shown to act as a mediator in binding ^{18}F to albumin (Carlson, Armstrong & Singer, 1960a).

Homeostasis, adaptation and mobilization

Following any mode of ingestion of F, the F in blood plasma will be elevated above the normal resting level, and homeostatic mechanisms will operate to restore the level to normal.

The disappearance of ^{18}F from blood following intravenous injection of ^{18}F has been studied in rats. The nature of the ^{18}F disappearance curve suggests that it may be a composite of several curves, possibly reflecting equilibration of ^{18}F in extracellular and intracellular fluids, skeletal deposition and urinary excretion (Wallace-Durbin, 1954). The ^{18}F disappearance curve in ruminants has been found to be resolvable into four components similar to comparable curves reported for [45]Ca (Perkinson et al., 1955). Similar plasma ^{18}F disappearance curves have been reported in humans (Carlson, Armstrong & Singer, 1960b).

The efficiency of regulation of the plasma F level has been demonstrated in humans (Singer & Armstrong, 1960). The mean plasma F content of four populations using drinking water containing 0.15, 1.1, 1.1 and 2.5 ppm F was approximately the same, the values being 0.14, 0.15, 0.19 and 0.16 ppm F respectively.   A slight, but significant, elevation of the plasma F level (0.26 ppm) was noted in a population drinking water containing 5.4 ppm F. No significant or prolonged rise of plasma F level was detected following ingestion of 1 mg of F; and little diurnal variation of plasma F was observed beyond a very slight rise following the intake of food.   In the dog, after one year of daily administration of 1 g and 5 g UF_4 per kg body-weight, the blood F level was reported to be 0.25 ppm and 1.25 ppm respectively (F. A. Smith, cited by Voegtlin & Hodge, 1949).   In subjects with metabolic bone diseases, administration of doses of NaF 50 to 100 times greater than the normal F intake did not increase the plasma F level more than four- or five-fold and, after withdrawal of NaF, the F levels reverted to the normal pretreatment level (Armstrong et al., 1964).

While the rise in plasma F level is controlled by skeletal sequestration and by urinary, dermal and faecal (gastrointestinal) excretion, there seems to be a self-regulatory mechanism whereby an elevated plasma fluoride level such as can result from renal failure (Stookey, Crane & Muhler, 1963) or from continuous ingestion of fluoride restrains intestinal absorption of F (Lawrenz, Mitchell & Ruth, 1940).

While homeostatic mechanisms seem to operate well in certain species (the rat and the human), they seem to be less efficient in others—for example, cattle and chickens.   In chicks receiving a natural basal diet containing 25 ppm F and the same diet with 300, 600 and 900 ppm supplementary F, for two weeks from one day of age, the plasma F levels were reported to be 0.23, 2.1, 3.1 and 5.2 ppm respectively (Suttie, Phillips & Faltin, 1964). However, to evaluate correctly the differences in efficiency and pattern of F homeostatic mechanisms in various species, it would be necessary to have data on plasma F levels, determined preferably by the same method, in different species receiving identical doses of F over similar periods of time.

Acquisition of fluoride by soft tissues

The F content of soft tissues and body-fluids is extremely low in comparison with that of hard tissues.   This fact could be explained in more than one way.

First, it is possible that the avidity of the hard tissues for the circulating F is so strong and the renal excretion of F operates to such an extent that the fluoride level in plasma and other body-fluids is kept too low to boost the soft-tissue fluoride level appreciably.   If this hypothesis were correct, the fluoride levels in blood and soft tissues would be higher in species devoid of hard tissues than in species with hard-tissue structures after a similar degree of fluoride ingestion.   Unfortunately, no reliable data in respect of this are as yet available.   According to Carlson, Singer & Armstrong (1960), more

[18]F appeared in the soft tissues of nephrectomized rats than in those of control animals after intraperitoneal administration of the isotope.

Secondly, it is possible that physico-chemical characteristics of cellular membranes do not favour significant intracellular transport of F. For example, barley root membrane is permeable to the Cl ion, which is actively absorbed against a concentration gradient of 1 in 300, but is not permeable to the F ion despite a very favourable concentration gradient (Venkateswarlu, Armstrong & Singer, 1965). In studies of the *in vivo* intestinal absorption of initially equal concentrations of Cl and F in the lumen, a more than 3 to 1 discrimination in favour of Cl as against F has been observed (Armstrong, Venkateswarlu & Singer, 1961). Rat gastric mucosal membranes acquire less F than Cl from the plasma and also subsequently secrete less F than Cl in the gastric juice (Venkateswarlu, 1962).

Administration of 1 mg F daily for 90 days to weanling rats failed to demonstrate any increase in the F contents of heart, liver and kidney even as fluoride saturation of the skeleton was approached (Wagner, Stookey & Muhler, 1958). However, in the absence of data on the plasma F levels, it is not possible to say whether the absence of rise of F in the soft tissues was due to the lack of attainment of an adequate level of circulating F or to the very limited permeability of the cell membrane to the F ion.

Normally, the F levels of most soft tissues are below 1 ppm but slightly in excess of the plasma F levels (0.1-0.2 ppm). Aorta and placenta have more F than other soft tissues (Ericsson & Ullberg, 1958; Gardner et al., 1952; Sita & Venkateswarlu, unpublished data; Smith et al., 1960), presumably because they develop zones of calcification in which circulating F can be trapped (Ericsson & Hammarström, 1964). Increased deposition of Mg in soft tissues seems to facilitate increased retention of F in these tissues (Foster et al., 1960; Griffith, Parker & Rogler, 1963a).

Besides intracellular Ca and Mg, intracellular colloids could also play a role in the acquisition of F by soft tissues. Although intracellular proteins carry a net negative charge at physiological pH, the possibility of their binding anions like F has been indicated. Since, in the binding process, the negativity of the protein is decreased, a simultaneous uptake of a greater number of protons than the number of anions is postulated (Engel et al., 1961). The role of Ca in the binding of F by albumin has already been mentioned.

Despite decreased skeletal retention and increased excretion of F in older rats, their soft tissues have been reported to contain more F than the soft tissues of younger animals (Wagner, 1962b). Whether, owing to the decreased rate of sequestration of circulating F by the adult skeleton, the plasma F level in the older rats is elevated, thus facilitating progressive accumulation of F in the soft tissues, or whether the F-binding constituents of the tissues (Mg, Ca, or proteins with a predilection for F) could increase with the age of the rats is not known and requires investigation.

It has been observed that, following ^{18}F administration, relatively vascular tissues such as liver, spleen and intestine acquire more ^{18}F per gram of tissue than the less vascular tissues like skin and muscle. [18]F concentrations, with the exception of those in the kidney and salivary glands, paralleled the blood ^{18}F level at all times. Thyroid did not accumulate ^{18}F and its ^{18}F concentration did not exceed the blood ^{18}F level at any time in the course of 9 hours of the experiment (Wallace-Durbin, 1954).

Hein et al. (1956) reported that thyroid, kidneys and adrenal glands (all blood-rich organs) contained the highest concentration of [18]F 30 minutes after oral administration or 10 minutes after intravenous administration of the isotope.

The distribution of ^{18}F in the soft tissues of rats on low-fluoride and high-fluoride diets was studied at 80 and 120 minutes after intraperitoneal injection of [18]F. To add another dimension to the study of fluoride metabolism, a labelled chloride ([36]Cl) was administered simultaneously with ^{18}F and the relative distribution of the isotopes was determined (Venkateswarlu, 1962). In the following, [18]F_{tw} and [36]Cl_{tw} denote the ^{18}F and [36]Cl counts per minute per gram of tissue water (tw) while [18]F_{pw} and [36]Cl_{pw} denote the ^{18}F and [36]Cl counts per minute per gram of plasma water (pw).

No difference was found in the values of the ratio [18]F_{tw}/[18]F_{pw} for corresponding tissues in rats on low-fluoride and high-fluoride diets. The ratio was less than 1.0 in all tissues except the kidney and the tail tendon. The magnitude of the ratio for the kidney is undoubtedly due to the role of the organ in concentrating fluoride from the plasma in the process of formation of urine.

In this study, the stomach is a particularly interesting organ in that it concentrates chloride and secretes HCl. The results indicated that the stomach wall and the gastric juice had a larger content of [36]Cl than of ^{18}F, compared with their plasma levels, suggesting a discrimination in favour of chloride. Gastric wall was the only tissue among those examined in which the ratio under discussion was found to be less than 1.0 in all examples. This ratio appeared to be even lower in the gastric juice, suggesting preferential secretion of chloride. This finding is in contrast to that with the kidney and urine, in which the ratio was in favour of the fluoride ion.

Although the [18]F_{tw}/[18]F_{pw} and [36]Cl_{tw}/[36]Cl_{pw} ratios in tendon could be influenced by loss of water during dissection of the tissue, the ratio ([18]F_{tw}/[18]F_{pw})/([36]Cl_{tw}/[36]Cl_{pw}) would not be affected in similar circumstances. In the case of animals sacrificed 80 minutes after isotope administration, the latter ratio was definitely less than 1.0. However, in those animals which were allowed to live for 120 minutes, the ratio was more than 1.0, indicating a preferential uptake and sequestration, progressing with time, of ^{18}F by the tendons. These observations are of interest in relation to the several publications in the literature describing hypercalcification of certain tendons in humans who had consumed, for long periods of time, drinking water with a high fluoride level (Shortt et al., 1937; Singh, Jolly & Bansal, 1961).

However, if such a calcification of the tendon (an organic matrix) is dependent on its prior acquisition of F, we do not as yet know exactly how F so acquired leads to subsequent calcification of the tendon. Recently attention has been called to the presence of organically bound F in the organic matrix of tooth enamel as distinct from the inorganic F in its mineral phase (Little, Casciani & Rowley, 1968). The significance, if any, of the organically bound F in the enamel is not known.

Acquisition of F by hard tissues

The bulk of the F administered by any route, on entering the extra-cellular fluid, is invariably sequestered by the skeletal structures, which have a variable propensity for acquiring fluoride.

The author of this section found no significant difference in the acquisition of intraperitoneally administered ^{18}F by corresponding hard tissues of rats which had ingested and retained significantly different amounts of fluoride (F in skeletal ash varying from 24 to 1727 ppm) (Venkateswarlu, 1962). Thus the previous fluoride load in the bones, within wide limits, is not of consequence in determining the amount of ^{18}F which can be acquired subsequently by the bones.

The ^{18}F thus acquired represents an increment of fluoride deposition and not an "exchange", because it was subsequently shown that bones of high F content did not exchange their fluoride with that of plasma in two hours following intraperitoneal injection of carrier-free radiofluoride (^{18}F) in saline (Armstrong & Singer, 1963a).

No more will be said here about the acquisition of F by hard tissues since this subject is extensively dealt with by Weidmann and Weatherell in Chapter 4, section 3, and by Zipkin in section 3 of this chapter.

Urinary excretion of fluoride

This aspect is covered in Chapter 5 (Hodge, Smith & Gedalia).

Placental transfer of fluoride

This aspect is covered by Gedalia in Chapter 4, section 4.

Mammary and salivary secretion of fluoride

These aspects are covered in Chapter 5 (Hodge, Smith & Gedalia).

Metabolic Interrelationships of Fluoride in Body-Fluids and Soft Tissues

Fluoride and general metabolism

Fluoridation of public water supplies for the control of dental caries has raised some questions about the health safety of concentrations of fluoride in communal water in the range 1-2 ppm. The epidemiological and experimental evidence for the safety of water fluoridation has been impressive and very massive.

Clinical studies in areas where the water is fluoridated and clinical and post-mortem studies in areas where the waters have a high natural fluoride content are reported in Chapter 8.

Some concern was expressed about reports of depression of blood pressure, increased heart rate and increased femoral blood flow in dogs following administration of 1 and 5 mg F by stomach tube (Richardson, Muhler & Bishop, 1955). However, it was subsequently demonstrated that the mere introduction of the stomach tube itself caused the decrease in blood pressure (Caruso & Hodge, cited by Smith (1962)).

Reports of renal changes in rats following ingestion of water containing 1, 5 or 10 ppm (Ramseyer, Smith & McCay, 1957) also caused some concern. But these observations could not be confirmed, and later it was established that the changes reported to be caused by F ingestion were no different from those normally seen in the kidneys of aged rats and were not readily traceable to F ingestion (Bosworth & McCay, 1962). Fluoride seemed to be implicated in the etiology of urinary stones, but no experimental evidence was obtained (Herman, 1956; Spira, 1956). Moreover, Venkateswarlu, Singer & Armstrong (1958) observed a slightly lower frequency of urinary stones in rats receiving a urinary-stone-inducing diet plus 10 ppm F in drinking water than in control rats which received the same diet, but no supplemental fluoride.

Renal handling of F was the same in normal rabbits as in rabbits in which chemical nephritis had been induced. Elderly patients with normal kidney function and a similar age-group of patients with long-standing kidney disease showed no difference in the range of urinary F concentrations (Smith, Gardner & Hodge, 1955). Thus kidney disease does not seem to accentuate the problem of renal handling of fluoride in an individual. The decrease in intestinal absorption of F as a homeostatic mechanism after nephrectomy has already been mentioned.

The question of iodine metabolism and possible interference by another halogen such as F is discussed in Chapter 7.

It is pertinent to mention here the reports from India of the incidence of skeletal fluorosis in areas with 3-5 ppm F in the drinking water (Pandit et al., 1940). Some of these reports have still to be critically evaluated and re-established. In all probability the F intake *via* water and food is very high in these localities because of the increased intake of water and salt to correct their heavy losses from the body in the tropical climate. Some samples of rock salt (75% NaCl) which have been used extensively as cooking salt till recently in regions such as the Punjab in India have been shown to contain F in concentrations as high as 200 ppm, corrected for 25% insoluble residue in the rock salt (Sita & Venkateswarlu, 1967). Daily consumption of 15-20 g salt (NaCl), in the form of rock salt, could result in the daily ingestion of 3-4 mg F over and above the F consumed in food, beverages (tea) and drinking water (sometimes contaminated with F sediments). However, quite contrary to expectations, the fluoride in the rock salt was not found to be biologically available. There was no increase in the skeletal F in rats receiving rock salt in the diet over that found in appropriate control rats (Raman, Sita & Venkateswarlu, unpublished data). Data on precise F intake and on faecal and urinary excretion of individuals from endemic areas of fluorosis would be most useful for a critical appraisal of the association of skeletal fluorosis with drinking waters containing relatively low levels of F.

Fluoride and carbohydrate metabolism

In certain circumstances F was found to depress respiration and stimulate fermentation in micro-organisms, and in other circumstances quite the opposite effects were observed (Runnstrom, Borei & Sperber, 1939). Stimulation of fermentation could be associated with depression of polysaccharide synthesis. In the presence of F (10-11 ppm), less ^{14}C-glucose was incorporated in the polysaccharides (Weiss, Schnetzer & King, 1964). At higher concentrations (20-200 ppm), CO_2 production was inhibited, presumably owing to a block of the enolase system resulting in accumulation of hexose phosphates (Nilsson, 1930). Such inhibition could be nullified by the addition of phosphate acceptors such as adenylic acid (Runnstrom & Hemberg, 1937).

In acute F poisoning of rabbits (2 hours after subcutaneous injection of 250 mg NaF per kg body-weight), glycogen decreased in liver and skeletal muscle and remained unaltered in the myocardium. Phosphorylase decreased in skeletal muscle only. In chronic fluorosis (oral doses of 50, 30 and 10 mg NaF per kg, daily for 3 months), mild to severe degeneration and almost complete disappearance of phosphorylase in the necrotic foci were found in the myocardia and liver, but no significant changes were observed in the skeletal muscle even with these extremely high doses (Iwase, 1958). In this context, one may recall the inhibitory effect of F on the role of HGF (the hyperglycaemic-glycogenolytic factor) and on epinephrine in the activation of muscle phosphorylase (Cori, 1950).

Zebrowski, Suttie & Phillips (1964) administered ^{14}C-glucose and ^{14}C-palmitate to rats which had received 0.1% NaF in the diet for 30-45 days, and observed that, in comparison with the controls, fatty acid catabolism was decreased and glucose catabolism unaffected, but glycogen turnover was depressed.

The degree of F exposure to which the above-mentioned experimental animals were subjected is never encountered in practical human nutrition and endemic fluorosis.

In a very severe case of skeletal fluorosis with spastic paraplegia, a glucose-tolerance test was found to be normal (Murthi, Narayana Rao & Venkateswarlu, 1953), as were the blood sugar levels of several fluorotic patients (Shortt et al., 1937). In a study of chronic experimental fluorosis in monkeys (Pandit & Narayana Rao, 1940), glycosuria was not observed, although the animals had developed a very advanced and severe form of osteosclerosis.

Fluoride and lipid metabolism

Study of the interrelationship of F and lipid metabolism assumes considerable importance in view of the implication that F plays a role in the incidence of arteriosclerosis (Exner & Waldbott, 1957). Epidemiologically, there is no evidence to support such an implication (Leone et al., 1954). In fact, Bernstein et al. (1966) found a higher frequency of roentgen-visible calcification of the aorta in low-fluoride than in high-fluoride areas.

Increasing the fat (Crisco,[1] corn oil, lard, cotton-seed oil) from 5% to 20% in F-supplemented rations aggravated the growth-retarding effect of fluoride in the rat and chick and also resulted in higher retention of F in the whole carcase, as well as in the femur and soft tissues (Bixler & Muhler, 1960; Büttner & Muhler, 1958a; Miller & Phillips, 1955). The higher retention of F, however, had no effect on serum cholesterol levels (Büttner & Muhler, 1958b).

The in vitro oxidation of fatty acids is reported to be inhibited by fluoride (Johnson & Lardy, 1950). As mentioned earlier, fatty acid catabolism was reduced in rats receiving 0.1% F in the diet for 30-45 days (Zebrowski, Suttie & Phillips, 1964); but 0.1% F in the diet amounts to an ingestion of 500-700 mg F per day, which is more than 100 times the 2-5 mg F ingested by any person via diet and water containing 1 ppm F.

Fluoride and protein metabolism

The urine of a fluorotic monkey was reported to darken on standing. The darkening was attributed to the presence of homogentisic acid (method of identification not mentioned) suggestive of an interference with the metabolism of phenylalanine and tyrosine (Pandit & Narayana Rao, 1940). However, F (10^{-3} M/litre final concentration, more than 100 times the tissue F concentration) added to guinea-pig-liver homogenates was not found to have any inhibitory effect on the in vitro oxidation of tyrosine (Venkateswarlu, 1955). Also, the patterns of urinary excretion of phenolic acids in fluorotic patients did not differ from those in normal humans (Saini et al., 1964).

---

[1] Proprietary name of a hydrogenated vegetable oil used for culinary purposes.

Other instances of fluoride-protein interrelationship—for example, the binding of F by dietary proteins in the gastrointestinal tract, by plasma proteins, by tendon, and by the intracellular proteins—have already been discussed, and the topic of fluoride and enzymes will be dealt with in some detail later in this section.

Fluoride and mineral metabolism

Fluoride and calcium.   A number of observations indicated interactions between calcium and F.   The distribution of F in the body was shown to conform to some extent to the pattern of distribution of calcium.   A positive relation between F deposition and metastatic calcification was observed when calcification-inducing diets were fed to rats and guinea-pigs (Stookey & Muhler, 1963).   Tissues such as aorta, which gradually accumulate calcium, also seemed to acquire increasing amounts of F.   Placenta seemed to accumulate F readily in its zones of calcification.   Calcium could mediate the binding of F by plasma proteins (Carlson, Armstrong & Singer, 1960a). Dietary Ca, by reducing F absorption, protected the organism against F intoxication (Lawrenz & Mitchell, 1941; Narayana Rao, 1942).

However, in natural conditions in humans, even on a restricted Ca diet, the daily ingestion of 7 and 14 mg F has no effect on the calcium balance (Wagner & Muhler, 1959).   Larger doses of F used in the treatment of cases of osteoporosis promote a positive calcium balance and give fair clinical results (Purves, 1962; Rich & Ensinck, 1961).   F in physiological doses has no influence on serum or salivary Ca and P levels (Knappwost & Tochtermann, 1955).   In the third trimester of pregnancy, both Ca and F are found to be lowered in serum, possibly coinciding with an active uptake of the elements by the foetus (Gedalia et al., 1963).

Fluoride and strontium.   An alarm was created by a proposition that F ingestion could enhance the skeletal acquisition and retention of ^{90}Sr from radioactive fall-out (Kerwin, 1958).   Analysis of human teeth, which keep once acquired mineral concentrations more stable than the bones, revealed no relationship between F and Sr in the tooth or any correlation of the tooth levels with F and Sr levels in drinking water (Steadman, Brudevold & Smith, 1958).   Experiments on rats revealed that F ingestion does not increase retention of ^{89}Sr and *vice versa* (Muhler, Stookey & Wagner, 1959; Rogers, Wagner & Stookey, 1961).   The metabolisms of Sr and F are not interrelated to warrant the above suspicion.

Fluoride and magnesium.   In rats receiving a high-lipid diet, the F : Mg ratio in soft tissues was closely related to that in mineralized tissues. In rats receiving high Mg and high F besides high lipid, the F : Mg ratio increased in soft tissues and decreased in mineralized tissues (Foster et al., 1960).   Whether this increase in F with respect to Mg could, to any extent, explain the increased toxicity of fluoride when ingested in conjunction with a high-lipid diet is an open question. Presumably Mg-dependent physio-logical enzyme mechanisms are decelerated by increasing F levels—for example, inhibition of enolase could result in less efficient utilization of carbohydrates.

Incorporation of 0.08% F and 0.25% Mg in chick rations caused a greater growth depression than did F alone. Chicks on Mg plus F developed a characteristic leg weakness which was not seen on Mg or F alone. Raising the Ca level of the diet did not prevent the interaction of Mg and F. Plasma alkaline phosphatase was elevated by F; enolase activity in muscle homo-genates was not impaired (Griffith, Parker & Rogler, 1963b). In chicks receiving supplemental Mg, increase in dietary F elevated Mg in plasma, bone, liver and kidney, but not in heart or muscle (Griffith, Parker & Rogler, 1963a).

In the dog, addition of F to the diet (200 ppm) prevented the development of gross aortic lesions and calcification of soft tissues inducible by a low-Mg diet (30 ppm). The mechanism of protection is not clear. Such protection was not detected in rats. While the lowering of the serum Mg level induced by low-Mg diet was not influenced by F in the dog, the level was further lowered by F in the rat (6-7 weeks' experiment) (Chiemchaisri & Phillips, 1963). However, in short-term experiments in the guinea-pig, the lowering of serum Mg on low-Mg diet was minimized by 450 ppm F in the diet (Thompson, Heintz & Phillips, 1964)—a finding which indicates the need for further investigations. Mg-F interrelationships may have something to do with the lower incidence of aortal calcifications found in a high-fluoride area (Bernstein et al., 1966).

The effects of Mg and/or ascorbic-acid deficiency, with and without addi-tional F in the diet, on the metabolism of connective tissues were investigated in guinea-pigs. Blood serum hexosamine was normal in fluorosis and Mg deficiency. In aorta, hexosamine was elevated and hydroxyproline depressed in guinea-pigs on low-ascorbic-acid diet, high-F/low-Mg diet and low-Mg/low-ascorbic-acid diet (Thompson, Heintz & Phillips, op. cit.).

Fluoride and iron. When iron (^{59}Fe) was administered by stomach tube to rats raised on iron-deficient or iron-supplemented diets, an enhanced uptake of ^{59}Fe by the blood was observed in rats receiving additionally either a prior dietary supplement of F (200 ppm) for 76 days or an oral dose of F, sufficient to complex the ^{59}Fe, immediately after the iron was admin-istered (Ruliffson, Burns & Hughes, 1963). It is difficult to explain the results on the basis of F facilitating the intestinal absorption of Fe, because Fe and F would appear to interfere with each other in intestinal absorption (Ruliffson & Hopping, 1963; Venkateswarlu, 1962). However, Stookey, Crane & Muhler (1964), who examined the entire gastrointestinal tract of the rat in F absorption studies, observed that the concomitant presence of

Fe enhanced F absorption. Whether F facilitates absorption of Fe in the stomach is not known. Whether the higher level of ^{59}Fe in blood could be a result of inadequate transport and utilization of plasma ^{59}Fe under the influence of F cannot be answered in the absence of data regarding the specific activities of blood Fe. Decreased *in vitro* incorporation of ^{14}C-glycocoll and ^{59}Fe in protoporphyrin by blood from rabbits receiving toxic doses of F has been proposed as the underlying cause of the hypersideroplasmatic hypochromic anaemia observed in fluorotic rabbits (Benard, Gajdos & Gajdos-Torok, 1958). The entire Fe metabolism as influenced by toxic doses of F would seem to merit further careful investigation, although ingestion of water containing about 1 ppm F is decidedly not known to have any adverse effect on normal Fe metabolism.

Fluoride and molybdenum. It has already been stated that some workers have found that Mo increases F absorption and, if confirmed, this might explain the reported increase of F levels in the bone and soft tissues of animals receiving a dietary supplement of Mo (Stookey & Muhler, 1962). However, recent reports throw doubt on this concept of an interaction of F with Mo (Adkins & Kruger, 1966; Büttner, 1961, 1963; Ericsson, 1966; Goodman, 1965). A combination of Mo and F was reported to be significantly more effective in reducing caries than F alone (Büttner, 1961; Jenkins, 1967; Malthus, Ludwig & Healy, 1964; Stookey, Roberts & Muhler, 1962). Molybdate itself may possess some anti-caries potentiality through its slight powers of inhibiting salivary acid production at pH 5 and reducing the *in vitro* solubility of calcium phosphate and enamel (Jenkins, 1967).

Fluoride and phosphate. Phosphate enhances fluoride absorption in the intestine presumably by counteracting the inhibitory action of intestinal calcium on F absorption (Bixler & Muhler, 1960). The formation of a fluorophosphate complex facilitating F transport has been also considered as a possibility. Absorption of fluorophosphate is interfered with less than that of F by calcium ions and for this reason, where calcium intake is very variable, monofluorophosphate has been suggested as a suitable form for fluoride in some caries preventive measures (Ericsson, Santesson & Ullberg, 1961).

Prolonged administration of F (20 mg/kg) to pups was reported to increase the serum organic phosphate and decrease the inorganic phosphate (Andreeva, 1957). In fluorotic rats, as compared with controls, subcutaneously administered ^{32}P was acquired more by muscle (not liver, brain, or thyroid) and bone. This has been interpreted as resulting from fluoride stimulation of the metabolic turnover of phosphate in muscle and bone. The animals were reported to excrete more urinary phosphate and the authors propose dietary supplementation with phosphate to correct for the alleged phosphate loss in fluorine intoxication (Gabovich, Bukhovets & Ermakova,

1960). Again, ingestion of 20 mg F per kg body-weight is never encountered in natural conditions. The interactions between fluoride and phosphate in enzyme mechanisms will be discussed later. An increase in dietary phosphorus from 0.14% to 0.71%, dietary calcium remaining constant, was reported to increase the appetite of growing rats and result in a distinctly heavier dry fat-free skeleton, although total retention and distribution of F in bones, teeth and soft tissues was not altered (Lawrenz & Mitchell, 1941).

Fluoride and sulfate. Sulfate presumably increases the intestinal absorption of F by counteracting, like phosphate, the inhibitory effect of intestinal Ca on F absorption (Stookey, Crane & Muhler, 1964).

Fluoride and chloride. The relative absorption of ^{18}F and ^{36}Cl by barley roots (Venkateswarlu, Armstrong & Singer, 1965), the relative intestinal absorption of ^{18}F and ^{36}Cl in the rat (Armstrong, Venkateswarlu & Singer, 1961), and the relative metabolism and transport of intraperitoneally administered ^{18}F and ^{36}Cl in rats on low- and high-F diets (Venkateswarlu, 1962) have been already discussed.

F at a level of 0.1% in chick rations was reported to be associated with hyperatrophy and histological changes in the proventriculi, and it was suggested that the production of HF instead of HCl could be the cause (Gardiner et al., 1959). No data on the HF or HCl content of the gastric juice were reported. It is pertinent here to point out an earlier discussion of a report that the gastric mucosa in the normal rat acquired a higher $^{36}Cl/^{18}F$ ratio than did the plasma and, further, that the gastric juice acquired a greater $^{36}Cl/^{18}F$ ratio than did the mucosa, possibly owing to a preferential acquisition and secretion of Cl over F by the gastric mucosa.

In a recent report, Cl has been considered an absolute requirement for the active intestinal transport of F in the secretory direction (Parkins & Faust, 1968). These findings await confirmation.

Fluoride and iodide. This aspect is dealt with by Demole in Chapter 7, section 5.

Fluoride and the effects of the parathyroid hormone

There is a dearth of knowledge on F and hormone interrelationships. At present our knowledge is essentially restricted to information concerning F and the thyroid gland (referred to above), and to a few limited studies on F and the parathyroid hormone, to be described now.

In bilaterally nephrectomized rats, peritoneal lavage with fluoride resulted in a significant increase in osteoclast count and activity as reflected by the proliferation of the osteoclasts into the bone trabecular zones. Similar changes were observed in nephrectomized fluorotic rats (in which the bone mineral is rendered less soluble) when calcium-free fluid was employed for peritoneal lavage. In both these situations (Talamage & Doty, 1962), where the plasma ionic calcium was lower than in the corresponding control rats, increased osteoclastic activity was observable only in parathyroid-intact rats and not in parathyroidectomized rats. Fluoride, possibly by lowering the plasma ionic calcium, indirectly stimulates the parathyroid glands. However, parathyroid function was reported to be normal in patients with chronic fluorosis (Singh et al., 1966).

In parathyroid-hormone-treated rats, the plasma F level was found to remain the same as that in the control rats, despite a rise in plasma Ca indicating mobilization of bone mineral and therefore release of bone F into the plasma. Failure to observe any rise in plasma F level was explained on the basis of efficient homeostatic mechanisms involving sequestration of plasma F by newly forming bone mineral and also renal clearance of F (Singer & Armstrong, 1964). It is possible that, even in parathormone-treated animals, skeletal sequestration of plasma F plays as dominant a role in the homeostasis of F as it does in normal animals. This proposition is borne out by the observation that acquisition of intraperitoneally adminis-tered ^{18}F by selected hard tissues was the same in parathormone-treated rats as in normal control rats (Venkateswarlu, Armstrong & Singer, 1966b).

Fluoride and vitamin metabolism

Some histological structures of the skeleton and teeth are adversely affected by fluorine intoxication and also by deficiency of vitamins A, C and D. This led to the comparison of fluorosis with various vitamin (and other nutritional) deficiencies and to considerable speculation as to the possibility of treating or preventing fluorosis by vitamin administration. The basic interrelationships remain to be understood; in no species has fluorine intoxication been cured or prevented unequivocally by administra-tion of any one or any combination of the above-mentioned vitamins. Attempts to relate the ameliorative effect of green leafy vegetables on fluo-rosis in rats to any of the dietary factors present in them have been unsuc-cessful (Phillips, cited by Suttie & Phillips (1959)).

Of all the vitamins, ascorbic acid seems to have attracted the maximum attention in connexion with fluoride metabolism. The interrelationship between vitamin C and F seems to require critical evaluation because of the suggested role of vitamin-C therapy in ameliorating fluoride intoxication, particularly after Pandit and co-investigators (1940) reported from India the co-existence of severe forms of human fluorosis and vitamin-C deficiency in a certain endemic area. This observation has been unjustifiably equated with aggravation of fluorosis by vitamin-C deficiency. Later Pandit & Narayana Rao (1940) demonstrated the ameliorative effect of vitamin-C-rich *foods* on fluorosis in monkeys (not *vitamin C alone* as misunderstood in some reviews). How far other factors present in vitamin-C-rich foods could contribute to the beneficial effects observed seems to have been un-fortunately overlooked.

Wadhwani (1952) induced fluorosis in monkeys kept on normal and scorbutic diets, noted higher mortality, stiffness of limbs and restricted movements in the latter group and observed dramatic improvement follow-ing vitamin-C therapy. This observation was interpreted as indicating that recovery from fluorosis was brought about by vitamin-C therapy, but it could merely reflect recovery from the experimentally induced scorbutic state by vitamin-C supplementation. The vitamin-C content of the "normal" basal diet was not given. Swelling of joints, reduced vivacity, restricted gait due to painful joints, etc. are commonly encountered in scorbutic guinea-pigs.

Wadhwani (1954) further claimed to have observed amelioration in fluorotic patients after administration of heavy doses of ascorbic acid; he reported improvement in radiological pictures. The vitamin-C status of the patients was not assessed before instituting the vitamin-C therapy. Con-ditions similar to chronic osteoarthritis, with osteophytic outgrowths, pseudoankylosis, and periosteal thickening, in chronic vitamin-C deficiency have been described by others (Mouriquand et al., 1940). One cannot rule out that the afore-mentioned radiological improvement could again be due simply to recovery from a chronic scorbutic state, which was reported by Pandit et al. (*op. cit.*) to be very prevalent in the area from which Wadhwani's patients came. The "aggravated" condition of fluorosis with vitamin-C deficiency as encountered in endemic fluorosis (Andreeva, 1959; Ivanova, 1959; Pandit et al., 1940; Wadhwani, 1954) might very well be a complex superimposition of the signs and symptoms of scurvy on those of fluorosis. The co-existing condition of scurvy responds to vitamin-C therapy while the basic condition of fluorosis does not. Extra vitamin-C administra-tion would not be expected to have a profound beneficial influence on frank fluorosis, unassociated with scurvy, as could be produced in experimental animals (Venkateswarlu & Narayana Rao, 1957).

There is no evidence to support the view that F ingestion enhances the body's need for ascorbic acid. In experiments with guinea-pigs, F (1 mg per 100 g body-weight for 24 days) was not found to increase the excretion of vitamin C from the body, nor was F (1 mg per kg body-weight for 24 days) found to cause increased utilization or destruction of vitamin C in the body-tissues (Venkateswarlu & Narayana Rao, 1957). The observation of a lowered vitamin-C content of soft tissues in the fluorotic guinea-pig reported by Phillips, Stare & Elvehjem (1934) should not be over-emphazised in the present context of practical human and animal nutrition; the level of F administered was extremely high (25 mg per kg body-weight daily) and is not encountered in spontaneous endemic fluorosis. Administration of extra vitamin C (10 times the optimal requirement) to fluorotic guinea-pigs did not produce any perceptible effects either on skeletal retention or on urinary and faecal excretion of fluoride. However, Muhler (1958) reported slightly increased skeletal deposition of fluoride in guinea-pigs receiving extra dietary vitamin C as compared with guinea-pigs on minimal vitamin-C intake. Again, in apparent contradiction to these observations, we have a report (Gabovich & Maistruk, 1963) indicating that vitamin C lowers the rate of F deposition in the hard and soft tissues of the guinea-pig and presumably increases the rate of F excretion.

Fluoride in extremely high concentrations might be expected to interfere with the role of vitamin C in the body. From a study of the activity of cellular oxidative mechanisms it was postulated that symptoms of scurvy and fluorosis result primarily from disturbances of specific phases of cellular respiration (Phillips, Stare & Elvehjem, 1934). Hauck (1934) believes that the interrelationships, if any, between fluorine and vitamin C, would be in the nature of fluorine interfering with the metabolism of vitamin C rather than with its storage. The specific mechanism by which the fluorine interferes with the role of vitamin C is not well established so far. It would appear that even if fluorine interferes with the metabolic function of vitamin C, it does not result in the production of all the phases of scurvy. Of the several guinea-pigs that were dissected, none of the fluorotic animals (not restricted to scorbutic diet) ever showed the characteristic signs of scurvy—haemorrhages, particularly at the costochondral junction—which were found in all fluorotic and non-fluorotic guinea-pigs rendered scorbutic by a vitamin-C-deficient diet (Venkateswarlu & Narayana Rao, 1957).

The significance of the finding of Phillips & Chang (1934) that fluoride ingestion causes an increased biosynthesis of vitamin C in the rat, which has been confirmed by Venkateswarlu & Narayana Rao (*op. cit.*), remains to be understood precisely.

Supplementary doses of vitamin D were found to have no therapeutic effect on experimental chronic fluorosis in young rats (Lindemann, 1965).

Fluoride and enzymes

General observations. Little is known about the *in vivo* effects of F at the low levels occurring naturally in body-fluids and soft tissues on enzymes and the various facets of general metabolism of the living organism. Low levels of fluoride have been reported to promote growth, flowering and higher yields of various plants. Perhaps such development of plants has been due to the stimulation of photosynthesis (Navara, 1963) by traces of fluoride and improvement in soil organic matter (Leroux, 1940) and nitrogen fixation (Fedorov, 1947) by soil micro-organisms under the influence of F. Traces of F stimulated the growth of embryonal cultures of chick heart and kidney (Hintzsche, 1954). In tissue-culture experiments employing murine leukaemic lymphoblasts (Albright, 1964), human HeLa and Minn. EE cells (Armstrong et al., 1965) and bone (Proffit & Ackerman, 1964), F was found to interfere with cell growth and metabolism only at levels higher than 10 ppm (5×10^{-4} M), which far exceeds the natural level of fluoride—below 0.2 ppm (10^{-5} M)—in body-fluids, thus providing a safety factor of 50 or more.

10^{-4} M NaF was found to inhibit parathyroid-induced resorption of five-day-old mouse calvaria explants in tissue culture. Such a concentration of F was not found to impair osteoid formation (Goldhaber, 1967). Subsequent radioactive studies showed that F concentrations of 10^{-6}-10^{-4} M activated, and higher concentrations inhibited, *in vitro* collagen synthesis. While resorption of preformed collagen in the explants was inhibited by F, resorption of poorly calcified collagen newly synthesized by the explant in the tissue culture was not inhibited by F. It was concluded that F does not directly inhibit the collagen-degrading enzymes but, by interaction with the (pre-existing) mineral phase associated with the preformed collagen, somehow protects the collagen matrix from such enzymes (Golub, Glimcher & Goldhaber, 1968). In this context, one may recall the view that proteolytic enzymes do not attack the tooth protein matrix until after it has been demineralized. It has been concluded that Ca salts protect the collagen from enzyme attack (Evans & Prophet, 1950). In tissue culture of bone, F probably reinforces or enhances a similar protective action of the mineral phase against the collagen-degrading enzymes as postulated in the case of dental tissues.

A decrease in proteins and Mg-dependent enzymes such as alkaline phosphatase and certain esterases in the serum of rats ingesting water containing 100 ppm F for 50 days was reported (Riekstniece, Myers & Glass, 1965). A slight decrease in the total plasma proteins and some variations in the quantitative pattern of plasma protein fractions in rats receiving 10-20 mg F per kg body-weight for six weeks were also reported (Moore & Wagner, 1968). However, whether the observed alterations are due to a specific effect of F or to the effects of a generalized toxic condition remains to be clarified. For example, liver glucose-6-phosphate dehydrogenase was found to be decreased in fluoride-fed rats. However, by regulating the food intake it was shown that the decrease in enzyme activity in fluoride-fed rats was a consequence of a direct effect of F on the pattern of food intake. The primary effect of excessive dietary fluoride was therefore considered to be on the regulation of food intake rather than on the control of tissue enzyme synthesis (Carlson & Suttie, 1966).

Fluoride and enzyme activation. At certain optimal concentrations, fluoride is reported to activate a variety of physiological processes—for example, yeast respiration (Borei, 1942); *Escherichia coli* fermentation (Opienska-Blauth, Kanski & Stobinska, 1949); enzymatic decomposition of nitromethane (rabbit liver) (Egami & Itahashi, 1951); synthesis of citruline (rat liver) (Cohen & Hayano, 1947); vibrio adenosinase (Agarwala et al.,

1954), pancreatic diastase (pig) (Wachsmann & Grutzner, 1902); respiration of gastric mucosa (frog) (Davies, 1949). Not much is known about the mechanisms of activation of these processes by F. It is likely that F, through its ability to complex certain metals, unmasks active surfaces of the enzyme previously covered by Ca or some other heavy metal. When a particular metabolic pathway is blocked by F, the cellular organization could stimulate and exploit an alternative pathway for cellular function which may appear as activation by F of the enzyme concerned. F could indirectly activate an enzyme. For instance, by inhibiting the phosphorylase-rupturing enzyme, F contributes to the conservation of tissue phosphorylase, a situation suggestive of activation of phosphorylase by F (Sutherland, 1951).

Fluoride and enzyme inhibition. Mechanisms of inhibition by fluoride of several enzyme systems have been investigated using fluoride concentrations several times higher than those present in normal body-fluids. To what extent the mechanisms as revealed by using such high concentrations of F would be operative at low levels of fluoride cannot be predicted. Nevertheless these studies lend an insight into the possible mechanisms, which seem to be many.

Fluoride can partly bring about enzyme inhibition by being adsorbed on (and thus blocking) the active sites of the enzyme required for formation of enzyme-substrate complex. This could be the reason why in some instances there is less inhibition of enzyme when F is added after the substrate (Marcuse & Runnstrom, 1943). In the presence of fluoride, a shift in the absorption spectrum of certain enzyme proteins—catalase (Ogura et al., 1950), cytochrome C (Borei, 1945)—has been noted; this could possibly mean direct combination of F with the protein. In some instances—yeast fermentation (Lipmann, 1929)—the combination is competitive and reversible, while in others—pancreatic lipase (Murray, 1929)—it is non-competitive and irreversible. Surprisingly lipases lose sensitivity to F on purification (Gyotoku, 1930); the action of F must be through some impurity or a labile component of the enzyme which is not directly involved in the enzyme function.

Susceptible isoenzymes are inhibited to various degrees by F, perhaps owing to differences in the order of reaction and in the affinity of F for the enzyme. Aerobic glycolysis is inhibited by F in Jensen rat sarcoma, but not in rat testis (Dickens & Simer, 1929). Human liver esterase is inhibited by F, but pancreatic and intestinal esterases are not (Gomori, 1955). Further, the activator requirement of the isoenzymes could be different. Mg-activated animal and plant glutamine synthetases are inhibited by F more than the corresponding Co-activated synthetases. F binding (Denes, 1954) with the metal activator is greater in the Mg-activated synthetases.

It was once presumed that F inhibition of some enzymes could be explained on the grounds that magnesium fluorophosphate inhibits competitively the activating effect of Mg^{++}. However, in the case of succinic dehydrogenase (Slater & Bonner, 1952) and enolase (Peters, Shorthouse & Murray, 1964), it has been shown that fluorophosphate is not inhibitory, although a mixture of F plus phosphate certainly is. F and phosphate seem to reinforce each other's affinity for the enzyme and bring about a greater inhibition than when present alone.

In cellular oxidation, involving the cytochrome system, F is believed to interfere with reduction of cytochrome in intact systems and oxidation of cytochromes in cell free systems. Fe in the porphyrin moiety of cytochrome C forms no complex with F at the physiological pH. Observations of combination of F and cytochrome oxidase separately with cytochrome C suggest competitive inhibition by F (Borei, 1945).

The fluoride inhibition curve of acid phosphatase differs from other inhibition curves. It is reversed by higher concentrations of F and augmented at low pH. The nature of inhibition was influenced by ionic strength, specific cations and protein concentration. Multivalent organic anions protected the enzyme against F inhibition (Reiner, Tsuboi & Hudson, 1955). Alkaline phosphatase can be protected against irreversible inactivation by F through prior incubation with alanine at pH 8.8 (Nguyen-van-Thoai, Roche & Roger, 1946).

No difference has been found in the intracellular concentration of enzymes in control bacteria and in bacteria subcultured for 20 days in increasing quantities of F (Williams, 1964). However, 1 ppm F slightly inhibited acid production by streptococci and lactobacilli although, at this concentration of F, the inhibition was small (Bibby, Van Kesteren & Volker, 1942). Following a prior prolonged exposure to F, acid production by lactobacilli was inhibited even in the absence of fluoride. Either some change in protein due to exposure to fluoride or continued adherence of F to protein could be one of the causes of low acid production (Clapper, 1947).

In instances where no effect of fluoride on bacterial metabolism can be observed, the problem of permeability requires recognition. At lower pH values, when the inhibition increases, undissociated HF seems to penetrate yeast cells, thus raising the pH outside the cells (Malm, 1940). While F plus glucose causes no inhibition of dephosphorylation in *Esch. coli*, F plus glucose plus succinate causes 80% inhibition; presumably succinate facilitates F permeability (Aubel, Grunberg-Manago & Szulmajster, 1949). Starvation also increases F permeability in yeast cells (Malm, 1947).

The enzymatic and other mechanisms by which fluoride inhibits dental caries are dealt with by Jenkins in section 4 of this chapter.

As mentioned earlier, we are still a long way from understanding precisely the biochemical mechanisms underlying the role of F, if any, in biological systems, particularly at the low levels F is present in body-fluids and soft tissues.

TABLE 1

PHYSIOLOGICAL PROCESSES AND ENZYMES INFLUENCED SLIGHTLY OR
MODERATELY BY LOW CONCENTRATIONS OF F (10^{-4} M/LITRE AND BELOW) [a]

Physiological process or enzyme involved	Source or material	Concentration of F (M/litre)	Reference
Activation by F			
Glucose fermentation	Esch. coli	10^{-5}	Opienska-Blauth, Kanski & Stobinska (1949)
Embryonal culture	Chick heart	1.25×10^{-5}	Hintzsche (1954)
Photosynthesis	Kidney bean (*Phaseolus vulgaris*)	3×10^{-5}	Navara (1963)
Fermentation	Yeast	5×10^{-5}	Slater (1951)
Respiration	Cancer tissue	10^{-4}	Sellei & Jany (1931)
Nitrogen fixation	Azotobacter	10^{-4}	Fedorov (1947)
Lipase	Liver	5×10^{-8}	Loevenhart & Peirce (1906-7)
Inhibition by F			
Calcification	Hypertrophic cartilage slices (rat)	10^{-5}	Robison & Rosenheim (1934)
Citric acid production	Aspergillus niger	5×10^{-5}	L'vov & Toupizina (1938)
Acid production	Streptococci and lactobacilli	10^{-5}	Bibby, Van Kesteren & Volker (1942); Clapper (1947)
Activation of acetate	Kidney and liver homogenates	10^{-4}	Aisenberg & Potter (1955)
Esterase	Pig liver	5×10^{-7}	Peirce (1913-14)
Acid glycerophosphatase	Sheep brain	6×10^{-6}	Mattocks & Holtan (1949)
Carbonic anhydrase	Rat incisor	10^{-5}	Kondo & Kuriaki (1961)
Adenosine triphosphatase	Cardiac muscle	10^{-5}	Hegglin, Grauer & Munchinger (1949)
Phosphomonoesterase	Serum	10^{-5}	Fleury, Courtois & Plumel (1950)
Phosphatase	Coconut kernel	10^{-4}	Sadasivan (1951)
Pyrophosphatase	Yeast	10^{-4}	Webb (1948)
Pyrophosphatase	Fire-fly	10^{-4}	McElroy, Coulombre & Hays (1951)
Glutamine synthetase	Animals and plants	10^{-4}	Denes (1954)
Acid phosphatase	Human saliva and prostate gland	10^{-4}	Smith, Armstrong & Singer (1950)
Isocitric dehydrogenase	Rat liver	10^{-4}	Doberenz et al. (1964)

[a] The F concentration in normal body-fluids and soft tissues is 5×10^{-6} to 5×10^{-5} M/litre. "Ionic" F in plasma is 5×10^{-7} to 2×10^{-6} M/litre.

Some of the physiological processes and enzymes reported to be activated or inhibited slightly or moderately by levels of fluoride below 2 ppm (10^{-4} M per litre) are shown in Table 1. It may be recalled that the F content of body-fluids is believed to be 0.1-0.2 ppm and of soft tissues to be around 1 ppm.

Is Fluorine an Essential Dietary Element?

The beneficial role of fluorine in the control of caries has been amply demonstrated by epidemiological studies, by the success of fluoridation of public water supplies as a mass caries-control measure, and by the reduction of experimental caries in animals by fluoride in the dietary. In the light of these experiences it is logical to ask: Is fluorine an essential element?

This question has not been satisfactorily answered because of the difficulties in the preparation of a fluoride-free diet and because of the lack of adequately sensitive methods for the determination of minute traces of fluoride. Passing reference may be made to investigations in this area by Sharpless & McCollum (1933), Lawrenz, cited by Mitchell & Edman (1945), McClendon (1944), McClendon & Gershon-Cohen (1953, 1954) and Maurer & Day (1957), and to a discussion by Muhler in Chapter 2, section 3.

In a more recent study a diet extremely low in fluoride was prepared to assess the fluoride requirement of the rat (Venkateswarlu, 1962). Two groups of rats received the low-F diet; one of these groups received double-distilled water and the other water containing 10 ppm F. There was a slight suggestion that the reproductive capacity of the animals in the low-F group was less than that of those in the other group. However, the difference between the two groups may have been only a chance result. It was originally intended to observe the rats through 3 to 5 generations before attempting to reach a decision as to the biological requirement for fluoride in the rat, but the experiment had to be abandoned because few animals reproduced beyond the third generation, and very few of the offspring were adequately nursed by the mothers. The cause of these unexpected developments may perhaps be traced to the artificial diet. Either some unknown deficiency was inadvertently created, or some toxic factor was produced in the preparation and storage of the diet in the refrigerator. Muhler (1951) attempted to prepare a fluoride-low synthetic diet and abandoned the experiments because the purified diet would not sustain reproduction. Maurer & Day (1957) found that only approximately half of the offspring born to female rats fed on a special F-low diet (F less than 0.007 ppm) could be successfully weaned, but from the observations they were able to make they concluded that fluorine was not essential in the rat. It may be well to point out that their conclusions were based on F analyses using a macrodistillation and titration method "sensitive to no less than" 1.0 µg F, whereas the F levels in the present writer's investigations (Venkateswarlu, *op. cit.*) were determined by microdistillation (Singer & Armstrong, 1959) and a microanalytical spectrophotometric method (Venkateswarlu, Armstrong & Singer, 1966a) capable of detecting as little as 0.1-0.2 µg F. In other words, it cannot be ruled out that some of the bones which were reported by Maurer & Day to contain no F might actually have contained some.

In another recent study (Doberenz et al., 1964) on the effects of a minimal F diet on rats, an increase in plasma isocitric dehydrogenase level with a concomitant decrease in the enzyme level in the liver was reported. 10^{-4} M F was found to inhibit liver isocitric dehydrogenase *in vitro*. The report, however, does not include observations on the *in vitro* effect of F on plasma isocitric dehydrogenase activity. The F content of the diet, determined by a macro-method, comparable in sensitivity to that of Maurer & Day, was reported to be less than 0.005 ppm and the mean F content in 91-day-old rat tibiae was 2.9 ppm.

In section 3 of this chapter some observations and hypotheses on the role of F in the formation and maintenance of apatitic structures are described. If these can be confirmed in experimental animals raised on fluoride-free diets, the essential nature of F for the development of calcified tissues would appear to be established.

3. EFFECTS ON THE SKELETON OF MAN (I. Zipkin)

Fluoride is a unique ion in that it continues to deposit in the calcified structures after the other constituents of bone have already reached a steady state. Thus, the major constituents—calcium, phosphorus, magnesium, carbonate and citrate—reach their maximum concentration early in life and remain essentially unchanged, even after administration of large amounts of the ion in question. Fluoride, on the other hand, showed a tenfold increase in bone following ingestion of each of four drinking waters with fluoride contents of <1.0, 1.0, 2.6 and 4.0 ppm, respectively.

About 96% of the fluoride found in the body is deposited in the bones, so that it becomes important to study the effect of this ion on the physical and chemical structure of bone as well as on its morphology and physiology. These effects of fluoride will be discussed as they relate to long-term exposure of man to levels of water-borne fluoride up to 4 ppm. The effects of levels as high as 8 ppm in the drinking water are discussed in detail by Leone in Chapter 8, section 2. Various factors affecting the deposition of fluoride in bone have been reviewed by Weidmann and Weatherell in Chapter 4, section 3.

The physiological effects of water-borne fluoride on the skeleton are a resultant of the effects on the chemistry, morphology, histopathology, X-ray density, and integrity or structure of both the inorganic and the organic phase of bone. In addition, the interplay of bone remodelling, fluoride deposition and mobilization may also influence skeletal physiology or function following fluoride exposure. It will be indicated that the various parameters mentioned do not interfere with the normal physiology of the skeleton in man ingesting water containing up to 4.0 ppm F and indeed up to 8.0 ppm F.

Effect of Fluoride on the Chemistry of Bone

Current theories propose that calcification of bone is preceded by a nucleation process in the early deposition of calcium and phosphorus on the chief organic matrix of bone, collagen, to form the mineral phase generi-

---

[1] The terms "apatite" and "apatitic" refer to compounds deviating from hydroxyapatite in theoretical calcium and phosphate content. They may contain other ions such as fluoride, carbonate or water within the lattice work and give X-ray diffraction patterns very similar to those of pure hydroxyapatite. The crystal structure of hydroxyapatite has recently been redetermined and refined from both X-ray and neutron diffraction data by Kay, Young & Posner (1964).

cally called hydroxyapatite, or $Ca_{10}(PO_4)_6(OH)_2$.[1] Statistically, the hydroxyls of any crystal of apatite in calcified structures may be partially or completely substituted isomorphically by fluoride. Thus, mixed crystals of hydroxy-apatite and fluorapatite may be present. In addition, the mineral phase of hydroxyapatite is presumed to be oriented along the collagen fibres, which are said to act as a sort of model or template for the deposition of the mineral. It would be important, therefore, to study various factors which might change the character or structure of collagen, since they might thereby alter the nucleation process and thus the deposition of mineral.

The chemical changes in bone with fluoride deposition will be related later in the text to crystallinity of the inorganic phase of bone—namely, apatite.

Inorganic constituents

The ash, fluoride, calcium, phosphorus, magnesium, sodium, potassium, and carbonate content of the iliac crest, rib and vertebra of individuals exposed to drinking water containing up to 4.0 ppm F for 10-87 years prior to demise has been reported by Zipkin, McClure & Lee (1960). Data from this study are given in Table 2.

Calcium, phosphorus and potassium in the bone ash were unaffected by mean concentrations of bone fluoride as high as 0.8%. There was a small decrease in sodium as the fluoride increased. The carbonate content decreased about 10%, whereas the magnesium increased about 15%, when the fluoride showed an eightfold increase.

At autopsy the bones of individuals whose drinking water contained 0.5 ppm F and who had been exposed to low concentrations of fluoride in

TABLE 2

ASH, FLUORIDE, CALCIUM, PHOSPHORUS, MAGNESIUM, SODIUM, POTASSIUM, CARBONATE AND CITRATE CONTENT OF SELECTED HUMAN BONES AS RELATED TO FLUORIDE CONCENTRATION OF THE DRINKING WATER[a]

Constituent	Percentage of constituent[b] in bones					
	Iliac crest		Rib		Vertebra	
	< 1.0 ppm[c]	4.0 ppm[c]	< 1.0 ppm[c]	4.0 ppm[c]	< 1.0 ppm[c]	4.0 ppm[c]
Ash.	53.5	58.6	56.0	57.4	49.8	52.3
F	0.08	0.69	0.08	0.70	0.10	0.80
Ca	38.8	38.4	38.8	38.4	37.8	37.8
P	17.5	17.7	17.5	17.7	17.5	17.5
Mg	0.50	0.57	0.50	0.60	0.50	0.61
Na	0.73	0.70	0.79	0.68	0.73	0.68
K	0.09	0.08	0.09	0.10	0.18	0.12
Carbonate . . .	5.83	5.20	5.41	5.19	5.31	4.55
Citrate	2.23	1.56	1.92	1.39	1.95	1.30

[a] After Zipkin, McClure & Lee (1960).
[b] Ash is expressed on a dry, fat-free basis. All other values are expressed on an ash basis.
[c] Concentration of F in drinking water.

the air showed normal values for Ca, P, F and ash (Call et al., 1965) similar to those reported previously by Zipkin, McClure & Lee (*op. cit.*). The highest levels of bone fluoride found in subjects with the most severe kidney disease (Call et al., *op. cit.*) were within the range for normal individuals drinking water containing less than 0.5 ppm F.

Organic constituents

The effect of fluoride on mucopolysaccharide and collagen turnover has been reported. No significant changes were seen in the incorporation of ^{35}S following a 10-fold increase in fluoride incorporation in the rat, which indicated that there was no synthesis of new polysaccharide in the femur, mandible, or pelvis (Zipkin, 1969). Rats receiving 10 ppm F for one month or for 10 months showed no change in total collagen, and only a group drinking water containing 50 ppm F for one month showed any significant decrease in total collagen synthesis of the calvaria (Peck, Zipkin & Whedon, 1965). New collagen synthesis was depressed in the calvaria of rats receiving 10 ppm F for 10 months or 50 ppm F for 2 or 4 weeks. Labelled proline was used as the marker in these experiments. In human subjects suffering from bone resorptive diseases, doses of 15-30 mg F per day for one year have been reported to reduce collagen synthesis, as measured by the *in vitro* incorporation of ^{14}C-proline by iliac crest bone specimens obtained at autopsy (Nichols & Flanagan, 1966). Bone organ culture experiments have also indicated diminished ^{14}C-proline uptake when the culture medium contains 10-20 ppm F (Golub, Glimcher & Goldhaber, 1968b; Proffit & Ackerman, 1964). In addition, degradation of collagen in bone organ cultures has been reported with medium containing as little as 0.2 ppm F, by direct chemical determination of collagen (Golub, Glimcher & Goldhaber, 1968b) and by histological techniques (Goldhaber, 1967).

Data have also been published on the relation of fluoride to the concentration of citrate in human bone (Zipkin, McClure & Lee, 1960). As shown in Table 2, the citrate content of the iliac crest, rib and vertebra decreased about 30 % as the fluoride increased about eightfold.

Effect of Fluoride on the Physical Structure of Bone

The effect of the consumption of drinking water containing up to 4.0 ppm F on histology, X-ray findings and bone density, as well as on the crystallinity of the apatite structure, will be discussed. The X-ray studies are discussed at greater length in Chapter 8, section 5.

Histology

The histology of bones of individuals exposed to low levels of fluoride in drinking water has been reported by Geever et al. (1958) and Weidmann,

Weatherell & Jackson (1963). The iliac crest, rib, vertebra and, in some cases, sternum of individuals drinking water containing <1.0, 1.0, 2.6 and 4.0 ppm F for at least 10 years prior to autopsy contained approximately 0.05% F, 0.15% F, 0.25% F and 0.40% F, respectively, on a dry, fat-free basis. Some 100 bone specimens as well as the intervertebral cartilage were examined histologically (Geever et al., *op. cit.*) for focal calcification of the periosteum and adjacent tendons and fascia, as well as for osteoclasia, osteophytosis and cortical thickness. Marrow sections were examined for haematopoiesis and for the degree and extent of trabeculation. Incidental changes due to aging were observed in all groups and were not significantly related to the fluoride intake.

Weidmann, Weatherell & Jackson (*op. cit.*) examined histologically the ribs of individuals drinking water containing <0.5, 0.8, and 1.9 ppm F for width of the cortex and number and thickening of the cortical trabeculae. No differences were seen in resorption areas of the trabeculae or of the compacta among the three groups.

Roentgenology

In an extensive paediatric study by Schlesinger et al. (1956) children drinking water containing 1.2 ppm F in Newburgh, N.Y., were examined at intervals over a period of ten years. Roentgenograms were taken of the right hand, both knees and the lumbar spine, and bone density as well as bone age was estimated. No differences of any significance could be found in any of the roentgenographic studies, including the bone-density and skeletal maturation (estimations of bone age) assessments. Previously, McCauley & McClure (1954) also found no adverse effect on the rate of ossification and maturation of the carpal bones of children aged 7-14 years continuously exposed to levels of water-borne fluoride as high as 6.2 ppm F.

Using step wedge techniques, Odland, Warnick & Esselbaugh (1958) found no difference in the bone density of the os calcis or the phalanx 5-2 of adolescents from two areas in Montana, one with 1 ppm F and the other with a negligible concentration of fluoride in the drinking water. Large differences in caries prevalence, however, were observed in the two areas.

Increased bone density or osteosclerosis was not apparent roentgenographically when the concentration of fluoride in the drinking water was less than 4 ppm (Geever et al., 1958; Morris, 1965; Stevenson & Watson, 1957), when the urinary fluoride concentration was less than 10 ppm (Largent, Bovard & Heyroth, 1951) or when the bone contained less than about 5000 ppm fluoride on a dry, fat-free basis (Weidmann, Weatherell & Jackson, 1963; Zipkin et al., 1958). Indeed, the fluoride content of bone has been used as a differential diagnosis between rheumatoid spondylitis and crippling fluorosis (Steinberg et al., 1955, 1958).

The increased bone density observed among 10-15% of individuals drinking water containing 8 ppm F (Leone et al., 1955) and the unusually high frequency of osteoporosis seen in Framingham, Mass. (Leone et al., 1960) among individuals consuming an essentially fluoride-free drinking water prompted a number of clinical studies on the effect of high levels of fluoride on resorptive bone disease (Rich, Ensinck & Ivanovich, 1964; Purves, 1962; Cohen & Gardner, 1964; Nagant de Deuxchaisnes & Krane, 1964; Higgins et al., 1965; Hodge & Smith, 1968). The effect of fluoride on bone density and on calcium balance in these studies has been equivocal. Field studies relating senile osteoporosis to water fluoride are reported elsewhere in this monograph.

No data appear to be available on the fluoride concentrations in resorbing human bone. Steinberg et al. (1958) reported that the bones of individuals in both fluoride and non-fluoride areas with various types of arthritis contained normal amounts of fluoride. It would appear that a conservative approach should be taken to the subject of elevated and prolonged administration of fluoride in various bone dyscrasias, as re-emphasized recently by Sognnaes (1965).

McClure (1944) has reported that bone-fracture experience and height-weight data of high school boys and young selectees of the Armed Forces were not related to fluoride levels of up to 6.0 ppm in the drinking water.

Crystallinity of bone apatite

The observation that an increase of fluoride in bone decreases the concentration of a number of chemical constituents, such as citrate, that are usually assigned to the surface of the apatite crystals of bone rather than within the lattice, prompted studies on the size and strain of apatite crystals as influenced by fluoride. For this purpose, X-ray diffraction techniques, as reviewed by Carlström (1955), using powdered specimens of bone were employed by Zipkin, Posner & Eanes (1962), Schraer et al. (1962) and Eanes et al. (1965). The theoretical considerations involved in the techniques employed for human bone were reported by Posner et al. (1963).

The X-ray diffraction patterns of powdered bone are poorly resolved when compared with authentic samples of well-crystallized hydroxyapatite. This lack of resolution is due to the small size and the imperfection of biological apatites. An increase in the degree of resolution using a template method (Posner et al., *op. cit.*), however, indicated an increased crystallinity associated with an increase in bone fluoride.

Relation to age. Robinson & Watson (1955) have made the most comprehensive study on the relation of crystal size to age in the human. They reported an increase in size under the electron microscope from an essentially non-crystalline unresolvable particle of less than 50 Å in the infant to crystals 1500 Å by 500 Å by about 100 Å in the senile subject. Enamel apatite is much more crystalline than the apatite of bone and may exceed 10 000 Å in length and 1000 Å in thickness. Larger crystals per unit mass would provide less surface than smaller crystals or, phrased otherwise, a reduced specific surface. Since most reactions occur at surfaces, large crystals would be more stable and less chemically reactive. The increase in crystal size with age would be expected to play an important role in the decrease in turnover exchange reactions in aging bone.

Relation to fluoride deposition in bone. Since the crystals of bone apatite are exceedingly small, show strain and imperfections and hence give a poorly resolved X-ray diffraction pattern (Zipkin, Posner & Eanes, 1962), it was not possible to measure the width at half maximum (β) of any of the characteristic peaks of apatite as an index of line broadening. The crystallinity, as previously mentioned, is inversely proportional to the degree of line broadening, so that a lower β value calculated from an over-all template (Posner et al., 1963) represents a higher degree of crystallinity.

Fig. 1 shows an unresolved X-ray diffraction powder pattern of a sample of iliac crest containing 0.224% F.

The increased resolution of a sample of iliac crest containing 0.873% F can be seen in Fig. 2.

The inverse relationship between fluoride content and β values for a large number of bones from individuals drinking water containing up to 4.0 ppm F is shown in Table 3.

TABLE 3

RELATION BETWEEN PERCENTAGE OF FLUORIDE IN HUMAN BONE
AND "CRYSTALLINITY" INDEX

Bone		New York City	Grand Rapids, Mich.	Colorado Springs, Colo.	Lubbock, Tex.
Iliac crest					
	Mean F	0.064 (12) [a]	0.205 (3) [a]	0.504 (10) [a]	0.711 (3) [a]
	β [b]	0.959	0.786	0.740	0.667
Rib					
	Mean F	0.082 (13)	0.273 (2)	0.495 (12)	0.842 (1)
	β	0.919	0.775	0.738	0.600
Vertebra					
	Mean F	0.088 (11)	0.280 (4)	0.606 (11)	0.802 (4)
	β	0.950	0.853	0.691	0.600
Mean					
	Mean F	0.078 (36)	0.253 (9)	0.533 (33)	0.773 (8)
	β	0.942	0.837	0.733	0.625

[a] The figures in parentheses indicate the number of comparisons.

[b] β is inversely related to crystallinity and a decrease in β is a measure of an increase in crystal size or state of perfection, or both.

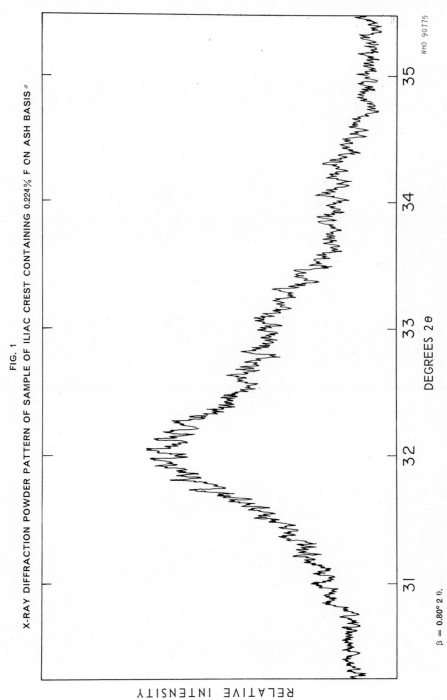

FIG. 1

X-RAY DIFFRACTION POWDER PATTERN OF SAMPLE OF ILIAC CREST CONTAINING 0.224% F ON ASH BASIS [a]

RELATIVE INTENSITY

DEGREES 2θ

$\beta = 0.80° 2\theta$.

[a] Reproduced, with permission, from Zipkin et al. (1962).

WHO 90775

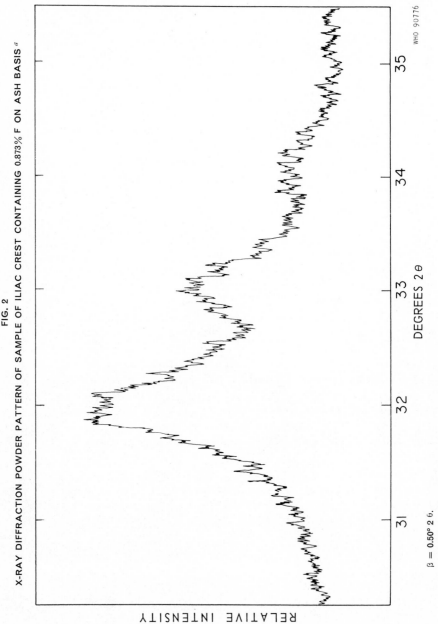

FIG. 2

X-RAY DIFFRACTION POWDER PATTERN OF SAMPLE OF ILIAC CREST CONTAINING 0.873% F ON ASH BASIS [a]

RELATIVE INTENSITY

DEGREES 2θ

$\beta = 0.50°$ 2 θ.

[a] Reproduced, with permission, rom Zipkin et al. (1962).

WHO 90776

While line broadening in X-ray diffraction patterns does not distinguish between the contribution of size or strain to crystallinity, low angle scattering studies by Eanes et al. (1965) have indicated that the enhancement of crystallinity is due in the main to increased size of the bone apatite crystals.

Increased crystallinity as a result of increased deposition of fluoride has also been demonstrated recently by Schraer et al. (1962) in rats and by Zipkin, Eanes & Shupe (1964) in cattle. Recent studies have also indicated increased bone crystallinity in the mouse (Zipkin, Sokoloff & Frazier, 1967) and in the chicken (Zipkin and associates, unpublished data) following administration of fluoride.

The enhancement of the crystal texture of bone apatite by fluoride may be due either to a direct effect of fluoride on the nucleation process to form large crystals of hydroxyapatite or to a displacement of such ions as carbonate (Bachra, Trautz & Simon, 1965; Grøn et al., 1963) and citrate (Patterson, 1954) which have been shown in *in vitro* studies to disturb crystallization of apatitic compounds.

Relation to chemistry of bone. It is generally agreed that Na, K and citrate do not occupy positions within the lattice of biologically synthesized apatites. The position of magnesium is still equivocal and recent evidence indicates that carbonate may at least partially substitute for phosphate in the apatite crystal (LeGeros, Trautz & LeGeros, 1965).

The increase in bone crystallinity may affect the concentration of those ions which are surface-oriented. As already mentioned, fluoride reduces the over-all surface per unit of mass of bone crystals thus delimiting the concentration of those ions found there, such as Na, K and citrate. It is also possible that such ions as calcium and phosphate as well as magnesium and carbonate may be adsorbed on the surface of the crystals as well as being incorporated within the lattice. It has also been postulated that magnesium is present as a cation complex $(MgOH)^+$ on the surface of the apatite crystal. The increase in magnesium with an increase in fluoride may be due to the formation of some ion complexes of Mg (OH, F) as a separate phase.

The decrease in carbonate with fluoride may be due to an increase in crystal perfection, thus enhancing the elimination of carbonate from the lattice, where it is presumed to substitute for phosphate. On the other hand, it is also conceivable that a simple displacement of surface-adsorbed carbonate occurs.

It is most difficult to resolve clearly the possibilities outlined since the crystals are small and show strain and imperfections, and hence only poor diffraction patterns are produced. Even when good resolution of the X-ray diffraction pattern is obtained, other techniques such as infra-red and solubility measurements as well as the electron microscope must be used. Present methods do not yet unequivocally establish the locus of an ion as extra- or intra-crystalline.

Possible Mechanisms for the Deposition and Mobilization
of Skeletal Fluoride

The deposition of fluoride in bone and its mobilization therefrom may be considered the resultant of at least two major processes. Vital metabolic processes of bone remodelling must play an important role in fluoride deposition, although major emphasis will be placed on physico-chemical considerations. Possible calcium phosphate precursors of apatite will be discussed as proposed by the workers in Dallemagne's laboratory (Dallemagne, 1964), by Brown et al. (1962) and by Hirschman & Sobel (1965). Conflicting views on the possible existence of a so-called "calcium defect" apatite will also be discussed. It thus seems feasible that more than one mineral phase may exist in calcifying structures.

Metabolic considerations

The ultrastructural organization of bone has been reviewed recently by Pautard (1964), and its relation to the formation and resorption of the skeleton has been discussed by Hancox & Boothroyd (1964).

It is generally believed that some of the apatite crystals are oriented along the collagen fibres (Glimcher, 1959) and that the mucopolysaccharide ground substance may also play a role in the nucleation and growth of the apatite crystals (Sobel, 1955). It is apparent, therefore, that factors affecting the organization of the organic matrix may alter the deposition of apatite and thus the incorporation of fluoride. Newly forming matrix is associated with active osteoblasts, while resorption of bone has been associated with osteoclasts at the resorbing site. Osteoblastic and osteoclastic activity may thus play a role in either "freeing" or "burying" active sites or surfaces of the apatite molecule. As bone ages and reaches a more or less "steady state" in the remodelling of its Haversion systems, less fluoride may be deposited. In addition, little fluoride is released from rat bone following discontinuance of fluoride administration (Zipkin, 1960) and this may in part be due to "buried" and relatively inaccessible apatite as a result of the decreased metabolic turnover of bone. The loss of fluoride is relatively small and may also be explained on physico-chemical grounds, which will be developed later.

Fluoride is not deposited uniformly throughout a given bone and may be related to the rate of growth and the degree of vascularization in various parts of the same bone. Thus, more fluoride is deposited in the epiphyseal than in the diaphyseal portions of bone (Zipkin & Scow, 1956).

The deposition of fluoride in non-physiological calcifications such as urinary calculi does not appear to follow the orderly processes of accretion and remodelling found in bone (Zipkin, Lee & Leone, 1958). Indeed, the concentration of fluoride in the calculi was higher than that in the bones of individuals with essentially the same fluoride exposure. In addition, the fluoride content of the urinary tract calculi of individuals from low-fluoride areas was not significantly different from that of calculi from individuals whose drinking water contained 2.6 ppm F. The bones, on the other hand, show about a five- to six-fold difference in fluoride concentration. Fluoride has been reported to be associated with a decrease in aortic plaque in human subjects (Bernstein et al., 1966), and both animal and *in vitro* models have been devised to study this phenomenon (Zipkin, I. et al., unpublished data). Factors affecting the biological deposition of fluoride are more completely discussed by Weidmann and Weatherell in Chapter 4, section 3.

Physico-chemical considerations

Fluoride appears to be associated with the mineral phase of bones and teeth almost exclusively, so that the deposition and mobilization of fluoride may be considered to simulate an *in vitro* reaction of fluoride with hydroxy-apatite. It would seem worth while at the outset, therefore, to consider the various formulae which have been proposed for the mineral phase of bone and to remember that none has been unequivocally proved to represent the true inorganic compound or compounds of bone. The major source of difficulty lies in the observation that "young" bone rarely attains the theoretical Ca/P weight ratio of 2.15 for hydroxyapatite, $Ca_{10}(PO_4)_6(OH)_2$.

As bone "matures" the Ca/P weight ratio approaches and may exceed that of stoichiometric hydroxyapatite. The composition of hydroxyapatite is variable, that is, the percentages of Ca and P may differ from the theoretical percentages, but the apatitic materials still give X-ray patterns virtually identical to that of stoichiometric hydroxyapatite. Hence, a number of formulae have been introduced to account for the non-stoichiometry of hydroxyapatite.

Synthetic apatitic calcium phosphates can be prepared with lower Ca/P ratios which give diffraction patterns similar to $Ca_{10}(PO_4)_6(OH)_2$ (Winand, Dallemagne & Duyckaerts, 1961; Armstrong & Singer, 1965). Reactions of fluoride with some of the proposed structures of the apatite series of compounds will be presented later.

1. Proposed formulae for the inorganic phase of bone:[1]

(a) $Ca_{10-x}H_x(PO_4)_6(OH)_{2-x}$, where $x = 0\text{-}2$ (proposed by Winand, Dallemagne & Duyckaerts (1961)). If $x = 1$ then $Ca_9H(PO_4)_6OH$ or $3Ca_3(PO_4)_2$, H_2O results which has been designated α-tricalcium phosphate hydrate by Dallemagne and co-workers. It has been postulated that both hydroxyapatite and $3Ca_3(PO_4)_2$, H_2O may co-exist as separate phases.

---

[1] von Kühl & Nebergall (1963) have proposed a general formula for synthetic apatites that does not necessarily include bone, but considers carbonate—namely: $Ca_{10-x-y}(HPO_4,CO_3)_x(PO_4)_{6-x}(OH)_{2-x-2y}$. When x and y are zero, stoichiometric hydroxyapatite results.

(b) $Ca_{10-x}H_{2x}(PO_4)_6(OH)_2$ (proposed by Posner, Stutman & Lippincott (1960)). When $x = 0$, then $Ca_{10}(PO_4)_6(OH)_2$ or hydroxyapatite results. The authors suggest that protons between the oxygens of phosphate ion. make up the defect in Ca so as to balance the molecule electrostatically-This view has been contested by Winand and associates (op. cit.) and Brown et al. (1962) on the ground that more than one apatitic phase may exist with a lower Ca/P ratio rather than merely a single phase of defect hydroxyapatite, thus accounting for the lower Ca/P ratio.

(c) Neuman & Neuman (1958) have proposed the formula Ca_{10-x} $(H_3O)_{2x}(PO_4)_6(OH)_2$, where hydronium ions (H_3O^+) may provide electro-neutrality by compensating for missing Ca.

(d) Octacalcium phosphate, $Ca_8H_2(PO_4)_6$, $5H_2O$, has been proposed by Brown (1966) as a calcium phosphate compound which because of its structural relationship to hydroxyapatite may co-exist with it in bone, particularly at initiation of deposition of the inorganic phase.

(e) Armstrong & Singer (1965) have suggested that the bone mineral is made up of microcrystals of hydroxyapatite with surface-coated ions derived from extracellular body-fluids (Ca, Mg, Na, K, carbonate, citrate and phosphate). It would be highly important to be able to determine by direct measurements the intra- and extra-crystalline proportions of these ions.

Thus, formulae have been proposed which require either hydrogen (formula b), hydronium ions (formula c), hydrogen with an accompanying loss of hydroxyl (formula a and formula of von Kühl & Nebergall) or loss of hydroxyl (formula of von Kühl & Nebergall) to maintain electrostatic balance. In addition, separate phases of "α-tricalcium phosphate hydrate" or octacalcium phosphate have been postulated to exist or layer with hydroxyapatite. And it has also been suggested that bone mineral is represented by microcrystals of hydroxyapatite with a variety of adsorbed ions. The relative proportions of surface and intracrystal components were calculated from theoretical equations (Armstrong & Singer, 1965).

2. Reactions of fluoride with apatitic calcium phosphates:

(a) Substitution. Since the fluoride ion is about the same size and shape as the hydroxyl ion, it can readily exchange isomorphically, with only a small decrease in the a axis from 9.42 Å for hydroxyapatite to 9.37 Å for fluorapatite (Carlström, 1955) as shown by X-ray diffraction data. Infra-red data by Elliott (1964) have also demonstrated the substitution of hydroxyl in synthetic hydroxyapatite by fluoride. The c axis remains unchanged at about 6.88 Å. The substitution of hydroxyl by fluoride is probably statistical in that some apatite crystals may show complete substitution, while, in others, mixed crystals may exist—namely, $Ca_{10}(PO_4)_6(OH, F)$.

McCann (1953) and Neuman et al. (1950), as well as other workers cited by Hodge & Smith (1965), have clearly demonstrated that, at low levels, fluoride reacts with synthetic apatites (McCann, op. cit.) as well as with bone

7. At low levels of fluoride concentration, the predominating reaction with the apatite, e.g., of bone, is presumed to be substitution for the hydroxyl. At high levels of fluoride concentration, it is postulated that CaF_2 forms. The latter compound has not been seen in bone, but has been identified after topical application of fluoride to enamel surfaces.

8. In addition to substitution of hydroxyl by fluoride in the apatite of bone, it appears that fluoride may enhance the rate of seeding of apatite. In other words, precipitation of apatite occurs at a lower concentration of calcium and phosphate ions than would be expected.

9. It has been suggested that the early microcrystals to appear in calcifying structures are probably not hydroxyapatite, but may be a hydrated tricalcium phosphate or octacalcium phosphate. Both these compounds have a Ca/P ratio lower than that calculated for hydroxyapatite. It has also been postulated that there is one phase in bone, namely, an apatite with missing calcium, that leads to a non-stoichiometric or so-called "defect" apatite.

10. It has been stressed that (a) there is no direct evidence of the state of fluoride in calcified structures, (b) more than one "species" of fluoride may exist, (c) a number of different calcium phosphates may co-exist, and (d) information is lacking on the state of the bonds between the organic and inorganic phases of bone.

4.   MECHANISM OF EFFECTS IN THE MOUTH (G. N. Jenkins)

The concentration of fluoride in the dental tissues follows a similar pattern to that of bone described in Chapter 4, section 3. The age of the subject and the fluoride intake in food and drink are the chief influences, but in enamel, from which cells and a circulation are absent, the uptake almost ceases after the age of about thirty. The F concentrations in deciduous teeth are consistently lower than those in permanent teeth formed under the same conditions.

It is now well established that, again as in bone, the distribution of fluoride within the tooth is not uniform. The fluoride levels in the outer layers of enamel are five to ten times higher than those in the inner layers. This probably arises partly because the outer layers are in contact with tissue fluid for a longer time after formation and before eruption than are the inner layers and partly because, after eruption, the outer enamel is in contact with the saliva. The secondary dentine, which forms slowly throughout life and has relatively prolonged contact with the tissue fluid of the pulp, has a higher F concentration than the more rapidly formed primary dentine. The rise in fluoride concentration with age in dentine is due partly to a rise in the concentration in the primary dentine and partly to the fact that the proportion of secondary dentine in the whole tooth increases with age.

Other effects of fluoride on the composition of teeth are discussed more logically after considering the relation between the fluoride concentration and the solubility of enamel and its caries resistance.

Fluoride Concentration of Enamel in Relation to Caries

Quite soon after the relation between fluoride and caries had been demonstrated, Armstrong & Brekhus (1938) reported that enamel from non-carious teeth contained a higher concentration of fluoride (0.0111 %) than did the surviving enamel from carious teeth (0.0069 %), but that the concentration in dentine did not differ in the two groups. This difference in enamel fluoride levels was of high statistical significance and referred to teeth varying in caries resistance but formed in areas without a high fluoride concentration in the water. For some years, these figures were quoted as being the only established chemical difference between enamel with high and enamel with low resistance to caries. A set of figures published later by McClure (1948) failed to confirm them, however. After it had become clear that the fluoride concentration of enamel was influenced by the age of the subject, Armstrong & Singer (1963b) reported that the teeth analysed in the earlier study came from subjects who differed sufficiently in average age to account for the difference in fluoride concentration in the enamel. There is still no explanation of why the fluoride concentration of the dentine showed no difference, however, since it is also affected by age.

Effect on carbonate and citrate of enamel

The question of the relation between the fluoride of enamel and caries resistance was re-opened by Nikiforuk (1961), who investigated the concentration on the *outer surface* of enamel in caries-resistant and carious teeth from individuals in towns with and without a high fluoride concentration in the drinking water. In view of the finding discussed in section 3 of this chapter that fluoride affected the carbonate and citrate concentrations of bone, Nikiforuk studied also the concentrations of those substances in the inner and outer enamel. His first published results (Table 4) suggested that the outer enamel of non-carious teeth from Toronto (0.1 ppm in water) contained a significantly higher fluoride concentration (136 ppm) than that from the surviving part of carious teeth (83 ppm). In Brantford, Ontario, where the fluoride content of the water is 1 ppm, the corresponding figures were 357 ppm and 229 ppm. Smaller differences in the opposite direction were found for the carbonate content of outer enamel (lower in the "fluoride town" and higher in the carious teeth). When the ratio of carbonate to fluoride was compared in the outer enamel from the four sets of teeth, very striking differences were obtained, the values ranging from 0.53 for non-carious enamel from a town with 1 ppm F to 2.45 for carious teeth from a town without fluoride. Later estimations (Nikiforuk, 1965) on larger

TABLE 4

MEAN VALUES FOR CARBONATE AND FLUORIDE CONCENTRATIONS IN OUTERMOST
LAYERS OF CARIOUS AND NON-CARIOUS TEETH[a]

	CO_2 (%)		F (ppm)		CO_2: F ratio $\left(\dfrac{\%\ \text{of}\ CO_2}{\text{ppm F}} \times 100\right)$	
	Carious	Non-carious	Carious	Non-carious	Carious	Non-carious
Deciduous . . . . (from fluoride town)	2.09	1.90	202	369	1.05	0.51
Deciduous . . . . (from non-fluoride town)	2.02	2.03	84	139	2.40	1.46
Permanent . . . . (from fluoride town)	1.86	1.79	285	425	0.65	0.42
Permanent . . . . (from non-fluoride town)	1.84	1.83	176	183	1.04	1.00

[a] After Nikiforuk (1965).

numbers of teeth confirmed the difference in the fluoride level and in the carbonate to fluoride ratio of carious and non-carious teeth from a fluoride town, but not from a town with no fluoride in the water. There was a correlation between fluoride and citrate on the surface enamel, but it was much weaker than that in bone. Brudevold, McCann & Grøn (1965) stated that their analyses failed to confirm the conclusions of Nikiforuk on the interrelation between carbonate and fluoride in enamel, but their results did, in fact, show a similar trend where the F concentration of the water supply varied from 0.1 to 1.6 ppm; it was at higher intakes that the relationship broke down.

Mode of Action of Fluoride in Dental Caries

The theories on the mode of action of fluoride that have attracted most attention are (a) that fluoride reduces the solubility of enamel in acid and (b) that fluoride acts as an inhibitor of the bacterial enzymes responsible for producing the acid which is believed to attack the enamel in caries. Other plausible theories are that fluoride affects the protein matrix of enamel (this suggestion has not been adequately investigated) and that it influences the shape of the tooth. It is possible, and perhaps probable, that fluoride may work in several ways. The possibility that mechanisms exist which have not so far been discovered must be borne in mind.

Reduction in solubility of enamel

It is very easy to demonstrate that if enamel is shaken with a solution of fluoride, even as dilute as 1 ppm, and then washed, its solubility in acid is reduced. Similarly, if as little as 0.1 ppm fluoride is present in an acid solution in which the solubility of enamel is tested, the solubility is reduced (Manly & Harrington, 1959). There is no doubt, therefore, that fluoride can reduce the solubility of enamel when it is present either in the enamel or in the solvent. The practical issue is whether fluoride intakes from concentrations known to be effective in caries (1 ppm or less in water) produce sufficiently large differences in the fluoride concentration of enamel or of the oral fluids to influence solubility. Curiously enough, the question has not been extensively studied and the available evidence is indecisive. Jenkins, Armstrong & Speirs (1952) compared the solubility of the intact outer enamel of groups of teeth from towns with water supplies containing 0, 1 and 2 ppm fluoride and all the results showed a trend towards lesser solubility in the "high fluoride" teeth, but not all the differences were statistically significant. Finn & DeMarco (1956) compared the solubility of ground, whole enamel from teeth formed in an artificially fluoridated area and in a control area and found the former to be slightly less soluble. Isaac et al. (1958) made an extensive study of layers of enamel ground off teeth formed under various fluoride intakes: they, too, found the enamel with the higher fluoride concentrations was less soluble, but the differences were small (less than 5%) and there were some anomalous findings. Taken as a whole, these results give general support to the theory that fluoride acts by reducing the solubility of enamel, although they are indecisive because there is no means of knowing whether these small and erratic differences are large enough to influence caries. The presence of fluoride in the plaque,[1] whose F concentration is influenced by that in drinking water (Dawes et al., 1965), may reduce the effectiveness of the acid formed by plaque bacteria in dissolving enamel.

Another aspect of this theory arises from the *in vitro* findings of Myers, Hamilton & Becks (1952) that fluoride is more readily bound by enamel which is changed by early caries than by normal enamel. The solubility of enamel in very early carious lesions in teeth from high- and low-fluoride towns was compared by Dowse & Jenkins (1957), who found a very much higher fluoride concentration and lower solubility in the carious enamel from the "high fluoride" teeth.

These results suggest a possible mechanism by which fluoride could reduce caries in teeth already erupted when they were first exposed to fluoride. If an early cavity is formed, then the enamel presumably becomes more permeable, which facilitates the entrance and binding of fluoride in depth to the surviving enamel. A reduction in solubility at this stage would be expected to slow the rate of development of the cavity.

At first, it was thought that fluorapatite, the main fluoride-containing constituent of enamel and the substance formed when hydroxyapatite is

---

[1] The dental plaque is the layer of bacteria, suspended in a protein matrix which deposits on the teeth, in which the acid believed to cause caries is formed. Owing to the technical difficulties involved in studying the minute amounts of plaque which can be collected, most work on acid production has been carried out on saliva.

treated with low concentrations of fluoride, was less soluble than hydroxy-apatite. In a tooth which had received fluoride, either during development or afterwards, the proportion of apatite in the form of fluorapatite would increase and so, according to this theory, the solubility would fall. Gray, Francis & Griebstein (1962) first raised doubts about this theory when they reported that the dissolution rates in acid of hydroxyapatite and fluorapatite, if compared over very short periods of time, did not differ. These workers found that the solubilities began to diverge only after several minutes' exposure to acid, and they concluded that the apparently lower solubility of fluorapatite arose as follows. As the fluorapatite dissolved, the calcium and fluoride ions released precipitated as an impermeable layer of calcium fluoride on the surface of the crystals, which remained undissolved, thus preventing solvent from reaching the crystal and dissolved ions from leaving it.

Another approach to this problem suggests that if apatite crystals form *in vivo* in the presence of concentrations of fluoride higher than usual, the carbonate in the crystals is reduced, and the solubility likewise, animal experiments having indicated that a low carbonate concentration in enamel is associated with a reduced solubility and a high caries resistance. As already mentioned, there is evidence of a fluoride-carbonate interrelationship in human enamel. More recently this concept has been replaced by the hypothesis, based on the finding that high concentrations of fluoride in a medium from which apatite is crystallizing improve the "crystallinity" of the apatite and that carbon dioxide has the opposite effect, that large, well-formed crystals, free from defects, dissolve less readily than small crystals with many defects. There is good evidence that this change in crystallinity occurs in human bone from subjects with a high fluoride intake for long periods (Zipkin, Posner & Eanes, 1962; Posner et al., 1963), but it seems, at present, to be merely a speculation that it occurs also in enamel. Bone is metabolizing and remodelling throughout life and has a much greater opportunity of being influenced by fluoride than has enamel, which, apart from the extreme outer surface, is in an environment where changes are minimal. Unless the enamel receives sufficient fluoride during its formation, it seems unlikely that the bulk of it could be influenced in the same way as bone.

Brudevold, McCann & Grøn (1965) have pointed out that many substances besides fluoride reduce the solubility of apatite (e.g., zinc, lead, tin, cadmium, copper) but only fluoride is known to reduce caries. They argue that fluoride must act through some unique property rather than through a property shared by many other substances. They have developed the idea, mentioned in section 3 of this chapter, that only in the presence of fluoride is an apatite deposited: in its absence, more soluble types of crystals such as brushite ($CaHPO_4$) or octacalcium phosphate are believed to be formed. This hypothesis can be considered in conjunction with the findings of Pigman, Koulourides & Newbrun (1960) that when whole teeth are treated with acid solutions, the enamel becomes soft and decalcified, but if they are then treated with a solution containing calcium phosphate and fluoride ions, a rehardening occurs following the precipitation of calcium phosphate on the enamel surface. If this occurs *in vivo,* the caries process can be pictured as short periods of decalcification, following the rapid acid formation that occurs after carbohydrate ingestion, alternating with periods in which precipitation of calcium phosphate occurs. The effect of fluoride is not only to favour the precipitation but also, Brudevold and co-workers suggest, to ensure that the salt precipitated is of the apatite structure which is less soluble than other possible crystalline forms. Although this is sometimes regarded as an alternative to the solubility hypothesis, it can be considered as a subtle explanation of the effect of fluoride on solubility. The concentration of fluoride in the solution will determine the proportion of fluoride present in the apatite and this can influence solubility, although perhaps indirectly, as suggested by Gray, Francis & Griebstein (1962).

It is doubtful whether the very small and intermittent rise in the fluoride concentration of the plasma brought about by the ingestion of the low concentrations of fluoride that are sufficient to reduce caries would influence the crystalline form of *developing* enamel. The effect is more likely to be important in the presence of the much higher fluoride concentrations in the plaque and near the crystals dissolving and reprecipitating in a carious lesion.

It is clear that although the facts give general, but not conclusive, support to the solubility theory, the mechanism by which fluoride may reduce solubility is at present extremely controversial.

Inhibition of bacterial enzymes

The well-known inhibitory effect which fluoride exerts on certain enzymes—including some of those concerned with glycolysis—raised the possibility that reduction in acid production, or in reactions associated with it, by the bacteria of saliva or the dental plaque might be the explanation of the anti-caries action. The validity of this theory depends upon the answers obtained to two questions:

(1)   What concentration of fluoride is necessary to bring about a decisive reduction of acid production?

(2)   What is the concentration of fluoride ions in the plaque?

Bibby & Van Kesteren (1940) investigated the effect of a range of fluoride concentrations on pure cultures of salivary bacteria and found that while 2 ppm F had a small but detectable effect on acid production, much higher concentrations were needed to affect bacterial growth. The concentration of fluoride in saliva is 0.1-0.2 ppm,[1] which is much below that which Bibby & Van Kesteren found was necessary even for the smallest detectable effect. In view of the striking evidence that fluoride could reduce the solubility of teeth *in vitro* (which, as already noted, preceded any evidence about the

---

[1] Recent studies with the fluoride electrode suggest that only some 20 % of the fluoride in saliva is present in a free ionic form (Grøn et al., 1968).

effect of fluoride on the solubility of teeth *in vivo*), the anti-enzyme theory received little attention.

Borei (1945) reviewed the evidence on the factors which influenced the inhibitory action of fluoride on enzymes and pointed out that if fluoride was added to an organism at an acid pH, its effect was greatly enhanced. This point was tested on salivary organisms and it was found that if fluoride was added to salivary bacteria at a pH of 5.0, as little as 6-10 ppm stopped acid production completely for some hours and even promoted a slight rise in pH, caused by alkali production, which was not only unopposed by acid production but even slightly stimulated (Jenkins, 1959, 1960). Of other workers in this field, Capozzi et al. (1967) studied the anti-enzymatic activity of the following fluorine compounds, not least with a view to their utilization in toothpastes: NaF, SnF_2, Na_2SiF_6, $MgSiF_6$, Na_2PO_3F and an amine fluoride indicated as GA297. In 4-mM concentration all these compounds inhibited lactic acid formation by lactobacilli, though Na_2PO_3F did so only after 24 hours. In tests with crystalline enzymes, enolase and phosphoglyceromutase were inhibited to the greatest extent.

Fluoride in plaque and its possible significance. Hardwick & Leach (1963) investigated the fluoride concentration in plaque from adults and found it surprisingly high, even in a town without fluoride in its water supply, averaging 66.9 ppm, with a range of 6 to nearly 180 ppm. It has been shown that the plaque fluoride is related to the fluoride of the drinking water (Dawes et al., 1965). Plaques collected from children in towns without fluoride and with 2 ppm in their water supplies averaged 26 ppm and 49 ppm respectively. It is not entirely clear why these figures were both *lower* than those obtained in the first investigation, but it is probably because there were several differences in procedure in the two surveys. These concentrations are several hundred times greater than those in saliva and could only remain in the plaque if the fluoride is present in some bound form, which has not yet been identified. Studies with the fluoride electrode show that the concentration of free ionic fluoride is below 1 ppm in plaque from a low-fluoride town and between 1 and 2 ppm in plaque from a town with 2 ppm in the water; in other words, about 95 % of the plaque fluoride is bound (Jenkins, Edgar & Ferguson, 1969). It has nevertheless been found that when samples of plaque from high (2 ppm) and low fluoride areas are allowed to stand with sucrose and the pH changes are measured, there is a significantly more rapid pH fall in the plaque from the low-fluoride town. These apparently contradictory results can perhaps be reconciled by the finding that if pure cultures of bacteria isolated from plaque are grown in fluoride-containing media they store fluoride and produce acid from sugar more slowly than fluoride-free controls. These results suggest that much of the fluoride of plaque may be inside the bacteria where it exerts an inhibitory effect.

Although the plaque fluoride has usually been considered in relation to anti-enzymatic effects, it also may influence caries by reducing the effectiveness of acid in dissolving enamel.

In addition to acid production, another type of activity by the plaque bacteria has recently been discovered, and although its importance in caries has not yet been proved, it seems likely. This activity is the synthesis of at least two types of polysaccharide from ingested sugar. It is very probable that the course of events in the plaque following the ingestion of sugar is as follows. Acid-producing bacteria rapidly convert some of the sugar to acid and the pH of the plaque falls and, more slowly, some sugar is built up into polysaccharide. When the sugar is all metabolized, acid production may continue from the stored polysaccharide and this may have the effect of lowering the pH still further or of prolonging the time during which the pH is low. It is believed that the enamel can only dissolve if the pH is below some critical figure, which varies from plaque to plaque but is in the neighbourhood of 5.5. The lower the pH reached, or the longer the time it is below the critical figure, the greater the decalcification will be expected to be. Two groups of workers (Kleinberg & Sandham, 1964; Weiss, Schnetzer & King, 1964) have shown that the synthesis of carbohydrate from glucose by oral bacteria, as well as acid production, is inhibited by concentrations of fluoride (2 and 4 ppm) well within those likely to be released when the plaque is acid.

Enzymatic site of inhibitory action. The enzyme of the Emden-Myerhof scheme which is most sensitive to fluoride is enolase (Warburg & Christian, 1942, confirmed by unpublished data of Jenkins). If enolase is the site of inhibition of glycolysis in the saliva or dental plaque, it would be expected that phosphoglyceric acid would accumulate instead of lactic acid. Repeated attempts by a variety of methods to demonstrate the presence of phosphoglyceric acid in saliva incubated with sugar and fluoride have failed (Jenkins, Ferguson & Edgar, 1967) and it seems unlikely that enolase, in spite of its great sensitivity, is the site of enzyme inhibition in saliva. Another piece of evidence suggesting that inhibition occurs at some stage much earlier than enolase is that if phosphoglyceric acid (which, according to Fosdick & Wessinger (1940), is more highly ionized than lactic acid) accumulated in lieu of lactic acid, the pH would fall to lower values in the presence of inhibitory concentrations of fluoride. In fact, fluoride greatly reduces the pH change, which implies that it inhibits some stage before that at which acid forms. It has been found that glucose utilization is reduced by fluoride, corresponding with diminished acid production, and it is concluded that a very early stage of glycolysis is inhibited—either hexokinase or the passage of glucose through the cell wall (Kleinberg & Sandham, 1964, and unpublished data from the writer's laboratory). There is evidence that hexokinase is not sensitive to low concentrations of fluoride (Berger et al., 1946); this, while it has not been thoroughly tested under a variety of conditions, increases the probability that glucose uptake by the cell is affected rather than any specific enzyme.

Bramstedt, Kröncke & Naujoks (1960) found that concentrations of fluoride of less than 1 ppm *increased* the rate of metabolism of sugar by certain organisms taken from the mouth. They suggested that this action might occur *in vivo* and result in a greater rate of removal of sugar, thereby reducing the time during which sugar is available for acid production. Although the acceleration—rather than the inhibition—of some enzyme action by low concentrations of fluoride has been well established by other workers, these paradoxical effects have not been demonstrated *in vivo*. The relation of the work of Bramstedt and associates to the action of fluoride in caries remains uncertain.

Source of fluoride in plaque. There are three possible sources from which the plaque can obtain fluoride: (1) saliva, (2) food and drink, and (3) the enamel surface. A few simple calculations show that most of it must come from either saliva or ingesta and not from the enamel surface. Although the fluoride concentration in plaque is high, the absolute amounts contained by the plaque in one mouth are minute owing to the small bulk of the plaque. If plaque is allowed to accumulate for a few days the average weight is only in the neighbourhood of 10 mg. If this contained 50 ppm fluoride, the weight of fluoride would be 0.5 μg, which is equal to the fluoride in 10 ml of saliva (assuming a concentration of 0.05 ppm) or in as little as 0.5 ml of drinking water containing 1 ppm. It is likely that the plaque fluoride is derived from the slow trickle of saliva or from the much larger but intermittent washes with drinking water. The work of Carlson, Armstrong & Singer (1960b) with ^{18}F had given grounds for expecting that the fluoride concentration in saliva would be related to that of plasma. This has been established by means of the fluoride electrode (Grøn et al., 1968). The increased fluoride of plaque in high-fluoride areas is probably largely derived from the slightly raised concentration of fluoride in the saliva.

It has been shown that the uptake of fluoride by the apatite of enamel is virtually irreversible, so it is most unlikely that enamel fluoride could diffuse into the plaque to provide a significant proportion of the plaque fluoride. If fluoride from the enamel enters the plaque at all, it could do so only by dissolving the apatite, thus releasing fluoride along with other constituents of enamel. It is clear that this process must be extremely limited in extent, otherwise the fluoride of the enamel surface would gradually fall with increasing age, when in fact it rises. Although only a tiny proportion of the plaque fluoride can be derived from the enamel, it is possible that it is of importance in caries because the release will occur into the innermost layer of plaque (which presumably influences the carious process more than the plaque as a whole), and at a time when the plaque is acid and the plaque bacteria are apparently most sensitive to fluoride.

Before the concentration in plaque had been measured, it had sometimes been suggested that the enamel surface, with its high concentration of fluoride, might exert an inhibitory effect on the plaque bacteria. The idea was supported by Briner & Francis (1962), who found that if a pure culture of *Lactobacillus casei* was incubated in a culture medium in contact with the ground surface of enamel either from a tooth with a naturally high fluoride content or from one which had received fluoride by "topical application" of a sodium or stannous fluoride solution, the bacteria produced less acid than when in contact with a control tooth. The conclusion that the fluoride in the enamel had inhibited the bacteria does not prove that an undamaged, natural tooth surface would exert a similar effect on the plaque bacteria, however, for the following reasons. The intact surface of the tooth is much less soluble than the ground surface used in the experiments of Briner & Francis and all enamel surfaces are much more soluble in the culture medium than in plaque or saliva, which contains concentrations of calcium and phosphate ions sufficient to saturate it over a wide range of pH and thereby prevent any enamel dissolving at all. In other words, such experiments are extremely prone to produce a "false positive" result indicating that the fluoride of enamel could exert inhibition.

Relative Importance of Systemic and Local Effects of Fluoride in Caries

If the mechanisms so far mentioned really are the means by which fluoride reduces caries, it is possible to discuss which of the actions are exerted systemically and which are local effects in the mouth responsible for the change which occurs after eruption. Epidemiological studies on caries rates in subjects who first received fluoride either before or after the eruption of their teeth have shown that the main effect requires the intake of fluoride during tooth formation: a smaller effect has usually been found, however, if fluoride is received after the teeth have erupted. For example, in Grand Rapids, Mich., after ten years of fluoridation, the 16-year-old group (who were 6-7 years old when fluoridation was introduced) showed a 26% lower DMF (decayed, missing, filled) rate than the controls, as compared with an approximately 60% reduction in the DMF rate of permanent teeth for the children born after fluoridation (Arnold et al., 1956). A similar post-eruptive protection was observed in Evanston, Ill., in the permanent, but not in the deciduous teeth (Hill, Blayney & Wolf, 1957). The fluoridation study carried out in Great Britain by the Ministry of Health (1962) reported reductions of 26% and 14% of caries in the deciduous teeth of 6- and 7-year-old children five years after fluoridation began (the figures for the 3-, 4- and 5-year-old children, whose teeth had formed under the influence of fluoride, were 66%, 57% and 50% respectively). However, Russell & White (1961) did not find such an effect after seven years' fluoridation in Maryland.

It is not known whether caries rates are affected in teeth which first receive fluoride many years after eruption, because no surveys appear to have been carried out among mature adults in areas with artificial fluoridation.

The action on the solubility of enamel is partly dependent on fluoride deposited in the enamel during formation, but is probably supplemented by the uptake known to occur on the enamel surface after eruption. The entry of fluoride into early cavities obviously occurs as a local effect after eruption and may play an important part in the post-eruptive reduction in caries.

If fluoride exerts an anti-enzymatic effect, it must be mostly local, following the uptake of fluoride from saliva or drinking water. The controversial question of whether any plaque fluoride can be derived from the enamel (i.e., from a largely pre-eruptive source) has already been discussed.

Effect of Fluoride on Size and Morphology of Teeth

Several observations on human subjects and experimental animals have shown that the size and morphology of teeth can be influenced by fluoride intake. It might be expected that smaller teeth and shallower fissures would reduce the contact points and other food-trapping areas.

Forrest (1956) and Ockerse (1949) commented on the well-rounded cusps and shallow fissures of human teeth from fluoride areas in Great Britain and South Africa, respectively, but presented no statistical data. Wallenius (1957) reported that teeth formed in a fluoride area were, on the average, 1.7% wider than those from a control area, contrary to the trend of other findings. In New Zealand, Cooper & Ludwig (1965) measured the mesiodistal and bucco-lingual diameters and the cusp depths of the lower first permanent molars of children in fluoridated and control areas and found the diameters about 2% smaller and the cusp depths 5% smaller in the fluoride area (Table 5). These differences were statistically significant, but it is debatable whether they are large enough to have a clinical effect on caries. Moreover, the effect on size and shape is apparently not specifically due to fluoride because some of these differences were observed also in Napier, a town where the intake of molybdenum was high because the vegetables had a high molybdenum content. Paynter & Grainger (1956) found that, in rats fed 12 ppm sodium fluoride (i.e., 6 ppm fluoride) in the diet, the size of the molar teeth was reduced and the proportion of molars with rounded fissures was higher than in the controls. Kruger (1962) studied the size and shape of the fissures in rats' molars after the injection of fluoride. A dose was employed which was much higher than would ever be received from food or

TABLE 5

EFFECT OF FLUORIDE INGESTION ON MORPHOLOGY OF HUMAN TEETH[a]

	Control	Fluoride	Significance of difference (P)
Lower 1st permanent molars			
Mesio-distal diameter (mm)	10.30 (86)[b]	10.11 (100)[b]	0.01
Bucco-lingual diameter (mm)	10.31 (99)	10.18 (100)	0.05
Upper 1st permanent molars			
Cusp height (mm)	2.68 (66)	2.54 (63)	0.01
Buccal convexity (mm)	0.35 (98)	0.31 (98)	0.01

[a] After Cooper & Ludwig, 1965.
[b] The figures in parentheses indicate the numbers in each group.

water: 0.108 mg of fluoride injected daily into each rat up to the age of 14 days—an amount which is approximately equivalent to 54 mg in a human baby. However, the rat needs about 10 ppm of fluoride in drinking water (i.e., ten times the human dosage) to reduce caries, and this species may be less sensitive than man to other effects of fluoride. Some of the morphological differences found by Kruger were statistically significant and some were sufficiently marked to be clearly visible in photographs without elaborate measurements. Other trace elements (boron and molybdenum) were observed to have similar effects on the shape of fissures—a finding which agrees with that of Cooper & Ludwig in the children's teeth in Napier, New Zealand.

Further points on the effect of fluoride on the morphology of human teeth are dealt with by Adler in Chapter 9.

There are several mechanisms by which fluoride (and other trace elements) could modify the morphology of the tooth, but it is not yet known which of them is effective. Some investigators have speculated that the fluorapatite crystals differ slightly in size from hydroxyapatite crystals. Others have pictured an inhibitory action on some of the enamel-forming cells which prevents growth in part of the enamel. It is believed that cusp formation depends on such a differential rate of enamel production on the part of the ameloblast (Kronfeld, 1935). It is possibly influenced at an even earlier stage in enamel development by local changes in the mitosis rate of the cells of the dental lamina which alter the intensity of its folding. The histology of developing teeth in animals treated with fluoride was examined by Kruger (1962), and although some damage to groups of ameloblasts was noted, it was inadequate to explain the eventual changes observed. Moreover, no histological changes were observed after the administration of boron, although this element produced an effect on tooth morphology similar to that of fluoride.

Fluoride and Non-specific Hypoplasia

Zimmerman (1954) pointed out that there was a type of enamel defect which could easily be confused with fluoride mottling but nevertheless differed from it in some respects (e.g., it was asymmetrical in distribution). This defect, usually referred to as "idiopathic mottling", occurs in areas without fluoride in their water supplies.

Forrest (1956) carried out a survey of the incidence of mottling in 324 children in areas of England where the water-borne fluoride varied between 0.1 and 5.8 ppm, and found that there was a higher incidence of idiopathic mottling in areas with virtually no fluoride than in those with 1 ppm. A similar finding was reported by Ast et al. (1956) in the Newburgh-Kingston fluoridation study. In Newburgh (with fluoride), 36 cases of non-fluoride mottling were observed among 438 subjects studied (8%), as compared with 19% among the 608 control subjects. The two reports cited above—one from an area with natural fluoride and the other from a locality where experimental fluoridation had been introduced—strongly suggest that a fluoride intake which is about the optimal for caries prevention *reduces* the incidence of idiopathic mottling. There is no adequate explanation of this reduction, nor is the cause of the non-fluoride mottling definitely known. Jackson (1961) reported that such mottling is more frequent on the upper permanent central incisor than on other teeth and suggested trauma of the deciduous predecessors as a main cause. Abscesses in the predecessors, which could damage the developing permanent teeth or lead to premature extraction, and thus trauma, seem an unlikely cause since they are most frequent on the molar teeth and would therefore lead to a high incidence of idiopathic mottling in their successors (the permanent premolars) which Jackson found did not occur.

Jackson (*op. cit.*) also suggested that a temporary increase in fluoride intake could not be dismissed as a cause of this type of mottling. While there can be no doubt that fluoride intake varies widely and could be exceptionally high for short periods (e.g., for periods during which larger amounts of foods high in fluoride such as tinned fish or strong tea were ingested), it is more difficult to explain the asymmetrical distribution on the teeth on a dietary basis. Jackson suggests that there may be periods of asynchronous development of homologous teeth, and if a period of high fluoride intake coincided with active growth of enamel in one tooth only, then a very limited asymmetrical defect might occur. However, the chances of these factors occurring simultaneously seem too small to account for the quite frequent occurrence of "idiopathic mottling".

A recent report (Richards et al., 1967) confirms the higher prevalence of non-fluoride enamel hypoplasia in low-fluoride areas only for regions with mean maximum temperatures below 80°F (27°C).

Mechanism of Other Possible Dental Benefits of Fluoride

As discussed in detail in Chapter 9, there is evidence that both periodontal disease and malocclusion are slightly less prevalent in fluoride areas. These benefits are probably secondary to the effect of F in reducing caries.

5. SUMMARY (I. Zipkin)

At least two efficient mechanisms act to maintain the concentration of fluoride in the body-fluids and soft tissues at low levels of concentration. These are the rapid and efficient excretion of fluoride by the kidney—discussed at length in Chapter 5—and the high avidity of the calcified structures for fluoride. Thus, fluoride is either eliminated in the urine or innocuously "sequestered" in the skeletal and dental tissues after consumption by the human at low levels of intake for long periods of time. Human body-fluids such as blood, milk and saliva contain 0.1-0.2 ppm F and these concentrations are little influenced by intakes of fluoride as high as 4 ppm F in the drinking water. Soft tissues such as heart, liver, lung and spleen contain less than 1 ppm F (wetweight). Kidney and aorta contain higher concentrations of fluoride, probably due in the former to the presence of concentrated filtered urine in the collecting tubules and in the latter to calcified areas, an age-related phenomenon. No evidence has yet been provided that fluoride ingested at 1 ppm in the drinking water affects intermediary metabolism of foodstuffs, vitamin utilization or either hormonal or enzymatic activity.

Levels of fluoride in the drinking water up to 4 ppm, which produced an eightfold increase in bone fluoride, did not alter the chemistry of the major constituents of bone, but reduced the concentration of carbonate and citrate by 10% and 30% respectively. The changes in the carbonate and citrate levels may play a part in the enhanced resolution of the X-ray diffraction patterns of bone, leading to a better crystalline texture which renders the apatite or mineral phase of bone more stable and perhaps more resistant to resorption. The deposition of fluoride reaches a plateau with age in human bone and only a small portion is very slowly released following removal of the fluoride source. It has been postulated that fluoride is necessary for the formation of apatite and hence for production of the mineral matrix of bone. Histologically, no changes were seen in human bone which could be related to its fluoride content.

Several clinical studies in the USA and in Europe have shown that a maximum in caries reduction (about 60%) is coincident with a minimum of mottling or dental fluorosis when the drinking water contains 1 ppm F. Non-fluoride opacities and malocclusion appear to be reduced in fluoride areas and somewhat less periodontal disease has also been reported. Concentrations of fluoride in saliva (0.1-0.2 ppm) are insufficient to produce cariostasis by inhibiting the growth or enzymatic activity of the oral bacteria. The very much higher levels of fluoride in plaque (20 ppm is a typical figure) are thought to be largely present inside bacteria, and there is evidence that they inhibit acid production. Fluoride is incorporated into the enamel of teeth to form fluorapatite, a less soluble apatite than hydroxyapatite, and the outer layer of "high fluoride" teeth shows a small but fairly consistent tendency to be less soluble *in vitro* than that of "low fluoride" teeth. If fluoride enhances the "crystallinity" of the enamel mineral as it does in bone, this perhaps introduces another factor to help explain the cariostatic effect of fluoride.

REFERENCES

Adkins, B. L. & Kruger, B. J. (1966) *J. dent. Res., 45*, 1205

Agarwala, S. C., Krishna Murti, C. R., Shrivastava, D. L. & Gupta, A. S. (1954) *Enzymologia, 16*, 322

Aisenberg, A. C. & Potter, V. R. (1955) *J. biol. Chem., 215*, 737

Albright, J. A. (1964) *Nature (Lond.), 203*, 976

Andreeva, V. S. (1957) *Fiziol. Ž. (Mosk.), 43*, 1183

Andreeva, V. S. (1959) *Vop. Ohrany Materin. Dets., 4*, No. 6, p. 25

Armstrong, W. D., Blomquist, C. H., Singer, L., Pollock, M. E. & McLaren, L. C. (1965) *Brit. med. J., 1*, 486

Armstrong, W. D. & Brekhus, P. J. (1938) *J. dent. Res., 17*, 393-399

Armstrong, W. D. & Singer, L. (1963a) *Fed. Proc., 22*, Abstr. No. 2906

Armstrong, W. D. & Singer, L. (1963b) *J. dent. Res., 42*, 133-136

Armstrong, W. D. & Singer, L. (1965) *Clin. Orthop.*, No. 38, pp. 179-190

Armstrong, W. D., Singer, L., Ensinck, J. & Rich, C. (1964) *J. clin. Invest., 43*, 555

Armstrong, W. D., Venkateswarlu, P. & Singer, L. (1961) *J. dent. Res., 40*, 727

Arnold, F. A., Jr, Dean, H. T., Jay, P. & Knutson, J. W. (1956) *Publ. Hlth Rep. (Wash.), 71*, 652-658

Ast, D. B., Smith, D. J., Wachs, B. & Cantwell, K. J. (1956) *J. Amer. dent. Ass., 52*, 314

Aubel, E., Grunberg-Manago, M. & Szulmajster, J. (1949) *C. R. Acad. Sci. (Paris), 228*, 715

Bachra, B. N., Trautz, O. R. & Simon, S. L. (1965) *Arch. oral Biol., 10*, 731-738

Baud, C. A. & Slatkine, S. (1965) In: *Proceedings of the Second European Symposium on Calcified Tissues, University of Liège, Belgium*, pp. 89-91

Benard, H., Gajdos, A. & Gajdos-Torok, M. (1958) *C. R. Soc. Biol. (Paris), 152*, 416

Berger, L., Slein, M. W., Colowick, S. D. & Cori, C. F. (1946) *J. gen. Physiol., 29*, 379-391

Bernstein, D. S., Sadowsky, N., Hegsted, D. M., Guri, C. D. & Stare, F. J. (1966) *J. Amer. med. Ass., 198*, 499-504

Berry, W. T. C. & Whittles, J. H. (1963) *Mth. Bull. Minist. Hlth Lab. Serv., 22*, 50

Bibby, B. G. & Van Kesteren, M. (1940) *J. dent. Res., 19*, 391-401

Bibby, B. G., Van Kesteren, M. & Volker, J. F. (1942) *J. dent. Res., 21*, 61-72

Bixler, D. & Muhler, J. C. (1960) *J. Nutr., 70*, 26

Borei, H. (1942) *Biochem. Z.*, **312**, 160

Borei, H. (1945) *Ark. Kem? Miner. Geol.*, **20 A**, No 8, pp. 1-215

Bosworth, E. B. & McCay, C. M. (1962) *J. dent. Res.*, **41**, 949-960

Bramstedt, F., Kröncke, A. & Naujoks, R. (1960) In: *Proceedings of the 5th Congress of the European Organization for Research on Fluorine and Dental Caries Prevention, Brussels, 1958*, Brussels, "Le Journal dentaire belge", p. 65

Briner, W. W. & Francis, M. D. (1962) *Arch. oral Biol.*, **7**, 541-550

Brown, W. E. (1962) *Nature (Lond.)*, **196**, 1048-1049

Brown, W. E. (1966) *Clin. Orthop.*, **44**, 205-220

Brown, W. E., Smith, J. P., Lehr, J. R. & Frazier, A. W. (1962) *Nature (Lond.)*, **196**, 1050-1055

Brudevold, F., McCann, H. G. & Grøn, P. (1965) In: Ciba Foundation, *Symposium on Caries-resistant Teeth*, London, Churchill, p. 127

Brudevold, F. & Messer, A. C. (1961) *J. dent. Res.*, **40**, 728 (Abstract)

Büttner, W. (1961) *Arch. oral Biol.*, **6**, 40 (Special Supplement: Proceedings of 8th ORCA Congress, London, July 1961)

Büttner, W. (1963) *J. dent. Res.*, **42**, 453-460

Büttner, W. & Muhler, J. C. (1958a) *J. Nutr.*, **65**, 259-266

Büttner, W. & Muhler, J. C. (1958b) *Proc. Soc. exp. Biol. (N.Y.)*, **98**, 620

Call, R. A., Greenwood, D. A., LeCheminant, W. H., Shupe, J. L., Nielsen, H. M., Olson, L. E., Lamborn, R. E., Mangelson, F. L. & Davis, R. V. (1965) *Publ. Hlth Rep. (Wash.)*, **80**, 529-538

Capozzi, L., Brunetti, P., Negri, P. L. & Migliorini, E. (1967) *Caries Res.*, **1**, 69-77

Carlson, C. H., Armstrong, W. D. & Singer, L. (1960a) *Amer. J. Physiol.*, **199**, 187

Carlson, C. H., Armstrong, W. D. & Singer, L. (1960b) *Proc. Soc. exp. Biol. (N.Y.)*, **104**, 235-239

Carlson, C. H., Singer, L. & Armstrong, W. D. (1960) *Proc. Soc. exp. Biol. (N.Y.)*, **103**, 418-420

Carlson, J. R. & Suttie, J. W. (1966) *Amer. J. Physiol.*, **210**, 79

Carlström, D. (1955) *Acta radiol. (Stockh.)*, Suppl. 121

Chiemchaisri, Y. & Phillips, P. H. (1963) *J. Nutr.*, **81**, 307

Clapper, W. E. (1947) *Proc. Soc. exp. Biol. (N.Y.)*, **65**, 333

Cohen, P. & Gardner, F. H. (1964) *New Engl. J. Med.*, **271**, 1129-1133

Cohen, P. P. & Hayano, M. (1947) *J. biol. Chem.*, **170**, 687

Cooper, V. K. & Ludwig, T. G. (1965) *N.Z. dent. J.*, **61**, 33-40

Cori, C. F. (1950) In: *First International Congress of Bio-chemistry, Cambridge, England : Report of opening and concluding sessions and three lectures*, Glasgow, Biochemical Society, p. 9

Dallemagne, M. J. (1964) In: *Proceedings of the First European Symposium on Calcified Tissues, New York, N.Y.*, New York, Macmillan, pp. 171-174

Davies, R. E. (1949) In: *First International Congress of Bio-chemistry, Cambridge, England : Abstracts of communications*, p. 579

Dawes, C., Jenkins, G. N., Hardwick, J. L. & Leach, S. A. (1965) *Brit. dent. J.*, **119**, 164-167

Denes, G. (1954) *Acta physiol. Acad. Sci. hung.*, **6**, 201

Dickens, F. & Simer, F. (1929) *Biochem. J.*, **23**, 936

Doberenz, A. R., Kurnick, A. A., Kutz, E. B., Kemmerer, A. R. & Reid, B. L. (1964) *Proc. Soc. exp. Biol. (N.Y.)*, **117**, 689

Dowse, C. M. & Jenkins, G. N. (1957) *J. dent. Res.*, **36**, 816 (Abstract)

Eanes, E. D., Zipkin, I., Harper, R. A. & Posner, A. S. (1965) *Arch. oral Biol.*, **10**, 161-173

Egami, F. & Itahashi, M. (1951) *J. Biochem. (Tokyo)*, **38**, 329

Elliott, J. C. (1964) *J. dent. Res.*, **43**, 959 (Abstract)

Engel, M. B., Joseph, N. R., Laskin, D. M. & Catchpole, H. R. (1961) *Amer. J. Physiol.*, **201**, 621

Ericsson, Y. (1966) *Acta odont. scand.*, **24**, 405

Ericsson, Y. (1967) *Caries Res.*, **1**, 144

Ericsson, Y. & Hammarström, L. (1964) *Gerontologia (Basel)*, **9**, 150

Ericsson, Y., Santesson, G. & Ullberg, S. (1961) *Arch. oral Biol.*, **4**, 160-174 (Special Supplement: Proceedings of 7th ORCA Congress, Hamburg, June 1960)

Ericsson, Y. & Ullberg, S. (1958) *Acta odont. scand.*, **16**, 363-374

Evans, D. G. & Prophet, A. S. (1950) *Lancet*, **1**, 290

Exner, F. B. & Waldbott, G. L. (1957) *The American Fluoridation Experiment*, New York, Devin-Adair

Fedorov, M. V. (1947) *C. R. Acad. Sci. URSS*, **55**, 259

Finn, S. B. & DeMarco, C. (1956) *J. dent. Res.*, **35**, 185-188

Fleury, P., Courtois, J. & Plumel, M. (1950) *Bull. Soc. Chim. biol. (Paris)*, **32**, 40

Forrest, J. R. (1956) *Brit. dent. J.*, **100**, 195-200

Fosdick, L. S. & Wessinger, G. D. (1940) *J. Amer. dent. Ass.*, **27**, 203-212

Foster, W. C., Sterling, W. A., Rush, J. P. & Rehm, J. A. (1960) *Fed. Proc.*, **19**, 253

Gabovich, R. D., Bukhovets, V. I. & Ermakova, N. A. (1960) *Vrach. Delo*, **6**, 627

Gabovich, R. D. & Maistruk, P. N. (1963) *Vop. Pitan.*, **22**, 32

Gardiner, E. E., Andrews, F. N., Adams, R. L., Rogler, J. C. & Carrick, C. W. (1959) *Poult. Sci.*, **38**, 1423

Gardner, D. E., Smith, F. A., Hodge, H. C., Overton, D. E. & Feltman, R. (1952) *Science*, **115**, 208-209

Gedalia, I., Kaplinski-Wertheimer, N., Mentzel, J., Brzezinski, A. & Zukerman, H. (1963) *Harefuah*, **64**, 191

Geever, E. F., Leone, N. C., Geiser, P. & Lieberman, J. (1958) *Publ. Hlth Rep. (Wash.)*, **73**, 721-731

Glimcher, M. J. (1959) *Rev. mod. Phys.*, **31**, 359-393

Goldhaber, P. (1967) *Israel J. med. Sci.*, **3**, 617

Golub, L., Glimcher, M. J. & Goldhaber, P. (1968a) In: *International Association for Dental Research, 46th General Meeting, San Francisco, Calif., USA, March 1968 ; Abstracts*, Chicago, American Dental Association, p. 97, Abstr. No. 240

Golub, L., Glimcher, M. J. & Goldhaber, P. (1968b) *Proc. Soc. exp. Biol. (N. Y.)*, **129**, 973

Gomori, G. (1955) *J. Histochem. Cytochem.*, **3**, 479

Goodman, F. (1965) *J. dent. Res.*, **44**, 564

Gray, J. A., Francis, M. D. & Griebstein, W. J. (1962) In: Sognnaes, R. F., ed., *Chemistry and prevention of dental caries*, Springfield, Ill., Thomas, chapter 5, pp. 164-180

Griffith, F. D., Parker, H. E. & Rogler, J. C. (1963a) *Fed. Proc.*, **22**, Abstr. No. 2352

Griffith, F. D., Parker, H. E. & Rogler, J. C. (1963b) *J. Nutr.*, **79**, 251

Grøn, P., McCann, H. G. & Brudevold, F. (1968) *Arch. oral Biol.*, **13**, 203

Gyotoku, K. (1930) *Biochem. Z.*, **217**, 279

Hancox, N. M. & Boothroyd, B. (1964) In: Clark, J. M. P., ed., *Modern trends in ortho-paedics, 4*, London, Butterworth, pp. 26-52

Hardwick, J. L. & Leach. S. A. (1963) In: *Advances in fluorine research and dental caries prevention*, Oxford, Pergamon, vol. 1, pp. 151-158; and *Arch. oral Biol.*, **8**, Spec. Suppl., pp. 151-158 (Proceedings of 9th ORCA Congress, Paris, June 1962)

Hauck, H. M. (1934) *J. agric. Res.*, **49**, 1041

Hegglin, R., Grauer, H. & Munchinger, R. (1949) *Experientia (Basel)*, **5**, 127

Hein, J. W., Bonner, J. F., Brudevold, F., Smith, F. A. & Hodge, H. C. (1956) *Nature (Lond.)*, **178**, 1295

Herman, J. R. (1956) *Proc. Soc. exp. Biol. (N.Y.)*, **91**, 189

Higgins, B. A., Nassim, J. R., Alexander, R. & Hilb, A. (1965) *Brit. med. J.*, **1**, 1159-1161

Hill, I. N., Blayney, J. R. & Wolf, W. (1957) *J. dent. Res.*, **36**, 208-219

Hintzsche, E. (1954) *Z. mikr.-anat. Forsch.*, **60**, 137

Hirschman, A. & Sobel, A. E. (1965) *Arch. Biochem.*, **110**, 237-243

Hodge, H. C. & Smith, F. A. (1965) *Biological effects of inorganic fluorides*. In: Simons, J. H., ed., *Fluorine chemistry*, New York, Academic Press, vol. 4, pp. 559-570

Hodge, H. C. & Smith, F. A. (1968) *Ann. Rev. Pharmacol.*, **8**, 395

Hodge, H. C., Smith, F. A. & Chen, P. S. (1963) *Biological effects of organic fluorides*. In: Simons, J. H., ed., *Fluorine chemistry*, New York, Academic Press, vol. 3

Isaac, S., Brudevold, F., Smith, F. A. & Gardner, D. E. (1958) *J. dent. Res.*, **37**, 254-263

Ivanova, N. A. (1959) *Vop. Ohrany Materin. Dets.*, **4**, No. 6, p. 29

Iwase, T. (1958) *Shikoku Igaku Zasshi*, **12**, 616, 624

Jackson, D. (1961) *Arch. oral Biol.*, **5**, 212-223

Jenkins, G. N. (1959) *Arch. oral Biol.*, **1**, 33-41

Jenkins, G. N. (1960) *J. dent. Res.*, **39**, 684 (Abstract)

Jenkins, G. N. (1967) *Brit. dent. J.*, **122**, 435-441

Jenkins, G. N., Armstrong, P. A. & Speirs, R. L. (1952) *Proc. roy. Soc. Med.*, **45**, 517-525

Jenkins, G. N., Edgar, W. M. & Ferguson, D. B. (1969) *Arch. oral Biol.*, **14**, 105

Jenkins, G. N., Ferguson, D. B. & Edgar, W. M. (1967) *Helv. odont. Acta*, **11**, 2

Johnson, R. B. & Lardy, H. A. (1950) *J. biol. Chem.*, **184**, 235

Kay, M. I., Young, R. A. & Posner, A. S. (1964) *Nature (Lond.)*, **204**, 1050-1052

Kerwin, J. G. (1958) *Dent. Dig.*, **64**, 58

Kleinberg, I. & Sandham, H. J. (1964) *J. dent. Res.*, **43**, 843 (Abstract)

Knappwost, A. & Tochtermann, H. G. (1955) *Dtsch. zahnärztl. Z.*, **10**. 1231

Kondo, K. & Kuriaki, K. (1961) *J. dent. Res.*, **40**, 971

Kronfeld, R. (1935) *J. Amer. dent. Ass.*, **22**, 1131-1155

Kruger, B. J. (1962) *J. dent. Res.*, **41**, 215; *Pap. Dep. Dent. Univ. Qd.*, 1960, **1**, No. 1 & 6

Kühl, G. von & Nebergall, W. H. (1963) *Z. anorg. allg. Chem.*, **324**, 313-320

Largent, E. J. (1948) *J. industr. Hyg.*, **30**, 92

Largent, E. J. (1961) *Fluorosis. The health aspects of fluorine compounds*, Columbus, Ohio State University Press

Largent, E. J., Bovard, P. G. & Heyroth, F. F. (1951) *Amer. J. Roentgenol.*, **65**, 42-48

Lawrenz, M. & Mitchell, H. H. (1941) *J. Nutr.*, **22**, 91-101

Lawrenz, M., Mitchell, H. H. & Ruth, W. A. (1940) *J. Nutr.*, **19**, 531

LeGeros, R. Z., Trautz, O. R. & LeGeros, J. P. (1965) In: *International Association for Dental Research, 43rd General Meeting, Toronto, Canada, July 1965 ; Abstracts,* Chicago, American Dental Association, Abstr. No. 17

Leone, N. C., Lieberman, J. & Geiser, P. A. (1960) *A.M.A. Arch. industr. Hlth,* **21,** 328

Leone, N. C., Shimkin, M. B., Arnold, F. A., Jr, Stevenson, C. A., Zimmerman, E. R., Geiser, P. A. & Lieberman, J. E. (1954) In: Shaw, J. H., ed., *Fluoridation as a Public health measure,* Washington, D.C., American Association for the Advancement of Science, p. 110

Leone, N. C., Stevenson, C. A., Besse, B., Hawes, L. E. & Dawber, T. R. (1960) *A.M.A. Arch. industr. Hlth,* **21,** 326-327

Leone, N. C., Stevenson, C. A., Hilbish, T. F. & Sosman, M. C. (1955) *Amer. J. Roentgenol.,* **74,** 874-885

Leroux, D. (1940) *C. R. Acad. Sci. (Paris),* **210,** 770

Lindemann, G. (1965) *Acta odont. scand.,* **23,** 575

Lipmann, F. (1929) *Biochem. Z.,* **206,** 171

Little, M. F., Casciani, F. S. & Rowley, J. (1968) In: *International Association for Dental Research, 46th General Meeting, San Francisco, Calif., USA, March 1968 ; Abstracts,* Chicago, American Dental Association, Abstr. No. 467

Loevenhart, A. S. & Peirce, G. (1906-7) *J. biol. Chem.,* **2,** 397

L'vov, S. & Toupizina, G. M. (1938) *C. R. Acad. Sci. URSS,* **21,** 307

McCann, H. G. (1953) *J. biol. Chem.,* **201,** 247-259

McCann, H. G. & Brudevold, F. (1966) *The mechanism of the caries-inhibiting effect of fluoride.* In: Kreshover, S. J. & McClure, F. J., ed., *Environmental variables in oral disease,* Washington, D.C., American Association for the Advancement of Science, p. 103

McCauley, H. B. & McClure, F. J. (1954) *Publ. Hlth Rep. (Wash.),* **69,** 671-683

McClendon, J. F. (1944) *Fed. Proc.,* **3,** 94

McClendon, J. F. & Gershon-Cohen, J. (1953) *J. Agric. Food Chem.,* **1,** 464

McClendon, J. F. & Gershon-Cohen, J. (1954) *Amer. J. Roentgenol.,* **71,** 1017

McClure, F. J. (1944) *Publ. Hlth Rep. (Wash.),* **59,** 1543-1558

McClure, F. J. (1948) *J. dent. Res.,* **27,** 287-298

McClure, F. J., Mitchell, H. H., Hamilton, T. S. & Kinser, C. A. (1945) *J. industr. Hyg.,* **27,** 159-170

McConnell, D. (1962) *Science,* **136,** 241-244

McElroy, W. D., Coulombre, J. & Hays, R. (1951) *Arch. Biochem.,* **32,** 207

MacGregor, J. & Brown, W. E. (1965) *Nature (Lond.),* **205,** 359-361

Malm, M. (1940) *Naturwissenschaften,* **28,** 723

Malm, M. (1947) *Ark. Kemi Miner. Geol.,* **25 A,** p. 187

Malthus, R. S., Ludwig, T. C. & Healy, W. B. (1964) *N.Z. dent. J.,* **60,** 291

Manly, R. S. & Harrington, D. P. (1959) *J. dent. Res.,* **38,** 910-919

Marcuse, R. & Runnstrom, J. (1943) *Ark. Kemi Miner. Geol.,* **16 A,** No. 20, pp. 1-27

Mattocks, A. M. & Holtan, S. D. (1949) *J. Pharmacol. exp. Ther.,* **96,** 114

Maurer, R. L. & Day, H. G. (1957) *J. Nutr.,* **62,** 561

Miller, R. F. & Phillips, P. H. (1955) *J. Nutr.,* **56,** 447-454

Ministry of Health (1962) *Report on public health and medical subjects No. 105,* London, HMSO

Mitchell, H. H. & Edman, M. (1945) *Soil Sci.*, **60**, 81

Moore, M. B. & Wagner, M. J. (1968) In: *International Association for Dental Research, 46th General Meeting, San Francisco, Calif., USA, March 1968 ; Abstracts*, Chicago, American Dental Association, Abstr. No. 281

Mouriquand, G., Dauvergne, M., Tete, H. & Edel, V. (1940) *C.R. Acad. Sci. (Paris)*, **210**, 515

Morris, J. W. (1965) *Amer. J. Roentgenol.*, **94**, 608-615

Muhler, J. C. (1951) *Fluorine in relation to specific problems of medicine and biology*, Bloomington (Thesis, Indiana University)

Muhler, J. C. (1958) *J. Amer. dent. Ass.*, **56**, 335

Muhler, J. C., Stookey, G. K. & Wagner, M. J. (1959) *Proc. Soc. exp. Biol. (N.Y.)*, **102**, 644

Murray, D. R. P. (1929) *Biochem. J.*, **23**, 292

Murthi, G. V. S., Narayana Rao, D. & Venkateswarlu, P. (1953) *J. Indian med. Ass.*, **22**, 396-399

Myers, H. M., Hamilton, J. G. & Becks, H. (1952) *J. dent. Res.*, **31**, 743-750

Nagant de Deuxchaisnes, C. & Krane, S. M. (1964) *Medicine (Baltimore)*, **43**, 233-266

Narayana Rao, D. (1942) *The role of calcium in chronic fluorine intoxication* (Thesis, Madras University)

Navara, J. (1963) *Biologia (Bratislava)*, **18**, 15

Neuman, W. F. & Neuman, M. W. (1958) *The chemical dynamics of bone mineral*, Chicago, University of Chicago Press, pp. 39-54

Neuman, W. F., Neuman, M. W., Main, E. R., O'Leary, J. & Smith, F. A. (1950) *J. biol. Chem.*, **187**, 655-661

Newesely, H. (1961) *Arch. oral Biol.*, **6**, 174-180 (Special Supplement: Proceedings of 8th ORCA Congress, London, July, 1961)

Newesely, H. (1965) *Dtsch. zahnärztl. Z.*, **20**, 753-766

Nguyen-van-Thoai, Roche, J. & Roger, M. (1946) *C.R. Soc. Biol. (Paris)*, **140**, 149

Nichols, G., jr & Flanagan, B. (1966) *Fed. Proc.*, **25**, 922

Nikiforuk, G. (1961) In: Mühlemann, H. R. & König, K. G., ed., *Caries Symposium Zürich*, Berne & Stuttgart, Huber, p. 62

Nikiforuk, G. (1965) *Tooth enamel*, Bristol, Wright, pp. 26-31

Nilsson, R. (1930) *Ark. Kemi Miner. Geol.*, **10 A**, No. 7, pp. 1-135

Ockerse, T. (1949) *Dental caries : clinical and experimental investigations*, Pretoria, Department of Public Health, Union of South Africa

Odland, L. M., Warnick, K. P. & Esselbaugh, N. C. (1958) *Bull. Mont. agric. Exp. Sta.*, No. 534

Ogura, Y., Tonomura, Y., Hino, S. & Tamiya, H. (1950 (*J. Biochem. (Tokyo)*, **37**, 153

Opienska-Blauth, J., Kanski, M. & Stobinska, L. (1949) *Ann. Univ. M. Curie-Skolodowska, DD*, **4**, 69

Pandit, C. G. & Narayana Rao, D. (1940) *Indian J. med. Res.*, **28**, 559-574

Pandit, C. G., Raghavachari, T. N. S., Rao, D. S. & Krishnamurti, V. (1940) *Indian J. med. Res.*, **28**, 533-558

Parkins, F. M. (1966) *Biochim. biophys. Acta (Amst.)*, **126**, 513

Parkins, F. M. & Faust, R. G. (1968) In: *International Association for Dental Research, 46th General Meeting, San Francisco, Calif., USA, March 1968 ; Abstracts*, Chicago, American Dental Association, Abstr. No. 98

Patterson, D. (1954) *Nature (Lond.)*, **173**, 75-76

Pautard, F. G. E. (1964) In: Clark, T.M.P., ed., *Modern trends in orthopaedics, 4*, London, Butterworth, pp. 5-25

Paynter, K. J. & Grainger, R. M. (1956) *J. Canad. dent. Ass.*, **22**, 519-531

Peck, W. A., Zipkin, I. & Whedon, G. D. (1965) *Clin. Res.*, **13**, 330

Peirce, G. (1913-14) *J. biol. Chem.*, **16**, 5

Perdok, W. G. (1963) In: *Advances in fluorine research and dental caries prevention*, Oxford, Pergamon, vol. 1, pp. 85-93; and *Arch. oral Biol.*, **8**, Spec. Suppl., pp. 85-93 (Proceedings of 9th ORCA Congress, Paris, June 1962)

Perkinson, J. D., Jr, Whitney, I. B., Monroe, R. A., Lotz, W. E. & Comar, C. L. (1955) *Amer. J. Physiol.*, **182**, 383-389

Peters, R. A., Shorthouse, M. & Murray, L. R. (1964) *Nature (Lond.)*, **202**, 1331

Phillips, P. H. & Chang, C. Y. (1934) *J. biol. Chem.*, **105**, 405

Phillips, P. H., Stare, F. J. & Elvehjem, C. A. (1934) *J. biol. Chem.*, **106**, 41

Pigman, W., Koulourides, T. & Newbrun, E. (1960) *J. dent. Res.*, **39**, 1117 (Abstract)

Posner, A. S., Eanes, E. D., Harper, R. A. & Zipkin, I. (1963) *Arch. oral Biol.*, **8**, 549-570

Posner, A. S., Harper, R. A., Muller, S. A. & Menczel, J. (1965) *Ann. N. Y. Acad. Sci.*, **131**, 737-742

Posner, A. S., Stutman, J. M. & Lippincott, E. R. (1960) *Nature (Lond.)*, **188**, 486-487

Proffit, W. R. & Ackerman, J. L. (1964) *Science*, **145**, 932

Purves, M. J. (1962) *Lancet*, **2**, 1188-1189

Ramseyer, W. F., Smith, C. A. H. & McCay, C. M. (1957) *J. Geront.*, **12**, 14-19

Reiner, J. M., Tsuboi, K. K. & Hudson, P. B. (1955) *Arch. Biochem.*, **56**, 165

Rich, C. & Ensinck, J. (1961) *Nature (Lond.)*, **191**, 184

Rich, C., Ensinck, J. & Ivanovich, P. (1964) *J. clin. Invest.*, **43**, 545-556

Richards, L. F., Westmoreland, W. W., Tashiro, M. & Morrison, J. T. (1967) *J. Amer. dent. Ass.*, **75**, 1412-1418

Richardson, A. W., Muhler, J. C. & Bishop, J. G. (1955) *J. Pharmacol. exp. Ther.*, **113**, 200

Riekstniece, E., Myers, H. M. & Glass, L. E. (1965) *Arch. oral Biol.*, **10**, 107

Robinson, R. A. & Watson, M. L. (1955) *Ann. N.Y. Acad. Sci.*, **60**, 596-628

Robison, R. & Rosenheim, A. H. (1934) *Biochem. J.*, **28**, 684

Rogers, W. E., Wagner, E. M. & Stookey, G. (1961) *J. dent. Res.*, **40**, 730

Ruliffson, W. S., Burns, L. V. & Hughes, J. S. (1963) *Trans. Kans. Acad. Sci.*, **66**, 52

Ruliffson, W. S. & Hopping, J. M. (1963) *Amer. J. Physiol.*, **204**, 171

Runnstrom, J., Borei, H. & Sperber, E. (1939) *Ark. Kemi Miner. Geol.*, **13 A**, No. 22, pp. 1-29

Runnstrom, J. & Hemberg, T. (1937) *Naturwissenschaften*, **25**, 74

Russell, A. L. & White, C. L. (1961) *Publ. Hlth Rep. (Wash.)*, **76**, 1087-1093

Sadasivan, V. (1951) *Arch. Biochem.*, **30**, 159

Saini, A. S., Singh, I. D., Bajaj, V. R. & Singh, A. (1964) *Indian J. med. Res.*, **52**, 1173

Savchuck, W. B. & Armstrong, W. D. (1951) *J. biol. Chem.*, **193**, 575

Schlesinger, E. R., Overton, D. E., Chase, H. C. & Cantwell, K. T. (1956) *J. Amer. dent. Ass.*, **52**, 296

Schraer, H., Posner, A. S., Schraer, R. & Zipkin, I. (1962) *Biochim. biophys. Acta (Amst.)*, **64**, 656-657

Sellei, C. & Jany, J. (1931) *Biochem. Z.*, **239**, 94

Sforzolini, G. S., Cusma, N. & Mastrantonio, A. (1964) In: *Advances in fluorine research and dental caries prevention*, Oxford, Pergamon, vol. 2, p. 213 (Proceedings of 10th ORCA Congress, Geneva, July 1963)

Sharpless, G. R. & McCollum, E. V. (1933) *J. Nutr.*, **6**, 163

Shortt, H. E., McRobert, G. R., Barnard, T. W. & Mannadi Nayar, A. S. (1937) *Indian J. med. Res.*, **25**, 553-568

Singer, L. & Armstrong, W. D. (1959) *Analyt. Chem.*, **31**, 105

Singer, L. & Armstrong, W. D. (1960) *J. appl. Physiol.*, **15**, 508-510

Singer, L. & Armstrong, W. D. (1964) *Proc. Soc. exp. Biol. (N.Y.)*, **117**, 686

Singh, A., Jolly, S. S. & Bansal, B. C. (1961) *Lancet*, **1**, 197-199

Singh, A., Singh, B. M., Singh, I. D., Jolly, S. S. & Malhotra, K. C. (1966) *Indian J. med. Res.*, **54**, 591-597

Sita, P. & Venkateswarlu, P. (1967) *J. dent. Res.*, **46**, 307

Slater, E. C. & Bonner, W. D., Jr (1952) *Biochem. J.*, **52**, 185

Slater, R. R. (1951) *Proc. Amer. Soc. Brew. Chem.*, p. 60

Slatkine, S. (1962) *Schweiz. Mschr. Zahnheilk.*, **72**, 1068-1086

Smith, F. A. (1962) *J. Amer. dent. Ass.*, **65**, 598

Smith, F. A., Gardner, D. E. & Hodge, H. C. (1955) *A.M.A. Arch. industr. Hlth*, **11**, 2-10

Smith, F. A., Gardner, D. E., Leone, N. C. & Hodge, H. C. (1960) *A.M.A. Arch. industr. Hlth*, **21**, 330-332

Smith, Q. T., Armstrong, W. D. & Singer, L. (1950) *Proc. Soc. exp. Biol. (N.Y.)*, **102**, 170

Sobel, A. E. (1955) *Ann. N.Y. Acad. Sci.*, **60**, 713-732

Sognnaes, R. F. (1965) *Science*, **150**, 989-993

Spinelli, M. A., Amdur, B. H. & Brudevold, F. (1964) *J. dent. Res.*, **43**, 864

Spira, L. (1956) *Exp. Med. Surg.*, **14**, 72

Steadman, L. T., Brudevold, F. & Smith, F. A. (1958) *J. Amer. dent. Ass.*, **57**, 340

Steinberg, C. L., Gardner, D. E., Smith, F. A. & Hodge, H. C. (1955) *Ann. rheum. Dis.*, **14**, 378-384

Steinberg, C. L., Gardner, D. E., Smith, F. A. & Hodge, H. C. (1958) *New Engl. J. Med.*, **258**, 322-325

Stevenson, C. A. & Watson, A. R. (1957) *Amer. J. Roentgenol.*, **78**, 13-18

Stookey, G. K., Crane, D. B. & Muhler, J. C. (1962) *Proc. Soc. exp. Biol. (N.Y.)*, **109**, 580-583

Stookey, G. K., Crane, D. B. & Muhler, J. C. (1963) *Proc. Soc. exp. Biol. (N.Y.)*, **113**, 366

Stookey, G. K., Crane, D. B. & Muhler, J. C. (1964) *Proc. Soc. exp. Biol. (N.Y.)*, **115**, 295-298

Stookey, G. K., Dellinger, E. L. & Muhler, J. C. (1964) *Proc. Soc. exp. Biol. (N.Y.)*, **115**, 298-301

Stookey, G. K. & Muhler, J. C. (1962) *Proc. Soc. exp. Biol. (N.Y.)*, **109**, 268

Stookey, G. K. & Muhler, J. C. (1963) *Proc. Soc. exp. Biol. (N.Y.)*, **113**, 720

Stookey, G. K., Roberts, R. A. & Muhler, J. C. (1962) *Proc. Soc. exp. Biol. (N.Y.)*, **109**, 702

Sutherland, E. W. (1951) *Ann. N.Y. Acad. Sci.*, **54**, 693

Suttie, J. W. & Phillips, P. H. (1959) In: Muhler, J. C. & Hine, M. K., ed., *Fluorine and dental health*, Bloomington, Indiana University Press

Suttie, J. W., Phillips, P. H. & Faltin, E. C. (1964) *Proc. Soc. exp. Biol. (N.Y.)*, **115**, 575

Talamage, R. V. & Doty, S. B. (1962) *Gen. comp. Endocr.*, **2**, 473

Taves, D. R. & Neuman, W. F. (1964) *Arch. Biochem.,* **108**, 390-397

Thompson, D. J., Heintz, J. F. & Phillips, P. H. (1964) *J. Nutr.,* **84**, 27

Venkateswarlu, P. (1955) *Biochemical investigations on fluorosis* (Thesis, Andhra University)

Venkateswarlu, P. (1962) *Studies on fluoride metabolism and transport* (Thesis, University of Minnesota)

Venkateswarlu, P., Armstrong, W. D. & Singer, L. (1965) *Plant Physiol.,* **40**,, 255

Venkateswarlu, P., Armstrong, W. D. & Singer, L. (1966a) *Indian J. med. Res.,* **54**, 455-457

Venkateswarlu, P., Armstrong, W. D. & Singer, L. (1966b) In: *Proceedings of the Fourth European Symposium on Calcified Tissues,* Amsterdam, Excerpta Medica Foundation, p. 107

Venkateswarlu, P. & Narayana Rao, D. (1957) *Indian J. med. Res.,* **45**, 377

Venkateswarlu, P., Singer, L. & Armstrong, W. D. (1958) *J. dent. Res.,* **37**, 69

Voegtlin, C. & Hodge, H. C. (1949) *Pharmacology and toxicology of uranium compounds,* New York, McGraw-Hill, p. 1366

Wachsmann, M. & Grutzner, P. (1902) *Pflügers Arch. ges. Physiol.,* **91**, 195

Wadhwani, T. K. (1952) *Indian med. Gaz.,* **87**, 5-7

Wadhwani, T. K. (1954) *J. Indian Inst. Sci.,* **36**, 64

Wagner, M. J. (1962a) *J. dent. Res.,* **41**, 667-671

Wagner, M. J. (1962b) *J. dent. Res.,* **41**, 1378

Wagner, M. J. & Muhler, J. C. (1959) *J. dent. Res.,* **38**, 1078

Wagner, M. J., Stookey, G. K. & Muhler, J. C. (1958) *Proc. Soc. exp. Biol. (N.Y.),* **99**, 102

Wallace-Durbin, P. (1954) *J. dent. Res.,* **33**, 789-800

Wallenius, B. (1957) *Odont. Revy,* **8**, 275-280

Walther, D. P. (1960) *J. dent. Res.,* **39**, 408 (Abstract)

Warburg, O. & Christian, W. (1942) *Biochem. Z.,* **310**, 384-421

Webb, E. C. (1948) *Biochem. J.,* **42**, 96

Weidmann, S. M., Weatherell, J. A. & Jackson, D. (1963) *Proc. Nutr. Soc.,* **22**, 105-110

Weiss, S., Schnetzer, J. D. & King, W. J. (1964) *J. dent. Res.,* **43**, 745 (Abstract)

Williams, R. A. D. (1964) *J. dent. Res.,* **43**, 946

Winand, L., Dallemagne, M. J. & Duyckaerts, G. (1961) *Nature (Lond.),* **190**, 164-165

Zebrowski, E. J., Suttie, J. W. & Phillips, P. H. (1964) *Fed. Proc.,* **23**, Abstr. No. 502

Zimmerman, E. R. (1954) *Publ. Hlth Rep. (Wash.),* **69**, 1115-1120

Zipkin, I. (1960) *J. dent. Res.,* **39**, 1115 (Abstract)

Zipkin, I., Eanes, E. D. & Shupe, J. L. (1964) *Amer. J. vet. Res.,* **25**, 1595-1597

Zipkin, I., Lee, W. A. & Leone, N. C. (1958) *Proc. Soc. exp. Biol. (N.Y.),* **97**, 650-653

Zipkin, I. & Likins, R. C. (1957) *Amer. J. Physiol.,* **191**, 549-550

Zipkin, I., Likins, R. C. & McClure, F. J. (1959) *J. Nutr.,* **67**, 59-68

Zipkin, I. & McClure, F. J. (1952) *J. Nutr.,* **47**, 611

Zipkin, I., McClure, F. J. & Lee, W. A. (1960) *Arch. oral Biol.,* **2**, 190-195

Zipkin, I., McClure, F. J., Leone, N. C. & Lee, W. A. (1958) *Publ. Hlth Rep. (Wash.),* **73**, 732-740

Zipkin, I., Posner, A. S. & Eanes, E. D. (1962) *Biochim. biophys. Acta (Amst.),* **59**, 255-258

Zipkin, I. & Scow, R. O. (1956) *Amer. J. Physiol.,* **185**, 81-84

Zipkin, I., Sokoloff, L. & Frazier, P. D. (1967) *Israel J. med. Sci.,* **3**, 719

CHAPTER 7

Toxic effects of larger doses of fluoride

B. R. BHUSSRY [1] — V. DEMOLE [2] — H. C. HODGE [3] — S. S. JOLLY [4] —
A. SINGH [5] — D. R. TAVES [6]

1. INTRODUCTION (A. Singh & S. S. Jolly)

Investigations of toxic effects of fluoride in humans have evoked a lively interest throughout the world because public health programmes of fluoridation for the prevention of dental caries have always been considered to involve the risk of remote cumulative intoxication. However, the indices of early intoxication are poorly defined and this has resulted in an element of speculation and confusion about the toxic potentialities of the fluoride ion. At the very onset, a clear distinction must be made between acute toxic effects, which result from a single massive dose, and the chronic toxic effect of large doses spread over a number of years. The latter may be confined to a minor physiological alteration or may produce a major crippling disease.

A number of biological effects have been ascribed to fluorides. Although many reports of such effects are unsubstantiated, several have been studied sufficiently to deserve careful summarization, including the effects on bones, teeth, kidney, thyroid, neurological functions and growth in general. Smith & Hodge (1959) have related the concentrations or doses of fluoride to the biological effects indicated in the tabulation below:

Concentration or dose of fluoride	Medium	Effect
2 parts per 1 000 million	Air	Injury to vegetation
1 ppm	Water	Dental caries reduction

[1] Professor of Anatomy, School of Medicine and Dentistry, Georgetown University, Washington, D.C., USA.

[2] Formerly Professor of Pharmacology, University of Lausanne, Switzerland.

[3] Professor of Pharmacology and Toxicology, School of Medicine and Dentistry, University of Rochester, N.Y, USA.

[4] Professor of Medicine, Government Medical College, Patiala, Punjab, India.

[5] Principal, Government Medical College, Patiala, Punjab, India. Dr Singh died in April 1966.

[6] Department of Pharmacology and Toxicology, School of Medicine and Dentistry, University of Rochester, N.Y., USA.

Concentration or dose of fluoride	Medium	Effect
2 ppm or more	Water	Mottled enamel
5 ppm	Urine	No osteosclerosis
8 ppm	Water	10 % osteosclerosis
20-80 mg/day or more	Water or air	Crippling fluorosis
50 ppm	Food or water	Thyroid changes
100 ppm	Food or water	Growth retardation
More than 125 ppm	Food or water	Kidney changes
2.5-5.0 g	Acute dose	Death

Clinical Observations of Acute Fluoride Intoxication

Current knowledge about the doses of fluoride that produce acute intoxication is derived principally from suicidal or accidental poisoning (Lidbeck, Hill & Beeman, 1943; Sharkey & Simpson, 1933). With the more widespread use of fluoride in industry, in agriculture and in the home, there is need for additional evaluation of acute toxic effects.

The acute lethal dose of fluoride for man is probably about 5 g as NaF (Goodman & Gilman, 1965). Although the precise doses of different fluorides are not known, the probable range is 2-10 g for soluble compounds such as hydrofluoric acid, hydrofluosilicic acid, potassium fluoride, sodium fluoride, sodium fluosilicate, and ammonium fluoride. The form of F used and the method and length of administration, as well as individual susceptibilities, have varied the toxic effects to such an extent that a comparison of the data obtained is scarcely warranted. However, there is evidence that fluosilicates are more toxic than either NaF or CaF_2 and that NaF is more toxic than CaF_2. The minimum fatal dose is determined by the carrying vehicle, by the promptness and completeness of vomiting and by the speed of initiation of therapy.

Acute fluoride intoxication, whether caused by ingestion or inhalation of relatively large amounts of fluoride-containing compounds, has not been so well described as chronic fluoride intoxication. This is due, in part at least, to the fact that acute fluoride intoxication is rare. In Roholm's (1937) world-wide survey of the published literature on the subject, 112 cases were recorded. Greenwood (1940) extended this survey and recorded 18 additional cases. From 1939 to 1957, 305 additional cases were recorded in the medical literature. The latter figure suggests a wider prevalence than really exists, because 263 cases of poisoning occurred in a single episode at the Oregon State Hospital (Lidbeck, Hill & Beeman, 1943). Thus, in the medical reports covering a period of 85 years, there were only 132 scattered cases of acute fluoride poisoning, with 303 additional cases related to two epidemic-type accidents.

The acute effects of the ingestion of massive doses of fluoride are first those of an irritant poison, and later become apparent in enzyme systems such as those engaged in metabolism, energetics, and cellular respiration and in endocrine functions. However, no system of the body can be considered exempt.   Thus, in cases of acute poisoning, early involvement of the alimentary, cardiovascular, respiratory and central nervous systems, with corresponding symptoms, is a characteristic feature and such cases commonly have a fatal outcome in two to three days.

The frequency of the symptoms reported in connexion with 34 fatal cases of acute fluoride poisoning as described by Roholm (1937) are shown in Table 1.   The best available description of massive, non-fatal intoxication by NaF is the case given by Peters (1948).

TABLE 1

FREQUENCY WITH WHICH SYMPTOMS WERE OBSERVED IN 34 FATAL CASES OF ACUTE FLUORIDE POISONING [a]

Symptoms	No. of cases
Vomiting	31
Pain in abdomen	17
Diarrhoea	13
Convulsions, spasms	11
General weakness and muscular weakness and collapse	8
Pain or paraesthesia in extremities	7
Paresis, paralysis	5
Difficulty in speech and articulation	5
Thirst	5
Perspiration	5
Weak pulse	5
Change in facial colour	5
Nausea	4
Unconsciousness	4
Salivation	3
Impaired swallowing	3
Motorial restlessness	2
High temperature	2

[a] After Roholm (1937).

The acute toxicity of fluoride manifests itself chiefly by local corrosive action, besides action due to absorption.   After ingestion of fluorine compounds in high doses, there is diffuse abdominal pain, diarrhoea and vomiting.   There is excessive salivation, with thirst, perspiration and painful spasms in the limbs.

It is obvious that rapid measures to empty the stomach and reduce fluoride absorption are most effective for preventing death or damage from massive fluoride ingestion.   Provoked vomiting, followed by the ingestion of a large volume of milk, will generally be the immediately available emergency treatment.   The same precautionary measures may be taken should a child ingest large quantities of caries-preventive fluoride tablets or fluoride toothpaste, regardless of the fact that the risks are very small in such cases according to calculations and limited experience.

Robinowitch (1945) described an interesting variant in his patient, who apparently took a large amount of NaF and died of the effects of altered calcium metabolism but without the appearance of severe gastroenteritis, which has been mentioned in almost all the other reports. Tetaniform spasms due to lowered serum calcium have been described in some of the cases of acute fluoride poisoning.

Similarly, the inhalation of gaseous fluorine leads first to irritation of the mucous membrane of the eyes and air passages and subsequently to symptoms due to absorption.

The irritant effects of fluoride, sometimes referred to as local effects, chiefly concern occupational injuries to the skin. More specifically, these local effects concern the corrosive action of:

(a)   solutions of fluoride-containing acids on the skin;

(b)   fluoride-containing acid vapours or gases on the eyes, nasal mucosa and face;

(c)   such vapours or gases on the respiratory tract.

The pathological changes in acute intoxication are haemorrhagic gastro-enteritis with a tendency to necrosis, acute toxic nephritis and varying degrees of parenchymatous damage in other organs—for example, liver and heart

TABLE 2

FREQUENCY OF PATHOLOGICAL CHANGES OBSERVED
IN 32 FLUORIDE-INDUCED FATALITIES [a]

Pathological changes	No. of cases
Corrosive phenomena in mouth, throat or oesophagus	8
Inflammatory or corrosive phenomena in stomach	30
Haemorrhagic stomach contents	10
Changes in duodenum	11
Changes in small intestine	16
Changes in large intestine	2
Corrosion of organs neighbouring stomach	2
Hyperaemia of abdominal organs	6
Acute nephritis	8
Degenerative changes in liver	3
Haemorrhage or oedema of lungs	5
Subendocardial haemorrhage	2
Discoloration of skin or mucus membrane	2
Sublevel haemorrhages, brain hyperaemia or oedema	1
No definite change	1

[a] After Roholm (1937).

muscle. The frequency of the gross pathological changes reported in connexion with 32 fatal cases of acute poisoning described by Roholm (1937) is shown in Table 2.

Acute Experimental Fluoride Intoxication

No description of acute fluoride intoxication would be complete without a reference to the experimental work, which has been more closely studied and whose results are better appreciated than the scantily studied clinical cases of intoxication. Tappeiner (1889) used dogs, rabbits, guinea-pigs and cats as experimental animals. As much as 0.5 g NaF per 100 g of body-weight was given internally and 0.15 g was given by injection sub-cutaneously and intravenously. The following characteristic symptoms were observed:

(1) A condition of drowsiness and weakness resulting from paralysis of the vasomotor centres;

(2) Cramps which attacked a single organ or the entire body and were epileptic in character;

(3) Paralysis of the vasomotor centres;

(4) Acceleration and deepening of the breathing with paralysis;

(5) Vomiting;

(6) Secretion of salivary and tear glands which was not controlled by atropine;

(7) Early rigor mortis following death.

Leone, Geever & Moran (1956), in their experimental work on dogs and mice on the acute and subacute toxicity of sodium fluoride, concluded that the mean acute lethal dose of sodium fluoride in unanaesthetized dogs in-fused to death by continuous intravenous infusion at the rate of 5.4 mg of fluoride ion per minute was 36.0 ± 0.5 mg/kg. The principal effects were progressive depression of blood pressure, heart rate and central nervous system with vomiting and defecation, all occurring with administration of approximately 20 mg/kg. At a mean dose of 30.6 mg/kg, there was a depression of the respiratory rate and a conversion to atrioventricular, nodal or ventricular rhythm with terminal ventricular fibrillation or asystole.

In a group of dogs infused intravenously with selected fractions of the acute lethal dose, an approximate LD_{50} was estimated to be 20 mg/kg. The major effects observed in this group were vomiting, defecation and central-nervous-system depression. In dogs given fluoride by mouth, single doses up to 3100 mg/kg produced only vomiting and diarrhoea and transient moderate depression. A slight drop in serum calcium followed the infusion of fluoride in another group of dogs in which serum Ca was determined. The pathological findings were chiefly those of generalized hyperaemia and acute focal haemorrhages.

The gross pathological changes in acute poisoning provide evidence of the potential toxic properties of fluoride and are an indication of the possible hazards and dangers inherent in a single exposure to a large concentration of F. But it must be emphasized that the response of tissues to the relatively minute concentration derived from natural sources or absorbed from in-dustrial contamination over long periods of time is quite different and does not simulate acute toxic effects.

2. CHRONIC TOXIC EFFECTS ON ENAMEL ORGAN

(B. R. Bhussry)

The influence of chronic fluorine intoxication on the structure of enamel organ during its formation results in the development of an endemic hypoplasia known as "mottled enamel". Reference to these hypoplastic lesions of enamel dates back to Eager (1901). On the basis of the clinical appearance of the teeth, Black and McKay originally introduced the term "mottled enamel" and defined mottled teeth as "characterized by minute white flecks, yellow or brown spot areas scattered irregularly over the tooth surface". The permanent teeth are particularly affected, although occasional mottling of the primary teeth may be observed.

Regarding the nature of the hypoplastic lesions, McKay & Black (1916) considered the possibility that mottled enamel resulted from the influence of some factors in the water supply of endemic areas. Further evidence concerning this hypothesis was provided by Kempf & McKay (1930) and McKay (1933) following clinical studies at Bauxite, Arkansas, and Oakley, Idaho, respectively.

The association of mottled enamel with the presence of fluoride in drinking water was suggested by Smith, Lantz & Smith (1931), Churchill (1931) and Velu (1931). Subsequent investigations revealed a quantitative relationship between the fluoride concentration of the water supply and the severity of mottled enamel (Dean & Elvove, 1935, 1936, 1937).

Classification of Mottled Enamel in Human Teeth

Dean (1933, 1934) noted a qualitative variation in the distribution of mottled enamel among persons using a common water supply containing fluoride and a quantitative diversity in the incidence among children from different endemic areas. He classified the degree of clinically observed mottling into seven categories, ranging from normal to severe. Since the degree of dental fluorosis may in part be related to the fluoride content of the water supply, the influence of regional climatic conditions on water consumption and therefore on total fluoride ingestion should be recognized (Arnold, 1943; Galagan & Lamson, 1953; see also Chapter 2, section 2, Chapter 8, section 4, and Chapter 9 of this monograph). The basis for each classification of mottling was as follows:

1. Normal—The enamel is translucent, smooth and presents a glossy appearance.

2. Questionable—Seen in areas of relatively high endemicity. Occasional cases are borderline and one would hesitate to classify them as apparently normal or very mild.

3. Very mild—Small, opaque, paper-white areas are seen scattered irregularly over the labial and buccal tooth surfaces.

4. Mild—The white opaque areas involve at least half of the tooth surface, and faint brown stains are sometimes apparent.

5. Moderate—Generally all tooth surfaces are involved, and minute pitting is often present on the labial and buccal surfaces. Brown stains are frequently a disfiguring complication.

6. Moderately severe—Pitting is marked, more frequent and generally observed on all tooth surfaces. Brown stains, if present, are generally of greater intensity.

7. Severe—The severe hypoplasia affects the form of the tooth. Stains are widespread and vary in intensity from deep brown to black. This condition may sometimes be referred to as "corrosion" type of mottled enamel.

On the basis of this classification, Dean et al. (1935) attempted to determine a mottled enamel index of the community. This was arbitrarily defined in terms of the "degree of severity of mottled enamel" observed clinically. Similar hypoplastic changes of a non-fluorotic nature have since been recognized and found to be more frequent in low-fluoride areas (cf. Chapter 6, section 4). Such changes probably account for the "fluorosis index" line that appears in the 0.1-1.0 ppm region in Fig. 4 of Chapter 9. The differential diagnosis between mild fluorosis and non-specific mottling may be difficult in individuals whose history of early fluoride ingestion is unknown; some morphological characteristics have been given by Nevitt, Frankel & Witter (1963).

Microscopic Appearance of Mottled Enamel in Human Teeth

The literature concerning the microscopic appearance and nature of fluorosed enamel is sparse. The series of mechanisms leading to the mottling of enamel during its development and mineralization are as yet not well understood. McKay & Black (1916) reported varying degrees of discoloration of the enamel surface in ground sections of mottled teeth. They observed a lack of interprismatic substance between the regular, well-formed enamel rods, and the presence of brown pigmentation in the outer third of enamel. Williams (1923) demonstrated that areas of fluorosed enamel were more easily permeable to dyes and silver nitrate than normal enamel, possibly owing to the developmentally defective nature of the outer enamel.

Ainsworth (1933) reported the presence of irregular white and brown patches in the enamel of teeth in schoolchildren from Maldon, England. On examination of ground sections of these teeth under ultraviolet light, Ainsworth found that while sound enamel normally fluoresces bright blue, the brown stain in the mottled enamel did not fluoresce. He suggested that the stains may be of extraneous origin, and the lack of interprismatic substance of enamel may provide a pathway for the stains, thus confirming the earlier observations of Williams (1923).

Erausquin (1934) considered the permeability of the external zone of mottled enamel as being similar to that of the "immature unerupted enamel". Applebaum (1936) used soft X-rays to examine sections of mottled teeth and reported a decreased X-ray density in the outer portion of fluorosed enamel. He observed that the X-ray radiolucency of enamel was directly related to the severity of mottling in teeth.

Newbrun (1957) employed the microradiographic technique and confirmed Applebaum's findings of decreased X-ray density in the outer third of mottled enamel. The microdensitometric tracings of fluorosed teeth showed distinct hypocalcification in that region.

On the basis of histological and controlled decalcification studies of mottled enamel, Bhussry (1959a) demonstrated the presence of brown pigmentation in the outer third of enamel which was resistant to solubility in acids (Fig. 1, I & II). His observation that pigmented areas emitted a high intensity of fluorescence (Fig. 1, III) when examined under ultraviolet light was in contradiction to that of Ainsworth (1933).

Microradiographic observations of fluorosed enamel (Bhussry, unpublished data, 1965) demonstrate areas of subsurface hypomineralization (Fig. 1, IV). Although diffuse radiolucent patches are always apparent, the variation in the X-ray density along the enamel rods and cross striations is obvious. This pattern is limited to the outer zone of mottled enamel.

Gustafson (1961) utilized the polarized light and microradiographic techniques to demonstrate variations in the radiodensity and birefringence in irregular hypomineralized areas of fluorosed enamel, which were more pronounced along the striae of Retzius. An arcade appearance at the dentino-enamel junction was observed in mottled enamel.

Gerould (1945), using electron microscopy, demonstrated that sections of mottled enamel etched with HCl exhibited much finer detail of background structure than did similarly treated normal enamel. He suggested that structural differences may be due to the reduced acid solubility of the fluorapatite of mottled enamel as compared with the hydroxyapatite of normal enamel.

Awazawa (1962) prepared replicas for electron microscopic examination of teeth showing varying degrees of mottling. He reported that the enamel was relatively rich in organic material while there was a deficiency of the inter-rod substance. The enamel rods on the tooth surface were poorly mineralized with abnormal crystal size.

Investigations in Experimental Animals

Fluorosis in the white rat is manifested as a pronounced alteration in the development and appearance of the incisor teeth. The influence of fluorine on the developing teeth of experimental animals always appears to be identical, regardless of the mode of fluoride administration (McClure, 1939).

FIG. 1

MOTTLED ENAMEL IN HUMAN TEETH

I. Unstained ground section through a mottled tooth. The smooth surface contour and pigmentation in the outer third of enamel are obvious. Scattered irregular hypocalcified areas (h) in the body of enamel are common. (Magnification: × 25)

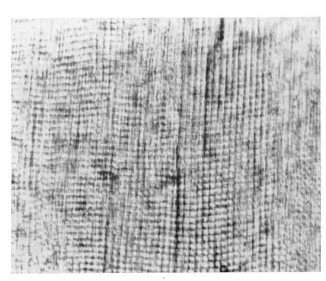

II. Detail view of the subsurface pigmented region of mottled enamel shown in I. The structure of the enamel rods and cross striations suggests disturbance (hypocalcification) in this area. (Magnification: × 250)

III. Fluorophotomicrograph of the ground section shown in I. Note the increased intensity of fluorescence pattern corresponding to the pigmented area observed in the outer third of enamel. (Magnification: × 25)

IV. Microradiograph of the section shown in I. The subsurface radiolucency (r) is limited to the area of pigmentation. Hypomineralization along the enamel rods and cross striations is obvious (h). (Magnification: × 250)

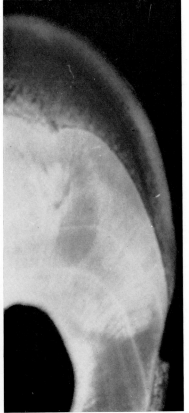

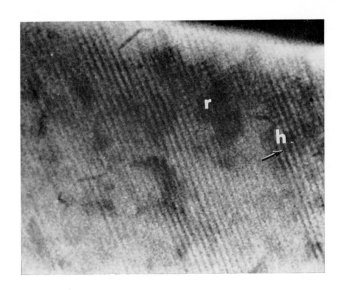

FIG. 2

EFFECT OF FLUORIDE ON THE DEVELOPING TEETH OF RATS

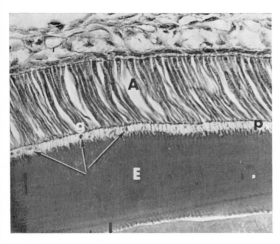

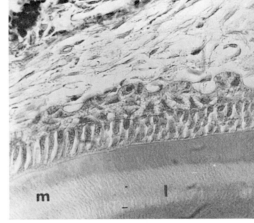

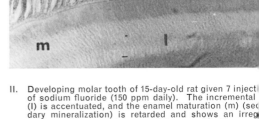

I. Developing molar tooth of 10-day-old rat given 7 injections of sodium fluoride (150 ppm daily). The zone of pre-enamel matrix (p) is wider than that observed in the controls. Small acidophilic globules (g) are usually present in the area of Tomes' processes of the ameloblasts (A). The newly formed enamel matrix (E) appears normal in texture and staining reaction. (Masson trichrome stain; magnification: × 250)

II. Developing molar tooth of 15-day-old rat given 7 inject of sodium fluoride (150 ppm daily). The incremental (I) is accentuated, and the enamel maturation (m) (sec dary mineralization) is retarded and shows an irreg pattern. (Masson trichrome stain; magnification: ×

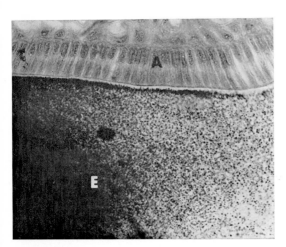

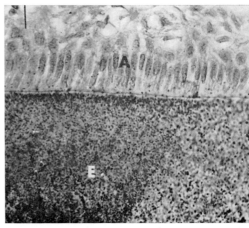

III. Developing molar tooth of 15-day-old control rat. The black silver precipitate in the cuspal region demonstrates the amount and pattern of enamel mineralization. (von Kossa staining reaction; magnification: × 400)

IV. Developing molar tooth of 15-day-old fluoride-treate (same animal as in II). The decreased aggregation intensity of silver precipitate in the enamel matrix suggests delayed mineralization. The black band at junction of the ameloblasts (A) and enamel matrix ind ing mineral deposition is absent. (von Kossa sta reaction; magnification: × 400)

FIG. 3
MOTTLED ENAMEL IN A CHILD FROM AN ENDEMIC FLUOROSIS
AREA IN PUNJAB

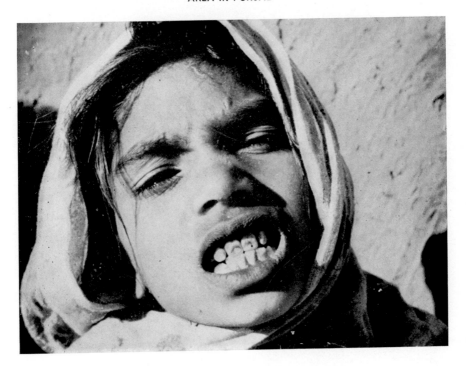

FIG. 4
PELVIS FROM AN ADVANCED CASE OF FLUOROSIS, SHOWING THE
ABNORMAL APPEARANCE OF BONES AND THE LAYING-DOWN OF IRREGULAR BONE

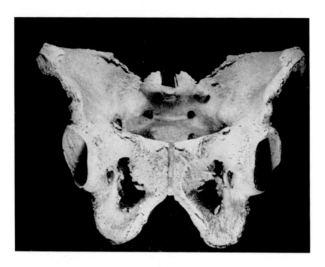

I. Front view.

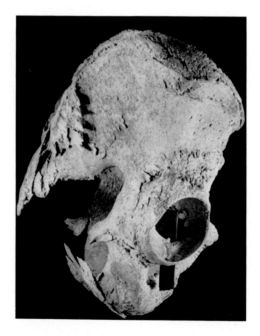

II. Side view.

FIG. 5

MANIFESTATIONS OF ADVANCED FLUOROSIS IN FOREARM BONES AND FEMUR

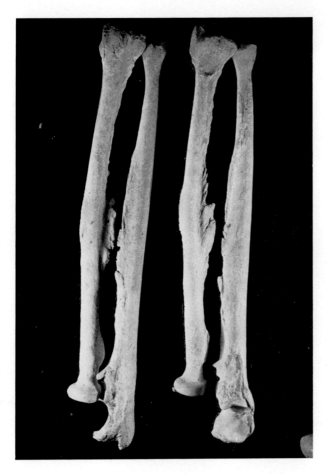

I. Forearm bones, showing gross degree of calcification of interosseous membrane.

II. Femur, viewed from each side, showing irregular bone formation.

FIG. 6

MANIFESTATIONS OF ADVANCED FLUOROSIS IN VERTEBRAE

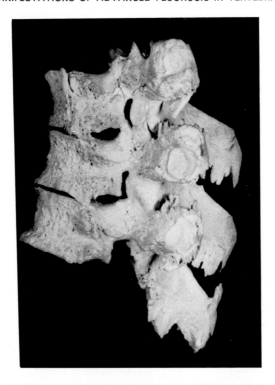

I. Fused dorsal vertebrae, showing narrowed intervertebral
foramina and irregular osteophytes.

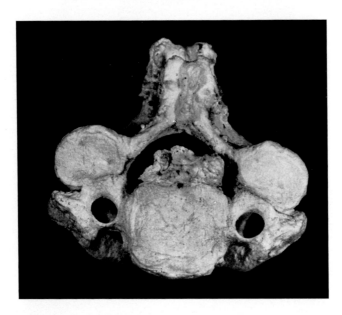

II. Third cervical vertebra, showing a huge exostosis projecting into the
spinal canal.

FIG. 7
MANIFESTATIONS OF ADVANCED FLUOROSIS IN SKULL [a]

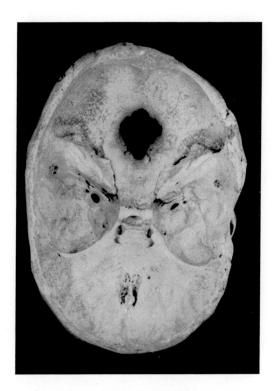

Base of skull, showing irregularity of the foramen magnum.

The initial report concerning the structural changes in the teeth of experimental animals following sodium fluoride ingestion (0.2-0.02%) was made by McCollum (1925). The rats developed overgrown upper incisor teeth without characteristic pigmentation. Chaneles (1929) observed changes in the structure and arrangement of the enamel-forming cells in the teeth of rats fed fluorides. Similar incisor teeth were observed in animals fed rock phosphate (Tolle & Maynard, 1928), cryolite (Smyth & Smyth, 1932), and sodium fluoride and calcium fluoride (Arkansas Agricultural Experiment Station, 1926). McClure & Mitchell (1931) could not produce similar changes in the teeth of swine following sodium fluoride injection (1.03% and 0.06%).

Experimental fluorosis in the white rat was also demonstrated by Smith, Lantz & Smith (1931). The teeth of rats given sodium fluoride (0.02%, 0.05% and 0.1%) either in drinking water or in food showed mottling of enamel after a one-month experimental period. The investigators concluded that sodium fluoride would influence the developing tooth structure irrespective of the mode of administration. Velu (1931) confirmed these findings by feeding calcium fluoride and rock phosphate containing about 3-4% fluorine to white rats. Bethke et al. (1933) demonstrated hypoplasia of tooth enamel in rats receiving fluorine in the diet.

Sebrell et al. (1933) observed changes in the teeth of rats given concentrated drinking water (following evaporation) from an endemic mottled-enamel area. The incisor teeth lost their normal orange colour and appeared white. Distilled water containing 150 ppm sodium fluoride when given to rats as drinking water induced similar alterations in incisor teeth. However, when the concentration of sodium fluoride in such synthetic drinking water was increased to 500 ppm, the water proved to be exceedingly toxic and only a few animals survived. The teeth of these animals were chalky white and brittle. Dean et al. (1934) demonstrated minute striations on the incisor teeth of rats receiving 25 ppm sodium fluoride in drinking water daily for 23 days. The severity of alterations in the teeth of experimental animals was proportional to the concentration of fluoride in the drinking water received by the animals (25 ppm, 50 ppm, 150 ppm, 300 ppm, 500 ppm). The initial appearance of minute striations was followed by the formation of irregular brown patches and, finally, the enamel became white and brittle. Schour & Smith (1934, 1935), and Schour (1934) reported that developing enamel and enamel-forming cells were the first to respond to intraperitoneal injections of sodium fluoride. The disturbances of the ameloblastic layer were reflected in the newly formed enamel matrix, which was poorly mineralized, while the rate of apposition was not affected (Schour & Poncher, 1937). The same workers observed that the cumulative action of fluorine produced a further toxic effect on the ameloblasts, and a disturbance of both appositional growth and mineralization of the enamel matrix. This resulted in hypoplastic defects of enamel.

Histochemical and microradiographic aspects of the influence of various concentrations of sodium fluoride on the developing teeth of rats were investigated by Bhussry (1959b, 1960). Five groups of ten animals, 3-10 days of age, were given intraperitoneal injections of 10, 25, 45, 70 and 90 μg of sodium fluoride daily for up to 20 days. Only two animals in the 90-μg group survived. All experimental animals demonstrated abnormalities of amelogenesis, the degree of severity depending upon the amount of fluoride received. There was a wide zone of pre-enamel matrix, suggesting a delay in homogenization of the Tomes processes of ameloblasts. The apposition and mineralization of enamel matrix was retarded and calcification disturbances were obvious (Fig. 2, I-IV). Large patches of uncalcified enamel matrix were evident and accentuated incremental lines in enamel were occasionally present. There was a distinct reduction in the mucopolysaccharides and glycoprotein-staining components of enamel matrix.

Parikh (1960, 1961) and Weber & Yaeger (1964), using microradiographic techniques, investigated the calcification pattern in the developing teeth of newborn animals receiving toxic doses of sodium fluoride. They reported a disorganization of the ameloblastic layer and the presence of large radiolucent areas in the enamel microradiographs indicating a disturbance in the pattern of enamel mineralization. Allan (1963) observed narrow hypermineralized striae of Retzius preceded by a hypomineralized zone in the forming enamel matrix of 3-day-old pups injected with 2% sodium fluoride in doses of 10 mg/kg to 50 mg/kg body-weight. However, when sodium fluoride was given to pups during the period of enamel mineralization, diffuse hypomineralization of the mature tissue was noted.

The possibility that fluorosis may bear a relationship to calcium metabolism has been suggested by various investigators (Hauck et al., 1933; Lantz & Smith, 1934).

The deposition of elevated levels of fluoride in rachitic animals has been observed by two investigators (Schultz, 1936; Kempf & Nelson, 1941). Morgareidge & Finn (1940) found that 300 ppm fluoride added to the drinking water of rats fed a rachitogenic diet reduced the severity of developing rickets by increasing the bone density.

Zipkin, Likins & McClure (1959) demonstrated an increase in the ash content of the femur and mandible of rachitic animals receiving fluoride. However, the fluoride content in the teeth was not altered by the rachitic condition of the animals. Cicardo et al. (1955) showed that daily administration of fluoride to rats resulted in an increased uptake of radiocalcium by long bones, while Comar et al. (1953) prepared autoradiographs of femurs from pigs following fluoride administration (1000 ppm in diet). He observed the removal of ^{45}Ca originally deposited in the epiphyseal region—an observation suggesting that fluoride intake caused an increased rate of bone resorption in the primary spongiosa. Likins et al. (1959) reported that the percentage of radiocalcium was significantly less in the tooth enamel

of fluoride-treated rats, but could not find any difference in the deposition of radiocalcium in bone.

Information concerning the histological and histochemical aspects of the effect of fluoride on the developing teeth—and, specifically, on the enamel organ—of rats fed calcium-phosphorus deficient diets is sparse.

Irving (1943a, 1943b) and Irving & Neinbar (1946) demonstrated changes in the calcification of dentine in fluoride-treated animals receiving diets containing various amounts of calcium-phosphorus.

Bhussry (1960) observed that when pregnant rats fed a high-calcium, low-phosphorus diet (4-5 : 1; Steenbock rachitogenic diet) were given 100 μg of sodium fluoride in water subcutaneously, the developing teeth of their offspring, although not normal, showed an improvement in the quality and mineralization of enamel matrix in comparison with those which did not receive any fluoride. Disturbances in the ameloblastic layer and cells of the stratum intermedium during amelogenesis were not as severe. The enamel matrix demonstrated an unusual increase of mucopolysaccharide and glyco-protein-stained material in the organic matrix.

In the developing teeth of animals which received a vitamin-D supplement (100 IU of Viosterol in cottonseed oil) in addition to sodium fluoride (Bhussry, 1961), the ameloblastic layer demonstrated considerable improvement. The pattern and quality of enamel mineralization appeared similar to that in the teeth of normal control animals of the same age. The enamel matrix, at times, exhibited an accelerated process of maturation.

When pregnant rats fed a vitamin-D deficient diet normal in calcium-phosphorus ratio (chick basal diet) were given 100 μg of sodium fluoride in distilled water subcutaneously (Bhussry & Werth, 1962), the developing teeth of their offspring demonstrated minimal changes in the ameloblasts and the enamel matrix. When these animals received a vitamin-D supplement (100 IU of Viosterol in cottonseed oil), the enamel matrix was of normal texture and staining quality. It could not be distinguished from the enamel matrix of normal developing teeth. These studies suggest a relationship between fluoride intake and calcium-phosphorus ratio in the diet.

Chemical Studies of Mottled Enamel

Information regarding the chemical aspects of the organic material in the mottled enamel of teeth is limited. Bowes & Murray (1936) demonstrated a higher protein content in fluorosed enamel than in non-mottled enamel. This finding was confirmed by Bhussry (1959a), who reported a higher nitrogen content in mottled enamel than in sound enamel. He could not, however, detect any significant differences in density determinations (see Table 3).

Chemical analysis of the inorganic content by Armstrong & Brekhus (1937), Bowes & Murray (1936), Montelius & McIntosh (1933), Smith

TABLE 3

COMPARISON OF MOTTLED ENAMEL AND SOUND ENAMEL

	Density (g/cm³)		N₂ content (mg/g)		N₂ content (mg/cm³)	
	No. of teeth	Mean ± SE [a]	No. of teeth	Mean ± SE [a]	No. of teeth	Mean ± SE [a]
Mottled enamel	161	2.88 ± 0.02	105	0.75 ± 0.05	105	2.17 ± 0.15
Sound enamel	261	2.81 ± 0.02	282	0.56 ± 0.02	243	1.59 ± 0.06

[a] The standard error is based on the within-group standard deviations (pooled estimate), which are: density, 0.29; nitrogen (mg/g), 0.57; nitrogen (mg/cm³), 1.54.

& Lantz (1932) and Ockerse (1943) did not show any significant difference (ash basis) in the calcium, phosphorus, magnesium and carbonate content of mottled and non-mottled teeth. This may partially explain the lack of differences in the density determinations of these teeth (Bhussry, 1959a). It should be mentioned that it has not been possible to find any further investigations dealing with the density and hardness of mottled enamel.

The fluoride concentration in human enamel at various levels of fluoride ingestion has been discussed by Weidmann and Weatherell in Chapter 4, section 3. The data from various investigations suggest that the concentration of fluoride in the surface enamel is linearly related to the fluoride level of the drinking water.

An observation of great theoretical interest is that although the outermost layer of shark's teeth contains more than a hundred times the fluoride content of human mottled enamel, there are no signs of disturbance in its mineralization. Using biophysical and chemical methods, Glas (1962) demonstrated that the size and orientation of the apatite crystallites in the shark "enamel" and its degree of mineralization was the same as in human enamel. In contrast to the hydroxyapatite occurring in human enamel, the inorganic phase of shark's "enamel" consists of an almost pure fluorapatite, which is formed during normal mineralization (Büttner, 1966). Unlike human enamel, which is of epithelial origin, the shark "enamel" develops from mesodermal tissues (Kvam, 1950) and has been referred to as "durodentin" and "petrodentin" (Schmidt & Keil, 1958; Lison, 1941). This suggests that the epithelial enamel organ of human teeth demonstrates specific sensitivity to fluorides.

Various investigators (Gedalia et al., 1959, 1961; Gardner et al., 1952; Ziegler, 1956) have reported that fluoride ingested during pregnancy is probably accumulated in the placental tissue. Ericsson and co-workers (Ericsson & Ullberg, 1958; Ericsson & Malmnäs, 1962; Ericsson & Hammarström, 1964) and Dustin (1963), however, demonstrated that the placenta permits a limited passage of fluoride to the foetal skeleton. Using ^{18}F they observed accumulations of fluoride in foetal skeletal tissues during intra-

uterine calcification.   Brezezinski, Bercovici & Gedalia (1960) found that when pregnant mothers received fluoride (0.55 ppm) in drinking water there was an increase in the fluoride content of foetal femora with advancing age. Gedalia et al. (1964) reported that although fluoride is incorporated in the calcifying foetal teeth, the accumulation is significantly less than that in the femora.   Fleming & Greenfield (1954) conducted a histological study to observe changes in the teeth and jaws of mice following administration of very large doses of sodium and calcium fluoride (60-100 μg daily) to the female parent during gestation.   Structural alteration of the ameloblastic layer resulted in the retardation of enamel matrix formation and its mineralization.   Calcium fluoride seemed to be more toxic to the foetuses than sodium fluoride.   It is obvious that there is a considerable lack of histological information regarding the influence of the mothers' receiving fluoride during pregnancy on the developing teeth of offspring.

Discussion and Summary

Epidemiological studies have verified the association of water-borne fluorides at levels of 1 ppm with the production of significant immunity to dental caries.   However, the influence of toxic levels of fluoride in drinking water on the structure of enamel organ during its formation result in the development of an endemic hypoplasia known as "mottled enamel".   Although there appears to be a relationship between the amount of fluoride ingested and the clinical manifestation of dental fluorosis, there are numerous factors which may cause wide individual variations.

The microscopic appearance of human mottled enamel depends upon the severity of the hypoplastic lesion.   In mild and moderate dental fluorosis the enamel surface continuity is maintained, while in the severe variety it is broken due to pitting.   The outer third of mottled enamel shows pigmentation and a decreased X-ray density suggesting hypocalcification.   These areas are less soluble in acids, have a greater permeability to dyes and emit fluorescence of higher intensity than normal enamel.

Investigators using experimental animals have demonstrated that the influence of fluoride on teeth always appears to be identical, regardless of the mode of fluoride administration (in drinking water, in the diet or by injection).   The gross changes in teeth include the appearance of minute striations followed by formation of irregular brown patches, and finally the enamel becomes brittle.

Microscopic observations of developing enamel indicate disturbances in the ameloblastic layer and a retardation in the apposition and mineralization of the enamel matrix produced by these cells.   The role of reduced mucopolysaccharides and glycoprotein-staining components of enamel in calcification is not well understood.   Histological and chemical evidence in

fluoride-treated animals fed diets with varying calcium-phosphorus ratios suggests the possibility that fluorosis may bear a relationship to calcium metabolism.

Although it has been established that fluoride ingested during pregnancy may pass through the placenta and be accumulated to a limited extent in the foetal skeleton and teeth, its effect on the teeth of offspring is not clear.

Chemical investigations of mottled enamel suggest an increase in the organic material, but no significant difference in the calcium-phosphorus ratio of mottled and non-mottled teeth.

It is obvious from the above studies that fluoride influences both the organic and the inorganic phase during development of the enamel organ. The possible mechanisms of action at physiological concentrations have been summarized by Jenkins (1962) as follows:

(a) ionic exchange with hydroxyl of the apatite in the calcified tissues;

(b) influence on the precipitation of mineral from saturated solutions of calcium phosphate;

(c) inhibition and, in some cases with low concentrations, activation of enzymes.

Although there is considerable evidence to support each of these aspects of fluoride action, none of them in itself is conclusive. It is possible that they are all interrelated, and further investigations will be necessary to explain the mechanism of formation of the hypoplastic lesions known as mottled enamel.

3. CHRONIC TOXIC EFFECTS ON THE SKELETAL SYSTEM *

(A. Singh & S. S. Jolly)

The chronic toxic effects of fluoride on the skeletal system have been described from certain geographical regions of the world where drinking water contains excessive quantities of natural fluoride. This form of chronic intoxication was first described in India from the State of Madras as early as 1937 (Shortt et al., 1937). Subsequently cases of endemic fluorosis have been reported from other parts of India, particularly from Punjab (Singh et al., 1962a, 1962b, 1963), and sporadically from other parts of the world, notably Ceylon (Clark, 1942), China (Lyth, 1946), South Africa (Ockerse, 1942), Japan (Hamamoto et al., 1954), Saudi Arabia (El Tannir, 1959), the USA (Leone et al., 1954; Zipkin et al., 1958), Canada (Kilborn, Outerbridge & Lei, 1950), and Europe (Odenthal & Wieneke, 1959). Besides endemic fluorosis, chronic toxic effects of fluoride on the

* The authors wish to thank Dr B. M. Singh, Dr O. C. Mathur, Dr K. C. Malhotra, and other members of the staff of the Patiala Medical College who helped in the preparation of this section.

skeletal system have also been observed in relation to industrial exposure to fluorides such as cryolite, and in fact it is the pioneer studies of Roholm (1937) that have paved the way for further contributions on this subject.

The precise dose of ingested or inhaled fluoride which results in well-recognized skeletal changes has not been fully evaluated. However, certain broad conclusions are possible at this stage. In fluoridation studies in adults which envisage a daily intake of 0.5-2 mg of fluoride, no evidence of storage, as defined in terms of abnormal density of bone, has ever been demonstrated.

At higher levels of ingestion—from 2 to 8 mg daily—when signs of fluorosis appear in teeth mineralized during the ingestion period, certain other factors (climatic conditions, malnutrition, age, storage, other constituents of water and, possibly, individual variations in absorption) may be involved. Under such conditions and over a number of years, skeletal fluorosis may arise, characterized by an increased density of bone and demonstrated in adults radiographically. The data put forward by McClure et al. (1945), although no longer regarded as accurate, indicate that the limit of total fluoride which may be ingested daily without hazardous body storage is of the order of 4-5 mg daily. In areas of endemic fluorosis, levels of ingestion of fluoride from diet and water over 8 mg daily are common, although in certain regions in India, changes typical of skeletal fluorosis have been stated to occur at estimated lower dosages (Singh et al., 1962b).

The bone changes and skeletal abnormalities in endemic fluorosis are not as marked as those in industrial fluorosis, although in hyperendemic areas the skeletal changes are almost identical to those seen in the heavy exposure of industrial fluorosis. The severity of the fluorosis indicated by the degree of mottling in the teeth is not proportionally reflected in the bone, which is natural considering the metabolic differences of these tissues and the different periods of development of enamel and bone fluorosis.

Clinical Features

The dental and skeletal changes in endemic fluorosis provide important clinical diagnostic criteria. Whereas dental fluorosis is easily recognized (Fig. 3), the skeletal involvement is not clinically obvious until the advanced stage of crippling fluorosis. However, radiological changes are discernible in the skeleton at a much earlier stage and provide the only means of diagnosing the early and relatively asymptomatic stage of fluorosis. Such early cases are usually in young adults whose only complaints are vague pains noted most frequently in the small joints of the hands and feet, in the knee joints and in the joints of the spine. These cases are frequent in the endemic areas and may be misdiagnosed as rheumatoid or osteo-

arthritis. In later stages, there is an obvious stiffness of the spine, with limitation of movements, and, still later, the development of kyphosis. There is difficulty in walking, due partly to stiffness and limitation of the movements of various joints and partly to the neurological lesions of advanced cases. Similarly, some of the patients complain of dyspnoea on exertion because of the rigidity of the thoracic cage. In Roholm's series of industrial fluorosis cases, the gastrointestinal symptoms of lack of appetite, nausea and constipation were as frequent as the symptoms of stiffness of joints, but the former have not been described in the different studies of endemic fluorosis.

The various skeletal changes in endemic fluorosis are best described under the following headings:

Gross changes in the skeleton

The gross changes in the skeleton in cases of endemic fluorosis are quite distinctive and characteristic. The excessive quantities of fluoride which are ingested are deposited in the skeleton over the years. Singh et al. (1962a) had a unique opportunity of studying a complete macerated skeleton of an individual who had lived in an endemic area where the water had a fluoride content of 9.5 ppm. All the bones were observed to be heavy and irregular and to have a dull colour due to irregular deposition of fluoride. The sites of muscular and tendinous insertions were rendered abnormally prominent by excessive periosteal reaction with development of multiple exostoses. Irregular bone was laid down along the attachment of muscles and tendons in the extremities as well as in joint capsules and interosseous membranes (Fig. 4 and 5). This irregularity is particularly helpful as a diagnostic feature in doubtful and borderline cases where the density of the bones is not markedly increased.

Maximum changes are detected in the spine with calcification of various ligaments, particularly the yellow, intertransverse and interspinous ligaments, resulting in marked osteophytes. The vertebral bodies are larger than normal and show marked lipping (Fig. 6, I). The vertebrae show altered proportions and measurements in all the planes, but the striking abnormality is the gross reduction of the anteroposterior diameter of the spinal canal. In one of our cases, this diameter was reduced to 2 mm at the level of third and fourth cervical vertebrae (Fig. 6, II). Since the average anteroposterior diameter of the spinal cord in the cervical enlargement is 8 mm and the bulge of the ligamentum flavum has also to be accounted for, it is evident that compression of the cord is almost inevitable. The vertebrae are also fused at many places—a fact which explains the marked limitation of movements and the resemblance of the disease to spondylitis ankylopoietica. The intervertebral foramina are narrowed and rendered irregular—a finding which explains the presence of radicular manifestations. A similar post-mortem

study of an advanced case who had a "poker back" was reported by Lyth (1946). There was fusion of all the vertebrae from the second cervical vertebra downwards with the ribs and bones of the pelvis. There was a fracture at the level of the eighth dorsal vertebra so that the lower dorsal vertebrae, lower ribs, lumbar vertebrae and pelvis came out in one piece and the upper ribs and vertebrae in another. The bones were held together by masses of new bone laid down in the joint capsule, ligaments and tendons. The long bones showed numerous spiky exostoses, especially along the attachment of muscles. The spinal canal was not more than 1.2 mm in diameter at the level of the second cervical vertebra.

In the skull the changes are not so conspicuous, although the bones are thick and heavy with no diploë. The floors of the cranial fossae are irregular and the clinoid process of the sella turcica is fused. The margins of the foramen magnum are also rendered irregular and narrow owing to the projection of osteophytes (Fig. 7). The smaller foramina in the skull are usually not altered, thus explaining the absence of cranial nerve involvement in advanced cases of endemic fluorosis.

The ribs are large, with rough surfaces and osteophytes projecting along the attachments of muscles, membranes and ligaments.

The other bones, including those of the limbs, the sternum and the mandible, have many prominent osteophytes at the attachments of ligaments, membranes, tendons and muscular insertions, thus making the various markings and ridges thick and prominent. The interosseous membranes between the tibia and fibula and between the radius and ulna are calcified in variable degree in most of the cases (Fig. 5, I).

There is thickening and calcification in most of the ligaments and in many of the capsular attachments such as the sacroiliac and sacrotuberous ligaments (Fig. 4, I). The thyroid cartilage is also calcified in most of the cases.

The irregular bone deposition is obvious clinically, in a large percentage of cases, as bony excrescences of varying size. These are usually seen near the knee joint along the anterior border of tibia and near the olecranon. The skeletal changes result in limitation of movements, particularly of the cervical spine, lumbodorsal spine, joints of the lower extremities and joints of the upper limbs, in that order.

Besides the gross structural changes described above, there is an appreciable increase in the weight of fluorotic bones. The total weight of the normal skeleton is variable. It was found to be 4957 g in Americans by Ingalls (1931). In Asians, Lawrence & Latimer (1957) found it to be 2882 g. In a case of fluorosis, the weight of the skeleton was 6190 g, as compared with 2520 g in a normal control of similar proportions (Singh et al., 1962a). The coefficient of weight to length showed that, in general, fluorotic bones were nearly twice the normal weight, but that the vertebral column, pelvis and scapulae were many times heavier.

Radiological changes

The radiological changes of skeletal fluorosis are diagnostic. Roholm (1937) distinguished three stages in the evolution of skeletal fluorosis.

Stage 1. The spinal column and the pelvis show roughening and blurring of the trabeculae.

Stage 2. The trabeculae merge together and the bone has a diffuse structureless appearance. The bone contours become uneven. These changes are most marked in the pelvis, spine and ribs. The medullary cavities may be narrowed and the ligaments show early calcification.

Stage 3. The bones appear as marble-white shadows, this appearance being most marked in the axial skeleton. The configuration is woolly. The bones of the extremities show irregular periosteal thickening with calcification of ligaments and muscular attachments. The cortex of long bones is thick and dense, and the medullary cavity is diminished. The interosseous membrane also shows calcification.

The radiological patterns of endemic fluorosis are almost identical to those of industrial intoxication described in cryolite workers, except that stage 1 is hardly ever seen in endemic fluorosis cases, most of which show the changes of stages 2 and 3. In general, the radiological appearance is as follows:

The most pronounced changes are seen in the vertebral column, particularly in the cervical and lumbar region. Osteosclerosis and irregular osteophyte formation is noted in the vertebral body, the transverse and spinous processes, and the pedicles and laminae. Beak-like lipping and the chalky white ground-glass appearance of the entire vertebral column are the characteristic radiological features. There is calcification of the intervertebral ligaments (Fig. 8 and 9). As a result of irregular exostoses, there is encroachment on the intervertebral foramina and the spinal canal (Fig. 10 and 11). Next to its spinal manifestations, osteosclerosis is most evident in the pelvis, along with calcification of the sacrotuberous and sacrospinous ligaments. Irregular periosteal bone formation is observed along the tendons and fascial and muscular attachments including the interosseous membranes of the forearm and legs, the linea aspera, the deltoid tuberosity, the lower margins of the ribs, the attachment of the Achilles tendon, the tibial tubercle, and the greater trochanter of the femur. Skiagrams of the chest reveal the peculiar contrast of a marble-white bony cage with radiolucent lungs (Fig. 12). The changes in the skull are not very striking, although there is thickening of the vault with sclerosis near the suture lines. The sella turcica and the nasal sinuses are normal and there is no significant narrowing of the basal foramina.

It must be emphasized here that the advanced radiological changes described above and reported from hyperendemic areas like Punjab (Singh et al., 1963) and Andhra Pradesh (Siddiqui, 1955) are not universally seen in the population as a whole. The development of skeletal fluorosis certainly depends on the length and level of exposure to natural fluoride in the water and soil, and possibly on particles suspended in the drinking water (cf. Chapter 2, section 5, and Chapter 4, section 3). It has been suggested that the advanced radiological changes seen in the endemic areas in India are due to malnutrition, although its exact role in the causation of skeletal fluorosis has not been finally elucidated. There is clinical and experimental evidence (Pandit et al., 1940) that malnutrition may predispose to the development of crippling fluorosis, because in other parts of the world where the level of fluoride in the water supply is almost the same the incidence of crippling fluorosis is so low (Leone et al., 1954). It has been alleged that the description of these advanced and bizarre radiological changes has created a bias in the interpretation of the physiological effects of fluoride. However, Leone et al. (*op. cit.*) also observed increased bone density, with or without condensed trabeculation with a ground-glass appearance, in 10-15% of persons exposed to a water supply containing 8 ppm fluoride. These observations did not bear any resemblance to the advanced findings described in cases of long exposure to cryolite or rock phosphate dust or to those attributed by Indian investigators to excessive fluoride in domestic water supplies.

Histopathology

Although there are many histopathological reports on experimental fluorosis (Weatherell & Weidmann, 1959), the data in human intoxication are scanty. Our observations are based on biopsy specimens obtained either from the tibia or iliac crest or from the spine at the time of laminectomy. In general, the compact bone shows disordered lamellar orientation and an enlarged, poorly formed Haversian system, resembling the changes described in experimental animals (Fig. 13). In the spongy bone, areas of osteoid tissue are found among well-formed trabeculae. Some of the irregular deposits of osteoid tissue extend into the attached muscle. The bone trabeculae are very dense in places and contain a considerable amount of calcium. The areas around the vascular spaces stain deeply with eosin. In some cases the muscular attachments to the bones may show areas of irregular calcification.

Among the effects of high fluoride ingestion may be the calcification of tendons, ligaments and, occasionally, muscles, as well as the stimulation of osteoblastic activity. Some bones are more prone to exostosis formation than others: the vertebrae, ribs and pelvis, for instance, are more susceptible than the long bones. In an advanced case, however, the entire skeleton is

involved. Such localized deposition of new bone, frequently found at the sites of muscle and tendon attachments, would seem to suggest that a significant factor in the development of the lesions is the rich blood supply of these sites. Exostosis formation is not always so restricted —sometimes the entire surface of a bone may be invested with new tissue resulting in an over-all increase in thickness. Blood supply is therefore not the sole factor governing the induction of fluorotic exostoses. The extensive production of new bone in the fluorotic skeleton is usually accompanied by increased bone resorption. It has been suggested that exostoses are formed in order to reinforce a weakened bone (Weinmann & Sicher, 1955). However, the few descriptions of chronic skeletal fluorosis in man suggest that there is a greater tendency towards the formation of new bone than towards the destruction of existing bone. Histologically, the exostoses consist of coarse, primary woven bone in which secondary lamellar replacement is minimal. The low degree of mineralization, as indicated by the calcium:nitrogen ratio of the bone, is partly due to a wide seam of uncalcified osteoid found in the fluorotic bones of both man and animals.

Skeletal fluorosis has been likened to a number of bone diseases: the dense radiographic picture of the skeleton has resulted in comparison with osteosclerosis; the presence of broad osteoid seams has suggested osteomalacia; the way in which bone formation may proceed side by side with bone destruction is reminiscent of Paget's disease; and the often extensive resorption points to osteoporosis. Certainly, fluorotic bones can exhibit signs common to each of these conditions, but a unique distinction is the presence of high levels of fluoride in the bone.

Geever et al. (1958b) made autopsy studies of 99 bones from 37 persons who had resided 10 years or more in communities where the drinking water contained 1-4 ppm of naturally occurring or artificially added fluoride and 33 controls from areas where the drinking water contained less than 0.5 ppm fluoride. The microscopic examination showed no significant difference between the fluoride-exposed group and the control group. It is, therefore, possible to conclude that the histopathological changes of endemic fluorosis occur only at higher levels of intake than 1-4 ppm.

Chemical Composition of Fluorotic Bones

There are very few studies of the chemical composition of bones in human cases of chronic fluorine intoxication (Zipkin et al., 1958; Zipkin, McClure & Lee, 1960), although considerable literature is available on experimental animals. The skeleton is the most important site of deposition of fluoride in the body. McClure & Zipkin (1958) analysed the fluoride content of the bones of persons exposed to drinking water containing 0.1-4 ppm fluoride and concluded that the concentration of fluoride in the bones increased in an

FIG. 14

PATIENTS SUFFERING FROM ADVANCED ENDEMIC FLUOROSIS

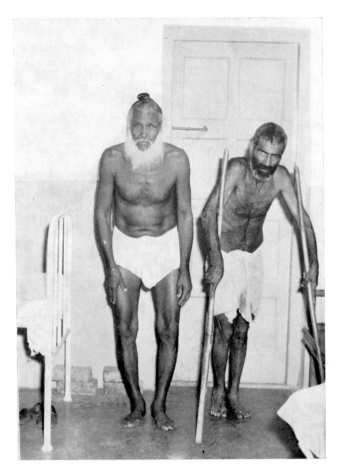

The gross degree of invalidism and the kyphotic deformity of crippling fluorosis are quite obvious.

FIG. 13 [a]

HISTOPATHOLOGICAL PICTURE OF BONE BIOPSY
SHOWING DISORDERED LAMELLAR PATTERN

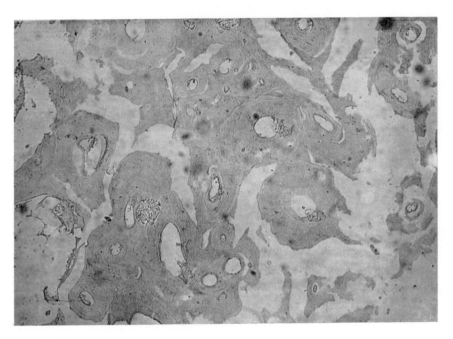

[a] Reproduced, with permission, from Singh & Jolly (1961).

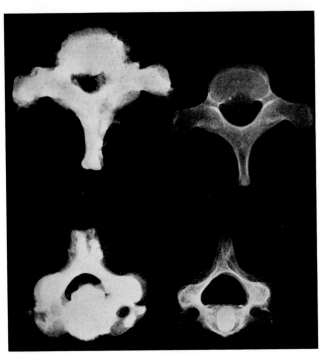

FIG. 11 [a]

POST-MORTEM SKIAGRAMS
OF FLUOROTIC DORSAL AND
CERVICAL VERTEBRAE (LEFT)
AND OF CORRESPONDING
NORMAL VERTEBRAE (RIGHT)

Marked narrowing of the spinal canal
is apparent.

[a] Reproduced, with permission, from
Singh & Jolly (1931).

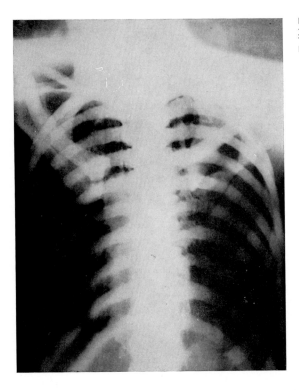

FIG. 12
X-RAY OF THE CHEST SHOWING
THE CONTRAST OF CHALKY WHITE
BONY CAGE WITH RADIOLUCENT LUNGS

FIG. 10 [a]

**POST-MORTEM SKIAGRAM OF THE CERVICAL SPINE FROM A CASE
OF FLUOROSIS (LEFT) AND OF A NORMAL CERVICAL SPINE (RIGHT)**

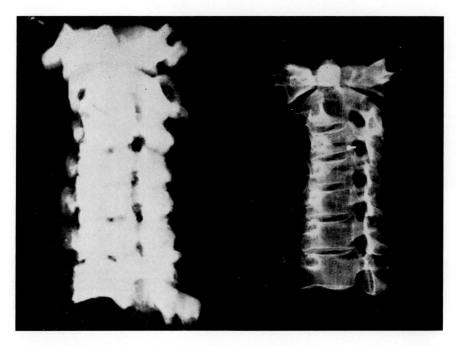

The chalky white appearance of fluorotic bones and the markedly narrowed intervertebral foramina are quite obvious.

[a] Reproduced, with permission, from Singh & Jolly (1961).

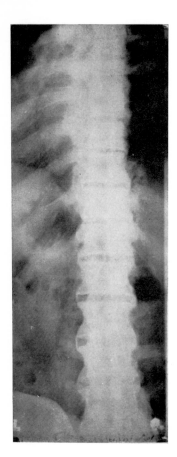

FIG. 8

SKIAGRAM OF LUMBODORSAL SPINE SHOWING
OSTEOSCLEROSIS AND MARKED OSTEOPHYTOSIS

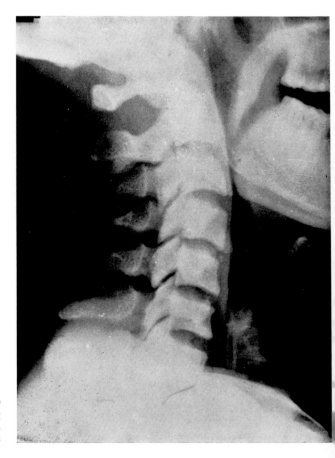

FIG. 9
SKIAGRAM OF CERVICAL SPINE
SHOWING MARKED OSTEO-
SCLEROSIS

essentially linear fashion and that, for a given level of fluoride in the drinking water, the iliac crest, ribs and vertebrae contained similar concentrations of fluoride. A recent study of the deposition of fluorides in bones which have also been examined histologically furnishes very valuable information regarding the levels of fluoride tolerated in bone without any harmful effects. McClure, McCann & Leone (1958), from a chemical analysis of the skeletal tissues of two women, have provided additional evidence regarding the threshold level of fluoride which may be tolerated by human skeletal tissues. As much as 0.5-0.6% fluoride in one of the subjects did not prove to be a physiological hazard. It must be concluded in the light of the available evidence that human skeletal tissues may have a very high degree of physiological tolerance to accumulation of fluoride. Roholm (1937) found 0.21-0.89% fluoride in the bones of two cryolite workers whose skeletal tissues showed evidence of increased calcification and trabeculation. The successful management by the body of this deposited fluoride is largely dependent upon the elimination of fluoride *via* the urinary tract. For this reason, study of the fluoride content of the urine in relation to the fluoride exposure may be of special value as a measure of the suspected health hazard attached to cumulative bone fluorosis. That all fluoride deposited in the skeleton is not fixed irreversibly is shown by its mobilization following a reduction in fluoride intake. Brun, Buckwald & Roholm (1941) reported that men who had absorbed fluoride from cryolite dust maintained a high level of fluoride in the urine for as long as 7 years following the period of exposure. Similarly, Largent & Heyroth (1949) and Largent (1961) found that urinary excretion of fluoride in excess of the intake continued at a progressively decreasing rate for as long as 2 years after the ingestion of large amounts of fluoride.

The deposition of fluoride in the bone takes place mainly by two mechanisms. In the first, fluoride exchanges with hydroxyl ion on the surface of existing crystals. In the second, new bone is formed by osteoblastic and osteoclastic activity. However, the precise mode by which the fluoride exerts its deleterious effects is not known. It is probable that there are initially changes in the chemical composition and deposition of bone salts in the organic matrix, possibly mediated by altered enzyme reactions. Roholm (1937) believed that the fluorides were probably deposited in the form of calcium fluoride along with calcium phosphate of the bone, but the work of Weidmann, Weatherell & Whitehead (1959) demonstrated a decrease of carbonate and an increase of magnesium in the exostotic bone—a finding which suggests replacement of Ca or HCO_3 groups in bone salts and a precipitation of MgF_2 upon or within the bone matrix. Zipkin and his associates (1958) studied fluoride deposition in human bones after prolonged ingestion of fluoride in drinking water, and came to the conclusion that the mean concentrations of fluoride in the various bones were proportional to the fluoride level of drinking water up to 4 ppm, and there is no indication in their data that these human calcified tissues approached their theoretical capacity of about 3.5% fluoride. Concentrations of fluoride as high as 5480 ppm in dry, fat-free bone and 10 800 ppm in bone ash may be present without producing any apparent tissue damage. The fluoride content in our studies (Singh et al., 1963) ranged from 700 to 7000 ppm (dry weight) against a normal of 200-300 ppm in persons from a non-fluorotic area. Smith & Hodge (1959) pointed out that, in human beings, osteosclerosis would be evident in a small proportion of the individuals with skeletal concentrations of fluoride of the order of 6000 ppm.

Zipkin, McClure & Lee (1960) tried to establish a relation between the fluoride content and the chemical composition of human bone. They studied 69 samples of human bone (iliac crest, ribs and vertebrae) obtained from 23 individuals, 26-90 years of age, who had consumed drinking water containing up to 4 ppm fluoride for 10-87 years. The bones were analysed for calcium, phosphorus, magnesium, sodium, potassium, carbon dioxide and citrate. The percentages of calcium and phosphorus in the dry, fat-free bones were normal, although the bones contained as much as 0.4% fluoride.

Over a tenfold range in concentration, no relation was apparent between the fluoride present in bone ash and either the calcium or the phosphorus content. As the level of fluoride in the ash increased (0.08-0.8%), there was a slight increase in magnesium and a decrease in carbon dioxide. The citrate content decreased markedly with increased fluoride. These data support the hypothesis that fluoride is deposited in mature bone largely at the expense of surface-limited ions like sodium, potassium, magnesium, carbon dioxide and citrate, which are presumed to be confined to the surface of the apatite bone crystals.

As regards magnesium, the apparent increase which accompanies fluoride deposition may be explained by its affinity for fluoride. The observed reduction in citrate concomitant with the increase in fluoride suggests that citrate, which is assigned to positions on the crystal surface, may be replaced by fluoride through ion-exchange processes.

Deformities and Crippling Fluorosis

This advanced stage of fluoride intoxication results from the continuous exposure of an individual to 20-80 mg of fluoride ion daily over a period of 10-20 years. Such heavy exposure is associated with a level of at least 10 ppm in the drinking-water supply. In the areas surveyed by us (Singh et al., 1962b), this level was not only common but was often exceeded. Moreover, besides the fluoride ingested from the water, there were additional sources of ingestion such as vegetables grown in the fluorotic soil and food processed and cooked in the fluoride-rich water. Therefore, it is not surprising that cases of crippling fluorosis are seen in such numbers in endemic areas of Punjab and Southern India.

The crippling deformities are due partly to mechanical factors and partly to the immobilization necessitated by pain and paraplegia. The commonest deformities are kyphosis, flexion deformity of the hips, flexion deformity of the knees and fixation of the chest in the position of inspiration due to calcification of cartilages. The advanced picture of crippling fluorosis is strikingly uniform. The quadriplegic patient bent with kyphosis and with markedly restricted movements of his spine, with contractures of hips and knees, provides a grim picture of the result of excessive fluoride intake (Fig. 14). Owing to the extreme fixation of the spine, the body moves as a single unit with each attempt to straighten any portion of it.

Neurological Complications of Fluorosis

The neurological manifestations have been exclusively reported from India. Credit for the earliest description of neurological complications in fluorosis must be given to Shortt, Pandit & Raghavachari (1937), who reported ten such cases from the Nellore district of Madras. A few sporadic cases have also been described from other parts of India (Murthi, Narayana Rao & Venkateswarlu, 1953; Janardhanan & Venkaswamy, 1957; Chhuttani, Wahi & Singh, 1962), but the only authentic study is that of Siddiqui (1955). We have tried to define the neurological pattern of this disease and have designated it as a radiculomyelopathy (Singh & Jolly, 1961). Our interest in this problem was aroused by the fact that while investigating obscure cases of paraplegia in Punjab, we were struck by the osteosclerosis and osteophytosis of all the vertebrae shown on radiography (Jolly, Singh & Singh, 1961). Subsequently it was noticed that nearly all such cases were coming from a limited geographical area of the Punjab.

Such neurological complications occur only in very advanced cases where the ingestion of large quantities of fluorides has continued for at least 20 years. Thus only 42 of our 409 cases of skeletal fluorosis had neurological complications and the description of such complications is based on an analysis of these cases (Singh et al., 1963).

Despite the alarming radiological appearance, the changes in the spine do not produce many symptoms. Usually the only complaint is of vague pains in the back and in the extremities. The symptoms of the spinal-cord lesion tended to develop slowly and progress insidiously. In two cases, the onset was sudden and was related to trauma, which in normal circumstances would not have resulted in sequelae.

Symptoms may be due to a lesion of one or more nerve roots or to involvement of the spinal cord.

Radicular features

The most important manifestations were muscular wasting, acroparaesthesiae, and pain referred along the nerve roots. Subjective complaints such as acroparaesthesiae and pain were almost universal, although such complaints were elicited only after specific questions about them. The most important feature was the weakness and wasting of muscles. This was usually asymmetrical, involving most often the small muscles of one or both hands. This localization was present in twelve cases and in two was the only finding. In the remaining ten it was associated with an extensive radiculomyelopathy. The mechanism is probably similar to that found in cervical spondylosis and due to compression of anterior roots by the lower parts of the foramina. Some muscular wasting may be the result of atrophy from disuse. The accompanying muscle fasciculations and fibrillation often led to a mistaken diagnosis of motor-neurone disease.

Myelopathic features

The earliest symptom of spinal-cord involvement observed in all cases was weakness of both lower limbs. This usually started in one leg, with later progression to the other. In 12 cases, after a variable interval, the upper limbs became involved, producing a spastic quadriplegia. Paraesthesiae in one or more limbs were frequent. The pattern resembled in many ways that of spondylitic myelopathy. In general, the symptoms progress fairly rapidly with progressive deterioration and restriction of activity. The signs of fluorotic myelopathy result chiefly from narrowing of the spinal canal or intervertebral foramina, and compression may occur at a single site or at multiple sites. Muscular wasting was not a prominent manifestation in our cases, being noted in only 12 cases. It was usually confined to the muscles of the hand or forearm, being most conspicuous in the former. Fasciculation was observed in only two cases. The site of muscular wasting could not always be correlated with the site of compression. Although wasting of the hands was likely to be severe when the last cervical and first dorsal segments of the cord were compressed, it was at times equally severe with protrusion at a higher level, suggesting interference with the blood supply to the lower segments of the cervical enlargement. Muscle tone in the extremities was usually increased. This was due predominantly to upper motor neurone involvement, although the muscular and skeletal changes of fluorosis were often a contributing factor. In four advanced cases the spasticity was extreme: it was impossible to bend one limb individually and the whole of the skeleton consequently moved as one unit. This was partly explained by development of contractures around the knees and hips. The upper limbs were involved in 18 cases, while the disease was mainly confined to the lower limbs in 19.

Thirty-one of the 42 neurological patients had some type of sensory disturbance, although the sensory changes tended to be patchy. In 12 cases, sensory loss resembled that due to compression by a tumour, all modalities of sensation being affected below a sharp level, usually around the umbilicus.

Light touch was less involved than other sensations. The posterior column was more severely affected than the spinothalamic tracts. In the upper extremities, paraesthesiae and sensory disturbances were confined to a single dermatome distribution in nine cases, while in two others there was a "glove" distribution involving both hands.

The tendon reflexes were usually exaggerated in the lower extremities, although, in advanced cases, contractures of the knee made it difficult to elicit reflexes. The deep reflexes in the upper limbs were exaggerated in 15 cases and absent in three. An inverted supinator jerk was present in nine cases. The abdominal and plantar reflexes were usually compatible with a bilateral pyramidal lesion, the latter being extensor in 37 patients, equivocal in two, and flexor in three. Hesitancy or incontinence of micturition was noted in 22 patients. In advanced cases, paraplegia-in-flexion gradually ensued, with flexor spasms. The active and passive movements of the spine were restricted and painful, and a kyphotic deformity was present in ten patients.

Certain other neurological features, such as impairment of auditory nerve function (Siddiqui, 1955), headache and tetaniform convulsions (Waldbott, 1961), electroencephalographic disturbances (Waldbott, 1955), and meralgia paraesthetica (Chhuttani, Wahi & Singh, 1962) have been described but were not observed by us. It was difficult to enter the subarachnoid space by either the lumbar or the cisternal route, owing to calcification of the intervertebral disks and ligaments. Consequently the composition and dynamics of the cerebrospinal fluid could be studied in only 13 cases. In three, the proteins were increased to more than 200 mg/100 ml. Cerebrospinal fluid pressure was low, indicating a partial block in the subarachnoid space. Myelography was possible in only four cases: in one patient, the dye remained in the cisterna magna for three days; in the second there was delay in the transit of the dye in the cervical region; and in the other two there was a complete block at D8 and C3 respectively.

Thus, the clinical picture of fluorotic myelopathy may closely simulate that of cervical spondylosis, extramedullary and intramedullary tumours of the spinal cord, subacute combined degeneration of the cord, syringomyelia and motor-neurone disease. However, in view of the distinctive clinical pattern and the radiological findings, the diagnosis of fluorosis can be readily established.

4. CHRONIC TOXIC EFFECTS ON THE KIDNEYS

(H. C. Hodge & D. R. Taves)

While there appears to be no doubt that fluoridation is safe for persons with normal kidneys, the remote possibility that fluoride may aggravate intercurrent renal disease has not been conclusively ruled out. Renal failure should cause fluoride retention, leading to higher tissue fluoride concentrations and a smaller margin of safety than for normal individuals.   In this section, the relevant information on the pathological and functional effects of toxic doses is reviewed and current work on the safety of the use of fluoridated water by patients suffering from renal failure is summarized.

Pathology

Fluoride-induced renal pathology, with the causative agent established beyond reasonable doubt, has never been reported from chronic exposures in man.   The nearest to such a finding came from the gross and histological studies of tissues of ten former cryolite workers by Roholm (1937), who stated that "poisoning with cryolite produces *considerable changes of bones and ligaments, but no changes—or at the most doubtful changes—of the organs*".   Roholm described the necropsies of two workers in detail: one, a man employed for 24 years in a cryolite factory, showed moderate chronic interstitial nephritis, thus raising some uncertainty as to a possible role of fluoride; the other had been employed for about 9 years.

In the first patient, the kidneys were normal in size.   On microscopic examination, the glomeruli were well-preserved.   A number of tubuli were dilated, "cystic" in places, and contained serous fluid.   Such "a slight grade of chronic nephritis, preponderantly of interstitial type", is at least reminiscent of the pattern of renal pathology in chronically exposed animals.[1]   In the second patient, the kidneys, normal on gross examination, were, except for some stasis, also normal microscopically.   The nephritis of the first worker, by no means proven to be a result of cryolite exposure, thus constitutes the only, and at best doubtful, human example of a chronic fluoride effect.

Autopsy examinations have undoubtedly been conducted on tissues of persons with more than minimal fluoride exposures.   Few   descriptions have been published, but three can be cited: (1) Neither incidental renal pathology nor renal disease as a cause of death (both recorded by autopsy examination) differed significantly with the duration of exposure to drinking water containing 2.5 ppm F (Geever et al., 1958a).   (2) The post-mortem examination of men who had lived in an industrial area of Utah, where chronic fluoride intoxication had been observed in cattle and sheep and vegetation damage recognized, revealed no gross or histological effects in kidney tissues (Call et al., 1965).   (3) No renal abnormalities ascribed to

---

[1] After prolonged exposures, macroscopically, the animal kidneys were pale and small, with uneven surfaces.   Microscopically, the lesion resembled interstitial nephritis (Bond & Murray, 1952; Taylor et al., 1961a).   Varying degrees of degeneration of the tubular epithelium were found, along with evidence of regeneration and greatly increased amounts of fibrous tissue as exposure continued.   Dilated tubules were often described at the cortico-medullary junction (Pindborg, 1957) apparently involving the loops of Henle and the convoluted tubules.   Glomerular changes were inconstant.   Vascular degeneration was sometimes present.   Such pathology has been described in several species—for example, rats, pigs, calves, dogs, guinea-pigs and rabbits.

fluoride were found at the autopsy examination of an elderly woman who for 34 years had consumed water containing 8 ppm F (Leone, Stinson & Sunbury, 1960).

Acute Effects after a Large Single Dose

The effects on the kidney of an overwhelming single dose of fluoride, an acute toxic nephritis, have been repeatedly observed in human patients fatally poisoned by accident or intent. The principal findings, which are quite different from the pattern of chronic kidney pathology, are (a) congestion and cloudy swelling of the renal tubular cells; (b) hyperaemia and fatty degeneration of the tubular epithelium; and (c) not limited to the kidney, widely distributed acute visceral hyperaemia. Experimental animals show entirely comparable effects. If the individual survives, regeneration occurs during recovery. Since the acute effects have no applicability in water fluoridation, they will not be discussed further.

Dose Response

No renal pathology ascribed to fluoride has been found in experimental animals maintained for protracted periods on diets or drinking water containing 50 ppm F or less. The borderline water concentration at which some individuals of certain species (but not all) exhibit changes is about 100 ppm (Hodge et al., 1964), which in the rat, for example, is roughly equivalent to a daily dose of 10 mg/kg. This dose is far greater (perhaps 10-30 times) than that received by Roholm's cases and held by Møller & Gudjonsson (1932) to cause crippling fluorosis. Only in one report, a study of rats maintained for periods of up to 520 days on drinking water containing 1, 5 and 10 ppm F, has kidney pathology ever been ascribed to fluoride in experimental animals consuming F levels comparable to those in human drinking water supplies (Ramseyer, Smith & McCay, 1957). However, a larger and more rigorous study from the same laboratory (Bosworth & McCay, 1962) failed to show any differences between the control and the treated animals, and identified the pathology as the renal pathology of old, diseased rats and *not* fluoride effects. The absence of progressive renal pathology in residents who had lived for a long time in a community where the water supply naturally contained 2.5 ppm F (Geever et al., 1958a) is consistent with the absence of renal changes in occupational exposures as well as with the considerable body of quantitative animal data.

Functional Effects

The responses of scores of acutely poisoned patients have been summarized in Table 3 of Roholm's monograph (*op. cit.*) and in Table 7 of Hodge & Smith (1965). Goldemberg, in 1930, gave the name of "diabète insipide fluorique" to a syndrome comprising polyuria, thirst, nocturia and abnormally frequent micturition which developed in patients given intravenously 100 mg of sodium fluoride daily or every other day for 10 to 15 days; neither albuminuria nor glycosuria was detected (see Hodge & Smith, *op. cit.*).

Efforts to detect functional changes as a result of chronic fluoride exposures have been made in the cryolite industry, in endemic areas of fluorosis in India, and in communities with fluoridated water supplies in the USA. In the 68 cryolite workers examined by Roholm, only a few signs or symptoms referable to the kidney were found: (*a*) one woman complained of extraordinary thirst; (*b*) urinary albumin and sugar tests in most cases were normal; (*c*) signs of chronic nephritis were found in one man; and (*d*) one woman, a diabetic, had glycosuria. Time lost because of urinary and venereal diseases was minimal for the men but relatively high for the women.

In villagers of the Nalgonda district, not far from Hyderabad, Siddiqui (1955) discovered 32 advanced cases of skeletal fluorosis with neurological manifestations. The nutritional state of the people was deficient; most of the patients showed a mild degree of anaemia. Urea clearance was markedly depressed. In the somewhat similar study of ten hospitalized cases of advanced fluorosis in the Madras Presidency, Shortt et al. (1937) reported renal filtration rates below normal in six cases, but within normal limits or above in three. Urea clearance values were low, in some cases quite low. Kumar & Harper (1963) reported on a group of 19 patients in Aden whose skeletal radiographs revealed osteosclerosis and whose drinking water presumably contained excessive concentrations of F (one well, the water supply for 6 cases, showed "sodium fluoride to be present in 6 parts per million"). Albuminuria, present in 11 of 12 persons examined for it, is ascribed without supporting evidence to fluoride injury of the kidneys. These groups of patients had sustained many stresses—for example, varying degrees of malnutrition, hard work in a hot climate, and unknown intercurrent diseases. Fluoride cannot be held specifically responsible for the changes in kidney function.

A little evidence can be gathered from populations drinking fluoridated water in the USA. The children in the Newburgh-Kingston study excreted similar amounts of albumin and sugar whether the drinking water was fluoridated or not (Schlesinger, Overton & Chase, 1956). No greater incidence of albuminuria or glycosuria was found in populations whose drinking water contained 8 ppm than in residents of a nearby city where the water contained about 0.5 ppm (Leone et al., 1954). McClure found no differences in the urine samples of 101 young men who drank naturally fluoridated water (2.0-5.2 ppm) as compared with those of 394 young men who resided in low-fluoride areas (McClure, 1946).

Animals given sufficient fluoride, in single or repeated doses, excrete large volumes of dilute urine and are thirsty. The urine may or may not give positive tests for albumin, blood or casts; sugar is typically present;

chloride and nitrogen excretion are increased. Clearances of urea, creatinine and *p*-aminohippuric acid (PAH) are reduced (see review by Taylor et al., 1961b). These effects reflect severe renal tubular injury in the presence of renal congestion. Caruso (1961) found in acute experiments on dogs that renal tubular transport, as measured by Tm_{PAH} and Tm glucose, was also decreased. Large single doses of fluoride in experimental animals promptly increased urine volume; urinary chloride and nitrogen excretions increased (reviewed by Taylor, 1959). Fluoride in large doses can be classed as a depressant of kidney function.

These results can be compared with those of the few studies of kidney function in experimental animals given known amounts of fluoride for protracted periods. Two of 12 rats maintained on drinking water containing 100 ppm for six months had renal lesions, showed polydypsia and polyuria (Taylor et al., 1961a). In a study lasting a little over seven years, Greenwood et al. (1964) and Mangelson (1963) observed the effects of various fluoride supplements on dairy cattle: inulin clearances were normal in cattle whose dry ration contained 93 ppm F. PAH clearances were reduced at 49 ppm but not at 27 ppm. In rabbits, dogs, and rats, doses of 5-10 mg/kg or more for periods of up to nearly a year produced reductions in urea clearance, albuminuria, polyuria, polydypsia, glycosuria, and urine of low specific gravity.

Urinary fluoride excretion is not markedly reduced in children with renal disease (Schlesinger, personal communication, 1957), in elderly patients with advanced kidney disease, or in rabbits with severe renal tubular injury from uranium poisoning (Smith, Gardner & Hodge, 1955). However, these studies do not rule out the possibility of elevations in serum fluoride and accompanying increases in tissue fluoride concentrations. If bone formation is occurring, the elevated serum levels should result in an increased bone fluoride concentration. If no bone is being laid down, on the other hand, the rise in fluoride concentration in serum and soft tissue may be more marked.

Evidence of the efficacy of the skeletal absorption has been provided by Largent (1961, p. 54): fluoride doses given to nephritic patients were stored in abnormally high percentages (75-82%). Nephrectomized animals deposited extra fluoride in their skeletons (Carlson, Singer & Armstrong, 1960). Linsman & McMurray (1943) state that their patient with renal impairment such that death ultimately occurred in uraemic coma, and who had a history of long residence in areas of endemic dental fluorosis, exhibited osteosclerosis, a condition developing only when bone fluoride concentrations exceed about 5000 ppm F (dry, fat-free basis). Call et al. (1965) discerned the end result of this skeletal mechanism, i.e., elevated bone F values in some but not all patients who were suffering from advanced chronic renal disease and whose environment had contributed extra fluoride.

In none of these studies have the serum fluoride concentrations been recorded. The only published data (Singer & Armstrong, 1960) indicated no increase with renal failure, but more recent investigations, using new methods, revealed a 3-fold to 5-fold increase in the serum fluoride of patients with renal failure (Taves et al., 1968) and in partially nephrectomized rats (Taves & Morrison, unpublished data). The discrepancy is explained by identifying what each method measured: Singer & Armstrong first ashed the serum and then measured total fluoride, most of which has since been shown to be unavailable as fluoride ion prior to ashing.[1] The newer methods, which measure only the fluoride ion, indicate that the fasting "normal" fluoride ion concentration in human serum is about 0.2-0.4 μmol (0.004-0.008 ppm) when the drinking water contains only traces of fluoride, and about 0.5-1 μmol (0.01-0.02 ppm) in a community with fluoridated water. Patients with renal failure occasionally exhibit serum fluoride ion concentrations as high as 5 μmol (0.1 ppm). The risk to health represented by such values cannot be definitively assessed as yet.

In two patients (one during haemodialysis, the other under fluoride therapy in a multiple myeloma study), serum F concentrations of 20-30 μmol (0.4-0.6 ppm) for 6-12 months were observed without obvious adverse effects. Growth was retarded in normal intact rats on high F rations when serum F concentrations reached 15 μmol (0.3 ppm); serious toxic effects developed at 50 μmol (1.0 ppm) (Taves, D.R., Raisz, L. & Yuile, C., unpublished data). There seems therefore to be at least a 3-fold to 5-fold margin of safety,[2] other things being equal, for patients with renal failure.

Fluoridated Water, Haemodialysis and Bone Disease

Chronic haemodialysis, now widely employed, enables many patients with little or no kidney function to go on living for many years. It is of interest from the point of view of fluoridation because tap water is often used in the kidney machines, and it has been suggested that fluoride from this source contributes to the bone disease seen frequently in these patients.

During dialysis with fluoridated water, the patient takes up fluoride (10-20 mg per 6-14-hour dialysis) from the dialysis bath (Taves et al., 1968; Backer-Dirks, unpublished data). Such doses would present little or no toxic hazard for an adult with normal kidney function; some of the fluoride would be deposited in the skeleton and the rest rapidly excreted. The patient on haemodialysis, however, frequently has no renal function and poor bone formation; the critical determinant, therefore, is not dose but serum level. Severe osteodystrophy not yielding to therapy with calcium and vitamin D developed in most of a group of patients in the Ottawa General Hospital who underwent dialysis with fluoridated water. The

---

[1] The non-exchangeable serum fluoride is 3-5 μmol (0.06-0.1 ppm); available information indicates that the magnitude of this fraction does not change with the fluoride concentration of the drinking water (Singer & Armstrong, 1960; Taves, unpublished data).

[2] Prolonged maintenance of serum F concentrations of 5-15 μmol (0.1-0.3 ppm) will probably produce osteosclerosis, which under certain circumstances may have a beneficial effect (Taves, 1969).

elevated serum F concentrations found in these patients—average 18 μmol (0.36 ppm)—suggested that fluoride was complicating or causing the bone disease.   Patients in another locality, however, who received dialysis with fluoridated water for a period of three years, did not develop severe osteo-dystrophy.   A causal role for fluoride has not therefore been established. The reasons for the differences are under investigation; it may be that other elements present in the fluoridated water have important influences on bone health.   It appears likely that the serum fluoride concentrations reflect the severity of the bone disease, but are not the cause.   However, in the Ottawa patients, the elevated serum fluoride concentrations may have made the bone disease more difficult to treat once it had developed.   Judgements should not be made prematurely, since the effects of fluoride on bone take years to manifest themselves.   Those who for experimental or economic reasons continue to use fluoridated water for dialysis should watch both the bone status and serum fluoride concentrations of their patients.

5.   TOXIC EFFECTS ON THE THYROID (V. Demole)

The question of the toxic effects of fluoride on the thyroid is indeed a problem, since formerly fluorides were used as antithyroid medication in Graves' disease (exophthalmic goitre), while nowadays it appears that the same fluorides, when absorbed continually, even in excessive doses, have no harmful effect on the thyroid!

We shall briefly review the literature on this problem.   The volume of published work in this field is considerable, so that a selection must be made from the various publications.

1.   In the first place, we shall survey clinical experience in regard to the treatment of Graves' disease with fluoride—a form of therapy which led to an erroneous generalization.

2.   Secondly, we shall enumerate the main investigations of a possible iodine-fluorine antagonism that have been carried out on animals and man.

3.   We shall then review the results of demographic surveys, mainly American, undertaken with a view to determining the alleged goitrogenic effect of water containing fluoride.

4.   Finally, we shall mention certain investigations in Switzerland, not because of their extent but because they were carried out in a limited area where endemic goitre was prevalent before it was eradicated by the pro-phylactic use of iodides.

Treatment of Graves' Disease

Among the antithyroid drugs used in the first half of this century, men-tion must be made particularly of iodine, the oldest antithyroid drug, which even today occupies the first place in pre-operative preparation to promote involution of the gland, storage of colloid and fall of basal metabolic rate (BMR); while, on the other hand, it is essential to prevent goitre. "The explanation of this paradox is still being sought" (Goodman & Gilman, 1965; Rawson, 1949).

Fluorine has also been used in the treatment of Graves' disease. Prolonged administration of sodium fluoride, 50-100 mg daily, may cause clinical improvement and reduction of the BMR, but the therapeutic action is weak, inconstant and transitory, and some hazard may be involved. Therefore, this medication has been abandoned.

Recent studies with radioactive iodine and fluorine confirm the reduction of BMR effected by prolonged administration (for several months) of a daily dose of 5-10 mg of fluorine to patients afflicted with Graves' disease (Galletti & Joyet, 1958). The signs and symptoms of hyperthyroidism (tachycardia, tremor, loss of weight) were completely relieved in 6 of 15 patients studied. Both the BMR and the plasma PBI (protein-bound iodine) fell to normal levels. In the remaining 9 cases, this fluorine dosage was clinically ineffective, although an improvement of BMR or PBI level was often observed. Young patients did not respond at all to fluorine therapy. No appreciable uptake of ^{18}F by the thyroid could be detected either in the normal or in the hyperactive gland. No inhibition of the thyroidal iodine uptake was observed when fluoride was injected in excess simultaneously with carrier-free iodine.

In normal human subjects, fluorides have no effect (Korrodi et al., 1956). Forty patients with normal thyroid function were given sodium fluoride for several months. Regular observation was possible on 15 of these patients: ten who received 2-3 mg of fluoride daily for 6-14 months, and five who received 5 mg of fluoride per day for 2-5 months. Clinical as well as special thyroid-function tests failed to reveal any pathological findings. The data obtained on blood PBI, radioactive iodine uptake by the thyroid (24-hour values), BMR and serum cholesterol at the beginning and end of the test period showed only negligible variations within normal limits. Any damaging action of fluoride on the thyroid gland was considered improbable.

Additional experiments, on young rats, showed that the radioiodine uptake was not affected by high fluoride intake, either in animals receiving normal food or in those on a low-iodine diet.

On the basis of both the above investigations, it was concluded that there need be no hesitation regarding a general use of fluoride for the prevention of dental caries under the conditions prevailing in Switzerland.

Moreover, in normal animals, fluoride does not decrease the BMR or affect the activity of administered thyroid (Seevers & Braun, 1935; Phillips et al., 1935); nor does it inhibit the deposition of iodine in the thyroid or accelerate the iodine depletion.

Why does sodium fluoride exert a mild antithyroidal effect in hyper-thyroidic patients if it is inactive in normal persons? Nobody knows. Attempts to develop fluorine-containing drugs which would compete with thyronine have all failed. Substitution of one or several fluorine atoms for iodine atoms in the molecule of thyroxine or thyronine did not produce anti-thyroidal substances (Cortell, 1949; Roche, 1953). The compound 3-fluoro-thyronine is said to lower the BMR in mice (Litzka, 1936) and to delay tadpoles' metamorphosis (Kraft, 1936); however, it seems merely ineffectual in the treatment of Graves' disease (May, 1935) and certainly less active than several synthetic non-fluorinated preparations—for example, 3,5,3′,5′-tetrabromothyronine (Lerman & Harrington, 1949) and 3,5-diiodo-4-hydroxybenzoic acid or DIBB (Sheahan et al., 1951). All these drugs (fluorinated or not) have been swept away by the modern goitrogens thiourea and thiouracil, the first report of whose efficiency was published in 1943 by Astwood.

Iodine-Fluorine Antagonism

Baumann & Metzger (1949) suggested that the thyroid has an affinity not only for iodine but also for other members of the seventh periodic group of elements. Such an affinity has been demonstrated to a small extent for chlorine and bromine, but not for fluorine. No correlation was found between the fluorine content of the thyroid of patients with Graves' disease, the iodine content of the thyroid, the BMR of the patients and the fluoride content of drinking water (Evans & Phillips, 1938).

[18]F investigations have also failed to provide evidence of the affinity for the thyroid of fluorine. For example, no affinity was observed in rat experiments by Wallace-Durbin (1954). No appreciable uptake of ^{18}F by the thyroid could be detected in tests on normal humans or on patients with hyperactive glands (Galletti & Joyet, 1958). After intravenous injection of ^{18}F in mice and rats, no concentration of fluorine was found in the thyroid or the salivary glands (Ericsson & Ullberg, 1958).

In rabbit experiments, the ^{18}F concentrations in the thyroid and pituitary were determined 35-38 minutes after the injection, and compared with the simultaneous concentration in the maternal blood. The ^{18}F content of the tissues was of the same order as, or lower than, that of the maternal blood (Ericsson & Malmnäs, 1962).

Can plasma fluorine, whether ionized or bound, act on plasma iodine, ionized or bound? Numerous tracer studies on this problem have been reported. All have failed to demonstrate any effect of fluoride on ^{131}I distribution and metabolism. For example, high doses of fluorine given to rats by mouth during eight days had no influence on ^{131}I uptake in the thyroid (Demole, 1954). Neither acute nor chronic administration of sodium fluoride to the rat inhibited the uptake of ^{131}I by the thyroid gland.

The transport of the [131] I through the acinar cell stage into the colloidal phase, and the ultimate distribution in the blood plasma, were of equal magnitude regardless of the dosage of sodium fluoride used (Harris & Hayes, 1955).

In rats suffering from experimental fluorosis caused by administration of NaF or CaF_2 the thyroid was not hypertrophied and its histological structure and uptake of ^{131}I were normal (Demole & Lerch, 1956).

In tests on normal humans, 4 mg F daily, given for 10 weeks, did not affect the iodine-trapping ability of the thyroid (Levi & Silberstein, 1955).

In groups of rats kept on an iodine-deficient diet and receiving 0.005-0.5 mg fluoride in the food daily for 6½ months no goitrogenic effect of the fluoride was observed and the radioiodine uptake was not affected by high fluoride intake either in animals receiving normal food or in those on a low-iodine diet. The increased uptake of ^{131}I by the thyroid caused by the iodine-deficient diet was clearly evident and independent of fluorine intake (Korrodi et al., 1956).

In the rat, neither F nor Ca nor Ca + F enhanced the goitrogenic effect of iodine deficiency. There was no indication of an antagonism between fluoride and iodine in the thyroid (Puentes & Cremer, 1966).

Jentzer (1955), working with rabbits, claimed to have found pathological changes in the thyroid morphology following fluoride administration. The technique used in this work was, however, open to criticism (Demole, 1956). Gordonoff & Minder (1952) described the inhibition of thyroxine by fluorine in the rat. This paper was marred by faulty calculations (Demole, 1954).

Auskaps & Shaw (1955), Galletti et al. (1955), Mühlemann & Schneider (1956), Ramseyer, Smith & McCay (1957), Willer (1958), Gedalia et al. (1960), Waller (1961) and Hennig & Fritz (1961) have shown that in rats given high fluorine doses the thyroid function is generally not impaired. Later rat experiments, using ^{131}I-tracing and histological thyroid examinations, have given similar results (Ardelean et al., 1963; Saka, Hallag & Urgancioglu, 1965).

Clinical investigations have also failed to demonstrate any effect of fluorine on the thyroid: in children consuming water naturally fluoridated at 1.25 ppm (Demole, 1951); after tablet administration of 1 mg F daily (Held, 1953); in endemic goitre (Hoffmann-Axthelm, 1953); after administration of sodium fluoride (Gedalia et al., 1961); in areas of endemic fluorosis (Siddiqui, 1960); in cases of skeletal fluorosis (Hennig & Fritz, 1961); in workers exposed for 7-20 years to fluorine inhalation with urinary fluoride varying between 5 and 12 ppm (Demole et al., 1951); and in two cases of industrial fluorosis (Roholm, 1937). Similarly, Gabovich and collaborators (Gabovich & Verzhikovskaya, 1958; Gabovich, Bukhovets & Verzhikovskaya, 1960) found no effect on the thyroid ^{131}I uptake or function from fluoride doses of up to 0.1 mg per kg of body-weight or from drinking water containing 2 ppm F. Velicangil & Eser (1957) found no influence of endemic fluorosis (caused by 4 ppm F in water;

dental signs) on the endemic goitre in a Turkish area.   Similar results are reported from India (Chapter 8, section 3).

The publication of Benagiano & Fiorentini (1955) has often been quoted. These authors reported anatomical and functional thyroid change in rural populations near Rome using fluoride-rich drinking water.   Their work, however, has been severely criticized on account of lack of precision. It is now generally agreed that iodide concentrated by the thyroid tissue is oxidized to a higher valence state, such as I^+ (iodinium ion), which then displaces hydrogen from tyrosyl residues (Maloof & Soodak, 1963).   Anions which behave as iodide in the Hofmeister series or in their interaction with serum albumin have been tested for their combining capacity, in different oxidation states, with albumin (Wyngaarden, Wright & Ways, 1952).   Such anions as ClO_4^- and SCN^- combine much more strongly than I^-, and in rat experiments the former ions have discharged iodide from the thyroid, in contrast to fluoride, in 100-μmol doses (Scatchard & Black, 1949).

American Demographic Surveys concerning Fluorine

·Large-scale surveys concerning the effect of fluorine on dentition and general health have been carried out in the USA.   Some of these surveys are remarkable because of the number of subjects examined, the competence of the examiners, the precision of the investigations, the duration of the examinations and the validity of the controls.   No deterioration in the thyroid was reported.

The studies of Leone et al. (1954, 1955) and Geever et al. (1958a, 1958b) concerning water containing 0.5 to 8 ppm fluoride are of particular interest.

Leone et al. carried out a survey of two communities in Texas, one of 116 persons in Bartlett and the other of 121 persons in Cameron.   In Bartlett, the fluoride content of the water was 8 ppm until 1952, when an experimental defluoridation unit was installed, reducing it to about 1.2 ppm; in Cameron, the water contained 0.4 ppm fluoride.

The study began in 1943 and the participants, aged 15 to 68, were chosen at random from persons who had resided in the respective communities for at least 15 years.   The average length of fluoride exposure at the end of the survey in 1953 was 36.7 years.

In 1943, medical histories were taken and each participant was given a medical, X-ray, and dental examination; blood and urine studies were also performed.   These were repeated for all in 1953.

Characteristics studied included arthritic changes, blood pressure, bone changes, cataract and/or lens opacity, thyroid, cardiovascular system, hearing, tumours and/or cysts, fractures, urinary tract calculi, and gallstones.   No significant differences between the findings in the two towns were observed except for a slightly higher rate of cardiovascular abnormalities in Cameron and a marked predominance of dental fluorosis in Bartlett.

Geever et al. performed more than 700 post-mortem examinations on persons who had lived for many years in Colorado Springs, where the fluoride content of the water is 2.5 ppm.

The duration of residence in the area was over 20 years in 334 cases, 5-20 years in 130 cases, under 5 years in 188 cases, and unknown in 76 cases. The diagnoses were classified and the results tabulated according to the major causes of death. Incidental findings were: thyroid disease, gallstones, renal disease, urinary tract stones, liver diseases, peptic ulcer, diabetes mellitus, and pancreatitis. Comparative statistical analyses of the pathological findings revealed no significant differences that could be related to prolonged residence in the high-fluoride area.

A vital fact that the authors have not felt necessary to point out is that they were working in regions where the iodine intake (either natural or enriched through iodized salt) was sufficient to prevent endemic goitre.

Swiss Surveys and Experiments showing the Compatibility of Iodine and Fluorine

It may be mentioned that in Switzerland the prophylaxis of endemic goitre by means of iodized salt (at present 10 mg of KI per kg), commenced in 1922, has led to the disappearance of thyroid hypertrophy and cretinism as well as to a decrease in the prevalence of deaf-mutism.

Two findings are of importance in connexion with the supposed antagonism between iodine and fluorine:

1. The beneficial effect of iodized salt has been experienced by the whole Swiss population (about 6 million) irrespective of whether the fluoride content of the local waters is low (0.01-0.05 ppm), medium (0.1-0.5 ppm), or high enough for caries prevention (1-2 ppm), as is the case at Sembrancher (Valais) and at Kaisten (Aargau).

2. The increasing consumption of salt which has been both iodized and fluoridated (10 mg of KI and 200 mg of NaF per kg—i.e., 90 mg of F) has not led to the reappearance of endemic goitre, even in a minor form (Demole, 1951; Wespi, 1954). No goitrogenic effects have followed the fluoridation of drinking water in Basle (0.8-1.0 ppm) for more than four years, the fluoridation of water in Aigle (1-1.25 ppm) for three years, the daily administration of a fluoride tablet (1 mg of F) to all children in Geneva schools during 10 consecutive years (Held, personal communication, 1967) or the consumption of fluoridated milk in Winterthur (Ziegler, 1964).

The comments by Wespi-Eggenberger (1960) concerning the prevention of thyroid hypertrophy in the foetus by means of iodized and fluoridated salt administered to the mother during pregnancy may serve as a conclusion:

"Various papers ascribe to fluorine a goitrogenic effect, and the introduction of the fluorine prophylaxis has been rejected partly on this ground. The fact, however, that the newborn who have benefited from a combined iodine and fluorine prophylaxis are practically goitre-free, demonstrates that fluorine at the employed doses does not have any goitrogenic property... [and] that the goitre-preventing effect of the iodine is not impaired by the addition of fluorine".

Discussion

It appears that certain drugs which act upon the sick organism are inactive in the healthy organism. Antipyretics which decrease fever do not lower the body temperature of normal men and animals. Thus, it is not surprising that in the treatment of Graves' disease (exophthalmic goitre) fluorides sometimes lower the basal metabolic rate. In normal subjects the same fluorides have no effect on BMR, blood cholesterol or uptake of iodine by the thyroid.

The very instructive example of iodine is also worth stressing here. In the patient afflicted with Graves' disease, iodine promotes involution of the goitre. On the other hand, iodine prevents the development of endemic goitre. This example shows that each case must be considered separately and that generalizations are dangerous.

A tendentious interpretation of certain medical and biological observations led to the erroneous theory of iodine-fluorine antagonism. This theory had two unfortunate consequences. In the first place, it led chemists to synthesize inorganic and organic antithyroid fluorides, all of which were a disappointment. (Of all these drugs, there is not a single one still on the market.) In the second place, it resulted in an unjustified fear that fluoride decreased the thyroid function and encouraged the development of goitre.

Advances in biochemistry, in particular tracer studies, have led to a complete revision of the theory of iodine-fluorine antagonism. We now know that fluorine does not accumulate in the thyroid gland, that its presence does not decrease the uptake of iodine by the thyroid and that it has no effect on the synthesis of thyroxine.

The information derived from the large-scale demographic surveys in the USA, Great Britain and elsewhere indirectly confirms the facts we have mentioned above. Consumption of drinking water containing fluoride, either naturally or artificially, does not impair the thyroid function, nor does it change the morphology and histological structure of the thyroid gland. Even the consumption throughout life of water containing 6 or 7 ppm fluoride does not affect the thyroid function.

Endemic goitre and endemic fluorosis are two separate disease entities. Fluorosis may exist with or without goitre, just as goitre can be present without fluorosis. Each endemic has its own remedy: fluorosis is prevented by defluoridation and endemic goitre by administration of iodine. The two endemics co-exist when both iodine deficiency and an excess of fluorine are present.

In Switzerland, all the doctors of the present writer's generation witnessed the disappearance of endemic goitre and cretinism as a result of prophylactic iodine medication, which is always effective regardless of the fluorine content of the water.

At present, despite the increasing ingestion of fluorine in fluoridated water, fluoridated milk, tablets containing fluoride, etc., goitre has not reappeared, even in its most readily induced form—namely, neonatal thyroid hypertrophy.

Conclusions

The problem of the toxic effects of fluorine in relation to the thyroid may be regarded as settled: a specific toxicity of fluorine for the thyroid gland does not exist.

The main facts behind this statement are:

(1)   Fluorine does not accumulate in the thyroid.

(2)   Fluorine does not affect the uptake of iodine by the thyroid tissue.

(3)   Pathological changes in the thyroid show no increased frequency in regions where the water is fluoridated, either naturally or artificially.

(4)   The administration of fluorine does not interfere with the prophylactic action of iodine on endemic goitre.

(5)   The beneficial effect of iodine in threshold dosage to experimental animals is not inhibited by administration of fluorine, even in an excessive dose.

6.   SYSTEMIC AND VISCERAL INTOXICATION
(A. Singh & S. S. Jolly)

Since the dental and skeletal manifestations of fluorosis can be easily demonstrated and provide reliable evidence of the disease, other physical abnormalities tend to be overlooked. On the other hand, certain authors have drawn a lengthy list of manifestations attributable to fluorosis. For example, Spira (1953) has mentioned a number of complaints which the persons residing in an area with a high fluoride content in the water may have, including constipation, furunculosis, urticaria, dermatoses, alopecia and brittle nails. Spira's observations were based on the answers to a questionnaire circulated to 5000 military personnel during the Second World War, of whom 20 % had mottled enamel. He suggested that fluoride acts on the central nervous system to cause depression and melancholy, and on the central and vegetative nervous systems to affect certain endocrine glands. He postulated that parathyroid dysfunction explained the disturbance of calcium metabolism, brittle nails and changes in the skin and teeth, and that adrenal dysfunction explained low blood pressure, lassitude, and the gonadal involvement which resulted in "feminized males". This hypothesis has, however, never been substantiated. Similarly, Waldbott (1955) attributed urticaria, cephalgia, electroencephalographic changes and a host of other symptoms to allergic reactions to fluoride.

A sizable number of other biological effects have been ascribed to fluorides. Although many reports of such effects are unsubstantiated, several have been studied sufficiently to deserve a careful summary.

To study the problem of systemic intoxication, Singh et al. (1962c) submitted a detailed questionnaire to the population in some of the villages of Bhatinda district, one of the endemic areas in Punjab where the drinking water had a fluoride content of 10 ppm. There was no significant evidence of underdevelopment or undue anaemia or signs of any unusual nutritional deficiency amongst the population in the affected area. On the contrary, the rural area of Bhatinda district has one of the tallest and best-built male populations in the country. There was no evidence of goitre or hypothyroidism in the affected population. Detailed examination of the cardiovascular system, including electrocardiographic studies, revealed no abnormalities. Thus, the evidence from the clinical studies of fluorosis with regard to systemic intoxication is mostly of a negative nature, with the exception of dental, skeletal and neurological lesions.

Haemopoietic System

Various observers have recorded haematological findings in patients with fluorosis. Anaemia—possibly of a secondary type, from nutritional imbalance—was reported in Roholm's (1937) series of cases and recorded as due to partial obliteration of the medullary spaces by dense bone formation. In the series of Singh et al. (1963), the haemoglobin level ranged from 8 to 15.5 g per 100 ml. The principal difficulty lies in separating specific effects of fluoride from other factors such as malnutrition or other nutritional imbalance. In British surveys on industrial fluorosis (Agate et al., 1949) with much higher levels of fluoride intake, blood counts and haemoglobin levels were normal and, in fluorosed livestock, anaemia is not a conspicuous feature. No significant alteration in the factors of coagulation has been reported in any clinical series, but under experimental conditions coagulation is inhibited by fluoride at a relatively low level and fluorides are useful anticoagulants. Whether this is due to inhibition of the enzyme, prothrombokinase, to the precipitation of the Ca salts in an insoluble form, or to some other mechanism is not firmly established.

Metabolic Effects

Fluoride has an inhibitory effect on many enzyme systems (see Chapter 6, section 2). Assumptions have been based on *in vitro* findings that this fluoride effect must be exerted to some degree on metabolic processes in general.

However, it is demonstrated in Chapter 6, section 2 that enzyme inhibition in cells and body-fluids requires much higher fluoride concentrations than inhibition of purified enzymes.

While the *in vitro* toxicity of the fluoride ion for a number of enzymes is universally recognized, it is notable that there are hardly any recognizable clinical manifestations other than the dental and skeletal abnormalities.

Endocrine Effects

In the endocrine system, where the intermediary metabolism and synthesis of highly sensitive hormones involves enzymatic action, it is expected that interference with the mechanism by chemical agents would produce early and pronounced clinical effects. Considerable attention has consequently been given of recent years to the behaviour of fluoride in hormone chemistry and to the possible clinical disturbances of endocrine functions, particularly the thyroid gland. The effect on thyroid function is discussed in detail in section 5 of this chapter.

Of particular importance are the effects of fluorosis on the function of the parathyroid glands in regulating the level of calcium and inorganic phosphorus in the blood plasma by controlling deposition or removal from the skeleton and excretion by the kidney. Ritvo (1955), in describing the bone changes in fluorosis, pointed out that in many reports fluorosis and hyperparathyroidism exert a similar action on bone and that the final picture may be a combination of fluorosis and hyperparathyroidism. Differential diagnosis, however, can be easily made on the basis of the history and the serum concentrations of calcium, inorganic phosphorus and alkaline phosphatase. Radiological examination reveals a predominant osteosclerosis in fluorosis, while there may be a generalized decalcification of bone in parathyroid flisease. The characteristic and distinct skeletal changes of osteosclerosis and calcification of ligaments occurring in advanced stages of chronic fluorosis might indicate a disturbance of calcium metabolism. An antagonism between fluoride and calcium has been repeatedly assumed, particularly in experimental work, although there are very few detailed studies of calcium metabolism. Singh et al. (1966) studied the parathyroid functions in detail by estimating serum calcium, inorganic phosphorus, and alkaline phosphatase and carrying out phosphate-clearance and calcium-deprivation tests. They did not detect any significant alterations in the parathyroid function as revealed by these tests.

Although the striking and distinctive skeletal changes suggest a disturbance of calcium metabolism, the changes probably take place so slowly (extending over 20 years or more) that they are not reflected in the conventional parathyroid tests available at present. Information concerning the possible function of fluoride in other endocrine organs is lacking.

General Effects

Hagan (1957) has studied the effects of fluoride on general health as reflected in the mortality data collected from the comparison of a non-fluoride community with another in which fluoride is artificially added. This study did not reveal any relationship between mortality experience and the presence of fluoride in drinking-water supplies. Similarly, Leone et al. (1955) did not find any significant physiological or pathological abnormality in the Bartlett and Cameron survey except a high prevalence of dental fluorosis in Bartlett.

7. SUMMARY (S. S. Jolly)

The toxic effects of larger doses of fluoride are predominantly confined to the teeth and the skeletal system, with secondary involvement of the nervous system in advanced and crippling fluorosis. There is experimental evidence of the toxic effects of fluoride in large concentration on the thyroid and the kidney, but overt clinical disturbances in the function of these organs have not been described in endemic fluorosis.

The skeletal changes of endemic fluorosis show irregular deposition of fluorides in different bones of the body, particularly in the axial skeleton. The radiological changes of osteosclerosis along with marked osteophytosis are characteristic. There is a distinctive histopathological pattern in which the Haversian system is disorientated. The chemical composition of the bones is also altered, and there is a marked increase of fluoride content in the bone ash. In very advanced cases, owing to the irregular narrowing of the spinal canal and intervertebral foramina, the complication of radiculomyelopathy is superimposed on the skeletal lesions.

There is no evidence at present to show that the amount of fluoride likely to be absorbed from fluoridated water supplies can produce the type of skeletal defects described in this chapter. In India, some cases of fluorosis have been reported at low water-fluoride levels, but in these areas other factors may play a significant role—for example, other sources of fluorides or constituents of water other than fluorides. Nutritional deficiency may also be an aggravating or superpositioning factor in the endemic fluorosis in India.

REFERENCES

Agate, J. N., Bell, G. H., Boddie, G. F., Bowler, R. G., Buckell, M., Cheeseman, E. A., Douglas, T. H. J., Druett, H. A., Garrad, J., Hunter, D., Perry, K. M. A., Richardson, J. D. & Weir, J. B. de V. (1949) *Industrial fluorosis. A study of the hazard to man and animals near Fort William, Scotland,* London, HMSO (Medical Research Council Memorandum No. 22)

Ainsworth, N. J. (1933) *Brit. dent. J.,* **55,** 233

Allan, J. H. (1963) In: *Advances in fluorine research and dental caries prevention*, Oxford, Pergamon, vol. 1, p. 41; and *Arch. oral Biol.*, **8**, Spec. Suppl., p. 41 (Proceedings of 9th ORCA Congress, Paris, June 1962)

Applebaum, E. (1936) *Dent. Cosmos*, **78**, 960

Ardelean, I., Racoveanu, N., Manescu, S., Lupulescu, A., Diaconescu, M. & Ghelerter, L. (1963) *Igiena (Buc.)*, **12**, 301

Arkansas Agricultural Experiment Station (1926) *Bull. Arkans. agric. Exp. Sta.*, No. 215, p. 23

Armstrong, W. D. & Brekhus, P. J. (1937) *J. biol. Chem.*, **120**, 677

Arnold, F. A., Jr (1943) *J. Amer. dent. Ass.*, **30**, 499-508

Astwood, E. B. (1943) *J. Pharmacol. exp. Ther.*, **78**, 79

Auskaps, A. M. & Shaw, J. H. (1955) *J. Nutr.*, **55**, 611

Awazawa, N. (1962) *J. Nikon Univ. School Dent.*, **4**, 157

Baumann, E. J. & Metzger, N. (1949) *Proc. Soc. exp. Biol. (N.Y.)*, **70**, 536

Benagiano, A. & Fiorentini, S. (1955) *Schweiz. Mschr. Zahnheilk.*, **65**, 736

Bethke, R. M. et al. (1933) *J. dent. Res.*, **13**, 473

Bhussry, B. R. (1959a) *J. dent. Res.*, **38**, 369

Bhussry, B. R. (1959b) *J. dent. Res.*, **38**, 653

Bhussry, B. R. (1960) *J. dent. Res.*, **39**, 673

Bhussry, B. R. (1961) *J. dent. Res.*, **40**, 657

Bhussry, B. R. & Werth, M. (1962) In: *International Association for Dental Research, 40th General Meeting, St Louis, Missouri, March 1962 ; Abstracts*, Chicago, American Dental Association, Abstr. No. 285

Bond, A. M. & Murray, M. M. (1952) *Brit. J. exp. Path.*, **33** 168-176

Bosworth, E. B. & McCay, C. M. (1962) *J. aent. Res.*, **41**, 949-960

Bowes, J. H. & Murray, M. M. (1936) *Brit. dent. J.*, **60**, 556

Brun, G. C., Buckwald, H. & Roholm, K. (1941) *Acta med. scand.*, **106**, 261

Brzezinski, A., Bercovici, B. & Gedalia, I. (1960) *Obstet. and Gynec.*, **15**, 329-331

Büttner, W. (1966) In: *Advances in fluorine research and dental caries prevention*, Oxford, Pergamon, vol. 4, p. 193 (Proceedings of 12th ORCA Congress, Utrecht, Netherlands, June 1965)

Call, R. A., Greenwood, D. A., Le Cheminant, W. H., Shupe, J. L., Nielsen, H. M., Olson, L. E., Lamborn, R. E., Mangelson, F. L. & Davis, R. V. (1965) *Publ. Hlth Rep. (Wash.)*, **80**, 529-538

Carlson, C. H., Singer, L. & Armstrong, W. D. (1960) *Proc. Soc. exp. Biol. (N.Y.)*, **103**, 418-420

Caruso, F. S. (1961) *The effects of sodium fluoride on renal function in dogs*, Rochester, N.Y. (Thesis, University of Rochester)

Chaneles, J. (1929) *C. R. Soc. Biol. (Paris)*, **102**, 860

Chhuttani, P. N., Wahi, P. L. & Singh, S. (1962) *J. Indian med. Ass.*, **39**, 61

Churchill, H. V. (1931) *Industr. Engng Chem.*, **23**, 996

Cicardo, V. H. et al. (1955) *Rev. Soc. argent. Biol.*, **31**, 71

Clark, A. (1942) *J. trop. Med. Hyg.*, **45**, 49

Comar, C. L. et al. (1953) *Amer. J. Anat.*, **92**, 361

Cortell, R. E. (1949) *J. clin. Endocr.*, **9**, 955

Dean, H. T. (1933) *J. Amer. dent. Ass.*, **20**, 319

Dean, H. T. (1934) *Amer. dent. Ass.* **21**, 1421

Dean, H. T. & Elvove, E. (1935) *Publ. Hlth Rep. (Wash.),* **50**, 1719

Dean, H. T. & Elvove, E. (1936) *Amer. J. publ. Hlth,* **26**, 567

Dean, H. T. & Elvove, E. (1937) *Publ. Hlth Rep. (Wash.),* **52**, 1249

Dean, H. T. et al. (1934) *Publ. Hlth Rep. (Wash.),* **49**, 1075

Dean, H. T. et al. (1935) *Publ. Hlth Rep. (Wash).,* **50**, 424

Demole, V. et al. (1951) *Bull. schweiz. Akad. med. Wiss.,* **7**, 430

Demole, V. (1954) *Bull. schweiz. Akad. med. Wiss.,* **10**, 292

Demole, V. (1956) *Bull. schweiz. Akad. med. Wiss.,* **12**, 459

Demole, V. (1957) *Schweiz. Mschr. Zahnheilk.,* **67**, 314

Demole, V. (1962) *Bull. schweiz. Akad. med. Wiss.,* **18**, 356

Demole, V. & Lerch, P. (1956) *Helv. physiol. pharmacol. Acta,* **14**, C 62

Dustin, J.-P. (1963) In: *Advances in fluorine research and dental caries prevention,* Oxford, Pergamon, vol. 1, pp. 9-21; and *Arch. oral Biol.,* **8**, Spec. Suppl., pp. 9-21 (Proceedings of 9th ORCA Congress, Paris, June 1962)

Eager, J. M. (1901) *Publ. Hlth Rep. (Wash.),* **16**, 2576

El Tannir, M. D. (1959) *Amer. J. publ. Hlth,* **49**, 45-52

Erausquin, R. (1934) *Rev. Agrup. odont. (B. Aires),* **22**, 430

Ericsson, Y. & Hammarström, L. (1964) *Acta odont. scand.,* **22**, 523-538

Ericsson, Y. & Malmnäs, C. (1962) *Acta obstet. gynec. scand.,* **41**, 144-158

Ericsson, Y. & Ullberg, S. (1958) *Acta odont. scand.,* **16**, 363-374

Evans, R. J. & Phillips, P. H. (1938) *J. Amer. med. Ass.,* **111**, 300

Fleming, H. S. & Greenfield, V. S. (1954) *J. dent. Res.,* **33**, 780

Gabovich, R. D., Bukhovets, V. I. & Verzhikovskaya, N. V. (1960) *Gig. Tr. prof. Zabol.,* **2**, 26

Gabovich, R. D. & Verzhikovskaya, N. V. (1958) *Probl. Endokr. Gormonoter.,* **4**, No. 3, p. 49

Galagan, D. J. & Lamson, G. G., Jr (1953) *Publ. Hlth Rep. (Wash.),* **68**, 497-508

Galletti, P.-M. & Joyet, G. (1958) *J. clin. Endocr.,* **18**, 1102

Galletti, P.-M. et al. (1955) *Schweiz. Mschr. Zahnheilk.,* **65**, 753

Gardner, D. E., Smith, F. A., Hodge, H. C., Overton, D. E. & Feltman, R. (1952) *Science,* 208-209

Gedalia, I., Brzezinski, A. & Bercovici, B. (1959) *J. dent. Res.,* **38**, 548

Gedalia, I., Brzezinski, A., Bercovici, B. & Lazarov, E. (1961) *Proc. Soc. exp. Biol. (N.Y.),* **106**, 147-149

Gedalia, I., Brzezinski, A., Portuguese, N. & Bercovici, B. (1964) *Arch. oral Biol.,* **9**, 331-340

Gedalia, I., Gross, J., Guttmann, S., Steiner, J. E., Salman, F. G. & Weinreb, M. M. (1960) *Arch. int. Pharmacodyn.,* **129**, 116

Geever, E. F., Leone, N. C., Geiser, P. & Lieberman, J. (1958a) *J. Amer. dent. Ass.,* **56**, 499-507

Geever, E. F., Leone, N. C., Geiser, P. & Lieberman, J. (1958b) *Publ. Hlth Rep. (Wash.),* **73**, 721-731

Gerould, C. H. (1945) *J. dent. Res.,* **24**, 223

Glas, J. E. (1962) *Odont. Revy,* **13**, 315

Goodman, L. S. & Gilman, A. (1965) *The pharmacological basis of therapeutics. A textbook of pharmacology, toxicology, and therapeutics for physicians and medical students,* 3rd ed., New York, Macmillan

Gordonoff, T. & Minder, W. (1952) *Schweiz. med. Wschr.,* **82**, 972

Greenwood, D. A. (1940) *Physiol. Rev.,* **20**, 582

Greeenwood, D. A., Shupe, J. L., Stoddard, G. E., Harris, L. E., Nielsen, H. M. & Olson, L. E. (1964) *Fluorosis in cattle,* Logan, Utah (Agricultural Experiment Station, Utah State University, Special Report 17)

Gustafson, A.-G. (1961) *Arch. oral Biol.,* **4**, 67 (Special Supplement: Proceedings of 7th ORCA Congress, Hamburg, June 1960)

Hagan, T. (1957) *Effects of fluoridation on general health — as reflected in mortality data* (Paper presented at the American Association for the Advancement of Science Symposium, Indianapolis, Ind.)

Hamamoto, E., Fujiwara, H., Kimoto, H., Furutani, A., Yoshimatsu, M., Oota, N., Ohara, T. & Ado, H. (1954) *Proc. Japan Acad.,* **30**, 53

Harris, N. O. & Hayes, R. L. (1955) *J. dent. Res.,* **34**, 470

Hauck, H. M. et al. (1933) *Amer. J. Physiol.,* **103**, 489

Held, A.-J. (1953) *Bull. schweiz. Akad. med. Wiss.,* **9**, 132

Hennig, K. & Fritz, H. (1961) *Schweiz. med. Wschr.,* **91**, 79

Hodge, H. C., Downs, W. L., Smith, F. A., Maynard, E. A., Scott, J. K. & Gardner, D. E. (1964) *J. dent. Res.,* **43**, No. 5, Suppl., pp. 864-865

Hodge, H. C. & Smith, F. A. (1965) *Biological effects of inorganic fluorides.* In: Simons, J. H., ed., *Fluorine chemistry,* New York, Academic Press, vol. 4

Hoffmann-Axthelm, W. (1953) *Dtsch. zahnärztl. Z.* **8**, 757

Ingalls, N. W. (1931) *Amer. J. Anat.,* **48**, 45

Irving, J. T. (1943a) *J. dent. Res.,* **22**, 447

Irving, J. T. (1943b) *Nature (Lond.),* **151**, 363

Irving, J. T. & Neinbar, M. W. P. (1946) *J. dent. Res.,* **25**, 327

Janardhanan, T. & Venkaswamy, T. J. (1957) *Madras med. J.,* **1**, 1

Jenkins, G. N. (1962) *Nature (Lond.),* **193**, 23

Jentzer, A. (1955) *Schweiz. med. Wschr.,* **85**, 662

Jolly, S. S., Singh, I. & Singh, A. (1961) *J. Ass. Phycns India,* **9**, 13

Kempf, G. A. & McKay, F. S. (1930) *Publ. Hlth Rep. (Wash.),* **45**, 2923

Kempf, G. A. & Nelson, V. E. (1941) *Proc. Iowa Acad. Sci.,* **48**, 199

Kilborn, L. G., Outerbridge, T. S. & Lei, H. P. (1950) *Canad. med. Ass. J.,* **62**, 135-141

Korrodi, H. et al. (1956) *Helv. med. Acta,* **23**, 601

Kraft, K. (1936) *Hoppe-Seylers Z. physiol. Chem.,* **245**, 58

Kumar, S. P. & Harper, R. A. K. (1963) *Brit. J. Radiol.,* **36**, 497-502

Kvam, T. (1950) *K. Norske Videnskab. Selskab (Trondhjem)*

Lantz, E. M. & Smith, M. C. (1934) *Amer. J. Physiol.,* **109**, 645

Largent, E. J. (1961) *Fluorosis. The health aspects of fluorine compounds,* Columbus, Ohio State University Press

Largent, E. J. & Heyroth, F. F. (1949) *J. industr. Hyg.,* **31**, 134-138

Lawrence, E. W. & Latimer, H. B. (1957) *Amer. J. Anat.,* **101**, 445

Leone, N. C., Geever, E. F. & Moran, N. C. (1956) *Publ. Hlth Rep. (Wash.),* **71**, 459-467

Leone, N. C., Shimkin, M. B., Arnold, F. A., Stevenson, C. A., Zimmerman, E. R., Geiser, P. A. & Lieberman, J. E. (1954) *Publ. Hlth Rep. (Wash.)*, **69**, 925-936

Leone, N. C., Stinson, J. & Sunbury, R. T. (1960) *A.M.A. Arch. industr. Hlth*, **21**, 335

Leone, N. C. et al. (1955) *J. Amer. dent. Ass.*, **50**, 277

Lerman, J. & Harrington, C. R. (1949) *J. clin. Endocr.*, **9**, 1099

Levi, J. E. & Silberstein, H. (1955) *J. Lab. clin. Med.*, **45**, 348

Lidbeck, W. L., Hill, I. & Beeman, J. A. (1943) *J. Amer. med. Ass.*, **121**, 826

Likins, R. C., Scow, R. O., Zipkin, I. & Steere, A. C. (1959) *Amer. J. Physiol.*, **197**, 75

Linsman, J. F. & McMurray, C. A. (1943) *Radiology*, **41**, 497

Lison, L. (1941) *C. R. Soc. Biol. (Paris)*, **135**, 431

Litzka, G. (1936) *Arch. exp. Path. Pharmak.*, **183**, 427

Lyth, O. (1946) *Lancet*, **1**, 233-237

McClure, F. J. (1939) *Nat. Inst. Hlth Bull.*, No. 172, pp. 1-53

McClure, F. J. (1946) *Nondental physiological effects of trace quantities of fluorine*. In: Moulton, F. R., ed., *Dental caries and fluorine*, Washington, D.C., American Association for the Advancement of Science, pp. 74-92

McClure, F. J., McCann, H. G. & Leone, N. C. (1958) *Publ. Hlth Rep. (Wash.)*, **73**, 721-731

McClure, F. J. & Mitchell, H. H. (1931) *J. biol. Chem.*, **60**, 297

McClure, F. J., Mitchell, H. H., Hamilton, T. S. & Kinser, C. A. (1945) *J. industr. Hyg.*, **27**, 159-170

McClure, F. J. & Zipkin, I. (1958) *Dent. Clin. N. Amer.*, July, pp. 411-458

McCollum, E. V. (1925) *J. biol. Chem.*, **63**, 553

McKay, F. S. (1933) *J. Amer. dent. Ass.*, **20**, 1137

McKay, F. S. & Black, G. V. (1916) *Dent. Cosmos*, **58**, 477-484, 627-644, 781-792, 894-904

Maloof, F. & Soodak, M. (1963) *Pharmacol. Rev.*, **15**, 43

Mangelson, F. L. (1963) *Biochemical and physiological aspects on the use of p-aminohippuric acid and inulin for the measurement of renal function of cows receiving added dietary fluorine compounds*, Logan, Utah (Thesis, Utah State University)

May, W. (1935) *Klin. Wschr.*, **14**, 790

Møller, P. F. & Gudjonsson, S. V. (1932) *Acta radiol. (Stockh.)*, **13**, 269-294

Montelius, G. et al. (1933) *J. dent. Res.*, **13**, 73

Morgareidge, K. & Finn, S. B. (1940) *J. Nutr.*, **20**, 75

Mühlemann, H. R. & Schneider, R. (1956) *Schweiz. med. Wschr.*, **86**, 625

Murthi, G. V. S., Narayana Rao, D. & Venkateswarlu, P. (1953) *J. Indian med. Ass.*, **22**, 396-399

Nevitt, G. A., Frankel, J. M. & Witter, D. M. (1963) *J. Amer. dent. Ass.*, **66**, 65-69

Newbrun, E. (1957) *Microradiographic comparisons of demineralized and fluorosed enamel*, Rochester, N.Y. (Thesis, University of Rochester)

Ockerse, T. (1943) *J. dent. Res.*, **22**, 441

Ockerse, T. (1942) *Endemic fluorosis in South Africa*, Pretoria, Government Printers (Thesis, University of the Witwatersrand)

Odenthal, H. & Wieneke, H. L. (1959) *Dtsch. med. Wschr.*, **84**, 725

Pandit, C. G., Raghavachari, T. N. S., Rao, D. S. & Krishnamurti, V. (1940) *Indian J. med. Res.*, **28**, 533-558

Parikh, J. C. (1960) *J. dent. Res.*, **39**, 672

Parikh, J. C. (1961) *J. dent. Res.*, **40**, 710

Peters, J. H. (1948) *Amer. J. med. Sci.*, **216**, 278-285

Phillips, P. H. et al. (1935) *Amer. J. Physiol.*, **113**, 441

Pindborg, J. J. (1957) *Acta pharmacol. (Kbh.)*, **13**, 36-45

Puentes, F. & Cremer, H. D. (1966) In: *Advances in fluorine research and dental caries prevention*, Oxford, Pergamon, vol. 4, p. 213 (Proceedings of 12th ORCA Congress, Utrecht, Netherland, June 1965)

Ramseyer, W. F., Smith, C. A. H. & McCay, C. M. (1957) *J. Geront.*, **12**, 14-19

Rawson, R. W. (1949) *J. clin. Invest.*, **28**, 1330

Ritvo, M. (1955) *Bone and joint X-ray diagnosis*, London, Kimpton, and Philadelphia, Lea & Febiger

Robinowitch, I. M. (1945) *Canad. med. Ass. J.*, **52**, 345

Roche, J. (1953) *Actualités pharmacol.*, **6**, 175

Roholm, K. (1937) *Fluorine intoxication : a clinical-hygienic study, with a review of the literature and some experimental investigations*, London, Lewis

Saka, O., Hallag, P. & Urgancioglu, I. (1965) *New Istanbul Contr. clin. Sci.*, **8**, 87

Scatchard, G. & Black, E. S. (1949) *J. phys. Chem.*, **53**, 88-99

Schlesinger, E. R., Overton, D. E. & Chase, H. C. (1956) *J. Amer. med. Ass.*, **160**, 21-24

Schmidt, W. J. & Keil, A. (1958) *Die gesunden und die erkrankten Zahngewebe des Menschen und der Wirbeltiere im Polarisationsmikroskop*, München, Hanser

Schour, I. (1934) *Proc. Soc. exp. Biol. (N.Y.)*, **32**, 1

Schour, I. & Poncher, H. G. (1937) *Amer. J. Dis. Child.*, **54**, 757

Schour, I. & Smith, M. C. (1934) *Bull. Ariz. agric. Exp. Sta.*, No. 52, pp. 69-91

Schour, I. & Smith, M. C. (1935) *J. Amer. dent. Ass.*, **22**, 796

Schultz, J. A. (1936) *Rep. Iowa agric. Exp. Sta.*, p. 78

Sebrell, W. H. et al. (1933) *Publ. Hlth Rep. (Wash.)*, **48**, 437

Seevers, M. H. & Braun, A. H. (1935) *Proc. Soc. exp. Biol. (N.Y.)*, **33**, 228

Sharkey, T. P. & Simpson, W. M. (1933) *J. Amer. med. Ass.*, **100**, 97-100

Sheahan, M. M. et al. (1951) *Biochem. J.* **48**, 188

Shortt, H. E., McRobert, G. R., Barnard, T. W. & Mannadi Nayar, A. S. (1937) *Indian J. med. Res.*, **25**, 553-568

Shortt, H. E., Pandit, C. G. & Raghavachari, T. N. S. (1937) *Indian med. Gaz.*, **72**, 396-398

Siddiqui, A. H. (1955) *Brit. med. J.*, **2**, 1408-1413

Siddiqui, A. H. (1960) *J. Endocr.*, **20**, 101-105

Singer, L. & Armstrong, W. D. (1960) *J. appl. Physiol.*, **15**, 508-510

Singh, A., Dass, R., Hayreh, S. S. & Jolly, S. S. (1962a) *J. Bone Jt Surg.*, **44 B**, 806-815

Singh, A. & Jolly, S. S. (1961) *Quart. J. Med.*, **30**, 357-372

Singh, A., Jolly, S. S., Bansal, B. C. & Mathur, O. C. (1963) *Medicine (Baltimore)*, **42**, 229-246

Singh, A., Jolly, S. S., Devi, P., Bansal, B. C. & Singh, S. (1962b) *Indian J. med. Res.*, **50**, 387-398

Singh, A., Singh, B. M., Singh, I. D., Jolly. S. S. & Malhotra, K. C. (1966) *Indian J. med. Res.*, **54**, 591-597

Singh, A., Vazirani, S. J., Jolly, S. S. & Bansal, B. C. (1962c) *Postgrad. med. J.*, **38**, 150-156

Smith, F. A., Gardner, D. E. & Hodge, H. C. (1955) *A.M.A. Arch. industr. Hlth*, **11**, 2-10

Smith, F. A. & Hodge, H. C. (1959) *Fluoride toxicity.* In: Muhler, J. C. & Hine, M. K., ed., *Fluorine and dental health*, Bloomington, Indiana University Press

Smith, H. V. & Lantz, E. M. (1932) *J. dent. Res.*, **12**, 552

Smith, M. C., Lantz, E. M. & Smith, H. V. (1931) *Bull. Ariz. agric. Exp. Sta.*, No. 32

Smyth, H. F. & Smyth, H. F., Jr (1932) *Industr. Engng Chem.*, **24**, 229

Spira, L. (1953) *The drama of fluorine, arch enemy of mankind*, Milwaukee, Wis., Lee Foundation for Nutritional Research

Tappeiner, H. (1889) *Arch. exp. Path. Pharmak.*, **25**, 203

Taves, D. R. (1969) *Fed. Proc.* (in press)

Taves, D. R., Freeman, R. B., Kamm, D. E., Ramos, C. P. & Scribner, B. S. (1968) *Trans. Amer. Soc. artif. intern. Org.*, **14**, 412

Taylor, J. M. (1959) *Toxic effects of fluoride on the rat kidney*, Rochester, N.Y. (Thesis, University of Rochester)

Taylor, J. M., Gardner, D. E., Scott, J. K., Maynard, E. A., Downs, W. L., Smith, F. A. & Hodge, H. C. (1961a) *Toxicol. appl. Pharmacol.*, **3**, 290-314

Taylor, J. M., Scott, J. K., Maynard, E. A., Smith, F. A. & Hodge, H. C. (1961b) *Toxicol. appl. Pharmacol.*, **3**, 278-289

Tolle, C. & Maynard, L. H. (1928) In: *Record of Proceedings, Annual Meeting of the American Society of Animal Production*, p. 15

Velicangil, S. & Eser, S. (1957) *Z. proph. Med.*, **2**, 41

Velu, H. (1931) *C. R. Soc. Biol. (Paris)*, **58**, 750-752

Waldbott, G. L. (1955) *Acta med. scand.*, **156**, 157-168

Waldbott, G. L. (1961) *Arch. environm. Hlth*, **2**, 59

Wallace-Durbin, P. (1954) *J. dent. Res.*, **33**, 789-800

Waller, U. (1961) *Schweiz. Mschr. Zahnheilk.*, **71**, 561

Weatherell, J. A. & Weidmann, S. M. (1959) *J. Path. Bact.*, **78**, 233

Weber, D. & Yaeger, J. A. (1964) *J. dent. Res.*, **43**, 50

Weidmann, S. M., Weatherell, J. A. & Whitehead, R. G. (1959) *J. Path. Bact.*, **78**, 435

Weinmann, J. P. & Sicher, H. (1955) *Bone and bones : fundamentals of bone biopsy*, 2nd ed., St. Louis, Mo., Mosby

Wespi, H. J. (1953) *Schweiz. med. Wschr.*, **83**, 452

Wespi, H. J. (1954) *Praxis*, **43**, 616

Wespi-Eggenberger, H. J. (1960) *J. Indian med. Prof.*, **7**, 3281-3286

Williams, J. L. (1923) *J. dent. Res.*, **5**, 117

Willer, G. (1958) *Intoxication expérimentale par le fluor chez le rat*, Geneva (Thesis, Faculty of Medicine, N° 203).

Wyngaarden, J. B., Wright, B. M. & Ways, P. (1952) *Endocrinology*, **50**, 537-549

Ziegler, E. (1956) *Mitt. naturw. Ges. Winterthur*, **28**, 1-63

Ziegler, E. (1964) *Helv. paediat. Acta*, **19**, 343-354

Zipkin, I., Likins, R. C. & McClure, F. J. (1959) *J. Nutr.*, **67**, 59-68

Zipkin, I., McClure, F. J. & Lee, W. A. (1960) *Arch. oral Biol.*, **2**, 190-195

Zipkin, I., McClure, F. J., Leone, N. C. & Lee, W. A. (1958) *Publ. Hlth Rep. (Wash.)*, **73**, 732-740

CHAPTER 8

Fluorides and general health

N. C. LEONE [1] — A. E. MARTIN [2] — G. MINOGUCHI [3] — E. R. SCHLESINGER [4]
— A. H. SIDDIQUI [5]

1. INTRODUCTION (A. E. Martin)

The final assessment of the effects of any substance on man can be determined only by observations on man himself, and in making such observations, full consideration has to be given to the variations in the reactions of individuals and to the diverse effects of different environments. Epidemiological studies are therefore of great importance in determining the effects of fluorides on human health. The function of laboratory tests, including those using modern biochemical and tissue-culture techniques, and of experimental studies on animals and on man, is to provide essential background information and to confirm, explain, and, where necessary, fill in the gaps in the knowledge derived from the work of the field epidemiologist.

Epidemiological investigations are frequently difficult to interpret for the design of a study is governed by natural circumstances and by the availability of data. Information on the early signs of general fluorosis is obtained from areas where water supplies contain grossly excessive quantities of fluoride and from occasional cases of industrial fluorosis. Investigations based on comparisons between high- and low-fluoride areas offer some of the best material for research, and particularly convincing results have been obtained in the study of fluoridation projects such as the Newburgh-Kingston project described in Professor Schlesinger's contribution to this chapter. In this investigation baseline information was obtained from

[1] Commanding Officer, PHS Hospital, Galveston, Tex., USA.

[2] Senior Medical Officer, Department of Health and Social Security, Alexander Fleming House, London, England.

[3] Professor and Head of Department of Stomatology, Faculty of Medicine, Kyoto University, Kyoto, Japan.

[4] Professor and Head of Maternal and Child Health Program, University of Pittsburgh Graduate School of Public Health, Pittsburgh, Pa., USA.

[5] "Hasan Villa", Red Hills, Hyderabad-4, Andhra Pradesh, India.

medical examinations carried out before the start of fluoridation. Such information is obviously not available in natural fluoride areas, but good results have been obtained where an extensive series of observations is available, as in the mortality study of Hagan, Pasternack & Scholz (1954). Where data are more limited, as are those from the smaller series of areas investigated in the similar British mortality study of Heasman & Martin (1962), or where a comparison between a single pair of high- and low-fluoride towns is made, as in the Bartlett-Cameron study of Leone and his colleagues, greater care is needed in interpretation. In the Bartlett-Cameron study useful information was obtained by carrying out repeat medical examinations on the same group of people after a period of 10 years. In these types of investigations, careful attention has to be paid to the meaning which can be attached to aberrant results. Thus, in the study of Heasman & Martin, it was apparent that high fluorides were not the cause of a difference in mortality from cancer of the stomach, since an adjacent town using the same high-fluoride water supply was found not to have a markedly high rate of mortality. Again, the finding of a lower incidence of osteoporosis in Bartlett could be regarded only as a possible indication of a beneficial effect of fluorides until supporting evidence was obtained from further studies in the town of Framingham, and in high- and low-fluoride areas in North Dakota. The US studies of morbidity and mortality are supported by the valuable Soviet survey of the towns of Shchuchinsk and Kokchetav (Knizhnikov, 1958).

While epidemiological studies thus provide some of the most valuable information on the role of fluorides in the human body, it has to be realized that no single epidemiological study can in itself provide a rigorous proof of the safety of fluoridation of water supplies, even though a high degree of significance may be obtained from the findings. Within specified statistical limits individual studies may show an absence of any harmful effects. But the strength of the case for fluoridation is not based on the results of a single study; it is based on the mutually corroborative observations of many different workers. This is the picture which emerges from a consideration of the contributions to this chapter.

2. AREAS OF THE USA WITH A HIGH NATURAL CONTENT
OF WATER FLUORIDE (N. C. Leone)

Accumulated evidence derived from studies in the USA indicates that under American conditions the prolonged ingestion of fluorides, in concentrations of up to 8 ppm in a drinking water, does not produce harmful physiological effects in humans except for dental mottling (Leone et al., 1954). Moreover, an objectionable degree of mottling is observed only when fluorides are consumed during the ages of about 0-12 years and at levels in excess of 2.0 ppm.

While various authors have observed physiological changes by roentgenographic techniques, there is still no reliable evidence to support claims of harmful effects in persons living in high-fluoride areas (up to 8 ppm F) for long periods (15 or more years), when diet, hygiene and all other health factors are taken into consideration and the fluoride is delivered in consistent amounts from a reliable water supply and not in variable amounts from isolated pot-holes, streams or other unreliable water sources (Azar et al., 1961; Call, Leone & Davis, 1960; Leone et al., 1955, 1960; Stevenson & Watson, 1960). The clarified water from the latter sources may on analysis conform to the range described and studied, but the actual amount of fluoride in the water, as consumed, is greatly in excess of the analysis figures owing to the presence of fluoride-containing sediments which are found in unprocessed or in completely unpurified drinking water.

Actually, the accrued evidence points to a beneficial effect of fluorides on adult bone (Leone et al., 1955) and several clinical studies in which 20-60 mg of fluoride has been administered daily in the control of various bone and calcium-loss conditions bear out this concept (Leone, unpublished data; Purves, 1962; Rich, 1961; Rich & Ensinck, 1961).

Recognizable roentgenographic bone changes, attributed to high fluoride intake, have been identified and described by a number of authors, but such changes have never been observed in otherwise healthy subjects consuming a natural water supply containing less than 4 ppm fluoride (Azar et al., 1961; Roholm, 1937). The bone findings described in association with an elevated fluoride intake are increased bone density and coarsened trabeculation of a degree that may be desirable in our aging population. Harmful roentgenographic findings have not been described in man after intakes of up to 8 ppm fluoride in water (Azar et al., 1961; Knizhnikov, 1958; Leone et al., 1955; Stevenson & Watson, 1960).

There is little doubt that nature intended to impose daily contact with fluoride upon us, for 0.1 % of the earth's crust is composed of this element in different forms. In a few scattered areas of the world fluoride is found in high concentration in the form of cryolite (54.3% F) and fluorspar (48.0% F).

In the extensive high-fluoride areas of the USA nature has provided an environment of great practical and scientific importance for epidemiological studies. The main high-fluoride areas are in the south central part of the country, though additional areas are found in other parts. Texas, a south central state, with its vast fluoride areas, has provided some of our best epidemiological source material on the effects of fluoride on man. There can be found large stable population groups using water containing more than the desired 1.0 ppm fluoride for many years. Data from such areas are vital to the unbiased evaluation of research findings. A clearer concept of the areas

FIG. 1

GEOGRAPHICAL DISTRIBUTION OF FLUORIDE AREAS (1.5 ppm AND HIGHER) IN THE USA

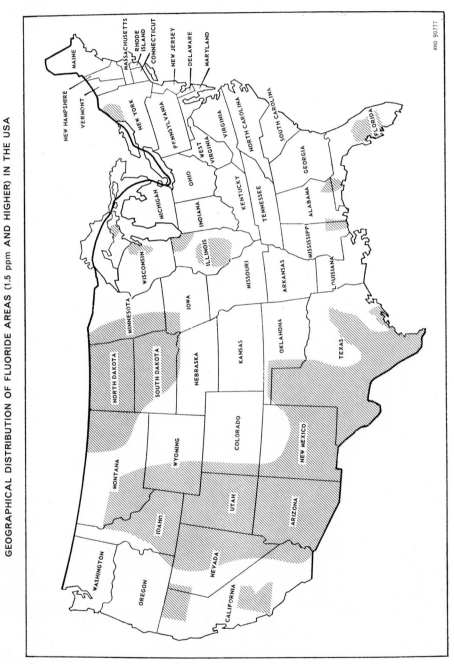

WHO 90777

▨ Areas where mottled enamel has been demonstrated by surveys and/or recorded in the literature.

under discussion can be obtained from the fluoride-distribution map of the USA shown in Fig. 1.

To clarify terminology, waters containing more fluoride than the physiologically desirable 1.0-1.5 ppm are regarded in this discussion as "high fluoride" waters.

Brief reference to the historical background of fluorides in man and, more specifically, to the high-fluoride areas of the USA will provide a better understanding of the nature of the problem and the extent to which it has been studied in the USA.

The earliest information on the effect of fluorides on man's dentition stems from a report by Eager, a US Public Health Service physician who was detailed to examine Italian emigrants in Naples. In his report to the Surgeon General, Eager (1901) stated: "One is struck by the frequency of a dental peculiarity common among the inhabitants of the Italian littoral and known as Denti di Chiaie, a defect first described by Professor Stefano Chiaie, a celebrated Neopolitan."

Specifically, the earlier epidemiological investigations in the USA stem from the astute observations of McKay and Black in Colorado Springs about 1908. These workers were the first to associate dental mottling with domestic water supplies (Black & McKay, 1916; McKay & Black, 1916). McKay, a practising dentist with an alert, open mind, had epidemiological direction in his thinking. His work gave impetus to Dean and others, who, using epidemiological techniques, proved beyond doubt that fluoride in drinking water produced recognizable dental changes under certain conditions.

These early American investigators found that when water contained concentrations substantially greater than 2 ppm F, there often developed dental defects, ranging from barely detectable white spots called dental mottling at the lower levels to unsightly brown, stained, hypocalcified or hypoplastic teeth at higher levels, i.e., 4-8 ppm F. They also noted a direct relationship between the amount of fluoride in the drinking water and the incidence of dental caries, observing, for example, that 1 ppm fluoride in drinking water, consumed during the tooth formative stage (0-8 years of age), was beneficial and responsible for a significant reduction in dental caries.

It was from these earlier interests and findings that a series of carefully planned, well-controlled studies were initiated to provide reliable information on the physiology of fluorides in man. Many of the studies were designed to be interrelated, each providing specific facets of information. Often they were paralleled by identical animal studies to support the epidemiological or other study results in man and to confirm definitive answers to the many questions that have been posed.

It is difficult to summarize effectively the great number of fluoride studies and the mass of information accrued. Therefore, a tabulation of documen-

TABLE 1

FLUORIDE STUDIES IN MAN AND SIGNIFICANT ASSOCIATED STUDIES

Area	F level (ppm)	Type of study	Material or effect studied	References
Texas	8.0	Epidemiological population study	1. Health status 2. X-ray—bone 3. Morbidity 4. Mortality 5. Dental 6. Urinary excretion of F	Leone et al. (1954) Leone et al. (1955); Stevenson & Watson (1960) Leone et al. (1954) Leone et al. (1954) Zimmerman et al. (1955) Likins et al. (1956); Zipkin & Leone (1957); Zipkin et al. (1956)
Texas and US fluoride areas	0.0-6.0	Epidemiological	Population — X-ray — bone fractures and height-weight (young men)	McClure (1944)
US fluoride areas	0.0-8.0	Human autopsy series (Epidemiological)	1. Human bone — F — chemical analysis 2. Human soft tissue — chemical analysis 3. Bone — F — microscopic 4. Human soft tissue — microscopic	Zipkin et al. (1958); McClure et al. (1958) Smith et al. (1960) Geever et al. (1958b) Geever et al. (1958a); Leone et al. (1964)
US fluoride areas	0.0 versus 8.0	Human autopsy study	Comparative autopsy study of bone and soft tissue (chemical analysis) (2 identical cases)	McClure et al. (1958)
Colorado Springs	2.5	Autopsy review	Pathological studies in man — morbidity and mortality studies (904 cases)	Geever et al. (1958a)
US fluoride areas	0.0-2.6	Clinical, epidemiological	Urinary and biliary tract calculi	Zipkin & Leone (1958)

TABLE 1

FLUORIDE STUDIES IN MAN AND SIGNIFICANT ASSOCIATED STUDIES *(concluded)*

Area	F level (ppm)	Type of study	Material or effect studied	References
Texas	3.5-5.5	Epidemiological	Radiographic survey — osseous development in hands and wrists of children	McCauley & McClure (1954)
US fluoride areas	0.0-4.0	Epidemiological	Human bone — F content and its relation to chemical composition	Zipkin et al. (1958, 1960)
Utah	—[a]	Human autopsy study	Bone — microscopic and chemical analysis Soft tissue — microscopic and chemical analysis	Call et al. (1960) Smith et al. (1960)
Crisfield, Maryland	0.0-3.48	Epidemiological	Thyroid function — studies in man — 0.02 ppm and 3.48 ppm F	Leone et al. (1964)
Texas	2.5-8.0	Epidemiological	Humans—X-ray studies in man with long exposure to F	Stevenson & Watson (1960)
North Dakota	4.0-5.8 0.15-0.3	Epidemiological	Lateral lumbar X-ray — humans	Bernstein et al. (1966)

[a] Airborne fluoride from steel mills.

ted evidence describing the source and nature of the pertinent high-fluoride studies is employed as a guide to what is known. By this means, a comprehensive presentation of the selective effects of fluorides on man, as determined through controlled studies, can be reviewed and evaluated, with greater detail available by reference to the original publications. Table 1 lists pertinent US fluoride studies in man with allied studies that have a direct bearing upon the interpretation of information now available; this table is designed to indicate the area, level of fluoride studied, type of study, material or effect studied, and references to original publications. Table 2 is similarly constructed but relates to significant associated fluoride studies in man and animals.

The available documented evidence derived from controlled studies makes it possible to summarize the physiological manifestations in man of long exposure to high fluoride levels. It can now be stated that under the climatic and living conditions met with in the USA:

1. According to epidemiological population studies, no impairment of or effect on the general health status could be detected among persons residing for an average of 37 years in areas where the water supply contains fluoride at the level of 8 ppm, and no systemic abnormalities or abnormal laboratory findings were observed that might be associated with ingestion of fluorides (Leone et al., 1954, 1955).

2. Roentgenographic examination of persons residing in high-fluoride areas showed an increased bone density and coarsened trabeculation with slight thickening of the cortical bone and periosteum in a limited number of those studied, but no harmful skeletal effects were identified. Actually, this X-ray study (Leone et al., 1955) provided evidence, later supported by other studies (Leone et al., 1960; Stevenson & Watson, 1960), that the described "fluoride bone effect" is in fact both beneficial and desirable in adult bone since it counteracts the osteoporotic changes of the aged and the effects of calcium-loss disease (Leone et al., 1955; Rich, 1961; Rich & Ensinck, 1961, McClure, McCann & Leone, 1958).

3. Prolonged high fluoride intakes up to 8 ppm do not affect morbidity or mortality (Leone et al., 1954; Geever et al., 1958a; Hagan, 1957; Knizhnikov, 1958).

4. The frequency of dental fluorosis, an expected finding in the planned studies, was found to be significantly higher in high-fluoride areas, but other dental conditions, such as gingivitis, horizontal and vertical alveolar bone resorption, dental caries, calculus, leukoplakia, soft-tissue abnormalities, pulp stones, periapical rarefaction, condensing osteitis, and dentigerous cysts, were no more frequent than in normal population groups (Zimmerman, Leone & Arnold, 1955). At lower levels of consumption, i.e., 1.0-1.5 ppm fluoride, there was ample evidence of the beneficial anti-caries effect of fluorides. This beneficial aspect is dealt with in detail in Chapter 9 of this monograph.

TABLE 2

SIGNIFICANT ASSOCIATED FLUORIDE STUDIES IN MAN AND ANIMALS

Area	F level (ppm)	Type of study	Effect studied	References
Laboratory	Toxic levels	Toxicological study (dogs, mice)	1. MLD 2. Toxicity 3. EKG 4. Physical effects 5. Serum calcium	Leone et al. (1956)

Utah	12.0–100	7½-year F-feeding study (cattle)	Blood system effects:
			1. Peripheral blood
			2. Blood chemistry
			3. Bone marrow
			4. Special studies
			  (a) electroplasmophoresis
			  (b) folic acid
			  (c) vitamin B_{12}
			  (d) blood enzyme
			5. Thyroid effects — PBI
			6. Liver function and spleen
				Hoogstratten et al. (1965);
				Leone et al. (unpublished data)
				
				Leone et al. (1964)
				Shupe et al. (1960)

Utah	12–100	7½-year F-feeding study (cattle)	Growth and development effects
			Fertility
			Reproduction
			Dental effects
			Bone — pathological
			  X-ray
			  chemical analysis (serial bone
			    biopsies)
			  microscopic
			Placental transfer
			Genetic, milk production and F content
			Urinary secretion of F
				Shupe et al. (1963)

Framingham, Mass.	0.04–8.0	Epidemiological X-ray study (humans)	Low-fluoride population (546 persons) — X-ray findings compared in identical bases with 8.0 ppm F area (Texas)	Leone et al. (1960)
Utah	12–100	Liver-function studies (cattle)	BSP in cattle fed 12–100 ppm F compared with control experimental herd (Beltsville)	Shupe et al. (1960)
Bethesda, Md. (NIH)	5	Clinical (humans)	Rate of F output in normal adults	Zipkin & Leone (1957)

5. The urinary excretion of fluorides is in direct proportion to the level of F intake and is not directly correlated with age according to studies in which age-groups of 7 through 16 years were compared with age-groups of 20 years and over (Likins, McClure & Steere, 1956; Zipkin & Leone, 1957; Zipkin et al., 1956).

6. Approximately 60% of the fluoride ingested is excreted within the first 24 hours at various intake levels. When there is a decrease in the amount consumed, there is a proportionate gradual but predictable decrease in the urinary fluoride output, indicating that the previously stored fluoride is being mobilized and excreted (McClure, 1944, Zipkin & Leone, 1957; Zipkin et al., 1956).

7. Young males in high-fluoride areas fail to reveal a relationship between bone fractures and fluoride exposure and their height-weight figures compare favourably with those of young men in other areas of the USA, indicating that fluoride exposure does not influence man's growth pattern (McCauley & McClure, 1954; McClure, 1944).

8. Autopsy studies of persons residing in 0-8 ppm fluoride areas provide clearly defined evidence that:

(*a*) There is a linear relationship between bone fluoride content and fluoride consumption, the highest bone fluoride content being found at high F levels (McClure, McCann & Leone, 1958; Zipkin et al., 1958).

(*b*) Soft tissues do not accumulate fluoride, regardless of the level of F consumption or the length of exposure, except the aorta and possibly the kidney where the F is probably adventitious (Smith et al., 1960; McClure, McCann & Leone, 1958; Azar et al., 1961).

(*c*) Occasionally, small isolated calcific plaques are found in the aorta which contain more fluoride than the immediate surrounding soft tissue. This is due to the affinity of fluoride and calcium for each other. However, in low-fluoride areas, such plaques are found in equal number and size, indicating that fluoride is not a factor in the formation of calcific plaques but a common finding at autopsy in aging adults (Smith et al., 1960; Geever et al., 1958a, 1958b).

(*d*) Histological examinations of bone from persons residing in communities with 1.0-4.0 ppm fluoride do not show any differences that can be related to fluoride intake. Microscopic changes incidental to aging and to non-fluoride-related conditions are observed in bone from both fluoride and non-fluoride areas (Geever et al., 1958a, 1958b; Azar et al., 1961) substantiating that demonstrable bone changes have not been identified in man by roentgenographic examination up to a level of 4 ppm.

(*e*) Similarly, no histological changes that might be associated with fluoride can be demonstrated in human soft tissue (Geever et al., 1958a, 1958b) when similarly exposed. Parallel animal studies support this finding (Shupe et al., 1963).

9. Comparative "matched" bone and soft-tissue studies from persons residing in high- and low-fluoride areas clearly demonstrate the effects of fluoride on bone density, increased fluoride and calcium in the bone, and the absence of soft-tissue change or the accumulation of fluorides in soft tissue (McClure, McCann & Leone, 1958).

10. Analyses of the findings of an extensive necropsy series, performed on persons from high-fluoride areas, revealed no significant association of morbidity, mortality, disease entity or other pathological condition which could be related to prolonged residence in a high-fluoride environment (Geever et al., 1958a; Hagan, 1957).

11. The fluoride content of urinary and biliary tract calculi is not affected by the level of fluoride intake according to a study in which renal calculi from high- and low-fluoride areas were compared (Zipkin & Leone, 1958).

12. A radiographic study of the hands and wrists of 2005 children, 7-14 years of age, residing in 3.5-5.5 ppm fluoride areas failed to demonstrate abnormal bone growth or developmental effects (McCauley & McClure, 1954).

13. Supporting human and animal studies demonstrate, through detailed blood studies, that prolonged administration of high concentrations of fluoride (a) does not produce gross histological or functional effects on the thyroid gland or the liver; (b) does not produce significant changes in the serum calcium, phosphorus or numerous other blood constituents studied; (c) may, at the 100 ppm or toxic level, in animals (which normally have a higher eosinophil level than man) slightly raise the total eosinophil count and lower the serum folic acid level; and (d) most important, does not produce anaemia or detectable abnormalities of the bone marrow or otherwise affect the haematopoietic system (Hoogstratten et al., 1965; Leone et al., 1964; Leone et al., unpublished data; Shupe et al., 1960).

14. The prolonged ingestion of fluoride does not affect thyroid gland size or function in either man or animals (Leone et al., 1964; Shupe et al., 1963).

15. The controlled feeding to cattle of fluoride in concentrations of 12-100 ppm for 7½ years does not affect fertility, reproduction or milk production or in any way produce abnormal effects in the offspring through repeated generations (Shupe et al., 1963).

16. The same studies also support the linear accumulation of bone fluoride (as described in man) which parallels the level of consumption, and, further, support human studies showing that while there is a linear increase in fluoride bone levels, the accumulation of fluoride in soft tissue does not occur (Shupe et al., 1963).

17. These and other studies also show a lack of histological evidence of abnormal change or fluoride effect in soft tissues (Shupe et al., 1963).

18. A limited placental transfer of fluoride has been demonstrated through the accumulation of low levels of fluoride in the bones of offspring,

but no growth or developmental effects have been observed (Shupe et al., 1963).

19. Liver-function studies in cattle, applying the same techniques as used in man, have demonstrated that high fluoride does not affect liver function and does not produce gross or microscopic change in the liver of animals fed 12-100 ppm F for 7½ years (Shupe et al., 1960, 1963).

20. Roentgenographic studies provide important information (Leone et al., 1960). When a controlled group of 546 persons in a low-fluoride area (0.04 ppm F) was compared with a group who lived in a high-fluoride area (8 ppm F), a statistically significant greater number of persons in the former group showed a decreased bone density, described by the radiologist as osteoporosis, a finding that supports the concept of a beneficial effect of fluoride on adult bone (Geever et al., 1958b; Bernstein et al., 1966).

In summary, it is evident that except for dental changes, long exposure to fluorides at what might be regarded as "high levels", i.e., 2.0-8 ppm F, does not produce harmful or otherwise abnormal effects in man but does in fact have an effect on adult bone that is beneficial and most significant to those persons in the post-menopausal or older age-groups.

3. FLUOROSIS IN AREAS OF INDIA WITH A HIGH NATURAL CONTENT OF WATER FLUORIDE (A. H. Siddiqui)

Epidemiology

In India, endemic fluorosis occurs with varying intensity in Andhra Pradesh, Madras, Mysore, Punjab and Kerala (Daver, 1945; Khan & Wig, 1945; Murthi, Narayana Rao & Venkateswarlu, 1953; Pandit & Narayana Rao, 1940; Pandit et al., 1940; Pillai, 1942; Raghavachari & Venkataramanan, 1940; Shortt, Pandit & Raghavachari, 1937; Shortt et al., 1937; Siddiqui, 1955; Singh et al., 1962; Venkateswarlu, Rao & Rao, 1952). The pioneer investigations were made by Shortt and his collaborators in 1937. Extensive survey work has been carried out in Andhra Pradesh, Madras and Punjab (Fig. 2, 3 and 4). Singh et al. (1962) have calculated that there is a belt covering at least one-fourth of the Punjab in which the fluoride content of the drinking water is high. This exposes roughly 5 million people to the toxic potentialities of the fluoride ion. An even larger population is exposed to high fluoride ingestion in Andhra Pradesh and Madras. The areas where the incidence of endemic fluorosis is high are shown in Fig. 2. Fig. 3 and 4 indicate the concentration of fluorine in well water and the number of specimens analysed in areas of endemic fluorosis. Singh et al. (op. cit.) recorded 16.2 ppm fluorine in certain areas of the Punjab, the highest figure reported from India.

FIG. 2
AREAS OF ENDEMIC FLUOROSIS

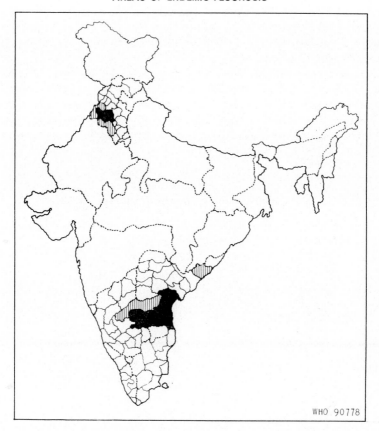

WHO 90778

Most foods are found to be poor sources of fluorine, even when grown in fluorine-rich soils, supposedly because the fluorine in the soil becomes converted to insoluble calcium salts. Tea and some other members of the family Theaceae, which grow in relatively acidic soils, are exceptional in their faculty for taking up fluorine. Fluorine in tea is in inorganic form. Quentin, Souci & Indinger (1960) found the fluorine content of Darjeeling and Assam tea to be 86.7 mg and 98.7 mg per kg dry weight, respectively. Tests on infusions of Assam tea, 3 g to 300 ml of water, allowed to stand for 5 minutes, showed that 90% of the fluorine was extracted by moderately hard tap water as well as by distilled water, and that a cup would supply 0.14 mg of fluorine. In a recent study Singer, Armstrong & Vatassery (1967) found 52-144 ppm F in five black teas and 336 ppm F in one green tea; 41-78% of this fluoride content could be extracted in the first infusion.

Sea foods may be rich in fluorine (5-15 ppm). Venkateswarlu (unpublished data) found the fluorine content of sea salt to range between 14 and 20 µg/g. About 11 g of sea salt are consumed on an average daily in India. Siddiqui (1955) reported high levels of fluorine, 0.09%, 0.11% and 0.15% respectively, in the sediments and mud samples obtained from wells in areas of endemic fluorosis.

Dental fluorosis occurs with varying intensity in the areas of endemic fluorosis (Fig. 3 and 4). Venkateswarlu, Rao & Rao (1952) found 0.9-1 ppm in Indian drinking waters to be associated with mottled enamel: almost the same amount which is being incorporated in the public water supplies in Europe and the USA as a mass caries-control measure. However, the

FIG. 3

FLUORIDE CONTENT OF WELL WATER IN ENDEMIC AREAS — I

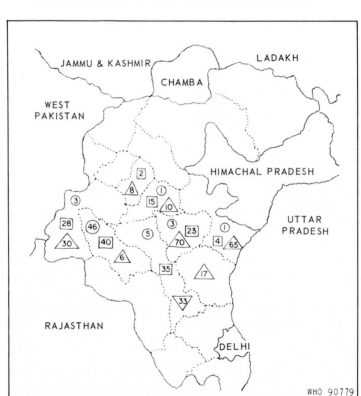

O More than 3 ppm.
□ Between 1 and 3 ppm.
△ Below 1 ppm.
The numerals indicate the number of specimens analysed.

FIG. 4

FLUORIDE CONTENT OF WELL WATER IN ENDEMIC AREAS — II

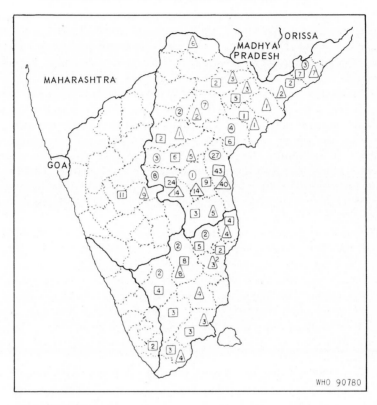

○ More than 3 ppm.
□ Between 1 and 3 ppm.
△ Below 1 ppm.
The numerals indicate the number of specimens analysed.

differences between India on the one hand and Europe and the USA on the other regarding the consumption of water, sediment in drinking water and the nutritional habits and general health status of the population have to be borne in mind in this connexion.

Clinical Observations

Children, apart from dental changes, do not suffer from ill-effects of fluorine-rich drinking water. Susceptibility to mottled enamel is restricted to a sharply defined age-group. The reason is that fluorine is deposited in teeth during the period of calcification of the crown of the permanent teeth.

This period extends from infancy, when the central incisors may be affected, to 16 years of age, when the calcification of the crown of the last teeth, the third molars, has been completed. Both sexes are affected with equal frequency. The condition is largely confined to the permanent teeth, although in areas of marked severity, sporadic instances of deciduous teeth being affected—evidence of placental transmission of fluorine—have been observed.

The changes are of two kinds. First, the enamel is abnormally opaque and chalky white. White blotchy areas are usually interspersed with areas of more or less normal enamel, a condition which has aptly acquired the descriptive term of mottling. This change is observable at the eruption of the tooth. Secondly, after eruption, an irremovable brown or black pigmentary substance is deposited in the defective enamel. The coloured areas form irregular patches or more regular transverse bands (Fig. 5) (Leone, 1960; Pillai, 1942; Raghavachari & Venkataramanan, 1940; Murthi, Narayana Rao & Venkateswarlu, 1953).

The degree of mottling depends largely on the amount of fluorine ingested. With increasing concentrations of F the effect becomes progressive, so that at 6 ppm the incidence of mottling is 100% (cf. Chapter 7, section 2 and Chapter 9). The most commonly affected teeth are the premolars and the second molars, though any tooth may be involved. The surfaces subjected to attrition show marked lesions. In severe cases of mottling, there is discrete or confluent pitting and the teeth often appear corroded. Caries in the mottled teeth is rare, but the enamel is rather brittle and inclined to chip off in the severe cases.

In the USA manifest mottling is reported to be associated with at least 3 to 4 ppm fluoride—a level at which many workers in India have recorded cases of skeletal fluorosis. In north-western Europe the degree of mottling has been found to be still less than that in the USA (Møller, 1965).

Such highly varying manifestations of fluorine intoxication in different parts of the world lead to the inference that there are factors, peculiar to each country, which influence the effect of fluorine in drinking water. For example, the consumption of water is greater in India than in temperate and subtropical countries. Fluorine-rich sediment in primitive wells has already been mentioned.

Venkateswarlu, Rao & Rao (1952) concluded that the incidence of caries and mottled enamel had a definite relationship with the fluorine content of water. However, the incidence of caries and mottled enamel varies considerably in communities exposed to nearly the same amount of fluorine in drinking water. Owing to the lack of information on the exact relationship between the incidence of dental caries and the fluorine content of waters, Venkateswarlu and co-workers (*op. cit.*) studied the relationship between the incidence of caries and the over-all manifestation of fluorosis in the community. An index for the degree of manifestation of fluorosis (as revealed by an examina-

FIG. 5
MOTTLING OF TEETH OBSERVED IN ENDEMIC AREAS

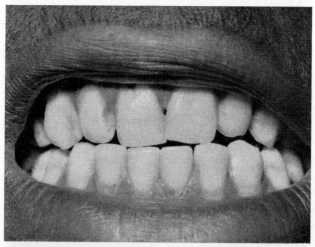

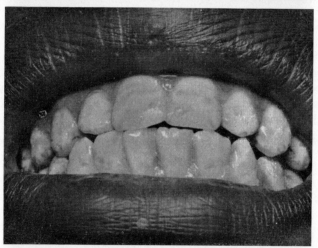

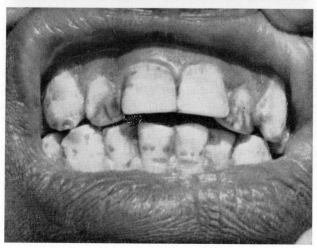

tion of mottled enamel prevalent in a community) designated as the dental fluorosis index (DFI) was established. It was concluded that the fluorine content of water remaining the same, the incidence of dental caries varied inversely with the DFI of a community.

This observation does not mean that nutritional and other factors, by lowering the toxicity of fluorine, should increase the chances of caries incidence. On the contrary, such factors, besides lowering the toxicity of fluorine, may by themselves effectively control caries incidence as well. It is interesting to recall in this context an observation by Dean et al. (1939) that the DMF rate per 100 children among Galesburgh subjects with mottled enamel was 200, while among those without mottled enamel it was 186. A low incidence of mottled enamel can co-exist with a low incidence of dental caries. It is therefore desirable to recognize the existence of other factors which contribute to a low caries incidence.

The optimal (sub-mottling) concentration of fluorine beneficial to dental health in India seems to be from 0.5 to 0.8 ppm in water.

Prolonged ingestion of water with a high fluorine content causes skeletal fluorosis in adults. There is an extraordinary uniformity in the signs and symptoms of intoxication. The initial symptom noted in India is a recurrent general tingling sensation in the limbs or all over the body. Pain and stiffness next appear, especially in the lumbar region but also involving the thoracic region and the cervical spine. Extension is more painful than flexion. The stiffness may increase until the entire spine, including the cervical region, appears to be one continuous column of bone. Accompanying the spinal disability, there is stiffness of various joints due to calcification of periosteal tissues, tendinous insertions of muscles and interosseous fasciae. This leads to various other disabilities, such as inability to squat. The bony and cartilaginous skeleton of the thorax is markedly affected and breathing becomes abdominal. The vertebral column becomes rigid and the patient develops a "poker-back". Bony exostoses can easily be seen or felt. By the time this condition is reached, the individual is between 30 and 40 years of age. Skeletal fluorosis, with special reference to conditions in India, is more comprehensively dealt with by Singh and Jolly in Chapter 7, section 3.

The patients exhibit cachexia, there is loss of appetite and signs of spinal root and cord compression appear with loss of sphincter control. The patient is finally bedridden while the mental powers remain unimpaired.

Involvement of the nervous system in skeletal fluorosis has been reported exclusively from India (Murthi, Narayana Rao & Venkateswarlu, 1953; Shortt et al., 1937; Siddiqui, 1955; Singh & Jolly, 1961). The spinal nerves and the cord are compressed by bony ingrowths in the spinal canal. The physical signs depend on the anatomical factors of maximum narrowing of the spinal canal or the intervertebral foramina and whether the compression is chiefly at a single site or is multiple. A patchy type of anaesthesia, muscular wasting, spastic paraplegia with sensory level, absence of vibration sense and loss of sphincter control are the usual neurological manifestations. The neurological changes resemble to a certain extent the clinical picture of cervical spondylosis. The pathogenic mechanism of root and cord compression is similar. However, the manifestations of cord compression are a more integral part of fluorosis and the root compression is much more common in cervical spondylosis.

Cases exhibiting radiological changes in the skull may suffer from a perceptive type of deafness. In the series reported by Rao & Siddiqui (1962)

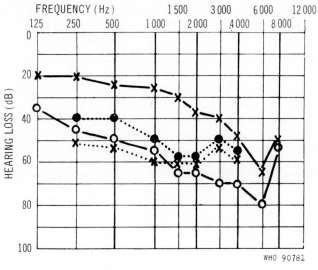

FIG. 6

AUDIOGRAM INDICATING HEARING LOSS OBSERVED IN CASES
OF SKELETAL FLUOROSIS [a]

[a] After Rao & Siddiqui (1962).

hearing loss commenced at 3000 Hz and was marked (up to 60 dB) at 8000 Hz (Fig. 6). Bone conduction seemed to be affected more than air conduction. Hearing loss was greater for higher frequencies. These workers postulated that hearing loss was the result of pressure on the eighth nerve during its passage through the narrowed and sclerosed internal auditory meatus.

Wilson (1941) reported a high degree of dental fluorosis in the goitrous area of the Punjab, India; however, no mention was made about the iodine intake, water sources were not analysed and the criteria for dental fluorosis did not exclude non-fluorotic mottling. The incidence of simple goitre, cretinism and deaf-mutism was investigated by Siddiqui (1960) in a known area of endemic fluorosis. With the possible exception of temporary thyroid enlargement in pubertal subjects, no relation was found between the incidence of goitre and the content of fluorine in the water supply.   No cases of cretinism or of deaf-mutism were seen.   Normal thyroid glands, both macroscopically and microscopically, were reported in two cryolite workers by Roholm (1937).   The fluorine-thyroid problem is more extensively covered in Chapter 7, section 5.

Factors influencing Severity

The severity of fluorosis has a definite relation to the concentration of fluorine in water, to the length of time of ingestion, to meteorological factors (for example, temperature), and possibly to the economic and nutritional status of the people, and the physical strain to which they are exposed.

The degree of disability and the time of onset of symptoms of the disease are related to the concentration of fluorine and to the length of time of its ingestion.   Siddiqui (1955) reported that symptoms of intoxication in Kamaguda village appeared in immigrants one to four years after their arrival.   The finding that it takes one to four years for symptoms to manifest themselves is at variance with that of Shortt et al. (1937), who concluded that a residence of 30-40 years in an endemic area was required for a definite picture of skeletal fluorosis to develop.   An exceptionally high fluorine content of water (11.8 ppm), excessive heat (46.1°C) and a poor state of nutrition, the diet being deficient in calcium and vitamin C (Table 3), may be possible factors responsible for the early development of skeletal fluorosis in Kamaguda.   The presence of signs of fluorosis in poultry, which is very resistant to fluorine (Peirice, 1940), also points to the intensity of intoxication in Kamaguda.

TABLE 3

COMPOSITION OF DAILY DIET IN KAMAGUDA VILLAGE [a]

Constituent	Amount
Protein:	
animal	$\left.\begin{array}{c}5.2 \\ 73.1\end{array}\right\}$ 78.3 g
vegetable	
Fats:	
animal	$\left.\begin{array}{c}8.9 \\ 19.9\end{array}\right\}$ 28.8 g
vegetable	
Carbohydrates	494.9 g
Total calories	2 618
Calcium	0.48 g
Phosphorus	1.78 g
Iron	39.1 mg
Vitamins:	
carotene	1 048 IU
vitamin A	176 IU
vitamin B₁	2 mg
vitamin C	23 mg

[a] After Siddiqui (1955).

Hot weather not only increases the water intake but also increases the concentration of fluorine and leads to the ingestion of abnormal amounts of

TABLE 4

RELATION BETWEEN TEMPERATURE AND FLUORINE CONTENT OF WATER[a]

Place of sampling	Temperature at time of sampling	Fluorine content of water (ppm) [b]	
		Well No. 1 [c]	Well No. 2 [c]
Kamaguda	$\begin{cases} 90° \text{ F } (32.2° \text{ C}) \\ 115° \text{ F } (46.1° \text{ C}) \end{cases}$	9.2 9.6	11.0 11.8
Yedvelli.	$\begin{cases} 108° \text{ F } (42.2° \text{ C}) \\ 115° \text{ F } (46.1° \text{ C}) \end{cases}$	5.5 5.8	6.5 6.8
Yellareddyguda	115° F (46.1° C)	5.2	6.7

[a] After Siddiqui (1955).
[b] Estimated by thorium nitrate titration method.
[c] The two wells are situated barely 100 yards (90 m) apart.

sediment (Table 4). The protective action of calcium against intoxication by large doses of fluorine has been noted by Ranganathan (1941) in rats, by Majumdar & Ray (1946) in bulls, and by Pandit & Narayana Rao (1940) in monkeys. Pandit & Narayana Rao (*op. cit.*) and Wadhwani (1952) found that administration of vitamin C lessened the severity of fluorosis in monkeys. This question is discussed in Chapter 6, section 2.

Lower temperatures, ingestion of smaller quantities of water and better nutritional conditions are undoubtedly factors responsible for the absence of crippling disabilities in countries such as Great Britain and the USA. This is well borne out by the studies of Leone (1960) and Stevenson & Watson (1960). A series of well co-ordinated investigations by Leone (*op. cit.*) in the USA has supported the concept that no clinically significant, adverse, physiological or functional effects, with the exception of dental fluorosis, are to be anticipated in persons whose water supply contains up to 8 ppm fluorine. In a review of approximately 170 000 X-ray examinations of the spine and pelvis of patients, mostly residents of Texas and Oklahoma, osteosclerotic changes were noted in only 23 by Stevenson & Watson (*op. cit.*). Each of these patients lived his entire life in an area in which the water contained fluorine in concentrations ranging from 4 to 8 ppm. No osteosclerotic changes were evident in this study in persons whose drinking water contained less than 4 ppm fluorine.

The degree of disability is also related to physical strain. It is most pronounced in manual labourers. Subjects pursuing sedentary occupations, such as the local village administrative officials and the school teachers, have less severe symptoms although they utilize the same sources of water supply. Pain and stiffness are most severe in the joints used most by the individual—for example, the wrists, shoulders and neck in the females, who are mostly engaged in household work, and the lumbar spine and the joints of the lower limbs in the males working in the fields. Radiological changes in the skull and the cervical spine, so seldom observed by Roholm and others, are frequently encountered in India: a fact which could be ascribed to the same phenomenon of strain. Most of the Indian patients reported were manual labourers who were accustomed to carry heavy loads on their heads.

4. JAPANESE STUDIES ON WATER AND FOOD FLUORIDE AND GENERAL AND DENTAL HEALTH (G. Minoguchi)

Investigations in Areas with a High Natural Content of Water Fluoride

At present, in Japan, water with over 0.5 ppm fluorine is being supplied from 158 sources to 42 communities. The exact number of consumers is unknown, but it is assumed that it is not over 200 000, or about 0.2% of the entire population of Japan, and this number is rapidly decreasing thanks to the advancement of water services. Owing to the geographical features of the Japanese Islands, there are no long rivers and little use is made of underground streams. Most of the fluorine-containing drinking water is obtained from small, shallow wells from which two or three families usually draw their water.

The highest fluorine concentration known today is well water containing 21.0 ppm fluorine which has been used by two or three persons for drinking over a long period (Minoguchi, Okumara & Takenouchi, 1957). In the past, the highest fluorine content in piped water supplies was 2.7 ppm, but at present there is only one district where there is 1.3 ppm (Iizuka, 1964). This means that we are unable to locate many people who drink water of the same fluorine concentration under the same or similar climatic and other environmental conditions. Therefore it is difficult to determine the concentration of fluorine in drinking water that causes dental fluorosis or osteosclerosis.

Dean and his colleagues (Dean, 1946) investigated the threshold of dental fluorosis in the mid-western region of the USA, and set the borderline limit for the appearance of dental fluorosis in the vicinity of Chicago at 1.0-1.5 ppm fluoride. But in Japan, in an investigation around the Kyoto district, it seems that the corresponding borderline limit is 0.8-1.1 ppm, i.e., appreciably lower than that in the central USA.

From the investigations in the Japanese Islands, which are long and narrow to the north and south, it was found that in general the people in the southern districts (which are hotter than the northern ones) seem to be afflicted with dental fluorosis at a lower water-fluoride concentration. In the Kyoto district, dental fluorosis was found in places where the water contained about 0.8 ppm. Many cases of rather severe dental fluorosis can be seen in districts where the fluorine content is over 1.1 ppm. From investigations of scattered small areas with a high water fluorine content, Hirata (1950) has reported the following facts.

He examined 270 schoolchildren afflicted with dental fluorosis in areas where the drinking water contained 1.0-5.0 ppm fluorine, and then divided them into three groups, mild, moderate and severe, according to the degree of dental fluorosis, without reference to the concentration of fluorine in the drinking water. Blood analyses were made in these patients. No changes were determined in the mild group, but in the moderate group a decrease (less than 6000/mm³) in white blood corpuscles was seen in 21.8% and a decrease (less than 3000/mm³) in the neutrophil number was seen in 32.7%. In the severe group, 47.2% showed a decrease in white blood corpuscles and 41.2% a decrease in neutrophil number. However, such abnormalities were not found in pupils beyond the age of puberty. X-ray examinations were made of the bones of the arms and hands of 29 children who showed moderate or severe dental fluorosis and accompanying neutrocytopenia. Abnormal signs, such as hypertrophy of the cortex of bones, shadow increase in the ossification centre of carpal bones, and serrating changes in the metaphyseal cartilage of the radius and ulna, were demonstrated.

Thus, abnormal blood and X-ray findings were not observed in persons with mild dental fluorosis. However, the investigation was mainly conducted during 1947-49, when nourishment and other factors were less satisfactory in Japan.

The results of Hirata's investigation emphasize that effects on the whole body should be considered, and the addition of fluoride to water to prevent tooth decay carried out with great care.

A few years later, Hamamoto (1957) discovered that 58 persons out of the 517 residents in one district in Okayama Prefecture, where 0.1-13.0 ppm fluorine was found in the wells, had reduced mobility in several joints. He estimated the content of fluorine in the drinking water and examined roentgenograms of the bones, and reported that 21 out of 33 persons who had drunk water containing over 5.0 ppm fluorine for over 10 years showed osteosclerosis-like symptoms, as did 2 of 97 children under 10 years of age.

From the above observations, it appears that in the central district of Japan, in communities where water with a fluorine concentration of over 5.0 ppm was continuously used as drinking water for over 10 years, there was a risk of contracting osteosclerosis.

Investigation in Yamashina where Water Fluoridation was introduced in 1952

Caries-preventive fluoridation of the water supply in the Yamashina district in Kyoto was initiated on 1 February 1952 at a level of 0.6 ppm.

As a result of Dean's investigation in the mid-western region of the USA (Dean, *op. cit.*), most of the fluoridation in the world has been conducted at

TABLE 5

DENTAL CARIES IN PERMANENT TEETH OF CHILDREN IN YAMASHINA (FLUORIDATED) AND SHUGAKUIN (CONTROL), KYOTO, AS OBSERVED AT 1964 EXAMINATION

Age (years)	District	Number of children examined	Number of children affected by caries	Percentage of children affected by caries	Number of permanent teeth examined	Number of DMF[a] teeth	DMF[a] rate (%)	Average number of DMF[a] teeth per child
7	Fluoridated	79	19	24.1*	512	25	4.9**	0.32
	Control	152	58	38.2	1 077	127	11.8	0.84
8	Fluoridated	76	32	42.1**	816	56	6.8**	0.74
	Control	127	91	71.7	1 344	269	20.0	2.12
9	Fluoridated	60	36	60.0**	791	89	11.3**	1.48
	Control	129	107	83.2	1 745	294	16.8	2.28
10	Fluoridated	63	37	58.7*	1 029	109	10.6*	1.73
	Control	81	63	77.8	1 435	194	13.5	2.90
11	Fluoridated	61	47	77.0*	1 257	135	10.7**	2.21
	Control	96	86	89.8	1 976	301	15.2	3.14
12	Fluoridated	72	59	81.9	1 756	200	11.4**	2.78
	Control	100	91	91.0	2 405	417	17.3	4.17
13	Fluoridated	53	45	84.9*	1 396	177	12.7**	3.34
	Control	115	108	93.9	3 061	509	16.6	4.43
14	Fluoridated	70	57	82.6*	1 888	267	14.1**	3.81
	Control	145	137	93.8	4 005	775	19.4	5.35
15	Fluoridated	104	91	87.5	2 893	383	13.2**	3.68
	Control	164	157	95.7	4 574	1 060	23.2	6.46

[a] DMF = decayed, missing, filled.
* Significantly differing from control at $P < 0.05$ in χ^2 test.
** Significantly differing from control at $P < 0.01$ in χ^2 test.

a level of 1.0 ppm; however, according to the investigations in the central district of Japan, there appeared to be a danger of causing dental fluorosis and possibly an abnormal blood picture at a concentration of 1.0 ppm. Moreover, osteosclerosis had been found to occur at a concentration of about 5 ppm, which was lower than that at which the condition had been observed in the USA. From the results of the above-mentioned investigation, it had been assumed that, in general, 0.8 ppm was the borderline of dental fluorosis occurrence around the Kyoto district, so the optimum fluoride concentration was naturally thought to be 0.6 ppm or 0.7 ppm. The level of 0.6 ppm was adopted with the aim of keeping well within the safety margin as regards the occurrence of dental fluorosis.

The Yamashina filter plant, which serves water to about 15 000 people living in the east side of Kyoto City, was chosen as the test area and the addition of 0.6 ppm fluorine, as sodium fluoride, started on 1 February 1952. The Shugakuin district, located in the north-east of Kyoto City, was selected as the control area because it is similar to the Yamashina district in its environment and in the general occupations of the people. Since the experiment began, the oral cavity and entire body of schoolchildren from 6 to 15 years of age have been examined periodically in both districts.

In October 1964, 12 years and 8 months after the start of fluoridation, the prevalence of dental caries was as shown in Table 5. In spite of the fact that caries of the permanent teeth of all the children in Kyoto district increased remarkably during the period 1952-64 (owing, no doubt, to the regional dietary changes during the period), the area where fluoride was added to the water had a considerably lower caries incidence than the control area. Especially in 7- and 8-year-old children, the number of carious teeth was reduced, being below 40% of that seen in the control district.

A comparison of the reduction in decayed teeth is difficult because the cause of tooth decay is complicated; but, as is shown in Table 6, the results after 10 years of fluoridation in Yamashina at a level of 0.6 ppm are almost equal to those obtained in Grand Rapids, Mich., at 1.0 ppm and only a little inferior to those observed among children over ten years of age in Newburgh, N.Y.

I. Ohmori (personal communication) dissolved with $HClO_4$ the enamel of the lingual surfaces of anterior teeth of 12-year-old pupils in the Yamashina district, after 13 years of fluoride addition to the water, and estimated the fluorine content to be 0.16%. This amount is about four times greater than the usual content of fluoride in the dental enamel. If the increase of fluorine in the dental enamel reflects an increase of resistance to dental caries, then it can be said that the purpose of fluoridation has been fully attained.

We have not seen any cases of dental fluorosis or other unfavourable side-effects in the people of Yamashina.

TABLE 6

PERCENTAGE REDUCTION IN DMF TEETH AFTER 10 YEARS OF FLUORIDATION [a]

Age (years)	Grand Rapids, Mich. [b]		Newburgh, N.Y. [c]		Brantford, Ont. [d]	Yamashina	
	1954/ 1944	Grand Rapids/ Muskegon	1954/ 1944	Newburgh/ Kingston	1954/ 1944	1962/ 1952	Yamashina/ Shugakuin
6	75	58			60	—	—
7	63	39	39.6	57.9	67	17	61
8	57	42			54	38	44
9	50	38			46	8	16
10	52	37			41	– 12	43
11	54	35	22.3	53.0	39	– 35	36
12	52	37			48	– 65	34
13	48	37	—	47.9	42	– 89	45
14	38	38			36	—	36
15	36	28	—	—	37	—	29
16	26	21	—	40.9	—	—	—

[a] Percentage reduction in DMF teeth $= 100 - \dfrac{\text{No. of DMF teeth per child}}{\text{A or B}} \times 100$, where A = No. of teeth per child at start of fluoridation and B = No. of DMF teeth per child in control area.

[b] Data from Arnold et al. (1956).

[c] Data from Ast et al. (1956).

[d] Data from Hutton, Linscott & Williams (1956).

Factors with an Influence on Fluoride Intake in Japan

While fluoridation in Yamashina was conducted at the level of 0.6 ppm, the reduction of decay in this district as compared with the control district was similar to that obtained in Grand Rapids (1.0 ppm added F) as compared with its control, Muskegon, Mich. The present writer would like to comment on why there is this difference in the optimum fluoride concentration.

It has been thought that, the temperature being higher in Japan than in the mid-western region of the USA, the amount of water consumed by the people may be higher. However, there is no actual evidence of any difference in the amount of water consumed in the USA as compared with Japan. In the second place, the Japanese people consume a rather large amount of marine products, such as fish, as their main protein source. This may cause dental fluorosis at a comparatively lower water-fluoride concentration. Besides this, there might be some difference in racial susceptibility to fluoride or other unknown factors. However, it is most appropriate to think that the major variables are the difference in climate and the difference in the amount of fluoride in food.

Climatic variation and fluoride optimum

Maier (1950) discussed the relationship of optimum fluoride concentration to climate and to an increase and decrease in the consumption of water according to seasonal changes in temperature. Since then, Galagan (1953) has compared the results of his investigation of dental fluorosis in Arizona, a hot district, with Dean's investigation in the cooler mid-western region of the USA. This relationship has been demonstrated in a graph with two straight lines showing the Community Fluorosis Index (hereinafter abbreviated CFI) at different concentrations of fluoride in the drinking water according to the different mean annual temperatures—50°F (10°C) and 70°F (21°C)—(see Fig. 7).

FIG. 7
COMMUNITY FLUOROSIS INDEX AS A FUNCTION OF WATER-FLUORIDE
CONCENTRATION AND MEAN ANNUAL TEMPERATURE [a]

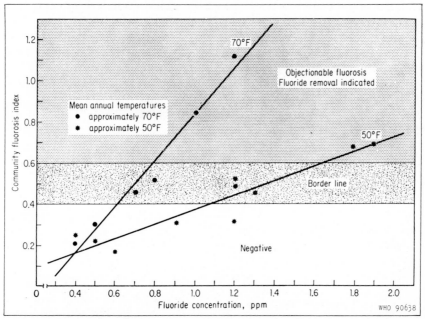

[a] Reproduced, with permission, from Maier (1963). Copyright McGraw-Hill Inc., 1963. The mean annual temperatures are based on the averages of the lowest and the highest temperature recorded in each 24-hour period.

Later, Galagan & Vermillion (1957) investigated the relationship of temperature to the consumption of drinking water of children in Antioch and Brentwood, Calif., and derived a formula for calculating the optimum fluoride concentration:

$$\text{optimum ppm } F = \frac{0.34}{E}, \text{ where } E = -0.038 + 0.0062\,t$$

(*E* is the estimated daily water intake for children through 10 years of age, in ounces per pound of body-weight; *t* is the annual mean of daily maximum temperatures in °F.)

From the formula Galagan calculated the optimum fluoride concentration of Tucson and Chandler in Arizona, which have a mean annual temperature of about 70°F, and found it to be 0.7 ppm.

However, the investigation of the Arizona district, which he had reported earlier, showed the CFI of Tucson (which has a 0.7 ppm fluoride water supply) to be 0.46 and that of Chandler (which has a 0.8 ppm fluoride water supply) to be 0.52. There is thus a risk of moderate dental fluorosis, and 0.7 ppm cannot be considered a safe amount for the people of Arizona. For this reason we think that the optimum fluoride concentration was calculated too high from Galagan's formula.

The difference between the two lines obtained in the Arizona/Mid-West comparison by Galagan (1953) should reflect a difference in physiological response due to the difference in temperature and the difference in the consumption of drinking water. Therefore, with these two trend lines as a basis, we have calculated the optimal fluoride concentration in drinking water as a function of CFI and annual mean temperature under the hypothesis that all the regression lines of the various annual mean temperatures (°F) that can be drawn between the 50°F and 70°F annual mean temperature lines pass through the point $x = 0.4$ and $y = 0.162$, which is the crossing-point of the 50°F and 70°F regression lines. The angle of the regression line expressed in t°F and $y = 0.021 + 0.353x$ is in proportion to the increase in annual mean temperature. This hypothesis may be considered to be established in this narrow space of 50°F and 70°F. As a result, we obtained the following formula:

$$\text{ppm F} = \frac{\text{CFI} - 0.162}{\tan (1.45585t - 53.3950)} + 0.4, \text{ where } t \text{ is the mean annual}$$

temperature in °F.

What this formula expresses is not only the difference in water consumption as related to seasonal temperature, but also the difference in water consumption due to differences in temperature between various geographical areas. For example, Kuno (1956) found that sweating conditions differ between people born and reared in areas with greatly different mean temperatures.

Our computation is illustrated in Fig. 8. The optimum fluoride concentration, the permissible fluoride concentration, and the limit fluoride concentration at each annual mean temperature are also illustrated in Table 7.

According to this formula, Tucson's optimum fluoride concentration would be 0.6 ppm; this cannot be said to be too high an optimum fluoride concentration in the light of the actual investigation results obtained in Tucson by Galagan (1953). The CFI at optimal fluoride concentration would be 0.374, calculated according to Galagan's formula with $y = 0.021 + 0.353x$. Dean (1946) stated that a fluorosis index below 0.4 is of little or no public health concern, while indices between 0.4 and 0.6 would be of borderline significance. Above an index of 0.6, the removal of excess fluoride is indicated; CFI = 0.6 thus gives the limit fluoride concentration.

FIG. 8

COMPARISON BETWEEN AMERICAN AND JAPANESE CITIES AS REGARDS OPTIMAL AND SUPRA-OPTIMAL WATER-FLUORIDE CONCENTRATIONS

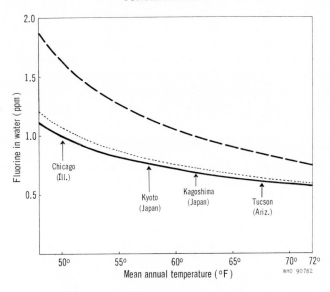

- – – – Positive borderline (limit) fluorine concentration.
- ·········· Negative borderline (permissible maximum) fluorine concentration.
- ——— Optimal fluorine concentration.

The optimum fluoride concentration of the Kyoto district, which has an annual mean temperature of 57.6°F (14.2°C), can be calculated as 0.762 ppm, the permissible maximum as 0.807 ppm, and the limit as 1.15 ppm. These figures are almost identical to the figures obtained from the investigation of the relation between dental fluorosis and the amount of fluoride in the water near the Kyoto district, which gave the borderline at 0.8 ppm and the limit at 1.1 ppm.

TABLE 7

RELATION BETWEEN FLUORINE CONCENTRATION AND MEAN ANNUAL TEMPERATURE

Mean annual temperature (°F)	Optimal fluorine concentration [a] (ppm)	Maximum permissible fluorine concentration [b] (ppm)	Limit fluorine concentration [c] (ppm)
50	1.000	1.074	1.640
51	0.956	1.024	1.548
52	0.916	0.979	1.465
53	0.880	0.940	1.393
54	0.849	0.905	1.329
55	0.821	0.873	1.270
56	0.796	0.844	1.218
57	0.773	0.819	1.170
58	0.752	0.795	1.127
59	0.733	0.774	1.088
60	0.714	0.752	1.048
61	0.698	0.734	1.015
62	0.682	0.716	0.983
63	0.667	0.700	0.953
64	0.654	0.685	0.925
65	0.640	0.670	0.897
66	0.629	0.657	0.874
67	0.618	0.644	0.850
68	0.600	0.632	0.828
69	0.597	0.621	0.807
70	0.587	0.610	0.786

[a] The CFI (community fluorosis index) of optimal fluorine concentration is 0.374, which is calculated in Galagan's trend-line formula, $y = 0.021 + 0.353x$, as $x = 1.0$ fitting (Galagan, 1953).

[b] The CFI of permissible maximum fluorine concentration is 0.4.

[c] The CFI of limit fluorine concentration is 0.6.

Fluoride content of Japanese food

In Japan sea-food and tea are among the staple foods and some particularly fluoride-rich kinds of both are consumed—e. g., shrimps: 30-50 ppm F (Iizuka, 1964; Minoguchi & Sato, 1964); seaweed: 6-14 ppm F (Iizuka and Minoguchi & Sato, *op. cit.*); and green tea: 336 ppm F, of which 66% is extracted in 3 minutes (Singer, Armstrong & Vatassery, 1967).

In order to calculate the amount of fluoride ingested from food daily by the Japanese, Sato, Yoshitake & Nakanishi (1965) determined the fluoride content of 127 types of food and applied this to the annual average consumption of food throughout Japan according to the 1960 National Nutrition Investigation (results of each food group and chart of nutrition intake) carried out by the Nutrition Section, Public Health Bureau, Welfare Ministry.

As a result, it was calculated that 1.38 mg of fluorine was ingested from food. The largest amounts were from marine products (0.39 mg), rice (0.33 mg), and green tea (0.25 mg) (Minoguchi & Sato, *op. cit.*). These figures are the average for the Japanese nation as a whole and in general correspond to the food intake of children from 13 to 15 years old.

In an investigation of the ordinary food of hospitalized patients in Kyoto University Hospital over one year (April 1963 to March 1964), the figure obtained was lower than the one above, registering 1.2 mg (Sato et al., *op. cit.*). In other investigations, Samejima (1959) has calculated it as 1.6-2.7 mg, Saito (1960) as 2.1-3.5 mg and Iizuka et al. (1963) as 0.48-2.64 mg. In contrast, McClure has reported the amount of fluorine ingested in the USA by children from 10 to 12 years of age as 0.056-0.56 mg (McClure, 1943) and by adults as 0.41-0.91 mg (McClure et al., 1945). Armstrong & Knowlton (1942) reported that the food in Minnesota Hospital contained 0.27-0.32 mg; Adamson et al. (cited by Elliott & Smith, 1960), reporting on Newfoundland residents who were assumed to take 3.1 oz (88 g) of codfish and 6 cups of black tea daily, obtained the figure of 2.74 mg daily, while Ham & Smith (1954), reporting on three women in Toronto, obtained 0.43-0.73 mg.

From all the reports except that of Adamson and co-workers, it appears that the Japanese ingest from 1.0 to 2.0 mg more fluorine daily from food than the Canadians or Americans.

However, these figures do not express the fluorine intake of infants and children from 6 months to 7 years of age—the period during which the main permanent tooth-crowns are being formed and dental fluorosis of the permanent teeth is caused.

Moreover, most of the fluorine in marine products exists in a very stable form bound to calcium phosphate, which is poorly soluble in water. Not all the fluorine can be considered to exert the same physiological action that fluorine dissolved in water ordinarily would.

It can, however, be assumed that Japanese children obtain more fluorine from food than American children of the same age, though the quantity has not been calculated exactly. If this food-borne fluorine shows a similar physiological effect to the water-borne fluorine, then under the same climatic conditions the fluoride concentration in drinking water which causes dental fluorosis would naturally be lower in Japan than in the USA.

Food Fluoride, Climatic Temperature and Dental Fluorosis

In fact, as stated earlier, the borderline of fluoride concentration in drinking water that was derived from actual investigation of dental fluorosis around Kyoto District, Japan, is 0.8 ppm, and the limit 1.1 ppm. Moreover, when the above formula derived from investigations in the USA is applied to the Kyoto vicinity, which has an annual mean temperature of 57.6°F (14.2°C), the borderline of fluoride concentration in drinking water is 0.807 ppm and the limit is 1.15 ppm. The latter figures are applicable to the Americans, whose fluorine intake from food is less than that of the Japanese. However, the difference is only 0.07 ppm at the negative borderline and 0.05 ppm at the limit, which can actually be considered zero.

Although the Japanese are thought to ingest a large quantity of food-borne fluorides, the fact that this does not appear as a difference in the sensitivity to fluorine in drinking water would lead to the assumption that a daily intake of food-borne fluorine corresponding to 1.0-2.0 mg in adults does not have any physiological effect on dental fluorosis.

What then would the optimum fluoride concentration be in the southern, subtropical zone of Japan, where the temperature is much higher than in the temperate zone of the country?

The limits of application of Galagan's formula are 50°F to 70°F (10-21°C) mean annual temperature. In districts where the annual mean temperature is below 50°F, the formula can hardly be applied because artificial methods of heating and clothing will prevent extremely low temperatures of the outside world from affecting the people directly (McPhail & Zacherl, 1965). When the three lines, the optimum fluoride concentration, the permissible concentration and limit concentration (according to appearance of dental fluorosis) are drawn from this formula at each temperature, the higher the annual mean temperature, the narrower the band width of the lines. If the interval between the optimum fluoride concentration and the limit fluoride concentration is considered the margin of safety, this interval will appear in the mid-western region of the USA, where the annual mean temperature is 50°F, as 0.64 ppm; in a district where the mean temperature is 60°F it would be 0.335 ppm, and in a district where it is 70°F it would be 0.199 ppm. That is, with increasing mean temperature, the margin of safety becomes progressively narrower, at 70°F being one-third of that at 50°F. If this computation were to be applied to a district of over 70°F, this margin would be 0.13 ppm at 75°F (24°C) and 0.10 ppm at 80°F (27°C), which indicates that it would be difficult to prevent the occurrence of dental fluorosis with fluoridation in a high temperature zone.

The relationship between the appearance of dental fluorosis and the nutrition of the residents in different districts was investigated and reported on by Massler & Schour (1952). In a low-nutrition district, dental fluorosis occured at a lower fluoride concentration.

At present, in the tropical areas of the world, the inhabitants cannot be said to be receiving the same adequate nutrition as the people in North American and European countries. Therefore, in tropical areas the nutritional state of the inhabitants, besides the climatic conditions, contributes to the risk of fluorosis at a lower fluoride concentration than can normally be expected.

In addition to temperature differences, there is a physiological difference in people who are born and reared in districts of high temperature, in that, as was reported by Kuno (1956), their sweating condition differs.

When we consider the precision that we can guarantee at present in the apparatus for supplying fluoride to waterworks, and—even more important—the individual variation in water consumption, the possibility of severe dental fluorosis occurring would be great in adding fluorine to drinking water in regions where the annual mean temperature is over 70°F, and in fact we think it would probably be impossible to avoid occurrence of the condition.

5. HEALTH STUDIES IN AREAS OF THE USA
WITH CONTROLLED WATER FLUORIDATION (E. R. Schlesinger)

Extent of Consumption of Fluoridated Water

The use of controlled fluoridation of public water supplies, at about 1 ppm fluoride, has grown steadily in the USA. By the end of 1967, there were 3827 communities, with a total population of nearly 72 million, which were being served by fluoridated water in the USA and Puerto Rico (US Department of Health, Education, and Welfare, 1968). In addition, some 10 million persons resided in communities in which the water supply contained about an optimal level of fluoride at its source. In recent actions, three populous states—Connecticut, Illinois, and Minnesota—have enacted legislation requiring fluoridation of municipal water supplies.

Besides those persons in the USA who have been receiving water with an optimal fluoride level at its source, more than 17 million persons have been drinking fluoridated water for at least 12 years. Despite this extensive experience with entire population groups—including pregnant women, children throughout their growing period, elderly persons, and persons with all types of long-term illnesses—there have been no well-documented reports of any adverse systemic effects or of symptoms of any kind that could be attributed to fluoridated water, although the medical profession and the general public in the communities concerned were fully apprised of the advent of fluoridation.

On the other hand, it has been a common experience for health officers to receive many complaints from local citizens about digestive disturbances and other disabilities caused by fluoridated water, even in advance of the actual date of initiation of water fluoridation (Hilleboe, 1956).

Controlled Long-term Study of Children (Newburgh-Kingston Study)

In the early 1940s, when water fluoridation was first being considered as a community measure for the prevention of dental caries, there was no body of practical experience to call upon. It is true that water with a fluoride level several times higher than that used in controlled fluoridation had been consumed over the lifetime of a sizable population group without any discernible adverse effects other than mottling of the teeth, and there was no scientific basis for thinking that the fluoride introduced into a community water supply differed in any way, including its physiological effects, from the same level of fluoride leached from the soil and rocks. Nevertheless, it appeared desirable to conduct a long-term controlled study of the health and the growth and development of two groups of children from infancy on, the only known variable in the two groups being the consumption of fluoridated water by the study group. This was the objective of the medical aspects of the Newburgh-Kingston (New York State) caries-fluorine study which was conducted for a period of ten years starting in 1944 (Schlesinger et al., 1956). The timing of these carefully controlled observations was particularly important, since the public and professional demand for fluoridation might preclude the possibility of long-term studies at a subsequent time.

The cities of Newburgh and Kingston, located about 30 miles (50 km) apart on the west bank of the Hudson River, were selected because of their comparability in size and in their demographic, social and economic characteristics. The two cities had similar upland reservoir water supplies, both of which were deficient in fluoride. The water supply of Newburgh, the study city, was adjusted to a fluoride level of 1.0-1.2 ppm, whereas the fluoride level of the Kingston water supply was allowed to remain at 0.05 ppm.

Since the annual medical examinations, the basic feature of the study, required the voluntary co-operation of the selected families over a period of ten years, a strict random sampling procedure was precluded. The selection of children was based, therefore, on the apparent residential stability of the families, and every effort was directed towards obtaining a broad scattering from all parts of each city, in proportion to population, and comparability of the two groups in respect of social and economic circumstances. With regard to race, for example, 4.6% of the Newburgh study group were Negro, in comparison with 3.6% in the total population of the city at the time; a similar relationship existed in Kingston.

A total of 817 children were enrolled in the Newburgh study group and 711 children in the Kingston control group. Most were enrolled at the start of the study, though small numbers of infants were added each year during the first three years of the study to ensure having in the study group some children whose mothers had been exposed to fluoridated water throughout pregnancy. Of the total Newburgh group, 500, or 61.2%, reported for their final examinations at the end of the study; 405, or 56.9%, of the Kingston group participated in the final round of examinations.

A detailed medical history was obtained by a paediatrician on the first visit to the research clinic, with interval information being added on a cumulative history form on subsequent visits. A physical examination was performed by the paediatrician on each visit, special attention being paid to the status of the skin and mucous membranes, the hair, and the thyroid gland. Physical measurements, including weight, height, and circumference of chest, were also made on each visit.

Laboratory studies were performed on both the Newburgh and Kingston children on the initial and final research clinic visits and on the Newburgh children on every third visit during the course of the study. These laboratory studies consisted of a routine urine analysis (including a microscopic examination of the urinary sediment), a haemoglobin determination, and total leucocyte and erythrocyte counts, with a differential leucocyte count on children whose total leucocyte count appeared to be outside normal limits.

On the roentgenograms of the right wrist and both knees, which were taken on each visit to the research clinic, special attention was paid to the rate of skeletal maturation and to density of the bone. On the final visit, a lateral roentgenogram of the lumbar spine was also taken, since the lumbar spine is among the earliest sites in the skeletal system to show evidence of osteosclerosis from exposure to excessive amounts of fluoride. The X-ray films were reviewed by an outstanding paediatric roentgenologist without reference to the clinical background or city of residence of the children.

Special ophthalmological and otological examinations were performed on groups of 25 children each year in Newburgh. The ophthalmological examinations included a test of visual acuity using the Snellen chart, plotting of the visual fields, measurement of the size of the blind spot, and slit-lamp examination of the cornea and lens. Otological examination encompassed pure-tone audiometry and a visual examination of the ear, nares and nasopharynx.

The findings from these examinations disclosed no differences of medical significance between the study and control groups that could even remotely be ascribed to fluoride. A threefold higher rate of tonsilectomies observed among the Newburgh children at the start of the study and on subsequent examination was attributable to differences in medical practice between the two cities. Comparable age-sex groups in the two cities followed closely similar patterns in height and weight.

Children with potentially significant health conditions were referred to their family physicians; in Newburgh, 4.0%, and in Kingston, 4.9% were so referred—a total of 39 children in the two cities. Obesity and urinary, blood and roentgenographic findings were the usual reasons for referral in both cities.

Estimation of bone age by two independent observers disclosed no significant differences in the level of skeletal maturation between comparable age-sex groups in the two cities. The second observer deduced the bone age from the X-rays of the wrist and knees, the only information given being the sex of the child under study.

All findings, whether or not considered to be of pathological significance or in any way related to the use of fluoridated water, were recorded. In certain of the findings, such as sclerotic epiphyseal ossification centres and the presence of sesamoid bones in roentgenograms of the hand and wrist, a somewhat higher proportion was found in one city, whereas in other findings, such as benign fibrous cortical defects in the roentgenograms of the knees, a greater proportion was observed in the other city.

No evidence of increased bone density could be discerned on roentgenographic examination. The absence of increased bone density in the lumbar spine after ten years of exposure to fluoridated water added weight to the negative observations of the wrist and knee on earlier examinations.

The haemoglobin level showed no significant differences between New-burgh and Kingston children. The mean for the two cities was very close, although a few more children in Newburgh had haemoglobin levels below 12.9 g per 100 ml. Similarly, a slightly higher proportion of children in Newburgh were found to have total erythrocyte counts below 4 400 000 per ml, but the difference between the two groups was found to be insignificant. The total leucocyte counts were essentially the same in the two cities, with a slightly higher proportion of children in Kingston showing a count over 10 000 per ml. Routine urine analysis also showed no significant differences between the findings in the two cities.

The findings on both the ophthalmological and the otological examinations in the Newburgh children fell well within the limits expected of any normal group of children of the age studied.

The quantitative excretion of formed elements in the urine in groups of 12-year-old boys in Newburgh and Kingston was the subject of a special study (Schlesinger, Overton & Chase, 1956) carried out because fluoride in highly toxic quantities had been reported to produce pathological changes in the kidneys of experimental animals. The Addis technique was used to detect any possible minimal irritative effect on the kidneys of the prolonged use of fluoridated water. These groups of normally active boys in the two cities failed to show any significant differences in their quantitative excretion of albumin, red blood cells, and casts.

The stillbirth and the maternal and infant mortality rates in Newburgh and Kingston were compared for the five-year period prior to the start of fluoridation and during the ten years of the study. The long-term downward trends were similar in the two cities and no change could be detected in the trend in Newburgh after fluoridation. The death rates from cancer and cardiovascular diseases were also examined in the two cities. These rates did not change, relative to each other, prior to or during the period of the study.

Statements on Adverse Systemic Effects from Fluoridated Water

Publications regarding adverse systemic effects from fluoridated water have often drawn analogies with the acute effects of toxic doses of fluorides or with the chronic effects of high levels of fluoride, particularly in hot climates. The latter observations have been further complicated by the effects of chronic malnutrition and by a high intake of dietary fluoride other than from drinking water. In citing the actual or stated systemic effects of high fluoride intake, the all-important factor of dosage has often been neglected. Many substances essential to life are toxic at excessively high levels, and this applies to oxygen and even to water itself.

The statements of two observers on adverse systemic effects, made in the USA, deserve specific mention. The first of these (Rapaport, 1959) suggests that Down's syndrome (mongolism) occurs more frequently in communities in which the water supplies contain more than 1 ppm fluoride than in communities with lower levels of fluoride. The numerator of the incidence rates of Down's syndrome presented was the number of cases reported on birth and death certificates, plus the number of children institutionalized for the condition. The denominator was the number of infants born to mothers who resided during their pregnancies in the years and in the communities under study. Based on a total of 48 cases reported, there was an incidence rate of 71.2 cases per 100 000 in the higher-fluoride communities, in comparison with a rate of 34.2 per 100 000, based on 67 cases, in communities with 0.2 ppm fluoride or less. The inadequacy of the case-finding method used is apparent from these figures. Down's syndrome has been found by other investigators to occur most often in the range of one per 600-700 births. In Rapaport's report, Down's syndrome is said to have occurred in only one per 1400 births in the higher-fluoride communities and in one per 2900 births in low-fluoride areas.

A well-conducted study in Great Britain (Berry, 1958, 1962) overcomes these deficiencies in case-finding. In this study, information was sought not only from institutions and vital records, but also from records of health officers which embraced cases detected at school entrance and in occupational centres, and from the personal knowledge of health visitors (public health nurses) and others concerned with the welfare of children with Down's syndrome. The over-all incidence of Down's syndrome was found to be one per 668 births, with insignificant variations in the rates in the communities served by water supplies containing different levels of fluoride.

Another widely cited publication is that describing allergic reactions to test doses of 15 mg sodium fluoride (Waldbott, 1963). These reactions are presented in a brief note and tabulation in an otherwise extensive review of acute fluoride intoxication. Of a selected group of 123 allergic patients tested, five developed a wide variety of symptoms and signs which developed five minutes to three hours after the test dose and lasted from twelve hours to ten days. Of the 21 symptoms and signs reported, only six occurred in more than one patient, and these were mainly of a nondescript nature, such as headache, nausea, vomiting, and epigastric pain. Physical findings such as muscular fibrillations, "cystitis", "spastic colitis", and facial oedema were each found in not more than one patient.

The absence of any suggestion of a clinical syndrome leads to the conclusion that a variety of unrelated conditions were presented as cases of so-called "fluoride intolerance". This was also the situation in an earlier publication (Waldbott, 1962), in which cases are reported from the literature as instances of fluorosis when, in reality, they represent unrelated clinical conditions among persons with vague or undocumented histories of excessive fluoride ingestion. These cases are then used as the basis for asserting that all these conditions are, therefore, manifestations of systemic fluorosis. The several original case reports in the paper were not documented by any independent observer. No cases of so-called "fluoride intolerance" ascribed to small doses of fluoride have been reported by other observers. In summary, there have been no adequately documented reports of any adverse systemic effects from fluoride ingestion even at levels several times greater than those used in water supplies for the prevention of dental caries.

6. INDUSTRIAL FLUORIDE HAZARDS (A. E. Martin)*

Industries emitting Fluorides

Fluorine is a ubiquitous element and traces of fluorides derived mainly from the combustion of coal and other fuels are to be found in all urban atmospheres. Localized areas of heavier pollution occur in various parts of the world as a result of certain specific industrial processes and may have a serious effect on agriculture.

The major sources of fluorine compounds in the atmosphere are well-known and in 1961 it was estimated that some 25 000 tons expressed as fluorine were emitted annually in England and Wales. Twelve thousand tons were derived from the industrial use of fluorspar (of which 10 000 were emitted during the manufacture of steel), 5000 tons from the industrial and domestic use of coal, 4500 tons from the heavy clay industry, 600 tons from the treatment of iron ores, 500 tons from the cement industry, and 150 tons from the pottery industry. Emissions from blast furnaces, from the chemical industry and from the manufacture of hydrofluoric acid, fertilizers, phosphorus and zinc production were negligible.

Such figures are of limited value for it is the localized areas of high pollution which may constitute the hazard. Moreover, the fumes may be discharged from tall chimneys giving satisfactory dispersal or alternatively they may be discharged at a low level with resulting heavy ground pollution. Heavy particulate matter will be deposited in the immediate vicinity of the emission whereas aerosol particles and gases will be dispersed over a wide area and a proportion will diffuse upwards and not reach ground level.

It is apparent that hazards may exist either from the deposition of fluoride particles on the ground and on herbage, or from the presence of fluorides in the atmosphere, where they may be inhaled by animals or man. Crops may be damaged and plant growth restricted by either, but it is the physical contamination of herbage which gives rise to the principal hazard, animal fluorosis.

* The author's thanks are due to the British Ministries of Agriculture, Fisheries and Food, Housing and Local Government, and Technology, to the Director of the Medical Research Council's Air Pollution Research Unit, and to the Warwickshire Clean Air Council for information contained in this section. He wishes also to acknowledge assistance received from Mr F. E. Ireland, Chief Alkali Inspector; Dr Ruth Allcroft of the Veterinary Laboratories, Weybridge; Dr B. T. Commins of the Air Pollution Research Unit; Dr D. Gall of the Warren Spring Laboratory; and Mr W. M. Lewis, City Analyst of Coventry.

Measurement of Fluorides

The amounts of fluoride deposited may be measured by the standard deposit gauge, the material collected being analysed and the results expressed either as total fluoride or subdivided into soluble and insoluble fluorides. This method is frequently used for monitoring emissions from individual industrial establishments.

Deposits in a rural area of England (Essex) have been found to average 0.69 g of soluble fluoride per 100 square metres per month, whereas in London values ranging from 0.58 to 2.6 g per 100 m² have been obtained, the excess over rural areas presumably being largely due to the combustion of coal. Measurements by local authorities at sites in Warwickshire have varied from 0.5 to 1.08 g per 100 square metres, the latter figure being recorded downwind from an aluminium works. In contrast to these readings, a monthly average of 4.5 g per 100 m² was measured near the centre of Rotherham at a distance of approximately 1½ miles (2.5 km) from a steel-works at that time using fluorspar in open-hearth furnaces, and an average of 3.64 per 100 m² was obtained at a site near the centre of the pottery industry in Stoke-on-Trent.

Deposit gauge readings are, however, of limited value for they are essentially an index of local pollution representative only of a small area round the gauge. The alternative method of measuring fluoride emissions is to use a volumetric apparatus to measure the gaseous and particulate matter in the atmosphere. Samples taken in the centre of London indicate a normal winter pollution of particulate matter of 0.05-0.09 μg per cubic metre expressed as fluorine. The concentration of gaseous fluorides is less than 0.05 μg per m³ so that the total fluoride content of the normal London air would be of the order of 0.1-0.15 μg per m³. During a period of exceptionally heavy pollution associated with severe fog, the amount of particulate fluoride rose to 0.8 μg per m³. In contrast, measurements of total particulate and gaseous fluoride over the winter months yielded an average of 0.7 μg per m³ at Rotherham and 1.9 μg per m³ at Stoke-on-Trent.

Similar, and in some cases rather higher, atmospheric concentrations have been reported from urban and rural areas of the USA (Cholak, 1960).

The Industrial Hazard in Man

In spite of continual vigilance by industrial health authorities, few cases of human industrial fluorosis have been identified and incidents have mostly been of a relatively trivial character. An exception was in the Danish cryolite industry where cases were identified and investigated by Roholm (1937). His descriptions still provide the classical account of severe human fluorosis due to the inhalation of fluoride dusts.

The cryolite industry

The mineral cryolite contains some 50% of fluorine and at the time of Roholm's investigations, many workers had been exposed to very heavy concentrations of the dust for long periods. Typical atmospheric dust concentrations were 30-40 mg per m^3 and in two enclosed areas of the works concentrations of up to more than 9000 mg per m^3 were found. Many of the exposed workers complained of acute gastric symptoms or shortness of breath, but it was difficult to say how far these might have been toxic symptoms due to cryolite, and how far they might have been a physical effect of the very heavy dust concentrations. Most of these symptoms disappeared quickly on leaving work. The most typical symptoms of fluorosis were complaints related to skeletal and muscular systems and 35% of the workers complained of pains, stiffness or rheumatic attacks. On radiological examination, 84% of exposed workers were found to exhibit evidence of osteosclerosis, the severity being related to both the duration of exposure and the concentration of dust inhaled. Faint or moderate pulmonary fibrosis was found in half the workers.

Roholm also traced previous workers in the industry. Although they were known to have been exposed to concentrations of dust at least as heavy as or heavier than workers currently employed in the industry, the number and severity of the cases of osteosclerosis was proportionately much lower. This was considered by Roholm to be a clear indication of the reversibility of the condition, a hypothesis confirmed by Likins, McClure & Steere (1956) who observed at Bartlett, Texas, that when a population ceased to be exposed to a high fluoride intake, fluoride excretion rates continued at a high level for a considerable time. A higher incidence of spondylitis deformans was found in workers who had left the industry. Cases of pulmonary fibrosis did not show any evidence of having deteriorated since leaving.

Roholm estimated that the workers engaged in the industry probably absorbed between 0.2 and 1 mg per kilogram of body-weight per day, the former figure being the more likely. The urinary excretion of two workmen, both with osteosclerosis and much exposed to dust, was 2.45 and 2.09 mg fluorine per day, as compared with two normal subjects whose daily excretion was 0.22 and 0.1 mg, respectively.

British experience : the Fort William incident

In Great Britain, apart from one incident, only occasional cases of human industrial fluorosis have been described and most of these have been asymptomatic. Thus Bridge (1941) described radiological changes in the workers at a factory using hydrogen fluoride. Wilkie (1940) similarly found radiological osteosclerosis in two workers employed in the manufacture of hydrogen and aluminium fluorides, and Bowler et al. (1947) found a case in an employee in a magnesium factory. Murray & Wilson (1946) described an episode where a family living adjacent to ironstone workings where calcining took place were exposed to heavy fumes over a period of years. Members of this family were found to be excreting from 1.6 to 4.6 ppm fluorine in the urine. They complained of muscular and joint pains, which they were convinced were due to the fumes, but radiological examination revealed no evidence of osteosclerosis.

The most notable incident in Great Britain occurred in an aluminium factory near Fort William, Scotland, and was investigated by the Medical Research Council during the years 1945-48 (Agate et al., 1949). Concentrations of fluorides in the factory atmosphere ranged from 0.14 to 3.13 mg per m^3 in the furnace room, while outside they varied from 0.22 mg at a distance of 200 yards (180 m) to 0.04 mg in the centre of Fort William, 1 mile (1.6 km) away.

None of the factory workers had complained of any symptoms and the incidence of aches and pains in the furnace-room workers was no greater than in other workers in the factory or in local residents. There was a suggestion that the furnace-room workers had rather more frequent digestive disorders and coughs, and the investigators themselves noted the irritating nature of the furnace-room fumes. No dyspnoea on exertion was found and no increased liability to suffer from fractures. There were no physical signs of skeletal fluorosis, but one furnace-room worker was suffering from anky-losing spondylitis which was thought by the investigators to be unconnected with fluorides. Among the other factory workers there was one case of chronic pulmonary fibrosis, and one of emphysema with a rigid barrel-shaped chest. Radiological examination revealed signs of osteosclerosis in 48 of the 189 furnace-room workers who were radiographed, the proportion of cases increasing with the time of exposure. Radiological signs included lipping of the dorsal and lumbar spines with beak-like exostoses, a granular, amorphous, and somewhat dense appearance of the pelvis, often with short bony exostoses, and plaques of dense bone on the tibia and fibula.

Workers in the factory showed an increased urinary excretion of fluoride, the amount being closely related to the severity of exposure; the average excretion of 65 heavily exposed workers in the furnace room was 9.03 mg per day. Outside the factory no clinical signs or symptoms among local residents were found and the incidence of mottled teeth in children in the vicinity did not differ appreciably from that in unaffected areas.

Other studies on industrial fluorosis

Other incidents resulting in human industrial fluorosis have been noted by Hodge & Smith (1965). A recent investigation is that of Derry-berry, Bartholomew & Fleming (1963) in an American phosphate fertilizer factory in which a group of 74 workers exposed to relatively high fluoride concentrations was compared with a matched control group of unexposed workers. In this study the fluoride exposure of the individual workers was estimated by repeated examinations of urine samples taken at the end of the night shift, and the percentage of specimens containing 4 mg per litre or more was calculated as an index of exposure for each person.

No disability attributable to fluoride was found in any of the workers. Minimal or questionable degrees of increased bone density were found radiologically in 23% of exposed employees, but in no case were the bone changes sufficient for them to have been recognizable as increased osseous radioopacity in routine radiological practice. No increase of abnormal findings relating to gastrointestinal, cardiovascular, metabolic or haemotological conditions was observed in the exposed group. Respiratory conditions, however, were more frequent, though these might have been due to the irritating properties of the acid gases. An apparent increase in albuminuria in the exposed group was found by Derryberry to be significant only at the 10% level of probability.

Miller (1955) quotes a report by Babayants from a super-phosphate factory with no purifying or recovery plant in the USSR. In a series of 56 tests during 1938-39, an average concentration of 0.98 mg per m³, with a maximum concentration of 18.4 mg, was recorded at a distance of 1000 metres from the factory. In a further series of 61 tests on the leeward side of the factory after the introduction of safeguards, the average concentration was found to be 0.050 mg per m³ at the same distance.

The Fluoride Intake of the Population

Suggestions have occasionally been made that where water is fluoridated at 1 ppm, the additional fluoride intake of the population in areas where there is industrial pollution might create a hazard. In most circumstances such fears may easily be discounted. The average man engaged on moderately strenuous work is known to inhale approximately 20 cubic metres of air per day. If, therefore, the fluoride pollution of the air of any place is known, it is a simple matter to calculate as an upper limit the maximum fluoride uptake on the assumption that all the fluorides inhaled are retained.

Using this method it was found that in Central London the fluoride intake of the average man would be of the order of 0.003 mg per day normally and 0.03 mg during a day of thick fog with exceptionally heavy pollution. Stoke-on-Trent and Rotherham have been among the most heavily polluted areas of the country. In the former, where the pollution was a generalized one covering the entire city and its environs, the intake of the average man would be of the order of 0.04 mg per day, and in Rotherham, where the pollution was more localized, the intake would be 0.01-0.02 mg. It is evident, therefore, that with these levels of pollution, even when allowance is made for the increased air intake of a workman engaged in a very strenuous occupation, the amount of fluoride absorbed from the atmosphere would be but a fraction of that shown by McClure (1949) and Longwell (1957) to be contained in his diet. By contrast, however, Lindberg (1964) has reported atmospheric fluoride concentrations of from 0.098 to 0.485 mg per m^3 near a super-phosphate plant in the USSR. This suggests maximum possible adult intakes of from 1.9 mg to 9.7 mg and high levels of fluoride intake were, in fact, confirmed by the finding of dental fluorosis and a low incidence of dental caries in schoolchildren in that area. Somewhat earlier, in an investigation of two USSR aluminium plants, Sadilova (1957) reported average atmospheric fluoride concentrations of 0.01-0.13 mg per m^3 in the ambient air in the vicinity of the plants, with maximum concentrations of 0.89 mg per m^3 at one plant and 0.61 at the other. An investigation of 2483 children in the vicinity was reported by this author also to have revealed increased dental mottling and diminution in the incidence of dental caries.

Other possible hazards are more remote. It has been shown that the increase in the fluoride content of the milk from cows suffering from fluorosis is negligible. There is no significant accumulation in the soft tissues and the prolonged boiling of bones from such animals has shown that there is no hazard in the making of soups and stews (Allcroft, 1956).

No appreciable increase occurs in the fluoride content of vegetables grown on soils rich in fluorides, and any hazard if it exists would arise from surface contamination of vegetables. From our knowledge of the amounts of fluoride deposited in affected areas of the United Kingdom, of the amounts of vegetables consumed by man, and from the practice of washing vegetables and discarding the outer and older leaves, it is apparent that any additional intake in the diet would also be negligible.

The relative unimportance of atmospheric fluorides as a human hazard has also been demonstrated in a recent study by Call and his colleagues (1965) of material from 127 autopsies in the State of Utah, where air pollution from industry was known to give rise to atmospheric fluoride concentrations of up to 0.8 μg per m^3, with a mean annual value of 0.24 μg.

Animal Fluorosis

It was the effects on animals in polluted areas which first drew attention to the importance of industrial fluorosis, and many reports have been published over the past 50 years. In the USA, the problem has been reviewed by Phillips et al. (1960) and, in Great Britain, a detailed investigation of the problem over an 8-year period has recently been completed (Burns & Allcroft, 1964; Allcroft, Burns & Herbert, 1965).

Cattle are the animals principally affected in Britain. As in man, dental lesions are the most sensitive clinical sign, but skeletal abnormalities are

the most characteristic feature in severe cases and lameness is frequently the
first sign noted by the farmer. An important cause of lameness in British
cases is fracture of the pedal bone. Debility and a loss of milk production
are a frequent result of the lameness, but in only a small number of cases
are dental lesions severe enough to cause difficulty in grazing and mastication.

Part of the British investigation was a survey of herds in industrial areas
to establish the distribution of animal fluorosis in England and Wales.
Fluorosis severe enough to cause economic loss was found on 170 farms in
17 different areas. Of these, 9 farms were so badly affected that cattle were
no longer kept, 61 were classified as severely and 100 as slightly affected.
In addition, a considerable number of farms were found to have cattle showing only dental lesions.

Control Measures and their Effectiveness

Standard methods for controlling fumes and arresting particulate emissions have done much to eliminate fluorine hazards in industry, and in the
United Kingdom it is now many years since a case of industrial fluorosis
occurred in a factory employee. Changing methods in industry have also
eliminated many of the sources of pollution. Thus, the sintering of iron
ores is replacing the older calcining process and a high proportion of the
fluoride is retained in the final sinter. In the pottery industry the use of
defluoridated Cornish stone and of higher chimneys is reducing pollution.
Emissions from the brick industry are still substantial and at present no
satisfactory method has been discovered for removing fluorides from the
fumes.

The major hazard is an agricultural one. The occasional farmer in a
heavily polluted area has had to give up animal husbandry and confine himself to arable farming; other farmers use flying herds in which cows are
brought to the farm as adults and stay for only a few lactations.

An important part of the British investigation was to examine the possibility of alleviating the effects of fluorosis in a self-contained dairy herd
in a polluted area of the pottery industry in Stoke-on-Trent. The results
showed that the feeding of mineral supplements, such as aluminium sulfate,
with or without additional calcium and phosphorus compounds, delayed
the effects of excessive fluorine intake but did not prevent them sufficiently
to be of practical value, and that good farming practices—in particular,
good pasture management—provided the best means of mitigating the ill-
effects.

7. SUMMARY (A. E. Martin)

By their wide distribution in nature, their inevitable presence in man's
food and drink and their consequent presence in the tissues of the human

body, fluorides form a natural part of man's environment, yet when present in excess they are known to be harmful. Studies of the geographical distribution of dental mottling in the USA were begun during the early decades of the century and the identification of fluorides in water supplies in 1931 led to a comprehensive survey designed, in the first place, to find the threshold limit for the avoidance of dental fluorosis and, later, to ascertain the concentration in a water supply necessary for optimum dental protection. When the artificial fluoridation of water was first considered, this survey provided a useful starting-point for a programme of specific epidemiological and experimental studies which, over the past three decades, has yielded a mass of data confirming the safety of fluoridation. This has been supplemented by independent studies from other countries which have provided further supplementary material for use in defining the upper limits of a safe fluoride intake. The results have shown that for the climatic, nutritional and environmental conditions under which the surveys have been carried out, a level of approximately 1 ppm fluoride in temperate climates has no harmful effects on the community. The margin of safety is such that it will cover any individual variation of intake to be found in such areas.

High levels of fluoride in drinking waters are found in some hot countries, such as India, China, Japan and parts of the Middle East and Africa, and some cases of osteosclerosis and crippling fluorosis have been observed. Occasionally, instances of harmful effects in these countries have been reported where there appear to be relatively low levels of fluoride in the drinking waters, and these findings were at first hard to reconcile with those of the American and European studies. In many of the reports, accurate medical histories are lacking and it is hard to ascertain how long or how consistently a person has consumed a particular water. Many of the reports also have been written primarily from a clinical angle and fluoride levels are found to be judged on inadequate analyses of water, often from shallow wells or water-holes where the mineral content may fluctuate from season to season.

Hot climates result in fluid intakes probably much higher even than those in the Arizona and Texas studies, and in addition populations have sometimes been exposed to severe nutritional deficiencies to a degree not experienced in the USA or Europe. Nevertheless, the apparent differences between countries have been puzzling and it was not until recently that information became available on which to base more accurate assessments. Dr Siddiqui has shown in his contribution the importance of taking into account a person's total fluoride intake as national dietetic habits may be responsible for considerable differences. The importance of considering the total fluoride intake emerges also in Professor Minoguchi's study of Japanese experience. Variations in total fluoride intake are therefore factors which must be taken into account when determining a country's fluoridation policy, for similar total fluoride intakes may be found where a water supply contains, for instance, 1 ppm in a temperate climate or 0.7 ppm in Arizona or 0.6 ppm in Japan. Each country should, therefore, make its own assessment of the desirable optimum concentration of fluoride in its water supplies.

REFERENCES

Agate, J. N., Bell, G. H., Boddie, G. F., Bowler, R. G., Buckell, M., Cheeseman, E. A., Douglas, T. H. J., Druett, H. A., Garrad, J., Hunter, D., Perry, K. M. A., Richardson, J. D. & Weir, J. B. de V. (1949) *Industrial fluorosis. A study of the hazard to man and animals near Fort William, Scotland,* London, HMSO (Medical Research Council Memorandum No. 22)

Allcroft, R. (1956) *Advanc. Sci., 12,* 494

Allcroft, R., Burns, K. N. & Herbert, C. N. (1965) *Fluorosis in cattle. 2. Development and alleviation,* London, HMSO (Animal Disease Surveys, No. 2)

Armstrong, W. D. & Knowlton, M. (1942) *J. dent. Res., 21,* 326

Arnold, F. A., Jr (1957) *Amer. J. publ. Hlth, 47,* 539-545

Arnold, F. A., Jr, Dean, H. T., Jay, P. & Knutson, J. W. (1956) *Publ. Hlth Rep. (Wash.), 71,* 652-658

Ast, D. B., Smith, D. J., Wachs, B. & Cantwell, K. T. (1956) *J. Amer. dent. Ass., 52,* 314-325

Azar, H. A., Mucho, C. K., Bayyuk, S. I. & Bayyuk, W. B. (1961) *Ann. intern. Med., 55,* 193

Bernstein, D. S., Sadowsky, N., Hegsted, D. M., Guri, C. D. & Stare, F. J. (1966) *J. Amer. med. Ass., 198,* 499-504

Berry, W. T. C. (1958) *Amer. J. ment. Defic., 62,* 634-636

Berry, W. T. C. (1962) *Med. Offr, 108,* 204-205

Black, G. V. & McKay, F. S. (1916) *Dent. Cosmos, 58,* 129-156

Bowler, R. G., Buckell, M., Garrad, J., Bradford Hill, A., Hunter, D., Perry K. M. A. & Schilling, R. S. F. (1947) *Brit. J. industr. Med., 4,* 216-222

Bridge, J. C. (1941) In: *Annual report of the Chief Inspector of Factories for the year 1939,* London, HMSO

Burns, K. N. & Allcroft, R. (1964) *Fluorosis in cattle. 1. Occurrence and effects in industrial areas of England and Wales,* London, HMSO (Animal Disease Surveys, No. 2)

Call, R. A., Greenwood, D. A., Le Cheminant, W. H., Shupe, J. L., Nielsen, H. M., Olson, L. E., Lamborn, R. E., Mangelson, F. L. & Davis, R. V. (1965) *Publ. Hlth Rep. (Wash.), 80,* 529-538

Call, R. A., Leone, N. C. & Davis, R. V. (1960) *A.M.A. Arch. industr. Hlth, 21,* 341

Cholak, J. (1960) *A.M.A. Arch. industr. Hlth, 21,* 312

Daver, M. B. (1945) *Indian med. Gaz., 80,* 332-336

Dean, H. T. (1946) *Epidemiological studies in the United States.* In: Moulton, F. R., ed., *Dental caries and fluorine,* Washington, D.C., American Association for the Advancement of Science, pp. 5-31

Dean, H. T., Jay, P., Arnold, F. A., McClure, F. J. & Elvove, E. (1939) *Publ. Hlth Rep. (Wash.), 54,* 862-888

Derryberry, O. M., Bartholomew, M. D. & Fleming, R. B. (1963) *Arch. environm. Hlth, 6,* 503

Eager, J. M. (1901) *Publ. Hlth Rep. (Wash.)*, **16**, 2576

Elliott, C. G. & Smith, M. D. (1960) *J. dent. Res.*, **39**, 93-98

Galagan, D. J. (1953) *J. Amer. dent. Ass.*, **47**, 159-170

Galagan, D. J. & Vermillion, J. R. (1957) *Publ. Hlth Rep. (Wash.)*, **72**, 491-493

Geever, E. F., Leone, N. C., Geiser, P. & Lieberman, J. (1958a) *J. Amer. dent. Ass.*, **56**, 499-507

Geever, E. F., Leone, N. C., Geiser, P. & Lieberman, J. (1958b) *Publ. Hlth Rep. (Wash.)*, **73**, 721-731

Hagan, T. (1957) *Effects of fluoridation on general health — as reflected in mortality data* (Paper presented at the American Association for the Advancement of Science Symposium, Indianapolis, Ind.)

Hagan, T. L., Pasternack, M. & Scholz, G. C. (1954) *Publ. Hlth Rep. (Wash.)*, **69**, 450

Ham, M. P. & Smith, M. D. (1954) *J. Nutr.*, **53**, 225-232

Hamamoto, E. (1957) *Medico-dental researches on fluoride*, Tokyo, Japan Society for the Promotion of Science, pp. 118-124

Heasman, M. A. & Martin, A. E. (1962) *Mth. Bull. Minist. Hlth Lab. Serv.*, **21**, 150

Hilleboe, H. E. (1956) *J. Amer. dent. Ass.*, **52**, 291-295

Hirata, Y. (1950) *Tokyo Iji Shinshi*, **67**, 9-14

Hodge, H. C. & Smith, F. A. (1965) *Biological effects of inorganic fluorides*. In: Simons, J. H., ed., *Fluorine chemistry*, New York, Academic Press, vol. 4

Hoogstratten, B., Leone, N. C., Shupe, J. L., Greenwood, D. & Lieberman, J. (1965) *J. Amer. med. Ass.*, **192**, 112-118

Hutton, W. L., Linscott, B. W. & Williams, D. B. (1956) *Canad. J. publ. Hlth*, **47**, 89

Iizuka, Y. (1964) *Jap. J. Hyg.*, **19**, 1-7

Iizuka, Y., Takaesu, Y., Egawa, T. & Ueda, K. (1963) *Jap. J. oral Hyg.*, **13**, 131-137

Khan, Y. M. & Wig, K. L. (1945) *Indian med. Gaz.*, **80**, 429-433

Knizhnikov, V. A. (1958) *Gig. i Sanit.*, **23**, No. 8, pp. 18-23

Kuno, Y. (1956) *Human perspiration*, Springfield, Ill., Thomas, pp. 327-335

Leone, N. C. (1960) *A.M.A. Arch. industr. Hlth*, **21**, 324-325

Leone, N. C., Geever, E. F. & Moran, N. C. (1956) *Publ. Hlth Rep. (Wash.)*, **71**, 459-467

Leone, N. C., Leatherwood, E. C., Petrie, I. & Lieberman, J. (1964) *J. Amer. dent. Ass.*, **69**, 179

Leone, N. C., Shimkin, M. B., Arnold, F. A., Stevenson, C. A., Zimmerman, E. R., Geiser, P. A. & Lieberman, J. E. (1954) *Publ. Hlth Rep. (Wash.)*, **69**, 925-936

Leone, N. C., Stevenson, C. A., Besse, B., Hawes, L. E. & Dawber, T. R. (1960) *A.M.A. Arch. industr. Hlth*, **21**, 326-327

Leone, N. C., Stevenson, C. A., Hilbish, T. F. & Sosman, M. C. (1955) *Amer. J. Roentgenol.*, **74**, 874-885

Likins, R. C., McClure, F. J. & Steere, A. C. (1956) *Publ. Hlth Rep. (Wash.)*, **71**, 217-220

Lindberg, Z. Y. (1964) *Gig. i Sanit.*, **29**, No. 12, p. 13

Longwell, J. (1957) *Roy. Soc. Hlth J.*, **77**, 361

McCauley, H. B. & McClure, F. J. (1954) *Publ. Hlth Rep. (Wash.)*, **69**, 671-683

McClure, F. J. (1943) *Amer. J. Dis. Child.*, **66**, 362-369

McClure, F. J., Mitchell, H. H., Hamilton, T. S. & Kinser, C. A. (1945) *J. industr. Hyg.*, **27**, 159-170

McKay, F. S. & Black, G. V. (1916) *Dent. Cosmos*, **58**, 477-484

McPhail, C. W. B. & Zacherl, W. (1965) *J. Canad. dent. Ass.*, **31**, 7

Maier, F. J. (1950) *J. Amer. Wat. Wks Ass.*, **42**, 1120-1132

Maier, F. J. (1963) *Manual of water fluoridation practice*, New York, McGraw-Hill, p. 57

Majumdar, B. N. & Ray, S. N. (1946) *Indian J. vet. Sci.*, **16**, 107-112

Massler, M. & Schour, I. (1952) *J. Amer. dent. Ass.*, **44**, 156-165

Miller, S. V. (1955) In: Ryazanov, V. A., *Limits of allowable concentrations of air pollutants*, vol. 2 (Translated by Levine, B. S., US Department of Commerce)

Minoguchi, G., Okumura, T. & Takenouchi, H. (1957) *J. Jap. stomat. Soc.*, **5**, 453-457

Minoguchi, G. & Sato, T. (1964) *Bull. Stomat. Univ. Kyoto*, **4**, 45-124

Møller, I. J. (1965) *Dental fluorose og karies*, Copenhagen, Rhodos (Thesis)

Murray, M. M. & Wilson, D. C. (1946) *Lancet*, **2**, 821

Murthi, G. V. S., Narayana Rao, D. & Venkateswarlu, P. (1953) *J. Indian med. Ass.*, **22**, 396-399

Pandit, C. G. & Narayana Rao, D. (1940) *Indian J. med. Res.*, **28**, 559-574

Pandit, C. G., Raghavachari, T. N. S., Rao, D. S. & Krishnamurti, V. (1940) *Indian J. med. Res.*, **28**, 533-558

Peirice, A. W. (1940) *Indian J. vet. Sci.*, **10**, 301-312

Phillips, P. H., Greenwood, D. A., Hobbs, C. S., Huffman, C. F. & Spencer, G. R. (1960) *The fluorosis problem in livestock production. A report of the Committee on Animal Nutrition*, Washington, D.C. (National Academy of Sciences — National Research Council Publication No. 824)

Pillai, S. C. (1942) *Indian med. Gaz.*, **77**, 19-20

Purves, M. J. (1962) *Lancet*, **2**, 1188-1189

Quentin, K.-E., Souci, S. W. & Indinger, J. (1960) *Nutr. Abstr. Rev.*, **30**, 810-811

Raghavachari, T. N. S. & Venkataramanan, K. (1940) *Indian J. med. Res.*, **28**, 517-532

Ranganathan, S. (1941) *Indian J. med. Res.*, **29**, 693-697

Rao, A. B. N. & Siddiqui, A. H. (1962) *J. Laryng. Otol.*, **74**, 94-99

Rapaport, I. (1959) *Bull. Acad. nat. Méd. (Paris)*, **143**, 367-370

Rich, C. (1961) *Sci. News Lett.*, **80**, 54

Rich, C. & Ensinck, J. (1961) *Nature (Lond.).*, **191**, 184-185

Roholm, K. (1937) *Fluorine intoxication : a clinical-hygienic study, with a review of the literature and some experimental investigations*, London, Lewis

Sadilova, M. S. (1957) In: Ryazanov, V. A., *Limits of allowable concentrations of air pollutants*, vol. 3 (Translated by Levine, B. S., US Department of Commerce)

Saito, H. (1960) *Boei Eisei*, **7**, 313-318

Samejima, K. (1959) *Jap. J. oral Hyg.*, **7**, 37-45

Sato, T., Yoshitake, K. & Nakanishi, H. (1965) *J. Jap. stomat. Soc.*, **14**, 262-263

Schlesinger, E. R., Overton, D. E. & Chase, H. C. (1956) *J. Amer. med. Ass.*, **160**, 21-24

Schlesinger, E. R., Overton, D. E., Chase, H. C. & Cantwell, K. T. (1956) *J. Amer. dent. Ass.*, **52**, 296-306

Shortt, H. E., McRobert, G. R., Barnard, T. W. & Mannadi Nayar, A. S. (1937) *Indian J. med. Res.*, **25**, 553-568

Shortt, H. E., Pandit, C. G. & Raghavachari, T. N. S. (1937) *Indian med. Gaz.*, **72**, 396-398

Shupe, J. L., Leone, N. C., Frame, C. F., Greenwood, D. A. & Miner, M. L. (1960) *A.M.A. Arch. industr. Hlth*, **21**, 348

Shupe, J. L., Miner, M. L., Greenwood, D. A., Harris, L. E. & Stoddard, G. E. (1963) *Amer. J. vet. Res.*, **24**, 964-979

Siddiqui, A. H. (1955) *Brit. med. J.*, **2**, 1408-1413

Siddiqui, A. H. (1960) *J. Endocr.*, **20**, 101-105

Singer, L., Armstrong, W. D. & Vatassery, G. T. (1967) *Econ. Bot.*, **21**, 285-287

Singh, A. & Jolly, S. S. (1961) *Quart. J. Med.*, **30**, 357-372

Singh, A., Jolly, S. S., Devi, P., Bansal, B. C. & Singh, S. S. (1962) *Indian J. med. Res.*, **50**, 387-398

Smith, F. A., Gardner, D. E., Leone, N. C. & Hodge, H. C. (1960) *A.M.A. Arch. industr. Hlth*, **21**, 330-332

Stevenson, C. A. & Watson, A. R. (1960) *A.M.A. Arch. industr. Hlth*, **21**, 340

US Department of Health, Education, and Welfare, (1968) *Fluoridation census, 1967*, Washington, D.C. (National Institutes of Health Publication No. 428)

Venkateswarlu, P., Rao, D. H. & Rao, K. R. (1952) *Indian J. med. Res.*, **40**, 535-548

Wadhwani, T. K. (1952) *Indian med. Gaz.*, **87**, 5-7

Waldbott, G. L. (1962) *Int. Arch. Allergy*, **20**, Suppl. 1, pp. 1-60

Waldbott, G. L. (1963) *Acta med. scand.*, **174**, Suppl. 400, pp. 1-44

Wilkie, J. (1940) *Brit. J. Radiol.*, **13**, 213-217

Wilson, D. C. (1941) *Lancet*, **1**, 211-212

Zimmerman, E. R., Leone, N. C. & Arnold, F. A., Jr (1955) *J. Amer. dent. Ass.*, **50**, 272-277

Zipkin, I. & Leone, N. C. (1957) *Amer. J. publ. Hlth*, **47**, 848-851

Zipkin, I. & Leone, N. C. (1958) *Proc. Soc. exp. Biol. (N.Y.)*, **97**, 650-653

Zipkin, I., Likins, R. C., McClure, F. J. & Steere, A. C. (1956) *Publ. Hlth Rep. (Wash.)*, **71**, 767-772

Zipkin, I., McClure, F. J. & Lee, W. A. (1960) *Arch. oral Biol.*, **2**, 190-195

Zipkin, I., McClure, F. J., Leone, N. C. & Lee, W. A. (1958) *Publ. Hlth Rep. (Wash.)*, **73**, 732-740

CHAPTER 9

Fluorides and dental health

P. ADLER [1]

1. INTRODUCTION

Although some earlier papers (Bunting, 1927; McKay, 1929; Dean, 1933) contain references to the low prevalence of caries among populations suffering from mottled enamel, the systematic investigations of Dean and co-workers (after the cause of this anomaly in development had been found to be excessive fluoride consumption) were the first to provide definite proof of the protective action of fluoride against dental decay. It had been repeatedly stated in the older literature that fluoride salts afforded protection against caries, but no adequate proof of this had been given.

The conditions under which mottled enamel appears were elucidated in the USA (Dean, 1954):

(*a*) Mottling occurs only when the dentition is *permanently* exposed to excessive fluoride during the development and calcification of the teeth. The permanent teeth are affected more frequently and to a greater extent than the milk teeth.

(*b*) As a rule, mottling is caused by the consumption of drinking water which is too rich in fluoride. The minimal threshold value at which a just perceptible change appears in the developing enamel of the permanent teeth was found to be 1.0-1.1 ppm for the people in the USA living in the temperate zone. At this concentration a small number of spots, gleaming like mother-of-pearl and hardly differing in colour from the rest of the enamel, develop on a limited number of teeth in scattered individuals. These spots are not noticeable to the layman and are in no way disfiguring. It is only after the fluoride concentration in drinking water exceeds 1.4-1.6 ppm that the first signs of more serious dental fluorosis appear: some of the teeth of a few

---

[1] Department of Stomatology, University Medical School, Debrecen, Hungary.

members of the population then show circumscribed spots, coloured light-yellow to brownish.   When the fluoride content exceeds 2.0 ppm, then brownish spots, varying from small to large in size, can be seen on numerous teeth in the great majority of the members of the exposed community.   When the fluoride content is more than 2.5 ppm, the enamel loses its smoothness: signs of serious dental hyperfluorosis appear, with hypoplastic zones and an often quite dark discoloration affecting extensive areas of the enamel of several teeth in the persons affected.   The degree of mottling thus runs parallel to the fluoride content of the drinking water, but this parallelism is by no means absolute, since, in addition to the fluoride content, the amount of water consumed—i.e., the quantity of fluoride ion ingested—also plays a part.   When the average annual temperature is high, then—because of the increased water consumption—small fluoride concentrations have a more harmful effect on the enamel than they do in the temperate zone (Galagan & Lamson, 1953).   Living and eating habits are also important; in cases of malnutrition, for example, the enamel has been found to be more susceptible (Schour & Massler, 1947).   In comparison with the amount consumed in water, the fluoride content of solid food plays only a minor role; however, in some special circumstances it, too, may be of practical importance (see Chapter 2, section 3 and Chapter 8, section 4).

(c)   A change in the drinking-water supply (conversion from water with excessive fluoride to fluoride-poor drinking water) causes the mottling to disappear in children born after the conversion (Dean & McKay, 1939), but mottling in already formed enamel is unaffected.

(d)   Disfiguring mottling is the first sign of a lesion caused by increased fluoride consumption, but it appears only at a late stage, on the eruption of the mottled teeth.   The ameloblast active in enamel formation is the most sensitive of all kinds of cells of the body to fluoride.   Other tissues, organs and functions are only affected by considerably higher fluoride concentrations.

After elucidating the question of the threshold of harmful concentration, the protective effect against caries was ascertained quantitatively.   Next, the naturally favourable conditions for the dentition occurring by chance in many places were artificially reproduced by enriching fluoride-poor drinking water with fluoride ion until the optimal concentration was reached.   Almost at the same time an attempt was made to bring about the desirable fluoride consumption by means of vehicles other than drinking water, primarily in order to provide protection against decay for population groups without a piped water supply.

In addition to increasing fluoride consumption to a desirable level, local fluoride application was also tried, after it had been shown that even fully developed enamel can take up fluoride from outside and that this also ensures a protective action against caries.   This local application took the form, on the one hand, of repeated brief application of fluoride solution to the teeth by the dentist or an auxiliary (referred to in the literature as "topical application") and, on the other, the use of toothpastes and mouthwashes containing fluoride.

In the following we shall first recapitulate the observations which led to the artificial enrichment of drinking water with fluoride. We shall then review the results given so far by this health measure and compare them with those achieved by other means of fluoride application, in an attempt to indicate the best method of caries prophylaxis with fluoride.

2. EFFECT OF FLUORIDE INGESTION ON CARIES EXPERIENCE

Fluoride Ingestion with Water

Caries of the permanent dentition in school-age children and adolescents consuming domestic waters with naturally occurring fluoride

Dean and co-workers (Dean, 1945, 1954) have clearly shown by systematic examination of 12- to 14-year-old children of both sexes in 21 cities in the

TABLE 1

SUMMARY OF DENTAL FINDINGS IN 7257 SELECTED WHITE SCHOOLCHILDREN, AGED 12-14 YEARS, IN 21 CITIES OF THE USA IN RELATION TO THE FLUORIDE CONTENT AND TOTAL HARDNESS OF THE PUBLIC WATER SUPPLY

City	Number of examinees	Domestic water		CER (DMF) count	First molar mortality	Upper incisor proximal surface caries	Percentage of caries-free examinees
		Mean F content	Total hardness				
		(mg per litre)		per 100 examinees			
Colorado Springs	404	2.6	27	246	4.7	2.48	28.5
Galesburg	273	1.9	247	236	15.0	3.66	27.8
Elmhurst	170	1.8	323	252	11.8	4.71	25.3
Joliet	447	1.3	349	323	19.5	10.74	18.3
Aurora	633	1.2	329	281	14.5	6.16	23.5
East Moline	152	1.2	276	303	15.8	1.63	20.4
Maywood	171	1.2	75	258	11.7	4.68	29.8
Kewanee	123	0.9	445	343	29.3	11.38	17.9
Pueblo	614	0.6	302	412	20.2	3.75	10.6
Elgin	403	0.5	103	444	20.3	32.26	11.4
Marion	263	0.4	209	556	25.1	26.24	5.7
Lima	454	0.3	223	652	55.9	25.89	2.2
Middletown	370	0.2	329	703	65.9	55.41	1.9
Zanesville	459	0.2	291	733	99.8	89.76	2.6
Elkhart	278	0.1	220	823	34.2	89.21	1.4
Michigan City	236	0.1	141	1 037	80.1	143.64	0
Quincy	330	0.1	88	706	71.2	70.00	2.4
Portsmouth	469	0.1	80	772	73.8	82.30	1.3
Waukegan	423	0	134	810	79.9	140.19	3.1
Oak Park	329	0	132	722	31.0	70.52	4.3
Evanston	256	0	131	673	42.6	85.16	3.7

USA that there is a definite relationship between the fluoride content of drinking water and caries experience: the higher the fluoride content, the lower the caries experience (Table 1).

Caries experience was expressed by the sum total of overtly carious, filled or extracted permanent teeth per person—DMF (decayed, missing, filled) or CER (caries, extractio, restauratio) count. The investigation was limited to children who had been born in the district concerned, had always resided there, and had always consumed the local water. In order to check the effect of the presence or absence of a drinking-water constituent (i.e., a varying concentration of fluoride), it was necessary to select for the survey localities whose water supply had undergone no change, at least during the lifetime of the subjects, but where the fluoride content of the water varied within given limits. The caries experience of children aged 12-14 years was investigated, since children in this age-group could still be completely reached in the schools. Apart from wisdom teeth, the permanent teeth have already erupted in the majority of children of this age, and numerous teeth known to be liable to caries (first molars, upper incisors, upper first pre-molars) had already been exposed for several years to cariogenic influences in the oral cavity.

While a considerable degree of regularity was evident in the antagonism between the fluoride content of the water and caries experience (Fig. 1), no

FIG. 1

RELATION BETWEEN DENTAL CARIES AND FLUORIDE CONTENT OF WATER [a]

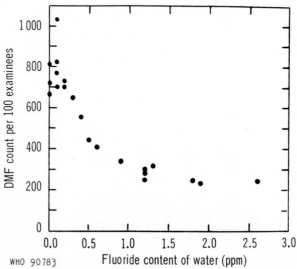

WHO 90783

[a] Based on the data obtained by Dean and co-workers from the examination of the permanent teeth of 7257 schoolchildren aged 12-14 years in 21 cities of the USA. (After Dean, 1954)

FIG. 2

RELATION BETWEEN DENTAL CARIES AND HARDNESS OF WATER [a]

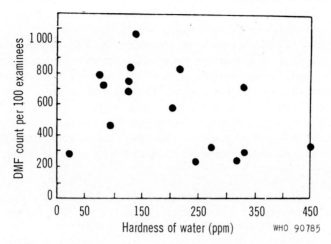

[a] Data from 16 of the 21 cities referred to in Fig. 1. (After Dean, 1945, 1954)

connexion could be detected between caries experience and water hardness (Fig. 2), which had been regarded as a determining factor in the development of caries since the time of Röse (1904).

As can be seen from Table 1 and Fig. 1, minor deviations from the general rule are visible in all the fluoride concentration ranges studied, so that caries experience is not strictly inversely proportional to fluoride content. Consequently, the data from the individual localities are best considered, not separately, but grouped according to the fluoride content of the water. For example, in Fig. 3, the average DMF count per 100 examinees

FIG. 3

DATA FROM THE 21 CITIES REFERRED TO IN FIG. 1
GROUPED ACCORDING TO FLUORIDE CONTENT OF WATER [a]

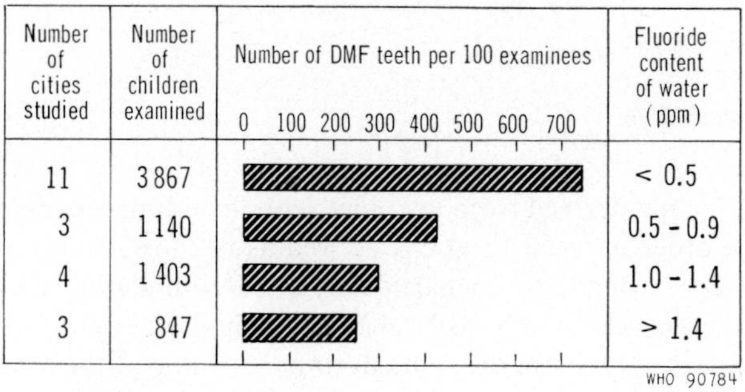

Number of cities studied	Number of children examined	Number of DMF teeth per 100 examinees 0 100 200 300 400 500 600 700	Fluoride content of water (ppm)
11	3 867		< 0.5
3	1 140		0.5 - 0.9
4	1 403		1.0 - 1.4
3	847		> 1.4

[a] After Dean (1945, 1954).

is shown for four—intentionally limited—ranges of concentration—namely, > 1.4, 1.0-1.4, 0.5-0.9, and < 0.5 ppm. This removes the small irregularities mentioned above (produced by minor differences in nutrition, general way of life, etc.) and clearly reveals the regular inverse correlation.

When mottling of the enamel in the various localities is also taken into account, it is found that a certain range of concentration exists where there is still no danger of any harmful dental hyperfluorosis, nor even of slight discoloration of the teeth, although the fluoride concentration already provides definite protection against caries. This protection is almost as great as that given by higher fluoride concentrations, including those causing a disfiguring mottling of the enamel. As can be seen from Fig. 4 (Hodge, 1950), this protective concentration is about 1.0-1.2 ppm for the temperate zone of the USA.

FIG. 4

RELATIONSHIP BETWEEN FLUORIDE CONTENT OF DRINKING WATER, CARIES EXPERIENCE AND DENTAL FLUOROSIS [a]

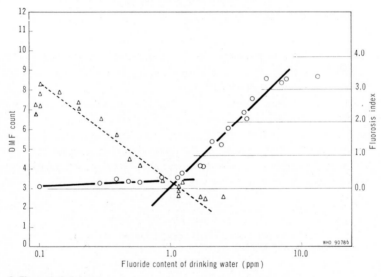

O Fluorosis index.
△ DMF count.

[a] After Hodge (1950).

The above data, derived from the older schoolchildren, were subsequently confirmed in other parts of the USA as well as in other countries and continents, and also extended. In particular, it was found that the protective effect on the permanent teeth exists already in children commencing school. Its extent appears to remain the same during the whole of the school-attendance period. Furthermore, the effect, expressed as a percentage of the caries

experience of the unprotected population, was *practically the same* in all parts
of the world. As compared with the results mentioned above, there were
differences between the various investigators in regard to the grouping of the
children by age and of the localities according to the fluoride content of
the drinking water, as well as in regard to the system used to characterize
caries experience.

FIG. 5

CARIES EXPERIENCE OF HUNGARIAN SCHOOLCHILDREN IN RELATION
TO FLUORIDE CONTENT OF WATER [a]

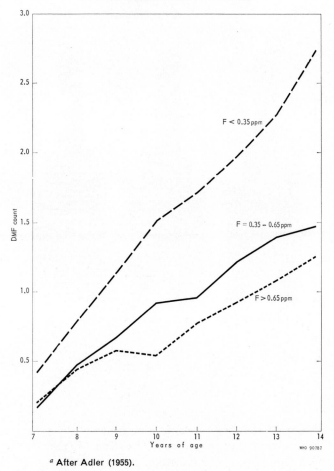

[a] After Adler (1955).

In Fig. 5 we show, as an example, the results of investigations made in
Hungary. Although the ranges of concentration of fluoride in the drinking
water vary from those chosen by Dean, Fig. 5 clearly demonstrates the
parallelism between fluoride content and protective effect, and this in a

population appreciably less attacked by caries. The protective effect can be seen to exist in all annual age-groups up to school-leaving age. The percentage protection is about the same in the individual age-groups and no distinct variation between the sexes can be detected (Fig. 6).

FIG. 6

CARIES PREVALENCE AND CARIES PROTECTION IN CHILDREN CONSUMING WATER WITH A MEDIUM (M) OR HIGH (H) CONTENT OF FLUORIDE, EXPRESSED AS A PERCENTAGE OF THAT IN CHILDREN CONSUMING WATER WITH A LOW (L) CONTENT OF FLUORIDE [a]

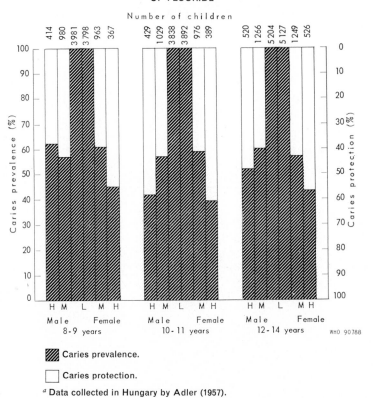

▨ Caries prevalence.

☐ Caries protection.

[a] Data collected in Hungary by Adler (1957).

According to Dean (Fig. 3), a fluoride content of 0.5 ppm is usually taken as the threshold value for the protective effect. In the case of a population whose composition, social structure, eating habits, general living standards and customs are all uniform, even small differences in the "sub-threshold" concentration range cause distinct variations in the caries experience of school-age children (see Fig. 7, concerning two adjacent villages in the Hungarian plain). The fluoride content of certain wells is higher in the village whose children have better teeth, even though the presumed

TABLE 2

COMPARISON OF THE FLUORIDE LEVEL IN THE WATERS
FROM ARTESIAN WELLS IN THE HUNGARIAN VILLAGES
OF NAGYLÉTA AND VÉRTES [a]

Fluoride level (mg per litre)	Number of wells with the particular fluoride level at	
	Nagyléta	Vértes
Lower than 0.1	0	0
Between 0.1 and 0.2	6	7
Between 0.2 and 0.3	4	1
Between 0.3 and 0.5	2	0

[a] Data from Csepura & Kovács (1953).

threshold value of 0.5 ppm is not reached in any of them (Table 2). Nevertheless, the small difference in fluoride content was sufficient to bring about
the changes in caries experience shown in Fig. 7.

FIG. 7

CARIES EXPERIENCE IN TWO ADJACENT HUNGARIAN VILLAGES
WITH SMALL DIFFERENCES IN THE FLUORIDE CONTENT OF THE WATER [a]

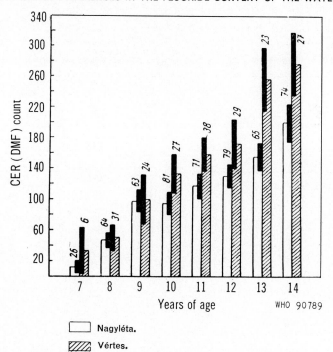

WHO 90789

☐ Nagyléta.

▨ Vértes.

[a] The black columns indicate the standard error; the figures at the top of the columns denote
the number of children examined.

TABLE 3

COMBINATION OF THE CARIES-PROTECTIVE EFFECT OF WAR-TIME DIET
AND INCREASED FLUORIDE INGESTION IN ENGLAND [a]

	1943		1949	
	North Shields	South Shields	North Shields	South Shields
Mean F level of domestic water (mg per litre)	0.25	1.4	0.25	1.4
Children of 12 years: [b]				
Percentage of caries-free examinees	4.8	25.8	26.4	50.6
Mean CER (DMF) count	4.3	2.4	2.4	1.3
expressed as percentage of North Shields count	100	55.8	100	54.2
expressed as percentage of 1943 count	100	100	55.8	54.8
Children of 5 years: [b]				
Percentage of caries-free examinees	11.6	27.0	26.4	28.0
Mean cer (def) count	6.6	3.9	4.4	3.5
expressed as percentage of North Shields count	100	59.1	100	79.5
expressed as percentage of 1943 count	100	100	66.7	89.7

[a] Data from Weaver (1950).
[b] The number of children at each examination in each age-group was 500.

TABLE 4

CER COUNTS AND DISTRIBUTION INTO DIFFERENT CER CLASSES OF BOYS
AND GIRLS, AGED 16-18 YEARS, IN HUNGARY, ACCORDING TO THE FLUORIDE
LEVEL OF THE DOMESTIC WATERS [a]

	F level *lower* than 0.35 mg per litre		F level *higher* than 0.35 mg per litre	
	Boys	Girls	Boys	Girls
Number of examinees	2 217	2 126	178	151
Number of CER teeth per examinee	4.01	4.81	2.12	2.78
Standard error	0.071	0.089	0.21	0.24
Percentage of caries-free examinees (CER O)	17.5	13.7	34.8	27.2
Percentage with 1 CER tooth	11.5	9.7	23.6	17.2
,, ,, 2 CER teeth	11.8	10.1	11.2	14.6
,, ,, 3 CER teeth	11.2	9.9	10.1	7.9
,, ,, 4 CER teeth	10.3	10.1	3.4	11.3
,, ,, 5 CER teeth	8.8	8.1	3.4	6.0
,, ,, 6 CER teeth	7.4	8.4	5.1	3.3
,, ,, 7-10 CER teeth	15.3	20.4	6.7	9.8
,, ,, 11 or more CER teeth . .	6.0	9.7	1.8	2.7
Highest number of CER teeth observed in one person	21	22	17	15

[a] Data from Adler (1957).
The groups consuming domestic waters containing more than 0.35 mg F per litre include all pupils of the grammar schools (gymnasia) in Szekszard and Hatvan who were born and continuously resident in the respective city, or whose residence there began before the end of the 6th year of life. While in Szekszard a public water supply exists, in Hatvan domestic waters are drawn from individual artesian wells. In no instance does the sum of the percentages, which have been corrected to one decimal place, in the columns differ from 100 by more than 0.2 %.

We regard as significant the finding that the protective effect of fluoride can combine with other factors in reducing caries experience. Thus in England the protective effect of fluoride-rich water on the permanent teeth has been demonstrated both alone and in combination with the caries reduction resulting from war-time diet (Table 3).

The protective action is not restricted to school-age children; it is also found in adolescents. For example, Table 4 shows the caries distribution among Hungarian adolescents aged from 16 to 18 years (Adler, 1957) who had consumed drinking water with a fluoride content above or below 0.35 ppm, respectively.

On the basis of data collected in the suburbs of Chicago, in particular, Arnold (1943) forecast that artificial enrichment of drinking water with fluoride would bring about:

(a)   a fall of nearly 60% in caries intensity;

(b)   a sixfold increase in the number of children still caries-free at school-leaving age;

(c)   a decrease of about 75% in the losses of first permanent molars during this period of life; and

(d)   a fall of about 95% in caries attack on the approximal surfaces of the upper incisors.

The success of this prediction will be commented on in the following.

Caries of the permanent dentition in school-age children consuming domestic waters with artificial addition of fluoride

The suggestion made initially by Cox (1939) that the protective action of increased fluoride consumption—confirmed epidemiologically and in animal experiments—should be utilized for public health purposes was first adopted in North America in the middle 1940s. Systematic studies on the various consequences of increased fluoride ingestion following the addition of fluoride to drinking water, studies extending over several years, were carried out in four towns—namely, Brantford, in Canada (control towns: Sarnia and Stratford), and Evanston, Grand Rapids and Newburgh, in the USA (control towns: Oak Park; Muskegon and Aurora; Kingston). The fluoride content of the drinking water was increased by the addition of sodium fluoride to about 1.2 ppm in Brantford and to 1.0 ppm in the other towns.

It should be remembered that this dosage applies to North American towns, and to inhabitants of the temperate zone. When the annual average temperature is higher, a lower fluoride level suffices to produce the same effect, and this also holds true in the case of dietetic habits involving increased consumption of liquid or fluoride-rich foods.

In view of the general interest in these studies, the partial results were published seriatim, leading many communities to introduce fluoridation without awaiting the completion of the investigations. Unfortunately, this also happened in Muskegon, the fluoride-poor control town of the Grand Rapids study, in the sixth year of the studies. The results obtained in the four studies are not only basically similar, but to a large extent even quantitatively identical. Nevertheless there are differences in presentation, in the time when the interim researches were made, in the grouping of the examinees by age, in the findings deemed worthy of communication, etc. Because of this it is not possible to summarize the results in a uniform manner. We can only enlarge on individual points in the results communicated. In addition, we shall refer to other studies carried out later elsewhere, so far as these results contribute to an understanding of questions which remain unsettled.

FIG. 8

GRAND RAPIDS: CARIES REDUCTION IN CHILDREN WITH LIFE-LONG
CONSUMPTION OF FLUORIDATED WATER (1.0 ppm) [a]

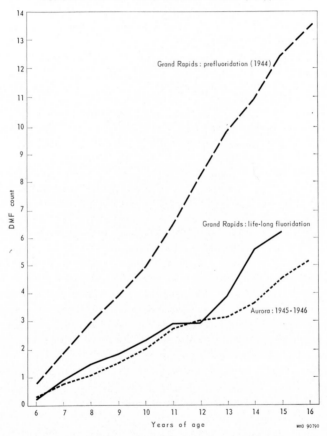

[a] For comparison, the caries prevalence in Aurora, with 1.3 ppm naturally occurring fluoride in the water, is shown.

The extent of the protection against caries attack on the dentition as a whole has been shown by concurrent findings to depend on the age when ingestion of fluoridated water commenced and the age when the results were recorded. The longer the period of "dental life" in an environment characterized by increased—presumably optimal—fluoride ingestion, the more distinct the protective action. The protective action throughout the compulsory school-attendance period and even afterwards is quite apparent (see Fig. 8, which shows the separately published longitudinal results of the Grand Rapids study combined into a single graph).

As regards the previously mentioned predictions of Arnold regarding the results of water fluoridation, it was found that:

(a) The fall in caries intensity among 12- to 14-year-old children was well up to expectations. As can be seen from Table 5, the protective effect

TABLE 5

CER (DMF) COUNTS OF CHILDREN OF 12-14 YEARS OF AGE AFTER DIFFERENT PERIODS OF FLUORIDATION OF THE DOMESTIC WATER IN THE USA AND CANADA [a]

Period of fluoridation (years)	CER (DMF) count per 100 children of 12-14 years of age, born and continuously resident at:							
	Grand Rapids	Mus-kegon	Aurora	Evan-ston	Oak Park	Brant-ford	Sarnia	Strat-ford
Before start	958	1 021	323	980	980	735		
2½				875				
3	833	932				768	794	255
5½				804				
6	762	952				610	855	312
7½				772				
9	527	836 [b]			951	489	884	302
10½				531				
12	477					378	775	270
15	415					323	746	233

[a] After 10 years of fluoridation in Newburgh the CER count per 100 children aged 13-14 years amounted to 610, as compared with 1170 in non-fluoridated Kingston.

[b] After 3 years of fluoridation of the domestic water.

is augmented in the case of increased fluoride consumption from birth (as compared with increased fluoride ingestion only at a later age). Thus it is not surprising that caries experience in Grand Rapids and Brantford, after 15 years of water fluoridation, fell to about 43-44% of the initial figure, and in Evanston and Newburgh, after about 10 years' fluoridation, to only about 52-54% (of the initial figure or of the figure determined contemporaneously in the control town).

(b) In regard to the number of caries-free dentitions among 12- to 14-year-old children, the predicted sixfold increase had already been attained in Brantford after fluoridation had been under way for 8 years. In the 14th year of the study, such dentitions were about 9 times as numerous as in the fluoride-poor control town of Sarnia. After 18 years, 11.8% of 16- to 18-year-old Brantford examinees had a caries-free dentition, as compared with only 0.41% of the same age-group in Sarnia. After 10 years of fluoridation, 13.5%, 10.7% and 5.6%, respectively, of 12-, 13- and 14-year-old schoolchildren in Grand Rapids were free from caries, whereas in Muskegon (where fluoride-enriched water had at that time already been consumed for more than 3 years) the corresponding figures were only 4.4%, 1.6% and 0%, respectively, giving an average of 9.9% for these three age-groups in Grand Rapids and 2.0% in Muskegon.

(*c*) In regard to the loss of the first molars, most reports contain no comparable figures. However, there are numerous comparable data (Table 6) on the over-all loss of teeth, involving chiefly the first molars. In Brantford, tooth mortality among 12- to 14-year-old children fell after 14 years of fluoridation (in comparison with data collected after the study had been under way for 3 years) by almost three-quarters; in Grand Rapids the figure fell after 15 years' fluoridation to almost the level found in Aurora at the outset. In New Britain, Conn., tooth mortality per examinee fell in 10 years from 0.93 to 0.23. In brief, the figures in Table 6 show that in this respect, too, fluoridation fulfilled expectations. Nevertheless, it should be remembered that in Sarnia—without any change in the drinking water—tooth mortality fell between 1948 and 1959 from 1.37 to 0.75 per person. Since loss of teeth depends *not only* on caries attack and progression but also, *inter alia*, on possibilities of treatment, the social status of the population, and the attitude of the dental profession to treatment of children in

TABLE 6

PERMANENT TOOTH MORTALITY OF CHILDREN AGED 12-14 YEARS
AFTER FLUORIDATION OF THE PUBLIC WATER SUPPLY AND IN
CONTROL CITIES

City	Level and duration of fluoridation	Tooth mortality per 100 examinees
Aurora	Natural, 1.2 ppm	25
Grand Rapids	F-deficient before start of fluoridation	84
	Fluoridation to 1.0 ppm through 10 years	41
	,, ,, ,, ,, ,, 15 ,,	27
Muskegon	F-deficient control city, in 1945	94
	,, ,, ,, 6 years later	96
Stratford	Natural, 1.3 ppm — contemporaneously with examination at Brantford after 14 years of fluoridation	22.5
Brantford	Fluoridation to 1.2 ppm through 14 years	22.3
Sarnia	F-deficient control city, in 1948	137
	,, ,, ,, 1959	75
New Britain, Conn.	F-deficient, before start of fluoridation	93
	Fluoridation to 1.0 ppm through 10 years	23
Ely, Minn.	Fluoridation to 1.2 ppm through 10 years:	
	children born and continuously resident in city	18
	children with partial exposure to fluoridated water	35

general and to root treatment in particular, as well as the attitude of the population to dental treatment in general, it is not certain that the impressive improvements revealed by the figures in Table 6 can be attributed solely to the favourable effect of fluoridation.

(*d*) The individual reports contain no specific data on the number of DMF upper incisor approximal *surfaces*. As the collected data of the Brantford study in Table 7 show, the number of DMF upper incisor *teeth*

TABLE 7

CARIES PREVALENCE IN UPPER INCISORS OF CHILDREN
AT BRANTFORD, STRATFORD AND SARNIA [a]

Age-group (years)	Year of examination	Number of CER (DMF) upper incisors per 100 children born and continuously resident at		
		Brantford [b]	Stratford	Sarnia
9-11	1948 1959	34 3	1 4	56 41
12-14	1948 1959	105 20	7 9	116 131
14-15	1961	25	19	123
16-18	1963	22	30	138

[a] Compiled from the reports of Brown (1959, 1961, 1963).
[b] Fluoridation at Brantford (to 1.2 ppm) started in 1945.

fell quite considerably as a result of fluoridation without reaching, however, the predicted 95% reduction. But these figures include the *foramina coeca* decay foci also so that they cannot be directly compared with Arnold's forecasts. However, in the Netherlands (Tiel-Culemborg study) the results were again close to those predicted, the protective influence of fluoridation on the approximal surfaces being greater than that on fissures and pits. The protective action exerted on the approximal surfaces also varies according to the type of tooth (weakest for the molars, strongest for the upper incisors) and even between the mesial and distal surfaces of the same tooth (Fig. 9), although it is true that these findings apply to teeth whose morpho-differentiation was already complete when fluoridation commenced (Backer Dirks, 1963).

Of the studies made elsewhere, Minoguchi's report on the results in Yamashina (control town, Shugakuin) is of fundamental importance (Minoguchi & Sato, 1964). After 11 years' fluoridation (0.6 ppm) caries experience in 12- and 13-year-old children rose from 1.49 and 1.85, respectively (average 1.67), to 2.46 and 2.64 (average 2.55), but nevertheless a protective

FIG. 9

TIEL-CULEMBORG STUDY: PERCENTAGES OF APPROXIMAL
TOOTH SURFACES WITH CAVITIES IN CHILDREN AGED 13-14 YEARS [a]

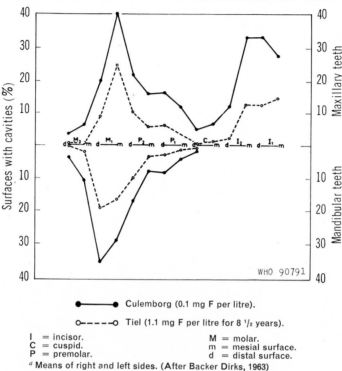

● —— ● Culemborg (0.1 mg F per litre).

○ – – – ○ Tiel (1.1 mg F per litre for 8 ¹/₂ years).

I = incisor.	M = molar.
C = cuspid.	m = mesial surface.
P = premolar.	d = distal surface.

[a] Means of right and left sides. (After Backer Dirks, 1963)

effect can be definitely shown to exist! For during the same period, there was an increase in the control town from 0.85 and 1.96, respectively (average 1.425), to 3.73 and 4.46, respectively (average 4.095). Thus, although in Yamashina caries experience rose by 53%, despite fluoridation, there was a protective effect of about 72% in comparison with the data for Shugakuin (since caries experience in the control town increased by 187% over the same period). Conditions similar to those in Japan may well exist in many other countries where the general living and eating customs and the social structure of the population have undergone extensive changes over a comparatively short period of time, with a resulting increase in caries experience. This shows that the periodic examination of the population in control towns also is of the greatest importance!

Protection of the teeth in adults

The far-reaching similarity between caries experience in children and adolescents following water fluoridation and that observed in subjects living

TABLE 8

NUMBERS OF CER (DMF) TEETH PER 100 ADULTS IN AREAS WITH HIGH AND LOW FLUORIDE LEVELS IN THE DOMESTIC WATER, AND DIFFERENCES BETWEEN THE TWO TYPES OF AREA (IN ENGLAND, HUNGARY AND THE USA) [a]

| Age group [b] | England | | | | Hungary | | | | United States of America | | | | | | | |
| | | | | | | | | | Colorado Springs—Boulder | | | | Aurora—Rockford | | | |
	A[c]	B[d]	B-A	%[e]	A[c]	B[d]	B-A	%[e]	A[c]	B[d]	B-A	%[e]	A[c]	B[d]	B-A	%[e]
1	1 000	1 620	620	38.3	284	733	449	61.3	540	1 404	864	61.5	878	1 692	814	48.2
2	1 250	1 930	680	35.2	535	927	392	42.3	649	1 649	1 000	60.6				
3	1 620	2 150	530	24.7	734	1 080	346	32.1	706	1 827	1 121	61.4	1 103	1 765	662	37.5
4	1 920	2 280	360	15.8	888	1.150	262	22.8	917	2 182	1 165	58.0				
5	2 200	2 640	440	16.7	930	1 314	384	29.2	1 027	2 167	1 140	52.6	1 241	1 800	559	31.1
6					1 096	1 413	317	22.5								
7					1 365	1 536	171	11.1					1 258	1 834	576	31.5
8					1 412	1 685	273	16.2								

[a] Compiled from: Adler (1951b, 1953); Bruszt (1962); Englander & Wallace (1962); Forrest, Parfitt & Bransby (1951); Russell & Elvove (1951).

[b] 1 = 21-25 (20-24) years
2 = 26-30 (25-29) ,,
3 = 31-35 (30-34) ,,
4 = 36-40 (35-39) ,,
5 = 41-45 (40-44) ,,
6 = 46-50 (45-49) ,,
7 = 51-55 (50-54) ,,
8 = 56-60 (55-59) ,,

The age-groups in parentheses apply to group B in Hungary and to all groups in the USA.

[c] A = CER (DMF) count in the "fluoride" areas (South Shields, Slough and Colchester in England, with 0.82, 1.45 and 0.9 ppm, respectively; Kunszentmárton in Hungary, with about 1.1 ppm; Colorado Springs, with about 2.5 ppm, and Aurora with 1.2 ppm, in the USA).

[d] B = CER (DMF) count in F-deficient areas (North Shields, Ipswich and Reading in England, with 0.07, 0.3 and 0.1 ppm, respectively; 12 agricultural communities in southern Hungary, with less than 0.3 ppm; Boulder, with 0.1 ppm, and Rockford, with 0.1 ppm, in the USA).

[e] $\% = 100 - \dfrac{100\ A}{B}$.

in places where the drinking water has a naturally high fluoride content justifies the assumption that the protective effect of fluoridation also remains the same in later years, like that of a naturally fluoride-rich water. It is therefore of interest to review the available data on the caries protection in adults afforded by naturally fluoride-containing water. Table 8 shows the results of four surveys—one in England, one in Hungary (only among women) and two in the USA (among both men and women). The statistics reveal that the protection continues up to—and beyond—the age when periodontal disease commences to play a large part in tooth mortality, even in advanced countries. But it is noteworthy that the absolute difference in the DMF count between "protected" and "unprotected" subjects decreases with advancing age in England, in Hungary and in the Aurora-Rockford study, whereas in the Colorado Springs—Boulder investigation it increases slightly. However, in Colorado Springs the fluoride content of the drinking water is appreciably greater than in the protected localities of the three other studies. Moreover, if the protective effect is expressed in the usual way, as a percentage of the caries experience of the unprotected control group, then there is a distinct tendency for it to fall with increasing age in Colorado Springs also.

Effect on caries of the deciduous teeth

For characterization of the caries experience of milk teeth, the cer (def) count—analogous to the CER (DMF) count of the permanent teeth—can be regarded as reliable only *before* the second dentition commences. So as to exclude the loss of milk teeth by natural exfoliation, the cer (def) [1] count of the milk teeth is sometimes related to the number of milk teeth present. This number, however, depends not only on caries attack, but also on the quality and quantity of paedodontic care. It is therefore unsuitable for the unambiguous characterization of over-all caries experience. There is a time gap between the change of the incisors and that of the canines and molars, so that in early school age the temporary cuspids and molars can be used to assess caries experience in the (remaining) temporary dentition (number of cer or def temporary molars and canines per 100 examinees, where "e" indicates missing, presumably extracted, teeth). A refinement is to neglect missing temporary teeth when the corresponding permanent teeth have already erupted (Adler, 1953). The need to determine the caries experience of milk teeth during school age arises because of the difficulty of examining an unselected, representative part of the individual annual age-groups in preschool age. Another suitable index number—at least for comparative purposes—is the percentage of examinees with caries-free milk teeth in the various annual age-groups. This number, too, gives a picture which is better than the actual state of affairs.

---

[1] "e" means here "indicated for extraction".

TABLE 9

CHANGES IN DENTAL CARIES PREVALENCE IN THE DECIDUOUS TEETH
AFTER FLUORIDATION OF THE PUBLIC WATER SUPPLY
(IN THE UNITED KINGDOM [a] AND THE USA)

Study area	Mode of caries assessment [b]	Duration of fluoridation (years)	Age (years)	Change in the cer count per 100 examinees in fluoridated area			Change in the cer count per 100 examinees in control area		
				from	to	%	from	to	%
United Kingdom	1	5	3	380	129	— 66.1	353	332	— 5.9
	1		4	539	231	— 57.1	518	483	— 6.8
	2		5	581	291	— 49.9	566	539	— 4.8
	2		6	649	481	— 25.9	632	622	— 1.6
	2		7	706	605	— 14.3	708	689	— 2.7
USA (Grand Rapids— Muskegon) [c]	3	6-10	4	419	219	— 48.0	505	446	— 11.7
	3	7-10	5	537	245	— 54.4	682	525	— 23.3
	3	8-10	6	643	293	— 54.4	717	567	— 20.9

[a] Data from Ministry of Health, Scottish Office & Ministry of Housing and Local Government (1962).

[b] 1 = number of carious, extracted and filled deciduous teeth (total deciduous dentition);
2 = number of carious, extracted and filled deciduous molars and cuspids;
3 = number of carious, extraction-indicated and filled deciduous teeth.

[c] In Grand Rapids the post-fluoridation cer counts are the averages of published figures for 6, 7, 8, 9 and 10 years of fluoridation for the 4-year-old, for 7, 8, 9 and 10 years for the 5-year-old, and for 8, 9 and 10 years for the 6-year-old children. In the control city Muskegon the second assessment was made 7 years after the first one.

As concerns the caries experience of the temporary dentition and the fluoride protective effect at school age (in cases where naturally fluoride-rich water is consumed), it has been found (Adler, 1953) that the milk teeth are appreciably less protected than the permanent teeth of the same children.

In the case of water fluoridation, it appears that—as with the protection of the permanent teeth—the effect is increased when ingestion has continued for a long time, perhaps since birth. Table 9 gives a few results of the action of fluoridation on the temporary dentition; Table 10 shows that the protective effect on the milk teeth of younger schoolchildren is less marked than that on the permanent teeth, even when fluoride-enriched water is consumed.

Nevertheless, a protective effect can definitely be shown during school age. Whereas the above-mentioned 12 milk teeth were caries-free in only 11.1%, 4.7% and 1.8% (average 5.5%), respectively, of 6-, 7- and 8-year-old children in Kingston, the corresponding figures in Newburgh after 10 years of fluoridation were 37.0%, 27.9% and 24.9% respectively (average 29.6%). In Sarnia, as well as in Stratford, there was no change in the percentage of children with caries-free milk teeth after 11 years of un-enriched drinking water, whereas in Brantford the frequency of such teeth rose over the same period from a level originally the same as that in Sarnia to the same height as that in Stratford.

TABLE 10

CARIES REDUCTION IN THE DECIDUOUS AND PERMANENT TEETH OF CHILDREN
6–8 YEARS OLD AFTER FLUORIDATION OF THE PUBLIC WATER SUPPLY
(IN CANADA AND THE USA)

City	Year and conditions		cer count per 100 examinees		CER count per 100 examinees		Percentage caries reduction	
	First caries assess-ment	Second caries assess-ment	First assess-ment	Second assess-ment	First assess-ment	Second assess-ment	Decid-uous teeth	Perma-nent teeth
Brantford	1948 3 years after start of fluoridation	1957 12 years	495	252	140	40	49.1	71.6
Evanston	1946 prior to start of fluoridation	1958 12 years after	537	366	150	50	31.8	66.7
Grand Rapids	1944/45 prior to start of fluoridation	1954 10 years after	617	317	187	72	48.6	61.5

The reason why the milk teeth—even when ingestion of an increased (optimal) amount of fluoride commences before conception—are less protected than the permanent teeth is an unsolved problem. The fact that morpho-differentiation and the commencement of mineralization occur *in utero* and that the placenta acts as a barrier against the entry of increased fluoride into the foetal circulation may play some part (reviews: Chapter 4, section 4; Zipkin & Babeaux, 1965). This barrier is already effective against fluoride concentrations in drinking water. Carlos, Gittelsohn & Haddon (1962) showed that fluoride ingestion by the mother during pregnancy causes no difference in caries experience. Other studies of the same problem in the USA have given contradictory results (review: Babeaux & Zipkin, 1966), which might indicate that the fluoride ingestion that is regarded as optimal for the mother is of borderline significance for the expected child.

At the same time, however, it should be borne in mind that the milk teeth of 6- to 8-year-old children are approaching the end of their life and therefore cannot be compared with the permanent teeth of the same children, which are commencing their existence. A more suitable comparison is with the permanent teeth of adults at an advanced age (Table 8); such a comparison at least hints at a certain parallelism. No definite conclusions can be drawn. however, from the available data in regard to the causation of the definitely proven difference in the effect on the temporary and the permanent teeth.

Fluoride Ingestion with Salt

As a general vehicle for ensuring adequate fluoride ingestion, cooking salt comes next to drinking water; its enrichment with iodine already provides a reliable means of preventing goitre. Following recommendations to this effect, Wespi (1956) succeeded in having salt enriched with sodium fluoride put on the market in Switzerland, and the consumption over the whole country increased from 100 000 kg in 1955 to 3 134 900 kg in 1961 (Wespi, 1962). In addition to 10 mg of potassium iodide, this salt contains 200 mg of sodium fluoride per kilogram, corresponding to 90 mg of fluoride ion. The daily salt consumption per head of the adult population in Switzerland amounts to about 7 g, so that the enrichment ensures the consumption of at most 0.63 mg of fluoride daily. It can be assumed that the fluoride intake with salt is smaller in children, particularly infants.

Nevertheless, this enrichment (which is at least 50 % below the optimum for adults) has led to a statistically significant fall in caries experience as indicated by the CER—tooth surfaces count after 5½ years' unsupervised use as table and cooking salt (Marthaler & Schenardi, 1962). In extent and distribution over the various tooth surfaces, this reduction is similar to the one observed in Tiel by Backer Dirks, Houwink & Kwant (1961) following water fluoridation. The extent of the reduction achieved ranges in both boys and girls from 8 % to 28 % in the various annual age-groups. The report also shows the difficulties and inaccuracies in the selection of examinees and their allocation to the experimental and control groups.

Fluoride Ingestion with Flour

Flour has been used in some countries as a vehicle for calcium, iron, iodine and/or some vitamins, and it has also been suggested as a carrier for fluoride. It has been shown that the variations in flour consumption may be smaller than those in water consumption in some countries—for example, Denmark and the Netherlands. Fluoridation of flour, like salt, would have the advantages of requiring much less of the chemical and, with large-scale production, much simpler control measures than fluoridation of piped waters. However, before fluoride enrichment of flour or any other staple food can be recommended on a large scale a number of investigations have to be performed: mapping of the consumption variations in different countries and areas, testing of the systemic and dental absorption of fluoride from the respective vehicles, and clinical testing of the caries-preventive effects.

Fluoride Ingestion with Milk

On the daily administration over 3½ years of 1 mg of fluoride in the milk with school meals, a very distinct fall in caries was observed by Rusoff et al. (1962) in the multicuspidate teeth erupting during this period in children aged 6-9 years at the beginning of the experiment. The caries rate was 0.34 CER teeth per child in the experimental group as compared with 1.70 in the control group (corresponding to a drop of 80%). The protective effect was still detectable 18 months after stopping the enrichment of the milk, but had fallen to 50%. Because of the considerable divergence in caries attack affecting the first molars in the two groups at the beginning of the experiment, and in view of the smallness of the groups (65 and 64 children), the lower CER rate noted in the experimental group during the enrichment period can hardly be regarded as a valid proof of the alleged effect.

The results for a larger, but still insufficient, number of subjects in Winterthur, Switzerland, are shown in Table 11. The protective effect is definitely visible.

TABLE 11

DENTAL CARIES EXPERIENCE OF CHILDREN AFTER 6 YEARS OF CONSUMING
FLUORIDATED MILK (1 ppm F) AND OF CONTROLS IN WINTERTHUR,
SWITZERLAND [a]

Year of birth	1958	1957	1956	1955	1954
Fluoride group:					
Number of examinees	159	164	92	154	160
Age when milk fluoridation started (months)	prenatally		9–20	21–32	33–44
cer count per 100 examinees	522	655			
CER count " " "		22	212	277	310
Control group:					
Number of examinees	139	145	87	56	124
cer count per 100 examinees	713	801			
CER count " " "		59	268	325	452
Percentage caries reduction:					
in the deciduous teeth	26.6	19.2			
in the permanent teeth		62.7	20.9	14.8	31.4

[a] Data from Ziegler (1964) and Wirz (1964), collected in 1964.

The two experimental series cited give proof, which *a priori* seemed beyond doubt, that increased fluoride consumption can be suitably achieved by means of milk fluoridation too.

Fluoride Ingestion with Tablets

Protective ingestion of fluoride by systematic administration of fluoride tablets is feasible on a large scale primarily during school age, when it is possible to distribute the tablets in school and see that they are taken under the supervision of the teacher. Thus such administration is restricted to the days when children are attending school. Both these factors are disadvantageous as concerns the protective effect. Consequently, it is not surprising that the results of this method, as reported in various studies, are far behind those given by water fluoridation. However, several reports have indicated that increased fluoride ingestion beginning only at school age exerts a protective effect, not only on teeth erupting later on but also on first molars, which have already appeared when tablet administration commences. Some reports show that the effect persists for several years after the cessation of tablet administration, although it becomes weaker (Held & Piguet, 1956; Berner et al., 1959); other reports even mention an increasing effect (Schützmannsky, 1965).[1]

When tablet administration commences at an early age, the results are quantitatively better; indeed, in the somewhat small number of examinees reported on by Arnold et al. (1960), they were quite comparable to those given by water fluoridation. However, these subjects were not only few in number (only about half remaining of the original test group) but also a selected group of children of scientific workers at the US National Institutes of Health.

In the various trials carried out different doses were used, and sometimes even changed during the course of one and the same trial. Because of the fear that the tablets might cause mottling, the dose was often kept below the optimum level, which again may be responsible—at least in part—for the comparatively small effect.

Fluorides have been combined with vitamins A and D, and sometimes also with other protective factors, in a number of preparations as tablets, lozenges and drops, particularly in the USA (Wurdack, 1965). The philosophy behind these preparations has been that it would be easier to obtain the collaboration of the families for the distribution of preparations containing several recognized protective factors. The caries-preventive effect of such preparations is probably of the same order as that of simple fluoride tablets (Hennon, Stookey & Muhler, 1966; Margolis, Macauley & Freshman, 1967; Hamberg, 1967). For a good effect on already erupted teeth these preparations obviously have to be administered in a form that ensures contact with the tooth surfaces.

3. EFFECT OF LOCAL FLUORIDE TREATMENT ON CARIES EXPERIENCE

Since the discovery that the fluoride ion readily reacts with calcium phosphates, even with the apatite in dental enamel, great efforts have been made to develop efficient methods for incorporating fluoride ions into the enamel surface of erupted teeth locally, by topical fluoride applications. Such treatment was expected to promote dental health primarily through its

---

[1] This conclusion, however, was based on the percentage of DMF teeth in relation to the tooth count, which, because of the increasing number of permanent teeth erupting with advancing age, may vary in an erratic manner.

local effects upon the tooth surface, and secondarily—though to a minor degree—by retention and absorption of F.

Some F is retained after every local application of fluoride, particularly if high concentrations are used. Studies of this problem are summarized in Chapter 2, section 4.

The caries-protective effect apparently varies both with the method of application and with factors such as posteruptive tooth-age, previous cleaning and drying of the teeth, supply of fluoride from other sources, etc.

Many methods have been tested, beginning with the manual (topical) applications of rather concentrated solutions of sodium fluoride to the tooth surfaces. Later developments have included the use of solutions of different fluorides, such as stannous fluoride, fluoride—orthophosphoric acid combinations, and sodium monofluorophosphate; elaborate methods, such as the daily application of a fluoride gel in a splint specially fitted to the dental arch or the use of electrophoresis in order to accelerate ionic movement; and simpler methods, such as the use of fluoride-containing toothpastes and mouthwashes.

As regards the mode of action of topically applied fluorides, reference is made to Chapter 6, section 4. A detailed report on the extensive and rapidly growing literature on local fluoride applications has been regarded as falling outside the scope of this monograph. Only a few summarizing statements will be made in addition to references to some reviews and key articles (Campbell & Widner, 1958; Mühlemann & König, 1961; Brudevold, 1967; Torell & Ericsson, 1965).

Rather great variations are apparent in the reports on the caries-protective effects of even similar or identical topical fluoride applications. This may reflect the well-known difficulties of clinical caries registration, small but none the less important differences in experimental conditions, and inadequacies in the quantitative estimation of caries protection.

The careful, repeated manual painting of the tooth surfaces of children with 2% sodium fluoride solution seems to reduce the caries attack by a maximum of 40% during the following year, but thereafter little seems to be left of the protection. The reports on similar or single applications of stannous fluoride solutions vary between much higher and much lower figures.

The purpose of combining sodium fluoride and phosphoric acid—pH about 3.0—has been to obtain the markedly greater fluoride uptake by the enamel at lower pH while at the same time counteracting by the high concentration of phosphate ions the splitting of the apatite, with liberation of phosphate and formation of unstable CaF_2. Initial optimistic reports have been followed by more modest figures.

Mouth-washing or tooth-brushing with weak solutions of NaF at intervals of two weeks or more have been widely employed in Scandinavian schools with good reported results.

The incorporation of fluorides into toothpastes offers great promise for the daily, and practically automatic, application of F, but obviously only in persons who brush their teeth regularly. This incorporation has met with some difficulties regarding the compatibility of the fluoride and the polishing agents commonly used in toothpastes. A number of clinical tests with different formulations of fluoride toothpastes (generally containing 0.1% F) have given reductions of 20-30% in caries rates in schoolchildren; higher protection figures have also been reported, particularly with daily supervised toothbrushing.

The effects of topical fluoride applications in adults and the benefits of such applications in areas with optimal water fluoride concentrations cannot yet be regarded as quantitatively settled.

Few studies have been made on the possible reaction of the gingival tissues to local fluoride applications. Provided that the pH values of applied solutions are not so low as to cause superficial etching *per se,* the gingiva does not seem to react to topical applications of fluoride containing up to 2% NaF.

4. EFFECT ON SHAPE AND SIZE OF THE TEETH

It could hardly fail to escape the notice of investigators in fluoride-rich districts how greatly the appearance of the teeth differs from that in fluoride-poor districts. In fluoride-rich districts the teeth have a fine lustre, which tends to be yellowish rather than blueish, lower cusps with flatter slopes, and wide, easily visible sulci. At the beginning of our field studies, some of the writer's young clinical assistants endeavoured to determine—on the basis of the appearance of the teeth and without waiting for the results of the chemical water analysis—whether the district concerned was a fluoride-rich one. However, these differences were not described more closely, mainly because of their non-quantitative nature. Measurable differences in the form of the teeth were first reported in the Evanston study—namely, a fall in the frequency of deep but not carious fissures (termed "pre-carious") after the introduction of fluoride; this decrease became more and more pronounced as the period of fluoride consumption increased (particularly in children aged 6-8 years, but also in those aged 12-14 years). Nevertheless, on a more thorough study of the reports it is noticeable that the decrease in frequency was already distinct after water fluoridation had existed for only a short time—i.e., it was manifest also in the case of teeth whose morpho-differentiation had taken place and mineralization commenced in a fluoride-poor environment, which had at most become a favourable one only in the final stage of mineralization (decrease in the number of pre-carious fissures in 8-year-old children after 12-22 months' fluoridation, from 107.65 to 68.63; after 9 years' fluoridation, however, reduction to 24.04). Subsequent experience with fluoridation has shown that there is no, or hardly any, noticeable protective action on the occlusal surfaces of first molars whose morpho-differentiation and mineralization have taken place in a fluoride-poor environment (Backer Dirks, 1963; Russell & Hamilton, 1961).

Apparently contradictory reports on the influence of fluoride on tooth size in humans and experimental animals are referred to in Chapter 6, section 4.

Measurement of the Carabelli cusp (a fifth, not always well-marked, cusp of the upper first molar) in children at Newburgh and Kingston gave greater values at Newburgh. The fact that this difference is not statistically significant indicates, however, that genetically determined dental charac-teristics are unlikely to be changed by increased fluoride consumption (Cox, Finn & Ast, 1961).

5. EFFECT ON PERIODONTAL HEALTH

The multifaced antagonism between dental decay and periodontal disease renders specially important the question whether (and, if so, to what extent) the protection against caries afforded by increased fluoride ingestion is associated with an adverse effect on the health of the periodontal structures. Although suspicions of this nature have been expressed, there is evidence that increased fluoride consumption in no way harms the periodontium and may even be advantageous. The fact that continuous consumption of fluoride-rich water in childhood does not bring about or maintain any inflammatory condition of the gums was shown, *inter alia*, in the case of children aged 14-15 years by Russell (1957) (comparison between Newburgh, with 1 ppm fluoride, and Kingston, with about 0.2 ppm) and in 16- to 18-year-old children by the present writer (Adler, 1957) (comparison be-tween Szekszárd, with about 0.75 ppm, Hatvan, with about 0.4 ppm, and Eger, with about 0.2 ppm fluoride in the drinking water). Jirásková (1961) in Czechoslovakia, as well as Englander & White (1963) in the USA, found the periodontium to be in better condition among teenagers living in fluoride rich districts than among those in fluoride-poor districts, in regard to the number of teeth affected per person and the percentage of subjects with periodontal pockets (the Russell periodontal index remaining the same).

We feel that the comparisons made by Russell & White (1959) in the USA on the basis of studies of adults are more important. These studies, carried out in localities with a high fluoride content in the drinking water (Colorado Springs, 2.5 ppm; Bartlett, about 8 ppm), concerned the frequency of pockets and the numerical value of the Russell periodontal index; the findings were in no way worse than those in fluoride-poor control districts. The present writer, too, found among the female population of a fluoride-rich village that the number of permanent teeth lost up to an advanced age was not greater than that observed in fluoride-poor areas.

To sum up, data based on various criteria justify the conclusion that the possibility of increased fluoride consumption having an adverse effect on the periodontium can be definitely excluded. At all ages the reduction in the number of teeth lost as a result of smaller caries experience should have a favourable influence on the position of as well as on the load borne by the remaining teeth, and consequently also on the periodontium. This is probably the main explanation of the lower prevalence of periodontal pockets which is repeatedly encountered in fluoride-rich districts. However, it is worth mentioning that experimental osteoporosis in alveolar septa, provoked by steroids in animals, has been prevented or reduced by fluoride administration (Zipkin, Bernick & Menczel, 1965; Gedalia & Binderman, 1966; Levy et al., 1968).

6. EFFECT ON LOSS OF THE DECIDUOUS AND ON ERUPTION OF THE PERMANENT TEETH

As part of epidemiological investigations under the direction of Dean, it was shown by Short (1944) that 12- to 14-year-old children of both sexes in areas with fluoride-rich drinking water had fewer erupted permanent teeth per subject than those in localities with fluoride-poor water. With a fluoride content of 2.5 ppm, the difference was statistically significant, while with a lower content, already affording, however, a high degree of protection against caries (1.2-1.9 ppm), this was no longer the case. Consequently Short excluded the possibility that this phenomenon could result from smaller caries experience of the milk teeth. Meanwhile, a more refined method of investigation made clear the basic causes involved (Adler, 1951a). It was shown later that the "apparent delay in eruption" of certain permanent teeth—and at the same time the delay in the loss of individual milk teeth—does not depend directly on the fluoride content of the drinking water but on the caries experience of the deciduous molars (Adler [1]). The deciduous molars and the permanent premolars are practically the *only* teeth affected by this delay in exfoliation or eruption, respectively. Findings in Finland (Scheinin et al.,1964) and Denmark (Møller, 1965) support this conclusion.

In regard to the influence of water fluoridation, the reports from Grand Rapids, Brantford and many other places in North America and Europe give no details regarding the number of milk teeth and permanent teeth in the various annual age-groups of boys and girls. The relevant figures given in the Newburgh-Kingston study (although unfortunately not broken down by sex) agree very well with the explanation given above (Table 12): among 9- and 10-year-old children—but not in younger age-groups—the number of teeth in Newburgh after 8 years of fluoridation was distinctly smaller, as compared both with the prefluoridation value and with the control-town

---

[1] Academic dissertation, Budapest, 1956.

TABLE 12

MEAN NUMBER OF ERUPTED PERMANENT TEETH
BEFORE AND 8 YEARS AFTER FLUORIDATION OF
THE PUBLIC WATER SUPPLY [a]

Age (years)	Newburgh		Kingston	
	1944-45	1953-54	1945-46	1953-54
6	4.8	5.16	4.9	4.46
7	8.8	8.53	8.9	8.08
8	11.4	11.22	11.7	10.72
9	14.7	12.95	14.0	13.27
10	18.3	16.79	17.8	17.93

[a] Data from Ast, Finn & Chase (1951) and from Ast et al. (1955).

figures. In general, Carlos & Gittelsohn (1965) found no delaying effect on the change in dentition. Again, unpublished provisional data from Norrköping, Sweden (personal communication from A. Syrrist) show, after 6-9 years' fluoridation, no appreciable difference in the number of teeth (broken down according to type) compared with the control area either among 7-year-old or among 14-year-old boys and girls. Findings in the two fluoridation studies with younger children indicate that no general delay in the eruption of the permanent teeth is caused. Rather, premature loss of the deciduous molars, as a cause of the early emergence of the permanent premolars, is largely prevented. There seems to be no effect on the eruption of the milk teeth (Tank & Storvick, 1964).

7. EFFECT ON ORTHODONTIC ANOMALIES

When fluoride ingestion from water is adequate, there is less undesirable migration and tilting in the remaining teeth after loss of individual milk teeth and permanent teeth than there is when fluoride-poor water is consumed. As a result, anomalies of occlusion are also rarer. Thus, in Evanston, the frequency of malocclusion among 6- to 8-year-old children fell after 8 years of fluoridation from 37.51% to 29.54%, and among 12- to 14-year-old children, after 10 years of fluoridation, from 55.83% to 46.32%, while in Oak Park over the same period there was a slight increase in frequency. Before fluoridation, a second deciduous molar was lost in at least 6.2% of 6- to 8-year-old children, and this was combined with malocclusion in 3.4% of cases. These frequencies fell to 2.9% and 0.4%, respectively, after fluoridation. Of all the occlusion anomalies encountered, 13.4% before fluoridation and only 1.3% after 8 years' fluoridation were associated with the loss of one or more second deciduous molars (Hill, Blayney & Wolf, 1959). In older children, loss of the first permanent molar plays a great part in the etiology of anomalies in the positioning of the teeth. For example, Ast, Allaway & Draker (1962) found that among 50 children aged 13-14 years in Kingston who had lost one or more first molars there was not one with normal occlusion. In Kingston, 35.2% of children had lost a first molar and in Newburgh only 8.1%. Consequently, it is not surprising that class I anomalies (Angle's classification) were found more often in Kingston than in Newburgh. Surprisingly enough, however, in Kingston the frequency of class II and class III (Angle's classification) anomalies was also greater than in Newburgh, even among children who had not lost any first molars. A causal connexion of the last-mentioned differences in frequency with fluoridation seems to us all the less probable in that increased fluoride ingestion has been shown to have no effect on the growth and proportions of the facial bones (Ast, 1955; Salzman & Ast, 1955). None the less, it is true that differences in the frequency of distoclusion and mesioclusion were also found by Plater (1949), between Madison, with fluoride-poor drinking water, and Union Grove, with 1 ppm fluoride in the drinking water.

8.   CONCLUDING REMARKS

It has been shown that a certain level of fluoride consumption—especially when this is continuous from earliest childhood—affords considerable protection for both permanent and milk teeth against caries, without exerting any unfavourable influence on the appearance of the teeth or on the periodontium. The best way to ensure adequate fluoride consumption is by fluoridation of drinking water, which is a collective measure of benefit to all those drawing water for drinking and cooking purposes from a central water supply system. When nutrition is adequate, enrichment of the water so that it contains 1.0-1.2 ppm is advisable in temperate zones. In warmer regions the content should be smaller.

Experience to date indicates fluoridated drinking water to be superior to all other vehicles, since these do not ensure permanent and optimal ingestion of fluoride. For districts without a piped water supply system, the best alternative at present appears to be enriched cooking salt. Another possible vehicle is flour, whose consumption in some countries does not vary more markedly than that of water or cooking salt. Nevertheless, certain precautions are called for in the use of fluoridated salt and flour which are unnecessary with water fluoridation (risk of introduction into fluoride-rich areas).

The use of fluoridated milk is less promising, bearing in mind the wide variations in its consumption and its frequent distribution from small dairies or even farms, difficult to control.

Any hope of ensuring the continuous, large-scale administration of fluoride tablets or similar preparations in families is equally slim. However, in groups such as school-classes the administration of tablets may be feasible, and the distribution of fluoride together with vitamins A and D to pre-school children may obtain sufficient interest and collaboration from many parents. A caries-preventive effect of these measures seems established.

Methods of local fluoride application also carry promise in direct proportion to their caries-preventive effectiveness but in inverse proportion to the personal effort and orderliness or professional working time required. These considerations clearly point towards the use of fluoride-containing toothpastes or mouthwashes.

The outstanding ability of fluoride to prevent dental caries by mechanisms that are not yet fully understood warrants great efforts both in basic and applied research and in practical application of methods that can safely and effectively be utilized for the attainment of improved dental health, which is an integral part of human general health.

REFERENCES

Adler, P. (1951a) *Acta med. Acad. Sci. hung.,* **2**, 349-360

Adler, P. (1951b) *Dtsch. Zahn-, Mund- u. Kieferheilk.,* **15**, 24-30

Adler, P. (1953) *Schweiz. Mschr. Zahnheilk.,* **63**, 432-452

Adler, P. (1955) In: Rosenthal, W. & Hoffmann-Axthelm, W., ed., *Die Zahnkaries und ihre sozialhygienische Bedeutung,* Berlin, Volk und Gesundheit, pp. 56-68

Adler, P. (1957) *Dtsch. Stomat.,* **7**, 268-283

Adler, P., Straub, J. & Szeverényi, E. (1951) *Fogorv. Szle,* **44**, 187-189

Arnold, F. A., Jr (1943) *J. Amer. dent. Ass.,* **30**, 499-508

Arnold, F. A., Jr (1957) *Amer. J. publ. Hlth,* **47**, 539-545

Arnold, F. A., Jr, Dean, H. T., Jay, P. & Knutson, J. W. (1956) *Publ. Hlth Rep. (Wash),* **71**, 652-658

Arnold, F. A., Jr, Likins, R. C., Russell, A. L. & Scott, D. B. (1962) *J. Amer. dent. Ass.,* **65**, 780-785

Arnold, F. A., Jr, McClure, F. J. & White, C. L. (1960) *Dent. Progr.,* **1**, 8-12

Ast, D. B. (1955) *Amer. J. Orthodont.,* **41**, 45-54

Ast, D. B., Allaway, N. & Draker, H. L. (1962) *Amer. J. Orthodont.,* **48**, 106-113

Ast, D. B., Bushel, A., Wachs, B. & Chase, H. C. (1955) *J. Amer. dent. Ass.,* **50**, 680-685

Ast, D. B., Finn, S. B. & Chase, H. C. (1951) *J. Amer. dent. Ass.,* **42**, 188-195

Babeaux, W. L. & Zipkin, I. (1966) *J. oral Ther. Pharmacol.,* **3**, 124-135

Backer Dirks, O. (1963) *Brit. dent. J.,* **114**, 211-216

Backer Dirks, O., Houwink, B. & Kwant, G. W. (1961) *Arch. oral Biol.,* **5**, 284-300

Berner, L., Fernex, E., Held, A.-J. & Piguet, F. (1959) *Schweiz. Mschr. Zahnheilk.,* **69**, 798-802

Brown, H. K. (1954, 1957, 1959, 1961, 1962, 1963) *Dental effects of water fluoridation,* Ottawa (Reports to the Department of National Health and Welfare)

Brudevold, F. (1962) *Chemical composition of the teeth in relation to caries.* In: Sognnaes, R. F., ed., *Chemistry and prevention of dental caries,* Springfield, Ill., Thomas, pp. 32-88

Brudevold, F. et al. (1967) *J. dent. Res.,* **46**, 37

Bruszt, P. (1962) *Fogorv. Szle,* **55,** 102-111

Bunting, R. W. (1927) *Dent. Cosmos,* **70,** 1008

Campbell, I. R. & Widner, E. W. (1958) *Annotated bibliography. The occurrence and biological effects of fluorine compounds,* Cincinnati, Kettering Laboratory, University of Cincinnati, Ohio

Carlos, J. P. & Gittelsohn, A. M. (1965) *J. dent. Res.,* **44,** 509-516

Carlos, J. P., Gittelsohn, A. M. & Haddon, W., Jr (1962) *Publ. Hlth Rep. (Wash.),* **77,** 658-660

Cox, G. J. (1939) *J. Amer. Wat. Wks Ass.,* **31,** 1926-1930

Cox, G. J., Finn, S. B. & Ast, D. B. (1961) *J. dent. Res.,* **40,** 393-395

Csepura, G. & Kovács, E. (1953) *Dtsch. Zahn-, Mund- u. Kieferheilk.,* **19,** 48-52

Dean, H. T. (1933) *Publ. Hlth Rep. (Wash.),* **48,** 703

Dean, H. T. (1945) In: Gies, W. J., ed., *Fluorine in dental public health,* New York, Institute of Clinical Oral Pathology, pp. 19-30

Dean, H. T. (1954) *Int. dent. J.,* **4,** 311-337

Dean, H. T. & McKay, F. S. (1939) *Amer. J. publ. Hlth,* **29,** 590-596

Englander, H. R. & Wallace, D. A. (1962) *Publ. Hlth Rep. (Wash.),* **77,** 887-893

Englander, H. R. & White, C. L. (1963) *J. Amer. dent. Ass.,* **68,** 173-181

Forrest, J. R., Parfitt, G. J. & Bransby, E. R. (1951) *Mth. Bull. Minist. Hlth Lab. Serv.,* **10,** 104-111

Galagan, D. J. & Lamson, G. G., Jr (1953) *Publ. Hlth Rep. (Wash.),* **68,** 497-508

Gedalia, I. & Binderman, I. (1966) *J. dent. Res.,* **45,** 825-829

Hamberg, L. (1967) *Thesis,* Stockholm, Realtryck

Held, A.-J. & Piguet, F. (1956) *Bull. schweiz. Akad. med. Wiss.,* **12,** 453-458

Hennon, D. K., Stookey, G. K. & Muhler, J. C. (1966) *J. Dent. Child.,* **33,** 3

Hill, I. N., Blayney, J. R. & Wolf, W. (1959) *J. dent. Res.,* **38,** 782-794

Hodge, H. C. (1950) *J. Amer. dent. Ass.,* **40,** 436-439

Jirásková, M. (1961) *Arch. oral Biol.,* **6,** 209-213

Levy, B. M., Bernick, S., Hampton, J. K., Jr & Dreizen, S. (1968) In: *International Association for Dental Research, 46th General Meeting, San Francisco, Calif., USA, March 1968 ; Abstracts,* Chicago, American Dental Association, Abstr. No. 182

McKay, F. S. (1929) *Dent. Cosmos,* **71,** 747-755

Margolis, F. J., Macauley, J. & Freshman, E. (1967) *Amer. J. Dis. Child.,* **113,** 672

Marthaler, T. M. & Schenardi, C. (1962) *Helv. odont. Acta.,* **6,** 1-6

Ministry of Health, Scottish Office & Ministry of Housing and Local Government (1962) *The conduct of fluoridation studies in the United Kingdom and the results achieved after five years,* London, HMSO

Minoguchi, G. & Sato, T. (1964) *Bull. Stomat. Univ. Kyoto,* **4,** 45-124

Møller, I. J. (1965) *Dental fluorose og caries,* Copenhagen, Rhodos (Thesis)

Mühlemann, H. R. & König, K. G., ed., (1961) *Caries Symposium Zürich,* Berne & Stuttgart, Huber,

Plater, W. R. (1949) *Amer. J. Orthodont.,* **35,** 790-796

Röse, C. (1904) *Dtsch. Mschr. Zahnheilk.,* **22,** 735-748

Rusoff, L. L., Konikoff, B. S., Frye, J. B., Jr, Johnston, J. E. & Frye, W. W. (1962) *Amer. J. clin. Nutr.,* **11,** 94-101

Russell, A. L. (1957) *Amer. J. publ. Hlth,* **47,** 688-694

Russell, A. L. & Elvove, E. (1951) *Publ. Hlth Rep. (Wash.)*, **66**, 1389-1401

Russell, A. L. & Hamilton, P. M. (1961) *Arch. oral Biol.*, **6**, 50-57 (Special Supplement: Proceedings of 8th ORCA Congress, London, July 1961)

Russell, A. L. & White, C. L. (1959) In: Muhler, J. C. & Hine, M. K., ed., *Fluorine and dental health*, Bloomington, Indiana University Press, pp. 115-127

Salzman, J. A. & Ast, D. B. (1955) *Amer. J. Orthodont.*, **41**, 674-690

Scheinin, A. et al. (1964) *Acta odont. scand.*, **22**, 229-254

Schour, I. & Massler, M. (1947) *J. dent. Res.*, **26**, 441-442

Schützmannsky, G. (1965) *Dtsch. Stomat.*, **15**, 106-111

Short, E. M. (1944) *J. dent. Res.*, **23**, 247-255

Tank, G. & Storvick, C. A. (1964) *J. Amer. dent. Ass.*, **69**, 749-757

Torell, P. & Ericsson, Y. (1965) *Acta odont. scand.*, **23**, 287

Weaver, R. (1950) *Brit. dent. J.*, **88**, 231-239

Wespi, H. J. (1956) *Fluor-Vollsalz zur Kropf- und Cariesbekämpfung*, Basel & Stuttgart, Schwabe

Wespi, H. J. (1962) *Schweiz. Mschr. Zahnheilk.*, **72**, 323-331

Wirz, R. (1964) *Schweiz. Mschr. Zahnheilk.*, **74**, 767-784

Ziegler, E. (1964) *Helv. paediat. Acta*, **19**, 343-354

Zipkin, I. & Babeaux, W.L. (1965) *J. oral Ther. Pharmacol.*, **1**, 652-665

Zipkin, I., Bernick, S. & Menczel, J. (1965) *J. Amer. Soc. Periodont.*, **3**, 111

INDEX

INDEX

Absorption of fluorides, 75-91, 105
mechanism, 76-78
site, 78-80, 105
See also Gastrointestinal absorption of fluorides; Inhalation of fluorine
Acid production by salivary bacteria,
effect of fluoride on, 206
effect of molybdate on, 175
Acroparaesthesiae in fluorosis, 247-248
Adrenal glands, radioactive fluorine concentration, 168
Africa,
fluoride content of waters, 23-26
North, inhalation of fluoride-containing dusts, 61
Age, effect of,
on bone apatite crystallinity, 189-193, 205
on fluoride concentration,
in bone, 109-111, 121-125, 135, 167, 194
in dentine, 201
in teeth, 111-114, 121, 125-128
on urinary fluoride excretion, 153-154
Allergic reactions, 15, 262-263, 309
Aluminium ions, effect on fluoride absorption, 86
Ameloblast, effect of fluoride on, 116, 233-234
Americas, fluoride content of waters, 24, 26-27
See also United States of America
Anaemia, fluoride-induced, 382
in fluorotic rabbits, 175
in industrial fluorosis, 263
Anaesthetic agents, fluorinated, metabolism, 58
Animal fluorosis, 315-316
Anticariogenic agents, fluorinated drugs, 40-56
Antimalarial agents, fluorinated drugs, 59
Aorta,
fluoride content, 101, 167
in calcific plaques, 282

prevention of lesions in dogs, 174
Apatite,
effect of fluoride on rate of seeding, 198
synthetic, fluoride reaction with, 196-197
See also Bone apatite
Aqueous solutions, fluoride-containing,
as dentine obtundents, 56
ingestion of fluoride from, 44-45
Arteriosclerosis,
correlation with fluoride content of aorta, 101
role of fluoride in incidence of, 172
Arthritis, fluoride content of bone in, 189
Ascorbic acid, effect on retention of fluoride, 48, 177-179
Ash content of bone, effect of fluoride on, 186-187
Asia, fluoride content of waters, 24, 27-28
See also India; Japan
Atherosclerosis, 14
Atmosphere,
fluoride content, 19, 22
inhalation of fluoride from, 59-64
See also Industrial fluoride hazards
Australasia, fluoride content of waters, 24, 28

Bactericidal agents, fluorinated drugs as, 59
Beer,
fluoride absorption from, 105
fluoride content, 36
Blood plasma,
and stomach fluoride level, 168
fluoride content, 58, 94-96, 100, 104, 134, 145, 165-166, 214
control of, 96-97
fluorine, action on plasma iodine, 257-258
isocitric dehydrogenase activity, 184
radiofluoride concentration, 97
See also Foetal blood; Haemopoietic

PROMESSE DE PLUIE

www.editions-jclattes.fr

Donna Milner

PROMESSE DE PLUIE

Roman

*Traduit de l'anglais
par Laurence Kiefé*

JC Lattès

Titre de l'édition originale
THE PROMISE OF RAIN
publiée par Quercus, Grande-Bretagne, 2010

Couverture : atelier Didier Thimonier
Illustration : © James Hardy / Zen Shui / Corbis

ISBN : 978-2-7096-2992-8

À la mémoire de Hazel Huckvale,
qui a planté la graine

1

Ma mère mourut le même jour que Marilyn Monroe, le 4 août 1962, et comme la star de cinéma, on ne découvrit son corps que le lendemain. Quand elle était vivante, maman avait une sacrée présence. Comme on pouvait s'y attendre, elle connut une mort tragique. Une mort qui devait contraindre mon père à revenir dans le sein de la famille. Même si, durant les onze premières années de ma vie, il était rentré tous les soirs dans notre maison construite pendant la guerre dans les quartiers sud de Vancouver, une grande partie de lui-même se trouvait ailleurs. J'étais habituée à son absence ; je n'étais pas habituée à celle de ma mère.

Avec le temps, j'en vins à croire que c'était cette absence même qui m'avait brutalement réveillée alors qu'il faisait encore nuit, ce matin-là. C'était plus probablement une rafale de vent qui secouait la fenêtre de ma chambre ou la pluie qui tambourinait sur la vitre. Je n'en suis pas certaine. Je sais seulement qu'en ouvrant les yeux, je me sentis poussée à quitter mon lit pour me glisser sur le palier étroit entre les deux chambres. Debout dans l'ombre, le cœur battant, j'écoutai le silence de la maison avant de descendre l'escalier, m'arrêtant dans l'angle, l'oreille tendue.

En bas, je me dirigeai vers la porte ouverte à l'extrémité du vestibule pour jeter un œil dans la chambre de mes parents.

L'odeur familière du parfum de ma mère, *Soir de Paris*, me submergea tandis que j'examinais la pièce, mes yeux s'accoutumant à la pénombre. Une silhouette sombre dans un coin me fit sursauter. Mais ce n'était qu'une robe pendue à la porte du placard. La pièce, comme le lit froissé, était vide.

Enjambant les vêtements éparpillés par terre, j'allai caresser le tissu soyeux de la robe de maman. Même quand elle n'était pas dedans, cette robe vert clair lui ressemblait. C'était sa préférée, celle qu'elle appelait « l'arme absolue », « sa tenue du dimanche », et la seule qu'elle accrochait sur un cintre rembourré.

Le jour où le camion d'Eaton l'avait livrée, elle m'avait appelée dans sa chambre pour l'essayer devant moi. Penchée vers le miroir de la coiffeuse, elle avait mis du rouge à lèvres, poudré la petite bosse de son nez puis, la tête inclinée, jugé de l'effet produit. Satisfaite du résultat, elle avait repoussé les livres, les bas filés et les cendriers à moitié pleins avant de reculer de quelques pas pour prendre la pose.

— Qu'en dis-tu, Ethie ?

Je la trouvais parfaite, quoi qu'elle eût sur le dos. Mais quelque chose dans cette robe accentuait le pétillement vert de ses yeux noisette, le brillant de ses épaisses boucles rousses et rendait le semis de ses taches de rousseur, que la poudre ne pouvait masquer, encore plus exotique.

— Tu es belle, répondis-je, on dirait une star de cinéma.

Son reflet me rendit mon sourire. Elle se retourna pour me prendre dans ses bras, m'enveloppant de son parfum et de sa nouvelle robe verte, m'enveloppant de tout elle.

— Oh Ethie, soupira-t-elle, quel bonheur de s'entendre dire qu'on est belle ! Surtout par ma fille préférée.

Elle me lâcha et tourna sur elle-même pour examiner le dos de la robe qui soulignait ses fesses rondes.

Même à cette époque, je savais sans doute déjà qu'elle avait acheté cette robe pour punir mon père de quelque faute. Quand elle était fâchée contre lui, la solution de maman était de feuilleter le catalogue pour commander quelque chose au-dessus de leurs moyens. Papa gérait les finances de la maison. Nous étions en compte pour tout ce qui était indispensable, y compris les courses hebdomadaires, et il réglait les factures à la fin du mois. Tant qu'elle ne travaillait pas, en fait d'argent, ma mère ne disposait que de l'allocation familiale mensuelle, soit dix dollars par enfant. Papa estimait cela suffisant pour couvrir toute dépense supplémentaire.

— C'est une robe magnifique, non ? demanda maman.

Elle en paraissait enchantée. Je hochai la tête en souriant, mais j'étais persuadée qu'elle n'attendait aucune réponse.

— C'est un modèle classique, ajouta-t-elle en s'agenouillant pour me prendre à nouveau dans ses bras. Et je vais en prendre soin, promit-elle, pour que tu puisses en profiter quand tu seras grande.

Chaque fois que je la voyais dans cette robe, je m'imaginais ainsi vêtue plus tard. Vu la tournure des événements, je ne la porterai jamais.

Un mouvement dans l'ombre me fit faire volte-face. Mais je n'aperçus que des boucles rousses emmêlées et le visage surpris d'une gamine de onze ans en culotte et maillot de corps qui me regardait dans le miroir. Les tempes battantes, je ressortis de la chambre à pas de loup. Je vérifiai le salon et la salle de bains de l'autre côté du vestibule. Vides tous les deux. Puis je me tournai vers la cuisine et je le vis – mon père, assis tout seul dans l'obscurité, les yeux fixés sur la fenêtre. Je me figeai sur le seuil. Je savais que ce n'était pas le moment d'entamer la petite danse à laquelle j'avais souvent recours pour le ramener de là où il disparaissait quand il s'embarquait dans une de ses transes. Tapie dans l'ombre, je regardai la braise rouge de sa cigarette passer lentement de la soucoupe sur la table à ses lèvres.

Des phares balayèrent la fenêtre, éclairant sa silhouette. Sans lâcher la rue du regard, il ôta le mégot de sa bouche pour l'écraser dans la soucoupe débordante. Je reculai jusqu'au salon où, collée contre le mur de façade, je soulevai un coin de voilage.

Dehors, une voiture noir et blanc s'arrêta le long du trottoir. Les essuie-glaces cessèrent leur mouvement. Le pare-brise se couvrit de gouttes lumineuses, brouillant l'ombre des occupants. Au moment où les portières s'ouvrirent, dans la maison d'en face, quelqu'un écarta les rideaux de la chambre à coucher avant de les relâcher, en les laissant entrouverts.

Mme Manson. Le chien de garde du quartier, comme l'appelait maman – quand elle ne la traitait pas de pipelette. Et, tout comme moi, elle était en train d'espionner par la fente de ses rideaux les deux policiers qui descendaient de voiture devant chez nous.

Mon père recula bruyamment sa chaise. Fonçant hors du salon, je grimpai l'escalier à toute vitesse. Hors d'haleine, je m'assis sur la marche après le virage et me penchai en avant, aux aguets.

Cette visite qui devait changer nos vies à jamais s'annonça en frappant doucement.

— Howard Coulter ?

La porte s'ouvrit en grinçant et une voix très jeune prononça le nom de mon père. Plus jeune même que celle de Frankie – mon frère aîné, âgé de vingt ans. Tout comme la façon de s'annoncer, la voix paraissait trop douce, trop gentille, pour appartenir à un policier.

Mon père ne réagit pas. Le silence s'installa et une autre voix plus âgée, plus grave, demanda :

— Pouvons-nous entrer, monsieur Coulter ?

Brusquement, une main me saisit l'épaule. Je me retournai d'un bond : Kipper était penché sur moi, sa bouche molle ouverte pour former un mot. Je posai un doigt sur mes lèvres. Il me rendit mon sourire en imitant mon geste. Je tapotai la marche et il vint s'affaler à côté de moi. Bien qu'il fût mon aîné de trois ans, mon frère, avec son corps épais aux hanches trop larges, était plus petit que moi. Il passa son bras courtaud autour de mes épaules, sans rien comprendre au jeu mais ravi de faire partie de la conspiration. Nous devions avoir une drôle de dégaine, tous les deux, assis là dans le petit matin sombre, moi en sous-vêtements, occupée à entortiller une longue boucle de cheveux en tire-bouchon, et lui, quatorze ans, tout sourire, vêtu d'un pyjama bleu imprimé de nounours et coiffé d'un feutre rond.

Ce chapeau brun aux bords étroits et relevés était indissociable de Kipper. Il ne le quittait que pour dormir. Il l'accrochait tous les soirs au montant de son lit, prêt à s'en recoiffer dès qu'il ouvrait l'œil. Il l'avait hérité de papa – un cadeau d'anniversaire de maman – bien des années auparavant. Papa ne l'avait jamais porté. Kipper ne s'en séparait jamais.

En bas dans l'entrée, la voix trop jeune répétait le nom de mon père et le ton de compassion me fit soudain peur. Je me penchai en avant pour tenter de voir ce qui se passait. Une autre main vint m'agripper l'épaule et Frankie, pieds nus et sans chemise, passa entre Kipper et moi. Ses cheveux blond cendré, généralement peignés en arrière et soigneusement brillantinés, se dressaient comme des ailes de chaque côté de sa tête. Je sentis l'odeur de Brylcreem qui restait encore de son rendez-vous de la veille. Sans s'arrêter, il ordonna : « Allez vous coucher ! » et dévala les marches quatre à quatre en remontant la fermeture Éclair de son jean.

Kipper se leva pour retourner dans sa chambre, toujours prêt à obéir à Frankie sans poser de questions. Ce qu'en général, je faisais également. Mais pas cette fois. Je suivis mon grand frère. En bas, notre père – l'air tout petit et rétréci dans la pénombre de l'entrée – demeurait immobile, la main crispée sur la poignée de porte. Dans la pâle lumière du matin, la pluie ruisselait sur les deux policiers qui se tenaient devant lui.

2

Je savais qu'il était différent. À six ans déjà, je savais que mon père ne ressemblait pas aux autres pères. Les autres pères ne restaient pas à fixer le mur, quelques centimètres au-dessus du poste de télévision. Ils ne disparaissaient pas régulièrement dans un monde de silence, ils ne s'égaraient pas dans d'interminables randonnées sous la pluie de Vancouver. Mon père partait parfois pendant des heures, et même des jours entiers, pour ces expéditions dont il revenait larmoyant et trempé comme une soupe, mais l'esprit plus léger, comme si son humeur sombre avait été nettoyée, à l'image de l'atmosphère de la ville. Je savais que les autres pères jouaient au ballon avec leurs fils. Je les observais avec envie percher leurs filles sur leurs épaules pour les promener d'un bout à l'autre du jardin. Je savais qu'ils avaient conscience de la présence de leurs enfants. Je n'étais pas sûre qu'il en fût de même pour mon père.

L'année de mon entrée à l'école, maman m'autorisa à courir jusqu'en haut de Barclay Street à l'heure où il revenait de son travail à la scierie. Tous les soirs, j'attendais avec impatience que mon séduisant père, de la sciure de bois dans ses cheveux bruns qu'il commençait à perdre, descende du bus. Et tous les soirs, je repérais cette infime seconde de perplexité dans ses yeux bleu pâle quand il me trouvait plantée là. Dès qu'il disait « Salut, Ethie », c'était fini. Il posait son casque sur ma tête et me tendait sa gamelle cabossée qui puait le métal et les sandwiches à la sardine. Je rentrais à la maison en la balançant d'une main tandis que de l'autre je me cramponnais à lui, comme si je croyais qu'il était content de me voir.

Je compris vite la raison pour laquelle mon père était ainsi détaché du monde. Ou du moins, je crus comprendre.

La guerre. Ce mot flottait dans l'atmosphère de notre maison comme un fantôme. Il rôdait dans le regard vide de mon père et au fond des bouteilles de whisky posées en haut du réfrigérateur. Parfois, il surgissait bruyamment de ses cauchemars au cœur de la nuit et réveillait toute la maison par sa violence obstinée. Maman conservait un balai à côté de leur lit pour s'armer contre ces épisodes. Une fois, peu de temps après le retour de mon père, elle commit l'erreur de chercher à le toucher alors qu'il luttait contre les horreurs qui hantaient son sommeil. Son poing était venu la frapper pile entre les deux yeux, lui brisant le nez en même temps que le cœur de mon père, comme elle disait. Donc, depuis dix-sept ans, dès qu'il commençait à se battre contre ses cauchemars, elle sautait du lit pour attraper le balai et le poussait avec le manche. Dès qu'elle était certaine qu'il était complètement réveillé, elle revenait se coucher. Allongée dans mon lit, j'écoutais ma mère chantonner d'une voix fausse pour le calmer et je finissais par me rendormir. Le lendemain matin, mon père avait toujours un regard vide, épuisé, que seule la pluie à venir saurait faire revivre.

« C'est la guerre », confiait maman en conversant à voix basse avec les visiteurs pour tenter d'expliquer ses soudaines crises. Quand j'étais très jeune, à force d'entendre ma mère et Frankie utiliser ces mots en référence aux absences de mon père, j'imaginais « Laguerre » comme une personne. Mais je compris vite qu'il ne s'agissait que de souvenirs. Des souvenirs que mon père ne partageait avec nul autre.

Même si on disait régulièrement de notre maison de Fraserview, comme de toutes celles des vétérans de ce quartier au sud de Vancouver, qu'elle avait été construite pendant la guerre, on évoquait rarement la guerre elle-même. Jamais en présence de mon père. La guerre restait tapie, spectre sombre, dans les coins de notre vie, prête à surgir sans prévenir pour saisir mon père dans son étau de silence que seules les interminables promenades dans la ville ruisselante pouvaient desserrer. À l'époque de mon entrée à l'école primaire, chaque fois que je voyais s'assombrir les yeux bleus de mon père, je priais pour que la pluie arrive.

Il ne fallait généralement pas longtemps pour que mes prières soient exaucées.

— Quand on a vécu à Tahsis, on ne songe plus à se plaindre du temps à Vancouver, disait souvent ma mère. Vivre à Tahsis, c'est vivre dans une station de lavage.

Quand mon père était revenu de la guerre, avant ma naissance, la famille s'était installée sur la côte nord-ouest de Vancouver Island. Maman affirmait qu'elle soupçonnait papa d'avoir cherché du travail dans l'endroit le plus pluvieux du monde, et c'était Tahsis. En dépit des photos et des nombreuses histoires que racontait maman sur cette lointaine ville d'exploitation du bois, je m'imaginais mal vivre dans un endroit où les seuls moyens de transport étaient le bateau ou l'hydravion.

J'entendis un jour tante Mildred, la sœur de maman, déclarer que, si mon frère « est comme il est », c'était parce qu'il était né en plein ouragan, alors qu'il était périlleux de voler entre Tahsis et Victoria. Ces paroles m'avaient surprise. Assise sur le canapé du salon, je relevai la tête. À côté de moi, Kipper m'écoutait lire le livre posé sur mes genoux en tripotant le bord de son chapeau. Lorsque je me tus, il l'enfonça jusqu'à ses yeux en poussant un énorme soupir.

Dans la cuisine, tante Mildred était assise, encore vêtue de son imperméable ; elle me tournait le dos. Elle devait considérer qu'il faisait trop froid chez nous ou elle craignait de coller des poils de chien ou de chat sur ses vêtements chers. En tout cas, quand elle venait nous voir, la plupart du temps lorsque papa travaillait, elle n'ôtait jamais son manteau, comme si elle était en permanence sur le départ.

En face d'elle, maman haussa les sourcils. Elle fixa sa sœur par-dessus le bord de sa tasse.

— Je te l'ai déjà dit, la trisomie 21 n'est pas un accident de naissance, déclara-t-elle en soupirant. (Elle reposa sa tasse et continua, les coudes sur la table.) Le destin de Kipper était scellé au moment où il a été conçu. Le ciel n'a pas eu de remords de dernière minute.

— Malheureusement, murmura ma tante.

— Mildred !

La voix de ma mère était lourde de menace.

Ma tante garda le silence. Mais elle ne put résister à l'envie d'ajouter quelque chose. Elle en était incapable. Reposant bruyamment sa tasse, elle déclara en reniflant :

— Tout ce que je dis, Lucy, c'est que ce garçon devrait être dans une institution. Plus tu attends, plus ce sera difficile. Et ce serait vraiment mieux pour tout le monde. Sans compter qu'il serait plus heureux avec ceux de son espèce.

— On est de la même espèce, répliqua sèchement maman.

Elle leva les yeux et nos regards se croisèrent. Elle sourit.

— Et il est heureux avec nous, merci beaucoup, reprit-elle.

Ce qui était vrai. La plupart du temps.

Kipper s'appelait en réalité Christopher Adam. « En référence à saint Christopher », expliquait maman. Bien qu'elle ne fût pas catholique, elle estimait juste de donner à son fils le nom du saint patron des voyages, « étant donné que quelqu'un veillait sur moi durant ce voyage jusqu'à Victoria Harbour en pleine tempête ».

Elle m'avait raconté que j'étais à l'origine de son surnom.

— Dès que tu as su marcher, tu le suivais partout en l'appelant. « Kipper », c'est le nom que tu lui as donné alors.

Le surnom lui resta. Tante Mildred exceptée, tout le monde l'appelait ainsi.

En échange, je lui dois mon surnom. Incapable de recourber sa langue pour prononcer le *l* de Ethel, il a fait de moi Ethie. Un échange de bons procédés et un cadeau dont je lui suis éternellement reconnaissante.

Qui, si ce n'est Lucy Coulter, aurait eu l'idée de nommer un bébé Ethel ? Lorsque je fus assez grande pour m'en plaindre, elle m'expliqua qu'elle avait voulu m'appeler Lily mais que papa s'y était opposé.

— De mémoire, c'est la seule fois où ton père a refusé de céder.

Juste avant ma naissance, tante Mildred avait donné à notre famille sa vieille télévision noir et blanc. Ce fut le premier poste de maman. La première émission qu'elle regarda se trouva être le premier épisode de *I Love Lucy*[1]. Nulle autre que ma mère n'aurait interprété toutes ces premières fois comme le signe que, si elle avait une fille – qu'elle ne pouvait pas appeler Lucy –, elle devait la baptiser Ethel, comme l'amie de Lucy Riccardo. À chaque épisode du feuilleton, maman murmurait : « Ah ! les voilà, Lucy et Ethel », comme si j'avais besoin qu'on me rappelle d'où venait mon nom. Et chaque fois, j'enfouissais mon visage dans les coussins du canapé en gémissant. Si Kipper était là, il enfonçait son chapeau jusqu'aux yeux et gémissait de conserve avec moi.

---

1. Série télévisée américaine très populaire.

Mon frère s'appropriait les émotions de ceux qu'il aimait. En particulier les miennes. Lorsque je riais, il riait, fort, avec des vociférations qui simulaient la joie. Si je pleurais, il se mettait à brailler aussi, avec des sanglots étouffés ; de grosses larmes de désespoir jaillissaient de ses yeux rougis. Il reflétait mes émotions avec une telle rapidité et une telle intensité que, souvent, ses réactions me faisaient prendre conscience de ce que je ressentais. Avec le temps, j'appris à réfréner mes emportements, sachant qu'ils risquaient de déclencher chez lui une crise d'asthme.

Avec papa, il se comportait tout à fait autrement. Près de lui, il restait calme et paisible, quelle que fût l'humeur de papa. D'après maman, de nous tous, c'était Kipper qui comprenait le mieux notre père. Souvent, lorsque papa, assis dans le fauteuil rembourré du salon, s'enfonçait dans une de ses crises prédisparition, mon frère glissait son corps large et trapu à côté de la frêle carcasse de papa. Il l'entourait de son bras et, de façon régulière, tapotait son épaule osseuse ; ils demeuraient sans rien dire devant le poste de télévision, comme s'ils ne formaient qu'une seule personne.

La semaine dernière, il y avait eu des pluies diluviennes. Durant les premiers jours d'août, maman avait découpé dans le *Daily Province* les articles mentionnant le nombre inouï d'accidents d'automobile liés à cette pluviométrie record. Dans toute notre rue, des visages enfantins se morfondaient derrière des vitres zébrées de pluie tandis que les gouttières se remplissaient et que les caniveaux débordaient. Confinés à l'intérieur, les petits se sentaient floués devant ces vacances d'été tronquées. Leurs mères réagissaient de la même façon. Installées dans notre cuisine à boire du café, elles se racontaient comment leurs époux respectifs prévoyaient toujours les changements de temps. Ils les sentaient dans la douleur lancinante de leurs muscles autour du métal fiché profond. Ils les sentaient dans les cicatrices inégales et déchiquetées de leurs blessures de guerre. Et ils les sentaient dans leurs os fragilisés par les souvenirs de têtes de ponts balayées par les vents et de champs de bataille gelés en Europe. Maman ne se mêlait jamais à leurs conversations. Contrairement à bien des hommes de notre rue, papa était revenu de la Seconde Guerre mondiale apparemment indemne. Aucune médaille pour blessure au champ d'honneur n'était entreposée avec son vieil uniforme dans le sous-sol. Aucun shrapnel allemand incrusté dans sa chair ne permettait de prévoir la météo. Et, à la différence de ses voisins, il appréciait la pluie.

Au pic de cet orage d'été, le jeudi après-midi, papa avait cherché son blouson d'aviateur dans le placard de l'entrée. Il avait au moins deux tailles de trop et le cuir brun décoloré était tout desséché et cassant à force d'avoir pris la pluie. N'empêche, notre père portait toujours ce vieux blouson pour ses virées. Il l'avait enfilé, il avait remonté le col en peau de mouton et il était sorti de la maison. Alors que nous poussions tous un soupir de soulagement inaudible, Kipper avait saisi son ciré jaune et l'avait suivi. Frankie s'était levé d'un bond pour le rattraper mais maman lui avait fait signe de se rasseoir. Lorsque la pluie cessa en fin de journée, papa et Kipper rentrèrent, mouillés et frigorifiés, et tous deux affamés.

Pour le dîner, Kipper ôta son chapeau détrempé. Des touffes de cheveux fins, plus orange que roux, se dressaient en tous sens sur le sommet de son crâne. Mon père lui adressa un sourire mélancolique en l'appelant « mon-grand-trieur ».

— Oui, mon-grand-trieur, l'imita Kipper.

Nous avons tous dévisagé papa avec le même regard inter-rogateur.

— Mon-grand-trieur ? demanda maman.

— Oui, répondit lentement papa de sa voix douce. Kipper trie les gens en deux groupes. Ceux qui sont à l'aise avec lui et ceux qui ne le sont pas. Avec ce critère, on en sait suffisamment sur eux, ajouta-t-il avec un haussement d'épaules presque imperceptible.

Je regardai Kipper. Un petit pois s'échappa de sa cuillère et vint rejoindre les gouttes de sauce qui maculaient déjà la table autour de son assiette. Sans s'en soucier, il enfourna la cuillère bien pleine dans sa bouche. Un filet de bave mêlée de jus pendant de son épaisse lèvre inférieure, il mâcha bouche ouverte et avala avant de sourire à mon père.

Frankie jeta un coup d'œil à sa montre, s'essuya la bouche et se leva d'un bond.

— Faut que j'y aille, dit-il en ébouriffant les cheveux humides de Kipper. Je devrais peut-être te demander de trier mes petites amies, le taquina-t-il avant de courir à un nouveau rendez-vous.

— D'accord, Frankie, lui cria Kipper tandis que maman levait les yeux au ciel.

Pendant que nous finissions de dîner, je réfléchissais à ce qu'avait dit mon père. Indéniablement, Kipper provoquait toujours une réaction quand on le voyait pour la première fois. J'en avais été moi-même témoin à plusieurs reprises avec les gamins du quartier. Il y avait mes amis, qui l'acceptaient, et puis ceux qui ne l'acceptaient pas, soit en se moquant de lui soit en l'ignorant. D'une manière ou d'une autre, il ne laissait personne indifférent. Ce qui me surprenait, c'est que mon père fût suffisamment attentif pour le remarquer.

3

Des années plus tard, en discutant avec Frankie de cette nuit d'août 1962, nous avons découvert que nos souvenirs ne correspondaient pas. Il ne se rappelait pas nous avoir trouvés, Kipper et moi, dans l'escalier, ni nous avoir ordonné de retourner au lit. Il se souvenait seulement d'être arrivé dans le hall et d'avoir vu notre père devant la porte grande ouverte, avec la pluie qui entrait par rafales. Il avait alors allumé la lumière.

— Papa ?

Papa s'était lentement tourné en clignant des yeux comme s'il venait de se réveiller.

— Que se passe-t-il ? avait demandé Frankie en faisant entrer les deux policiers et en refermant la porte.

— C'est ta mère, répondit papa d'une voix bizarrement atone. Il y a eu un accident.

— Elle va bien ? s'enquit Frankie, en s'adressant aux deux policiers plutôt qu'à notre père.

Le plus petit des deux, dont la peau lisse était en harmonie avec sa voix trop jeune, jeta un coup d'œil à son collègue qui hocha la tête pour l'encourager à continuer.

— Non, répondit-il calmement.

Il ôta son chapeau ruisselant, le regarda puis releva la tête.

— Je suis navré, reprit-il. Votre mère...

— Elle est partie, Frankie, chuchota papa.

— Partie ?

Kipper, qui m'avait suivie jusqu'en bas, me saisit la main. Un petit sifflement s'échappait de sa gorge à chaque inspiration de ses poumons asthmatiques. Papa jeta un regard vacillant vers l'endroit où nous nous trouvions, derrière Frankie, mais sans manifester qu'il nous avait vus. Il passa la main dans ses cheveux en désordre et prononça les mots imprononçables :

— Votre mère est morte.

La phrase brutale résonna dans un silence assourdissant. Puis les hurlements commencèrent. Un chœur de gémissements de douleur animale s'échappant de nos bouches grandes ouvertes, à Kipper et moi. Je voyais mon frère manquer d'air à chaque cri qu'il poussait en écho, ses yeux, écarquillés d'horreur, chercher les miens et ses poings frapper son chapeau dans ses efforts pour imiter mon hystérie. Mais je ne parvenais pas à m'arrêter.

Ce fut Frankie, et non mon père, qui vint s'agenouiller devant moi et poser ses mains sur mes épaules.

— Ethie, arrête, m'intima-t-il d'une voix douce mais ferme. Tu ne facilites pas les choses.

J'essayai de ravaler mes larmes tandis qu'il serrait mon corps tremblant. Tout en luttant pour étouffer mes sanglots, je soulevai mon maillot de corps pour m'essuyer le visage.

Frankie se tourna vers Kipper. Il lui prit les mains et les lui fit remettre le long du corps.

— Regarde-moi, dit-il en prenant le visage de Kipper dans ses paumes. Il est temps de te comporter comme un grand garçon.

La poitrine haletante, Kipper hocha la tête et plaqua ses mains contre sa bouche, les larmes et la morve coulant entre ses doigts.

— Respire profondément.

Frankie inspira, lentement, longuement, et attendit que Kipper fît de même.

Puis il se releva et nous attira contre lui en nous tenant chacun par l'épaule ; il se tourna ensuite vers les policiers.

— Que s'est-il passé ? demanda-t-il.

C'est là que mes souvenirs divergent complètement de ceux de Frankie. Je ne me souviens absolument pas de l'explication que, d'après lui, ils ont donnée tandis que papa restait planté là, hébété. Peut-être étais-je également en état de choc, perdue dans ma vision intérieure de la voiture de ma mère, son Hudson verte toute ratatinée dans quelque rue luisante de pluie ou peut-être l'explication n'avait-elle aucun sens pour moi. Je ne me souviens que des paroles prononcées ensuite par Frankie et qui me sont parvenues comme à l'issue d'un long tunnel.

— Non, attendez, dit-il. Ce n'est pas possible. Il doit y avoir une erreur.

C'est l'espoir dans sa voix qui me secoua de ma torpeur.

Le plus âgé des policiers regardait un papier qu'il tenait dans sa main gantée.

— Je suis désolé.

Il le retourna pour nous le montrer.

Les épaules de Frankie s'affaissèrent une seconde avant que, moi aussi, je reconnaisse le nom de notre mère inscrit en gros sur le permis de conduire.

4

À l'arrière de la voiture de patrouille, Howard essayait de se ressaisir tandis que le policier au visage de poupon, assis à l'avant sur le siège passager, décrivait les faits. Vers minuit, expliqua-t-il, le propriétaire d'un bateau amarré en permanence à Coal Harbour avait remarqué de la lumière sur un voilier ancré non loin. Il avait téléphoné à la marina pour signaler ce qu'il pensait être un cambriolage.

Howard ne parvenait toujours pas à comprendre. Quel rapport y avait-il entre un voilier et Lucy ? Lui-même n'était jamais monté sur un voilier et il était certain qu'il en allait de même pour elle. Alors que le policier, mal à l'aise, racontait comment la police avait découvert les corps à bord, Howard se laissa aller à penser que tout cela n'était qu'une gigantesque erreur. Mais, dès qu'il vit l'Hudson verte sur le parking de la marina, il sentit la bile amère de l'espoir déçu envahir sa gorge.

S'obligeant à mettre un pied devant l'autre, il suivit les policiers sur le quai et dans le dédale des passerelles flottantes. La pluie avait cessé. Dans le ciel les mouettes plongeaient au gré du vent en réclamant l'aumône avec insistance. Le matin paraissait trop clair, la lumière trop vive tandis que le soleil levant brillait entre les nuages. Les premiers rayons rebondirent sur l'eau et se reflétèrent sur le bois verni d'un bateau amarré tout au bout du quai. Une petite foule de gens s'agitait devant. Les conversations à voix basse s'interrompirent à l'arrivée de Howard et de la police.

Un homme en complet veston – l'air décalé au milieu des badauds habillés de façon moins formelle – marchait de long en large devant un policier en uniforme qui griffonnait des notes.

— Merde ! Merde ! Merde ! marmonnait-il sans cesser d'arpenter le quai.

Puis son regard croisa celui de Howard et il s'arrêta net.

— Nom de Dieu, aboya-t-il, encore des spectateurs !

Le policier releva le nez de son carnet.

— Le mari de l'autre victime, expliqua-t-il.

— Merde ! répéta encore l'homme, brusquement calmé.

Le jeune policier se pencha vers Howard.

— Voilà Jeremy Telford, chuchota-t-il. Le propriétaire du bateau.

Ce nom était vaguement familier.

L'officier plus âgé, qui marchait devant, s'arrêta.

— Vous êtes prêt ? demanda-t-il à Howard.

Celui-ci hocha la tête. Il saisit un étai et se hissa sur le pont. Deux autres policiers étaient en faction de chaque côté de l'écoutille ouverte. Ils évitèrent le regard de Howard tandis que celui-ci descendait l'échelle de bois qui menait à la cabine.

En bas, mis à part le bruit des vagues qui clapotaient contre la coque et le bateau qui grinçait contre le bassin, il régnait un silence sinistre. On entrouvrit les hublots et les aérations. Trop tard. Howard fut brusquement pris de vertige, non à cause du roulis et des relents de gaz qui subsistaient dans l'air renfermé mais à la vue de deux verres à vin vides sur la table de la coquerie. Et le manteau bleu marine jeté dans un coin. L'imperméable de Lucy.

Dehors, la voix du propriétaire cria d'un ton angoissé :

— Ah, bon Dieu, on était prêts pour accueillir une exposition très importante la semaine prochaine. Ce soir, on devait fêter ça.

Sur le pont, un des policiers marmonna :

— On dirait qu'elle avait son idée sur la manière de faire la fête !

Le policier qui accompagnait Howard fronça les sourcils puis le poussa doucement en avant.

— Entrez, dit-il.

La porte qui donnait sur la couchette avant était ouverte. Un pinceau de lumière venue de l'écoutille éclairait le drap blanc recouvrant le matelas. Howard s'était cru fort, mais, lorsqu'on souleva le coin du drap, rien ne l'avait préparé à encaisser le coup brutal qu'il prit en pleine poitrine en voyant le corps de Lucy. Et la façon dont elle gisait recroquevillée contre son amie Marlene Telford. Ce fut alors qu'il comprit pourquoi le nom de l'homme d'affaires affolé sur le quai lui était familier. Il ne l'avait jamais rencontré mais il s'agissait sans nul doute du mari de Marlene.

Il secoua la tête, tentant de mobiliser son cerveau engourdi. À ses pieds, une bouteille de vin vide roula sur le sol de la cabine. La tache rouge sur le parquet en teck témoignait qu'elle avait été renversée. Quelque chose ne tournait pas rond. Lucy ici ? En train de boire ? Lucy ne buvait pas. Même la façon dont elle était habillée n'avait aucun sens, le vieux pantalon et la grande chemise qu'elle ne portait que pour faire le ménage. Qu'est-ce qui avait pu l'amener à sortir ainsi vêtue ? Lucy n'aurait jamais accepté de paraître en public sans s'être changée et maquillée.

Pourtant, même ainsi, même morte, elle était belle. Ses boucles auburn s'étalaient sur l'oreiller à côté de la crinière frisée et striée de gris de Marlene. Les taches de rousseur prenaient une teinte rose sur sa peau d'une blancheur de lait, contrastant avec le lin noir du corsage de son amie.

Il tendit la main pour lui caresser la joue et remarqua le mouchoir humide roulé en boule dans sa paume détendue. Tout en s'efforçant d'empêcher ses genoux de céder, il hocha la tête puis se détourna tandis que le policier rabattait le drap sur le visage de sa femme.

Il posa le sac sur la banquette. Voilà à quoi cela se résumait, les affaires de sa femme dans un sachet de papier brun. Il le déplia. La douce odeur musquée de Lucy se répandit dans la voiture. Il ferma les yeux en respirant profondément. Il se sentait la bouche sèche. Il avait besoin d'un verre. Il résistait à cette envie depuis qu'il s'était réveillé au petit matin, seul dans leur lit.

Son cœur se serra en revoyant l'image de Lucy recroque-villée en position fœtale sur le bateau, avec son amie qui la tenait par l'épaule comme pour la consoler. Il ouvrit les yeux et tenta de se rappeler à quoi elle ressemblait la dernière fois qu'il l'avait vue. Hier matin. Était-elle contrariée ? Il se sou-venait vaguement d'elle occupée à préparer le petit déjeuner, en peignoir ; elle les asticotait, Frankie et lui, en disant qu'ils pouvaient lui acheter un beau cadeau avec tout l'argent que rapportaient leurs heures supplémentaires. Était-ce hier ou un autre matin ?

Lucy lui avait reproché un jour de ne jamais se retourner quand il quittait la maison.

— Ça me donne l'impression que tu m'oublies au moment où tu sors, avait-elle dit. Il n'y a pourtant aucun risque que tu te transformes en statue de sel, avait-elle ajouté d'un ton chargé de sarcasme.

Si seulement il s'était retourné hier matin.

Il replia le sac en papier puis saisit le volant et laissa son regard errer sur Burrard Inlet. L'ironie de la situation le frappa brusquement. Le souvenir de la première fois où il avait vu ce paysage tourbillonnait dans sa tête, la brume le cachait en partie et c'était juste avant qu'il s'embarque pour une guerre imprévue. Il se retournait à ce moment-là. Il le faisait toujours, jusqu'à ce qu'il revienne au même quai quatre ans plus tard, vieillard de vingt-quatre ans, plombé par le fardeau d'une culpabilité trop lourde pour être partagée. Pas même avec Lucy. Il se l'était promis tant et plus, un jour, il lui raconterait, un jour, il lui avouerait tout. Mais, en dix-sept ans, il n'en avait jamais trouvé le courage.

Il s'affaissa sur le volant, cachant son visage au creux de ses bras. Au bout de quelques instants, on frappa à la vitre. Howard releva la tête et croisa le regard inquiet du jeune policier. Il se ressaisit, s'essuya les yeux d'un revers de manche et descendit la vitre.

— Ça va, monsieur ? s'enquit le policier.

Howard déglutit avec difficulté.

— Ouais, réussit-il à dire.

Mais ça n'allait pas du tout. Cela faisait très longtemps que ça n'allait pas du tout.

5

27 octobre 1941 : Dépôt ferroviaire
du Canadian Pacific, Burrard Inlet

Le grincement de l'acier contre l'acier arracha Howard au sommeil. Tout en se frottant la nuque, il se pencha pour regarder par la fenêtre. Le train fit halte bruyamment dans un ultime sursaut mais un brouillard épais obscurcissait sa première vision de Vancouver. Autour de lui, des soldats, plongés dans différents stades du sommeil, s'agitèrent.

— Nous y sommes, les gars, cria le brigadier Lawson du fond du wagon.

L'officier, un vétéran de la Grande Guerre, enjamba les corps endormis recroquevillés dans le couloir. Soldat de carrière jusqu'au bout des ongles, depuis sa moustache parfaitement taillée jusqu'à ses bottes luisantes, il traversa la voiture pour saluer ses hommes avant de passer dans le wagon suivant.

À en croire la rumeur qui courait dans le train, le commandant des troupes n'était pas vraiment heureux de son affectation. Avant d'être promu brigadier, Lawson s'était vu assigner la tâche d'évaluer la « préparation au combat » de toutes les unités canadiennes. Apparemment, il avait classé les Royal Rifles et les Winnipeg Grenadiers, les bataillons qui remplissaient ce train militaire, dans la catégorie C : préparation insuffisante. Si la rumeur était vraie, Howard se demandait ce que le chef allait faire des quatre cents hommes de renfort – dont Howard faisait partie – récemment venus grossir les rangs des deux bataillons. Nombreux étaient ceux qui n'avaient jamais tenu un fusil.

Il donna un coup de coude à son voisin ; celui-ci, réveillé en sursaut, se leva d'un bond. « Le destin nous attend, mon pote ! » s'exclama Howard en attrapant son sac et son casque pour le rejoindre dans le couloir. Il ne regretterait pas de quitter l'atmosphère enfumée du wagon surpeuplé. Tout en suivant le soldat Gordy Veronick, Howard sourit : même en se faufilant dans la bousculade, son copain d'enfance réussissait encore à plastronner. Lucy l'avait un jour décrit comme « tout en muscles et en panache », une remarque affectueuse que Howard trouvait particulièrement pertinente. Avec dix bons centimètres de moins que lui mais bâti comme un bulldog, les cheveux noirs et le teint olivâtre, Gordy était son meilleur ami, et ce depuis qu'ils avaient six ans.

Ayant grandi avec trois frères plus âgés, dont le dernier avait quatre ans de plus que lui, Howard avait parfois eu l'impression d'être un enfant unique, doté de cinq parents au lieu de deux. Aussi, lorsque sa mère lui raconta qu'un garçon de six ans, qui avait perdu ses parents dans l'épidémie de grippe, allait emménager dans la ferme voisine de la leur, la perspective d'avoir quelqu'un de son âge avec qui jouer le réjouit beaucoup. La première fois que Howard le vit débarquer dans la cour, il essaya de nouer des relations amicales.

À peine sa mère et la grand-mère de Gordy disparues à l'intérieur de la maison, le regard de Gordy se durcit.

— Howie ? En voilà un nom de tapette ! se moqua-t-il avant de s'éloigner d'un air supérieur.

Howard avait gardé ses distances tout le reste de l'été. Mais dans l'école à classe unique, impossible de l'ignorer plus

longtemps. À la fin du premier jour, Gordy était venu l'asticoter dans la cour de récréation. Peut-être l'avait-il choisi parce
que Howard était le plus grand de la classe, peut-être parce
qu'ils étaient voisins ou parce qu'il avait trois frères aînés alors
que Gordy était enfant unique. En tout cas, il s'était mis à
tourner autour de Howard comme un petit coq, puis il s'était
arrêté, les poings levés.

— En garde ! avait-il ordonné.

— En garde ? avait répété Howard.

— Allez, poule mouillée, viens te battre !

Les jambes bien écartées, Gordy boxait dans l'air. Il était
tellement comique que Howard éclata de rire. Avant de
comprendre ce qu'il lui arrivait, il se retrouva par terre, pris
dans un tourbillon de bras et de jambes qui s'efforçait de le
clouer au sol.

Tandis qu'il se battait avec Gordy dans la poussière, une
foule se rassembla autour d'eux pour les encourager. Au
moment où Howard réussissait à prendre l'avantage, quelqu'un
cria :

— Eh, Howie va se faire l'orphelin !

Les spectateurs se mirent à scander la phrase. Orphelin !
Orphelin !

Gordy se raidit puis ferma les yeux. Mais Howard avait eu
le temps de les voir se remplir de larmes. Il lâcha prise et le
laissa partir.

— Il a de la poussière dans les yeux, annonça-t-il en se
relevant. Il peut pas se battre.

Il se pencha, saisit Gordy par la main et le remit sur pieds.
Tandis qu'il l'entraînait plus loin, il lui proposa :

— Tu veux venir avec moi à la mare de Miller pour attraper
des têtards ?

Gordy s'essuya les yeux avec la manche de sa chemise.

— Oui, dit-il.

Ils firent quelques pas puis il ajouta :

— J'aurais pu te coller une raclée, tu sais.

— Je sais.

Depuis ce moment, Gordy était devenu le meilleur ami d'Howard. Ils faisaient tout ensemble, y compris s'enrôler dans les Winnipeg Grenadiers.

Alors qu'ils descendaient du train, Gordy s'arrêta brusquement sur la dernière marche.

— Ah, ça sent l'eau salée, les gars ! s'exclama-t-il.

Howard n'avait encore jamais senti l'odeur de l'océan. Il n'aurait su dire s'il l'aimait ou s'il la détestait, mais en tout cas cette forte odeur était indéniable.

— Ça sent comme le sexe, déclara quelqu'un, faisant écho à ses propres pensées.

— Ouais, comme une femme prête pour l'amour, répliqua un autre.

— Ou qui en sort tout juste, rétorqua Gordy.

Un rire parcourut les rangs des soldats en train de débarquer.

Howard pouffa et rejoignit ses camarades. Une petite bruine tombait. Il enfonça son calot et observa les officiers qui, d'un bout à l'autre du train, pressaient les soldats qui restaient.

— Avancez !

L'ordre fut relayé tout le long du flot d'hommes en uniforme.

— Mettez-vous en rangs !

Les troupes se bousculèrent pour obéir.

— Demi-tour droite ! En avant ! Marche !

— Eh bien, voilà au moins une chose qu'on sait faire ! marmonna Gordy.

Cette fois, personne ne rit.

Howard se mit à marcher au pas avec ses camarades vers l'embarcadère. Le bruit des milliers de bottes écrasant le gravier résonnait le long des rails du dépôt.

En approchant de l'extrémité du train, quelqu'un à l'avant cria : « Regardez à droite ! » et Howard tourna la tête en même temps que le reste des troupes.

Elle était debout sur la dernière marche du dernier wagon. Son manteau bleu nuit ne dissimulait pas sa jolie silhouette. Sa chevelure qui tombait aux épaules – une masse de boucles indisciplinées – encadrait un visage criblé de taches de rousseur. Même dans la lumière grise, Howard voyait ses yeux verts scruter les troupes qui défilaient devant elle. Lucy ! Au nom du ciel, mais qu'est-ce qu'elle faisait là ? Sous le choc, il perdit le rythme et vint heurter le grenadier qui marchait devant lui.

— Du calme, mec ! murmura le soldat, surpris. T'as jamais vu de gonzesse ?

Howard reprit le pas cadencé mais il réfléchissait à toute vitesse : comment sa Lucy se trouvait-elle ici, à Vancouver ? La dernière fois qu'il l'avait vue, c'était deux jours auparavant, au moment de s'embarquer à Winnipeg, en compagnie de ses trois frères. Comme tous les autres soldats qui disaient adieu à leur famille et à leurs proches dans la gare bondée, il s'était cramponné à elle jusqu'à la dernière minute. Alors que Gordy l'entraînait à reculons vers le wagon, elle leur avait crié :

— Veillez bien l'un sur l'autre !

— T'inquiète pas. Je vais m'occuper de lui, Luce ! avait lancé Gordy par-dessus son épaule. Je préférerais affronter Hitler en personne plutôt que d'avoir à te rendre des comptes s'il arrivait quelque chose à notre copain !

À peine Howard à bord, le train avait démarré. Il s'était faufilé jusqu'à la fenêtre mais il n'avait pas réussi à repérer son visage dans la foule qui faisait des grands signes. Il se demandait à présent comment elle avait pu monter dans le train. Et pourquoi. Lorsque sa colonne passa devant elle, leurs regards se croisèrent. Elle sauta à terre et, trimballant deux valises cabossées qui venaient taper contre ses jambes, elle courut pour le rattraper.

— Seigneur ! Lucy ! Qu'est-ce que tu fais là ? dit-il du coin de la bouche quand elle parvint à son niveau.

Devant, les soldats se démanchaient le cou pour apercevoir la belle fille qui essayait de marcher à leur allure.

— Sois pas furieux, Howie, haleta-t-elle. Si je t'avais dit que je voulais venir, tu aurais essayé de m'en empêcher.

— Mais comment...

Il tourna la tête et haussa les sourcils en voyant le visage souriant sur sa gauche.

— Ne me regarde pas comme ça, dit Gordy d'un air innocent. Salut, Luce, ajouta-t-il en se penchant en avant. C'est sympa de te voir ici.

— Salut, Gordy, répondit-elle en souriant avant de revenir à Howard. Non, il n'était pas au courant. Je savais qu'il serait incapable de te cacher quelque chose. Tes frères m'ont aidée. C'est eux qui m'ont fait monter dans le train.

— Ils étaient dans le coup ? Pourquoi personne ne m'a prévenu ?

— Tu m'aurais écoutée si je t'avais dit que je voulais venir ?

— Bon sang, non !

Howard lui jeta un coup d'œil puis s'obligea à regarder devant lui. Il luttait pour ne pas sourire de la détermination qu'on lisait sur le visage de Lucy tandis qu'elle marchait à ses côtés, la tête haute et le menton levé. Il ne pouvait s'empêcher d'être fier de la voir aussi obstinée.

— J'ignore où tu vas partir mais j'ai l'intention de rester le plus près possible de toi tant que tu ne seras pas revenu à la maison. Je vais m'installer ici à Vancouver, chez Mildred.

— Mildred !

La sœur aînée de Lucy l'avait toujours traitée plus comme sa fille que comme sa sœur cadette – une enfant qui, d'après elle, devait être constamment surveillée. Depuis le jour où elle avait rencontré Howard, elle ne s'était jamais donné la peine de masquer à quel point elle désapprouvait cette relation.

— Il n'y aura pas de problème, déclara Lucy d'une voix radoucie.

Mildred était donc aussi au courant. Tout le monde était au courant, sauf Howard. Lucy avait dû agir vite. Mais, à vrai dire, la vie allait vite en ce moment.

Quelques mois auparavant, Howard et Gordy livraient des blocs de glace dans les cuisines des ménagères de Winnipeg. Le Canada était entré en guerre depuis près de deux ans. Autour d'eux, les jeunes gens – que ce fût par conscience patriotique ou attirés par la promesse d'une paie régulière – s'enrôlaient massivement. Les trois frères de Howard étaient en garnison au centre d'entraînement de l'Air Force, à une bonne soixantaine de kilomètres de Winnipeg. En tant que benjamin, il avait été désigné pour rester à la maison avec leur mère veuve. Tout comme ses frères, il avait grandi en sachant que ses deux parents s'étaient engagés durant la Grande Guerre, elle comme infirmière et lui dans l'infanterie. Devant l'intensification de cette nouvelle guerre en Europe, Howard s'était senti poussé à suivre les traces de son père. Des affiches de recrutement l'assaillaient dans toutes les vitrines de magasin. Pourtant, alors même que sa mère, qui était en mauvaise santé, le pressait de partir, il avait refusé de la quitter. Et puis, deux mois auparavant, elle était morte. Trois semaines après l'enterrement, après avoir mis ses affaires en ordre, Howard, accablé de chagrin, s'était enrôlé. Contrairement à ses frères, il préférait rester sur le plancher des vaches. Comme son père, il choisit l'armée. Gordy signa le même jour.

Alors qu'ils se trouvaient au centre d'entraînement de Portage La Prairie, un officier supérieur, le lieutenant-colonel Sutcliffe des Winnipeg Grenadiers, avait réclamé des volontaires pour renforcer son bataillon. L'officier de haute taille, visage étroit et sourcils sombres assortis à son épaisse moustache, avait passé en revue les rangées de recrues qui avaient avancé d'un pas à sa demande. De ses yeux perçants il avait examiné chaque volontaire ; ceux qu'il refusait reculaient, la déception se lisant sur leurs traits. En arrivant devant Howard, ses sourcils en broussaille s'arquèrent tandis que le sergent de service, lisant ses notes, lui apprenait que le soldat Coulter n'avait pas encore achevé l'entraînement de base et n'avait jamais manipulé d'armes.

— Vous n'avez jamais tiré, soldat ? demanda Sutcliffe à Howard.

— Non, monsieur… Je veux dire si, monsieur. J'ai tué ma part de chiens de prairie dans notre ferme familiale.

— Vous vivez encore avec vos parents ?

— Non, monsieur, mes parents ont perdu la ferme à cause de la sécheresse.

Howard considéra qu'il était inutile de raconter que, moins de deux ans après avoir perdu la ferme, son père avait succombé à une crise cardiaque.

— Quel âge avez-vous, soldat ? s'enquit l'officier en plissant les yeux.

— Vingt ans, monsieur.

— Alors, de quand date votre dernier coup de fusil ?

— C'était il y a sept ans, monsieur.

— Quand vous aviez treize ans ? Sur des rongeurs ? Vous avez déjà raté votre cible ? insista Sutcliffe en secouant la tête.

— Pas sans le faire exprès, monsieur.

Une ombre de sourire gonfla la moustache de l'officier.

— Ce soldat est accepté, déclara-t-il en se tournant vers le sergent.

Il passa au suivant.

Deux semaines plus tard, Howard et Gordy montaient dans le train à Winnipeg avec les autres grenadiers, ignorant tout de leur destination finale.

Alors qu'ils approchaient de l'embarcadère, Howard sentit que Lucy avait du mal à se maintenir à sa hauteur. Chaque muscle de son corps se tendit pour l'aider. Il s'obligea à regarder droit devant lui.

L'eau sombre du Burrard Inlet apparut. Il fut submergé par une vague d'appréhension imprévue. Il n'était jamais monté sur une quelconque embarcation, encore moins à bord d'un bâtiment aussi imposant que cette carcasse grise qui dominait le quai. Tandis que les premiers soldats gravissaient les passerelles du *S.S Awatea*, la compagnie de Howard fit halte devant les entrepôts qui s'étendaient le long du quai.

Avec un soupir de soulagement, Lucy posa ses valises à terre.

— Je vais attendre ici jusqu'à ton départ, annonça-t-elle en se frottant les mains.

— Lucy, écoute-moi, répliqua Howard. Je veux que tu trouves un taxi pour aller immédiatement chez ta sœur. Nous ne savons pas quand nous allons partir.

— Soldat Coulter ! Rompez !

Howard fit un pas en avant, obligeant Lucy à se pousser. Derrière elle, le brigadier Lawson, sa badine coincée sous le bras, dévisageait Howard.

— Est-ce votre petite amie ? demanda-t-il.

— Ma femme, monsieur.

Le regard de Lawson passa de Howard à Lucy. La tristesse envahit brièvement ses traits, vite remplacée par une mine renfrognée. Il se pencha en avant jusqu'à presque toucher le visage de Howard.

— Soldat, grommela-t-il, vous avez jusqu'à ce que l'avant-avant-dernier homme monte sur la passerelle de ce bateau pour faire correctement vos adieux. Et, nom de Dieu, vous avez intérêt à être le dernier à grimper sur cette passerelle.

— Oui, monsieur !

Le brigadier le congédia d'un geste et s'éloigna.

Howard tendit les bras et Lucy se précipita. Elle l'enlaça et leurs lèvres se joignirent. Sous les huées et les sifflements des autres soldats, les lèvres de Lucy se déplacèrent vers les joues de Howard, vers ses paupières jusqu'à ce qu'ils se couvrent de baisers frénétiques. Howard finit par enfouir son visage dans la chevelure de sa femme. Il était d'ores et déjà submergé par l'odeur, le toucher, l'essence de sa femme. Sa femme depuis sept jours.

Il la connaissait depuis toujours. Enfin, presque. Ils s'étaient rencontrés à l'école primaire, lorsque le père de Lucy avait racheté le drugstore de Hamm. Dans la petite école de deux classes, l'arrivée d'un nouvel élève ne passait jamais inaperçue, mais celle de Lucy provoqua une scission parmi les enfants des deux dernières années. Il y avait ceux qui étaient intimidés par son aisance, son assurance, ses magnifiques yeux verts et sa crinière rousse et ceux qui étaient séduits. Howard et Gordy se trouvaient quelque part entre les deux. Et elle, elle décida de se lier à eux. Ils ne résistèrent pas longtemps et pendant les années qui suivirent le duo se transforma en trio. Puis ce fut le choc de la puberté. Ils entrèrent au lycée où les deux garçons attirèrent l'attention d'autres filles. Tout comme Gordy, qui commençait à se pavaner comme un coq dans un poulailler, Howard s'aperçut qu'il appréciait d'être remarqué et se mit à en jouer.

Un jour, alors qu'ils avaient tous deux seize ans, Lucy le surprit à l'heure du déjeuner assis sur la table d'une autre élève. En revenant de cours ce jour-là, elle l'accusa de se laisser embobiner par cette fille parce qu'elle avait comparé ses yeux bleu pâle à ceux de la coqueluche en vogue, Henry Fonda.

— Tu es devenu un dragueur et tu as la grosse tête, déclara-t-elle en faisant la moue.

— Quoi ? se moqua Howard. Serais-tu jalouse ?

Lucy serra ses livres contre son cœur et releva le menton.

— Et si je l'étais ?

Howard sourit.

— Tiens, dit-il, laisse-moi les porter.

Elle lui tendit ses livres et il les garda jusqu'à chez elle, signe universel qu'elle était sa petite amie.

Il ne tarda pas à remarquer chez Gordy un changement d'attitude. Depuis que la famille de Howard avait quitté la ferme pour s'installer en ville, Gordy passait les week-ends et même bien des nuits en semaine chez eux. Mais ce ne fut plus le cas. Un vendredi soir, Howard le coinça avant qu'il puisse monter dans le bus scolaire.

— Que se passe-t-il ? demanda-t-il.

— Je suis occupé.

— Ah oui ? À faire quoi ?

Gordy tapa du pied par terre.

— Écoute, reprit Howard, s'il s'agit de Lucy, rien n'a changé. On est toujours...

— C'est ta petite amie maintenant. Tu n'as plus besoin que je traîne dans les parages.

Howard scruta le visage de Gordy.

— Aucune fille ne viendra se mettre entre nous deux.

Gordy lui rendit son regard, comme s'il le mettait au défi.

— Ah oui ?

— Oui. Tu n'as qu'un mot à formuler.

— Nan, répliqua Gordy en souriant et en lui allongeant une bonne tape sur l'épaule. Elle a choisi. Ce qui me laisse l'intégralité des autres filles.

La famille de Lucy, et en particulier sa sœur Mildred, n'accepta pas aussi facilement ce tournant dans leur relation ; après avoir vu Howard en train d'embrasser Lucy sous le porche pour lui souhaiter bonne nuit, elle le traita de « petit voyou ».

La réponse indignée de Lucy parvint à Howard par la fenêtre ouverte.

— Ce « petit voyou » aide sa famille en livrant le *Winnipeg Tribune* tous les jours avant les cours et le *Star Weekly* le week-end.

Tout en s'éloignant, Howard n'avait pu s'empêcher de sourire quand elle avait ajouté :

— Et un jour, je l'épouserai !

Comme la famille de Lucy, il apprit vite que la jeune fille était une force avec laquelle il fallait compter. Mais, lorsque vint le moment de s'enrôler et qu'elle tenta de le convaincre de rester, de travailler pour son père et d'apprendre ainsi le métier, il resta ferme sur ses positions en dépit de tout l'amour qu'il lui portait.

— Je ne pourrais pas aller me recueillir sur la tombe de mes parents si je n'agissais pas alors que l'Allemagne piétine l'Europe une fois de plus, lui expliqua-t-il. J'aurais trop de mal à me regarder dans la glace.

Un mois plus tard, lorsqu'il lui avoua qu'il s'était porté volontaire pour une mission outre-Atlantique et qu'il allait partir bientôt pour une destination inconnue, elle avait déclaré :

— Alors, nous nous marierons avant ton départ.

Ses parents ne pouvaient pas s'y opposer. Mildred était tombée amoureuse d'un médecin de l'hôpital de Winnipeg où elle était infirmière. Ils s'étaient mariés et avaient emménagé à Vancouver. Howard ne savait pas très bien s'il était soulagé ou triste que Mildred ne fût pas là pour protester quand ils s'étaient dit « oui » devant l'employé municipal à la mairie.

Et maintenant, ils étaient là, accrochés l'un à l'autre sous la bruine, dans une ville inconnue, avec l'odeur de naphtaline qui s'échappait de son uniforme de laine trempé. Il la lâcha et recula d'un pas. Posant les mains sur ses épaules, il scruta son visage. Des yeux verts impénitents lui rendirent son regard.

— Lucy… que puis-je dire ?

Il essuya ses joues humides. Comment aurait-il pu être fâché contre elle ?

— Pourquoi ne m'en as-tu pas parlé ? reprit-il.

— Je n'allais pas prendre le risque que tu dises non, répondit-elle en reniflant. J'étais bien décidée à venir et je ne voulais pas perdre le temps qui nous restait en discussion. Pas question de le faire maintenant.

Il la serra à nouveau contre lui tout en jetant un coup d'œil sur la file de soldats qui diminuait.

— Va chez ta sœur, murmura-t-il dans ses cheveux.

— Non, répondit-elle en se raidissant dans ses bras. Je veux être là quand tu partiras.

— Ça n'a pas de sens, protesta Howard en reculant d'un pas. Je n'ai aucun moyen de savoir quand nous allons partir.

— Alors, j'attendrai jusqu'à ce que tu le saches.

— Merde, Lucy, ne sois pas aussi têtue. L'heure de notre départ est gardée secrète. Je peux très bien ne rien savoir avant.

— Alors, j'attendrai ici pour te voir partir. Pas question que tu t'embarques pour je ne sais quelle destination sans que je sois là pour te dire au revoir. Un point c'est tout.

— Ça risque de ne pas être avant demain.

Lucy haussa les épaules.

— Lucy…, l'implora-t-il.

Puis il vit le dernier groupe de soldats se diriger vers la passerelle.

— Il faut que j'y aille, reprit-il.

Il l'attira de nouveau à lui pour un ultime baiser. Il se força à la lâcher et se pencha pour reprendre son barda.

— Trouve un taxi, dit-il en marchant à reculons vers le bateau.

Il monta sur la rampe derrière le dernier soldat. Arrivé en haut, il jeta un coup d'œil par-dessus son épaule. Sur le quai plus bas, Lucy n'avait pas bougé entre ses deux valises, exactement là où il l'avait laissée.

— Vas-y, articula-t-il.

Il posa le pied sur le bateau sous les cris et les encouragements des soldats qui grouillaient sur le pont.

Gordy était appuyé au bastingage à côté de la passerelle.

— Si t'es pas un salopard verni ! s'exclama-t-il lorsque Howard le rejoignit. Quel adieu !

Howard laissa tomber son paquetage à ses pieds.

— Ouais. Sauf que maintenant elle refuse de quitter le quai avant de savoir l'heure de notre départ.

— Alors, je dirais qu'elle risque d'être plutôt mouillée.

La pluie tombait plus fort et les cheveux de Lucy pendaient en boucles emmêlées autour de son visage. Elle sortit un foulard de sa poche et le noua sous son menton. Très vite, le foulard se retrouva collé sur sa tête.

— Je vais aller explorer le bateau, déclara Gordy, voir si je peux apprendre à quelle heure on part.

— Merci.

Howard ôta son calot et attacha son casque métallique sans quitter Lucy des yeux. Sous la pluie qui tombait à verse, il cherchait comment lui ordonner de partir. Il ouvrit la bouche et la referma. Tu parles d'une efficacité ! Dans le ciel, le cri des mouettes rivalisait avec le grincement des grues qui chargeaient des marchandises dans les cales des navires alentour. Au-dessus de l'*Awatea*, les grues demeuraient immobiles.

Après ce qui parut durer une éternité, Gordy vint le rejoindre au bastingage.

— Ce rafiot est censé contenir cinq cents passagers, pas deux mille, expliqua-t-il. On est serrés comme des sardines en boîte. Tu n'imagines pas l'endroit où on va dormir. Il y a des hamacs suspendus partout – même dans la cuisine.

Il jeta un œil sur le quai.

— Elle est encore là ? reprit-il. Désolé, je n'ai pu avoir aucun renseignement officiel mais, à en croire la rumeur, on attend l'arrivée de matériel lourd. Il devrait être chargé dans la journée. On pourrait tabler qu'on partira au matin.

— Très bien, dit Howard, puis il mit les mains en coupe autour de sa bouche et cria à Lucy : Demain matin !

— À quelle heure ?

Howard haussa les épaules.

— Va-t'en maintenant. Tu ne peux pas rester ici toute la nuit.

Lorsqu'il vit qu'elle ne bougeait pas, il montra du doigt les entrepôts derrière le quai.

— Au moins, va te mettre à l'abri.

— Soldat Coulter !

Howard fit volte-face et se mit au garde-à-vous. L'austère officier chargé de la sélection des volontaires à Portage la Prairie, le lieutenant-colonel Sutcliffe, désormais commandant des grenadiers, le dévisageait d'un air sévère.

— Soldat, savez-vous combien d'hommes de cette compagnie j'ai perdus en route ? demanda-t-il.

Howard avait entendu dire qu'au moins vingt soldats avaient raté le train et que d'autres avaient disparu au gré des arrêts à travers tout le Canada.

— Non, monsieur, répondit-il cependant.

— Il y en a déjà trop et je n'ai pas l'intention d'en perdre encore un.

— Oui, monsieur.

— Si je vous accorde la permission de quitter le bateau pendant quelques heures, ai-je votre parole que vous reviendrez ?

— Oui, monsieur ! répondit Howard qui n'en croyait pas ses oreilles.

Le commandant lui tendit une feuille de papier.

— Vous n'avez que jusqu'à vingt et une heures tapantes pour régler votre problème.

Howard prit le document et fit le salut réglementaire.

Avant de s'éloigner, Sutcliffe murmura :

— Vous pourrez lui dire d'être ici demain matin à sept heures tapantes.

Sur la banquette arrière du taxi, Howard prit dans ses bras une Lucy trempée et frissonnante. Dans les rues, une nuée de parapluies noirs se déplaçait au-dessus de la foule qui se bousculait sur les trottoirs de Vancouver.

Le taxi s'arrêta à un feu rouge au coin de Granville et Georgia Streets. Howard regarda les piétons envahir les quatre chaussées du carrefour tandis que la circulation automobile attendait.

— On ne croirait jamais qu'on est en guerre, dit-il tandis que des hordes de clients entraient et sortaient sans arrêt du grand magasin Hudson's Bay.

Le trajet jusque chez la sœur de Lucy, à Vine Street, prit vingt minutes. Une fois la voiture repartie, ils contemplèrent l'imposante demeure victorienne à trois étages avant de sonner.

Howard poussa un sifflement.

— Ils auront sûrement de quoi te loger, remarqua-t-il.

— Montre-toi gentil, le gronda Lucy tandis qu'ils montaient les marches.

La dernière fois que Howard avait vu Mildred, il n'était qu'un gamin maigrichon de dix-sept ans à peine aussi grand qu'elle. À force de porter des blocs de glace de vingt-cinq kilos, son torse s'était développé et, avec son mètre quatre-vingt, il avait maintenant près de dix centimètres de plus que la femme qui vint ouvrir la porte.

Howard estimait que, comme sa sœur, elle était belle. Mais, contrairement à Lucy qui était tout en courbes douces, Mildred était sèche et anguleuse. Ses cheveux bruns étaient relevés à la dernière mode, soulignant ses pommettes hautes et les rides qui s'étaient creusées entre ses sourcils. À vingt-huit ans, se dit Howard, sa toute nouvelle belle-sœur avait déjà l'air d'une matrone.

Il fut surpris qu'elle ne le reconnaisse pas – son regard passa avec indifférence de lui à Lucy. En voyant sa sœur, cependant, elle laissa échapper un cri de surprise et la prit dans ses bras. Puis elle les fit entrer tous deux dans la maison. Howard eut l'impression que, en voyant son uniforme, le regard de Mildred s'était adouci. Ce qui le réconforta.

— Vous ressemblez à des rats noyés, dit-elle en aidant Lucy à ôter son manteau.

Elle jeta un coup d'œil sur la taille de sa sœur.

— Tu n'es pas… ?

— Mildred ! la coupa Lucy. Bien sûr que non. Et, pour ton information, nous sommes mariés, Howard et moi.

— C'est ce que je comprends. Vous nous réservez toujours des surprises, vous deux.

— Tu ne l'as pas prévenue que tu allais venir ? chuchota Howard à Lucy tandis qu'ils traversaient le vaste hall d'entrée.

— Comment aurais-je pu le faire ? répliqua Lucy. Je ne savais même pas si ton train se dirigeait vers l'est ou vers l'ouest.

Au salon, Mildred les fit s'installer sur le canapé avant de s'asseoir elle-même en face d'eux, droite comme un i sur la chaise assortie.

— Alors, qu'est-ce qui se passe, au juste ? demanda-t-elle.

Durant le quart d'heure qui suivit, Lucy parla sans arrêt. Elle raconta à sa sœur comment Howard avait perdu sa mère, son enrôlement dans l'armée, leur mariage, et maintenant cette mission secrète.

— Mais, dès que la guerre sera terminée, nous avons des projets, affirma-t-elle en se redressant. Quand nous serons revenus à Winnipeg, Howie fera des études de pharmacie pour que nous puissions travailler avec papa.

Pendant qu'elle parlait, Howard, assis à côté d'elle, se sentait mal à l'aise dans cette pièce haute de plafond, meublée de façon très formelle. Son uniforme humide le démangeait et il tripotait son calot en luttant pour ne pas céder à l'envie de se gratter.

— J'attendrai à Vancouver le retour d'Howard, conclut Lucy. J'espère pouvoir m'installer chez Sidney et toi – le temps de trouver du travail et un petit appartement.

— N'importe quoi ! l'interrompit sa sœur. Tu resteras ici avec nous aussi longtemps que tu en auras besoin. Ce n'est pas comme si nous manquions de place, ajouta-t-elle en adressant un sourire crispé à Howard.

On sentait de la tristesse dans cette dernière remarque. Après trois ans de mariage, elle et son mari, chirurgien à l'hôpital de Vancouver, n'avaient toujours pas d'enfant. Selon Lucy, elle était amèrement déçue de ne pas être tombée enceinte. Eh bien, elle allait à nouveau pouvoir materner sa sœur, songea Howard, surpris d'être soulagé par sa proposition.

— Alors, c'est réglé, dit Mildred d'un ton ferme en se levant. Maintenant, il est temps de vous faire à dîner avant que Howard reparte s'embarquer. Vous devez mourir de faim.

Lucy se laissa conduire hors de la pièce et Howard en profita pour se gratter avant de lui emboîter le pas.

— Bonne chance, fiston.

La voix rocailleuse du chauffeur de taxi rappelait à Howard celle de son père. Circuler en taxi deux fois dans la même journée était une extravagance encore inédite, mais ça valait le coup pour passer quelques minutes supplémentaires en compagnie de Lucy.

Le mari de Mildred n'était pas encore rentré de l'hôpital à l'heure où Howard avait dû repartir. Comme elle ne savait pas conduire, Mildred avait appelé un taxi en promettant que Sidney et elle amèneraient Lucy à l'embarcadère le lendemain matin.

Sur les quais, Howard regarda disparaître les feux arrière du véhicule. La pluie avait cessé. Il remonta tout de même son col et enfonça les mains dans ses poches. Originaire de la plaine, habitué à la morsure d'un froid bien franc, il se sentait transpercé par l'humidité de l'air de la côte Ouest. Comme un voleur, ce froid s'insinuait sous ses vêtements, pénétrant jusqu'à la moelle de ses os, lui dérobant jusqu'à la dernière once de chaleur. Frissonnant, il se dirigea vers les entrepôts bordant l'embarcadère. Il avait beau savoir que près de deux mille hommes étaient entassés à bord du bateau de l'autre côté, il se sentit soudain plongé dans une profonde solitude.

Il entendit du vacarme avant même d'atteindre l'embarcadère. Un grondement de voix chargées de colère lui parvint dans l'obscurité. Il accéléra l'allure. En tournant le coin, au milieu des entrepôts, il fut surpris de voir une foule de soldats, qu'il identifia pour la plupart comme des grenadiers, rassemblés sur le quai sous l'*Awatea*. Au-dessus, au bastingage, deux officiers braquaient des mitraillettes sur les hommes.

— Howard !

Gordy quitta le groupe avec lequel il était pour le rejoindre.

— Que se passe-t-il ? s'enquit Howard.

— Nous avons déserté le navire, expliqua-t-il et les mots s'entrechoquaient tant il était pressé de parler. Les conditions de vie sur ce rafiot sont impossibles. Avant d'être affecté au transport des troupes, ce bateau était un paquebot pour croisière de luxe en Nouvelle-Zélande. Mais les seuls qui vont en profiter, de ce luxe, ce sont les officiers. Les gars sont entassés comme des sardines dans un vrai bouge alors que les officiers ont des cabines, un salon et une salle à manger privés. Et ce soir, pendant qu'ils se tapaient la cloche, nous on a eu droit à des tripes aux oignons. Alors, nous protestons !

Howard s'efforça d'ignorer le pincement de culpabilité provoqué par le roastbeef et le Yorkshire pudding encore chauds dans son ventre.

— Ça ressemble plutôt à une émeute ! dit-il en montrant les mitraillettes.

— Tu crois qu'elles sont chargées ? railla Gordy. Bon Dieu, ils ont pas assez de munitions pour l'entraînement, alors tu crois pas qu'ils vont les gâcher pour nos malheureuses fesses ! De toute façon, on veut seulement obtenir quelques concessions. On a appris que certains de nos volants en route pour l'Angleterre ont quitté leur bateau à Halifax la semaine dernière et ils ont eu gain de cause. Nous sommes en train de négocier.

D'un signe de tête, il désigna le colonel Sutcliffe, qui tentait de se faire entendre par-dessus le vacarme.

— Pour l'instant, reprit-il, ils ont transféré cent vingt Royal Rifles sur le *Prince Robert*, notre bâtiment d'escorte, grommela-t-il. Ça nous fait une belle jambe. Maintenant, on nous accuse de mutinerie et de désertion. Merde, Howie, nous sommes les pantins dans cette armée. Allez donc ! Si suffisamment d'entre nous...

Un rugissement de protestation noya la fin de sa phrase.

Profitant de la confusion, deux soldats sortirent à reculons de la foule. Ils se précipitèrent entre les entrepôts et disparurent dans l'obscurité. En les voyant prendre la tangente, Howard sentit le démon de la tentation. L'espace d'un instant, il s'imagina partir, chercher Lucy et rentrer chez lui.

— Je croyais qu'en s'engageant, dit-il en se tournant vers Gordy, les gars renonçaient à chercher la bagarre. En tout cas, moi, j'ai sûrement pas signé pour aller me battre sur la nourriture et les conditions de logement. Et toi non plus, non ?

Il se fraya un chemin dans la bousculade. Quelques soldats lui emboîtèrent le pas tandis qu'il montait sur la passerelle. À mi-parcours, il jeta un coup d'œil à Gordy qui, avec un haussement d'épaules, le suivit.

À bord, ils s'accoudèrent au bastingage pour observer les négociations qui se déroulaient en bas. Ayant échappé à la menace du conseil de guerre et reçu la promesse d'une amélioration des conditions de vie, les hommes remontèrent lentement sur le bateau, sans cesser de grommeler. Une fois les passerelles retirées, Howard posa son bras sur les épaules de Gordy.

— Allez, dit-il, montre-moi le bouge.

Gordy n'avait pas exagéré. Les quartiers bondés puaient déjà la sueur et l'uniforme humide, rappelant à Howard un relent de chaussettes de laine portées trop longtemps. On identifiait également la puanteur âcre de la naphtaline. La plupart des uniformes de grenadiers, comme le sien, dataient de la dernière guerre. L'intérieur de sa tunique était marqué « 1918 ». Même ses sous-vêtements sortaient tout droit de la Grande Guerre. Il serait content d'échanger ces oripeaux qui grattaient pour les nouveaux uniformes promis au moment du départ.

Sous le pont, on avait suspendu des hamacs dans tous les espaces disponibles. Ils étaient si proches les uns des autres que Howard était persuadé qu'il suffirait qu'un homme bouge pour qu'ils bougent tous. Mais ça ne le dérangeait pas. Benjamin de quatre garçons qui avaient grandi dans une ferme où il n'y avait que deux chambres, il était habitué à dormir dans un espace restreint.

Il s'assit à une table de mess sous le hamac indiqué par Gordy et se pencha pour dénouer les lacets de ses grosses chaussures. Ce soir, il allait dormir.

Il sentit plus qu'il n'entendit un vrombissement. Les moteurs ? Il se redressa pour prêter l'oreille. Il était sûr que les moteurs tournaient au ralenti. Il renoua ses lacets en hâte et sortit de la salle au galop. Il grimpa un escalier et sur le pont, se précipita vers le bastingage. Sur l'eau noire attendait un remorqueur attaché au bateau. Howard fila vers bâbord pour regarder par-dessus l'épaule des autres hommes massés là. Le rugissement profond de la sirène vint confirmer les craintes d'Howard. Ils étaient en train de partir.

Sur le quai, en dessous, des dockers détachaient les grosses amarres. La surface noire de l'eau s'élargit entre le bateau et le quai. Puis, les moteurs tournant toujours au ralenti, le *S.S. Awatea* parut prendre son souffle avant de se mettre lentement en route.

Sous la proue, Howard voyait le sillage blanc du remorqueur qui fendait les eaux du bras de mer, entraînant l'*Awatea* derrière lui. Devant, sur l'eau sombre, le *NCSM Prince Robert* approchait des passes. Lorsque le bateau escorte disparut dans la brume sous le pont du Lion's Gate, il se rendit à l'arrière et s'accouda au bastingage pendant que les deux navires sortaient dans le port et jetaient l'ancre. Il n'avait nul besoin d'entendre les conjectures qui allaient bon train autour de lui pour comprendre pourquoi il y avait eu une modification des plans : après ce début de mutinerie sur l'embarcadère, quiconque aurait encore envie de quitter le bateau ce soir serait contraint de le faire à la nage.

Au loin, les lumières de la ville clignotaient dans la brume épaisse et Howard frissonna. Il se sentait vide. Tout en prononçant un silencieux adieu à Lucy, il tenta d'ignorer le sinistre pressentiment qui remplissait tout l'espace creux en lui.

6

Si je fermais les yeux vraiment fort. Si je ne bougeais plus le moindre muscle. Si je ne pleurais pas. Si j'étais sage – si j'étais sage – alors les mots prononcés par mon père ne seraient pas réels. Recroquevillée en boule sous ma couverture, entourant mes genoux de mes poings serrés, j'essayais de ne pas trembler. Je fermai encore plus fort les yeux et recherchai le visage de ma mère dans les éclairs qui jaillissaient derrière mes paupières. Je m'efforçai de la retrouver telle qu'elle était hier. Impossible de m'en souvenir. Les jours de la semaine passée se mélangeaient tous dans ma tête.

L'été, lorsqu'on n'allait pas à l'école, les journées paraissaient toutes identiques. Il était plus facile de ne pas perdre le fil du temps durant le reste de l'année. Pendant les périodes scolaires, maman travaillait deux jours par semaine. Le jeudi et le vendredi matin, elle emmenait Kipper avec elle à la galerie d'art de Marlene Telford dans Granville Street où elle travaillait.

Marlene ? Soudain me revint le souvenir d'hier matin.

Kipper et moi, nous avions dormi tard. Après avoir englouti mes céréales, j'avais crié au revoir à maman. Elle était dans la salle de bains, et je l'avais entendu dire quelque chose à propos d'aller en ville chez Marlene. Mais j'étais pressée. J'avais entraîné Kipper hors de la maison à toute vitesse, inquiète à l'idée de rater la première chanson à l'école biblique de la nouvelle église évangélique de la Cinquante et unième avenue. Tous les jours, à dix heures pétantes, nous chantions *I Will Make You Fishers of Men* (« Je ferai de vous des pêcheurs d'hommes ») et le professeur choisissait quelqu'un pour coiffer le chapeau de paille et porter la canne à pêche en bambou. Ensuite, il prenait une photo Polaroid du pêcheur choisi, photo qu'il fallait conserver. Peut-être serait-ce enfin mon tour.

Avec mon amie Ardith Price, nous participions au stage de deux semaines à l'école biblique qui promettait « gâteaux et travaux manuels ». Kipper adorait les chansons. Il aimait surtout *Onward Christian Soldiers* (« En avant, soldats du Christ »). Il se mettait à marcher au pas en entonnant les paroles de sa voix forte et monocorde, avec quelques temps de retard.

À la fin de la première journée, le professeur m'avait prise à part pour me souffler qu'il vaudrait sans doute mieux laisser Kipper à la maison la prochaine fois. Ses paroles provoquèrent chez moi un soulagement coupable parce que, ces derniers temps – et à l'évidence, je n'aurais jamais avoué pareille chose à maman –, j'étais rongée de ressentiment à l'idée de devoir toujours traîner mon frère partout où j'allais.

Mais, au lieu de décider de le garder à la maison, maman avait plissé les yeux quand je lui avais répété les paroles du professeur.

— On va s'occuper sans tarder de cette histoire ! s'était-elle exclamée. Ils peuvent l'empêcher d'aller en classe mais tu peux parier ta chemise qu'ils ne l'empêcheront pas de fréquenter l'école biblique, si j'ai mon mot à dire.

Le lendemain matin, elle nous a accompagnés à l'église. J'ignore ce qui s'est passé dans le bureau du pasteur mais, quand maman est ressortie, elle m'a dit d'emmener Kipper et d'aller rejoindre les autres élèves dans le sous-sol. Le professeur n'a plus jamais suggéré que Kipper reste chez lui. Mais il ne l'a jamais choisi, ni moi, pour faire le pêcheur d'hommes.

Maintenant, je regrettais de ne pas avoir attendu que maman sorte de la salle de bains hier matin. En revenant de cours, nous avons trouvé Mary, la fille adolescente d'Irene Manson, à la maison. Il y avait un message sur le bloc près du téléphone mural et un ragoût de thon surgelé décongelait dans l'évier. Le message, de l'écriture penchée de maman, si familière, avait fait sourire Frankie et papa ; après avoir passé l'après-midi en ville, elle irait chez Marlene jouer aux cartes.

— Je remarque qu'il n'est pas question de poker, souligna Frankie en riant, une fois la baby-sitter payée et partie.

Nous savions tous pourquoi. Maman refusait de dévoiler son vice secret à la grande commère du quartier – la mère de Mary, Irene.

À peine quelques jours plus tôt, Frankie s'était moqué de maman en lui disant que la police allait finir par défoncer la porte de l'appartement de Marlene dans le West End pour une opération commando contre cette officine illégale.

— Nous ne jouons que des pennies, avait protesté maman, amusée par les railleries de Frankie. Personne ne perd plus d'un dollar par soirée.

N'empêche, elle nous avait fait jurer le secret sur ses séances hebdomadaires de poker. Pour tout le monde – excepté notre voisine, Dora Fenwick – le mercredi soir, elle jouait au bridge. Elle ne voulait pas que sa sœur et les dames du quartier soient au courant de cette activité clandestine. La partie se terminait toujours très longtemps après l'heure à laquelle j'allais me coucher ; hier soir, je n'étais donc pas inquiète de ne pas la voir avant d'aller au lit. Pas plus que je n'avais pensé qu'on était samedi et non pas mercredi.

Je rejetai les couvertures. Bien que Frankie m'ait ordonné de rester au lit, je redescendis sans faire de bruit. Il était en train de discuter à voix basse au téléphone dans la cuisine ; je me faufilai dans la chambre de papa et maman et je me glissai dans leur lit. Je rabattis les draps et les couvertures par-dessus ma tête et enfouis mon visage dans l'oreiller de maman. Je sentis son odeur. Tout allait bien, donc. Elle ne pouvait pas être morte.

Morte ? Morte, la mouette malodorante que nous avions trouvée sur la plage la semaine dernière, Kipper et moi, et enterrée dans le sable. Mort, mon poisson rouge que Frankie avait fait disparaître dans la cuvette des toilettes après que je l'eus découvert le ventre à l'air dans son aquarium. Mort, notre vieux chien Pepper. « Le ciel le réclame », avait expliqué maman quand nous avions enterré le corps inerte de notre épagneul cocker noir enveloppé dans une vieille couverture de bébé, derrière la maison. « Désormais, il appartient au ciel. »

Mais ma mère n'appartenait pas au ciel. Et à partir de maintenant j'allais être tellement parfaite que le ciel n'insisterait pas pour la garder.

Aujourd'hui, à l'école biblique, j'allais accepter Jésus-Christ comme mon sauveur, ainsi que le professeur nous avait encouragés à le faire à la fin du cours tous les jours de la semaine. Contrairement à mon amie Ardith, quelques jours auparavant, j'avais refusé d'aller au premier rang m'agenouiller pour que la main du pasteur pousse Jésus de force dans ma tête jusqu'à atteindre mon cœur.

Après, Ardith me raconta qu'elle sentait la chaleur de Jésus-Christ dans son cœur.

— Maintenant, je peux lui demander n'importe quoi. Et quand je mourrai, j'entrerai au Royaume des Cieux.

Je ne savais rien de tout cela, je voulais simplement que ma mère n'aille pas dans un endroit pareil. Bientôt, moi aussi, j'allais pouvoir demander des services à Jésus.

L'odeur était en train de s'évaporer. Je déplaçai l'oreiller et inspirai à nouveau le doux parfum de ma mère.

Quelqu'un tira sur la couverture. Je jetai un œil et vis Kipper. Je repoussai les draps et il grimpa dans le lit. Il posa son chapeau sur la table de chevet puis se blottit contre moi.

Je me mordis l'intérieur de la lèvre. Je ne pleurerai pas. Je ne pleurerai pas. D'ici peu, maman allait débarquer en disant : « Il pleut, il mouille, c'est la fête à la grenouille », comme elle le faisait chaque fois qu'il pleuvait quand elle se garait devant la maison. Je me promis que, la prochaine fois, je ne râlerais pas lorsqu'elle répéterait cette comptine enfantine. Il était impossible que je ne l'entende plus jamais prononcer ces paroles bêtasses. Quel que fût l'endroit où elle avait passé la nuit, quelle que fût la raison qui l'avait empêchée de rentrer, ce que la police avait raconté à mon père était faux. Ils s'étaient forcément trompés. Il arrivait que les adultes se trompent.

Comme Frankie s'était trompé à propos des bébés crabes. « Ils vont mourir », m'avait-il dit quand j'étais rentrée de Birch Bay dimanche dernier avec des douzaines de minuscules crabes noirs qui grattaient les bords de mon seau. « Il leur faut l'océan, insista-t-il. Ils ont besoin d'eau salée. » Mais, une semaine plus tard, les crabes étaient toujours vivants dans notre vieux bac à sable. Tous les jours, je versais du sel de table dans une cruche remplie d'eau et j'allais les arroser. Je mettais de la nourriture pour poissons rouges dans les flaques de l'abri que je leur avais installé avec des coquillages, des cailloux et des bernaches ramassés sur la plage. On retrouvait même l'odeur de la plage. Mais les crabes devenaient tout mous, inertes. Peut-être aurais-je dû les rapporter jusqu'à l'océan et les libérer. Oui, c'était ce qu'il fallait faire. Aujourd'hui, on était dimanche. S'il ne pleuvait pas à nouveau, je demanderais à papa d'aller à Birch Bay cet après-midi. Maman adorait la plage.

Quand je me suis réveillée, un rayon de soleil passait entre les rideaux. On entendait une voix féminine dans la cuisine. Maman était revenue ! Je rejetai les couvertures et bondis hors du lit.

Tout le monde se tut lorsque je débarquai. Mon regard passa de papa à Frankie, affalés chacun à un bout de la table, puis de tante Mildred à oncle Sidney, accoudés au comptoir. Le front chauve de mon oncle luisait de sueur. Même les petites touffes de cheveux au-dessus de ses oreilles paraissaient humides. Il enleva ses lunettes et s'absorba dans leur nettoyage pendant que je les regardais d'un air interrogateur.

— Maman ? bredouillai-je.

Mon père releva la tête. Il ouvrit la bouche puis la referma. Je me tournai vers Frankie. Avachi devant son café, les épaules voûtées, mon frère avait les yeux rouges, épuisés, vieux et aussi vides que ceux de notre père.

— Mon petit ange, dit ma tante en s'agenouillant pour m'attirer à elle.

— Non.

Je reculai et vins éclater en sanglots contre la poitrine de mon père. Il m'entoura les épaules de son bras.

Derrière moi, tante Mildred se releva en poussant un soupir.

— Monte t'habiller, ma chérie, dit-elle. Oncle Sidney et moi, on t'emmène chez nous.

Ma tante me proposait souvent de venir chez elle et, la plupart du temps, ça me plaisait d'y aller. Chaque fois, j'étais certaine d'avoir des nouveaux vêtements, des poupées ou des illustrés. Des cadeaux auxquels j'avais rarement droit à la maison. Aujourd'hui, rien de tout cela ne comptait. Je secouai la tête en me cramponnant à papa.

— Je pense que c'est une bonne idée que tu y ailles pour un petit moment, déclara-t-il doucement.

— Kipper vient aussi ? demandai-je en m'essuyant les yeux d'un revers de manche.

Tante Mildred fouilla son sac à main à la recherche d'un mouchoir en coton.

— Je crois que ton frère ne serait pas bien chez nous, répondit-elle en me le tendant. Je ne saurais pas m'occuper de lui.

Vis-à-vis de Kipper notre tante faisait partie des gens du deuxième groupe. Quand elle nous rendait visite, elle l'ignorait la plupart du temps et il n'avait jamais dormi chez elle.

— Alors, je ne viens pas non plus.

Je suis sortie de la pièce en courant.

— Laisse-la tranquille, dit mon père derrière moi, d'une voix lasse.

En haut, j'enfilai un pantalon corsaire et un T-shirt et je mis mes tennis. Je sortis par le sous-sol et remontai l'escalier de béton.

Dans le jardin, l'air sentait l'herbe et la poussière humides, les vers de terre se montraient dans la pelouse détrempée et trop haute. Deux rouges-gorges sautillaient et ma présence ne les fit pas s'envoler. Ils continuèrent à chercher leur petit déjeuner pendant que j'examinais le vieux bac à sable où les crabes gisaient immobiles dans leur maison de fortune. Je m'agenouillai et les touchai du bout d'un bâton. Des bulles minuscules moussaient sous leurs yeux. Ils levèrent mollement leurs pinces pour saisir le bâton en remuant les pattes. Ils étaient encore vivants.

Je me relevai et entrai dans le sable trempé. Je me mis à taper du pied, encore et encore, écrasant méthodiquement les crabes sous mon talon jusqu'à les réduire en bouillie au fond du bac.

7

La porte de la cuisine s'ouvrit et Frankie sortit. Accroupie dans le bac à sable, les bras serrés autour des genoux, je l'observais. Il prit un paquet de Player's froissé dans la poche de sa chemise et porta une cigarette à sa bouche d'une main tremblante. Il dut s'y reprendre à trois fois avant de réussir à enflammer l'allumette. Appuyé contre le mur de la maison, il tira une bouffée puis, tenant la cigarette entre ses doigts, il observa la fumée qui montait en s'enroulant du bout rougeoyant. Quand il la remit à ses lèvres, il leva les yeux et m'aperçut. Sans hâte, il vint s'asseoir sur le rebord du bac, à côté de moi. Nous avons examiné ensemble le gâchis que j'avais fait tandis que sa cigarette se consumait.

— Je ne savais pas que tu fumais, dis-je.

— Je ne fume pas, répondit-il. C'est le paquet de papa.

Il prit une autre bouffée puis se pencha pour écraser dans le sable le mégot à moitié fumé, d'un mouvement lent et régulier qui évoquait beaucoup celui de notre père. En regardant son profil, la ligne sévère de sa mâchoire, les petites rides au coin des yeux qui n'étaient pas là hier, je compris pour la première fois pourquoi maman affirmait toujours qu'il ressemblait à papa comme deux gouttes d'eau.

Une boucle blond cendré retomba sur son front lorsqu'il

se redressa. Il la repoussa puis se leva en brossant le sable humide sur son jean.

— Je crois que nous ferions bien de rentrer, dit-il en soupirant.

Il me tendit la main et je le laissai me remettre debout.

Nous parvînmes en haut des marches, au moment où tante Mildred, dans la cuisine, demandait :

— Tu m'as entendue, Howard ? Je voudrais savoir ce que Lucy faisait sur un bateau à voiles ?

Un bateau à voiles ? Je me retournai vers Frankie. Et c'est à ce moment que je la vis : dans la rue, garée derrière la Volvo noire, neuve et rutilante de ma tante, il y avait l'Hudson verte de ma mère.

— Elle était avec Marlene Telford, répondit papa. Le bateau appartient au mari de Marlene.

— Marlene ! s'exclama tante Mildred d'un ton méprisant. Je ne comprends toujours pas.

Moi non plus. J'avais cru que maman avait eu un accident de voiture.

— Oxyde de carbone…, commença papa mais il s'interrompit en voyant Frankie passer devant moi pour pousser la porte.

Dans la cuisine, mon oncle et ma tante étaient accoudés au comptoir, exactement à l'endroit où ils se trouvaient quand j'étais partie. Toujours penché sur sa tasse de café, papa avait l'air hébété.

— Continue, papa, l'encouragea Frankie. Il faut que Ethie, elle aussi, soit au courant.

J'entendis tante Mildred reprendre son souffle.

— La police croit qu'il s'agit d'un empoisonnement à l'oxyde de carbone, déclara papa d'un ton hésitant en s'adressant à la table. À cause d'un chauffe-eau défaillant. Apparemment, aucune des deux n'avait pensé à ouvrir les aérations.

— Mais qu'est-ce qu'elle faisait là-bas, d'abord ? demanda tante Mildred.

La dureté de sa voix fit tressaillir mon père.

Oui, que faisait-elle là-bas ? J'attendais sa réponse. Il déglutit ; ses yeux passèrent du réfrigérateur à la cigarette pas encore allumée qu'il tenait entre ses doigts tachés de nicotine.

— J'aimerais bien le savoir. C'était un accident complètement inattendu. Je ne peux rien vous dire de plus.

— L'oxyde de carbone est mortel, intervint oncle Sidney, mais indolore. Elles ont dû simplement sombrer dans le sommeil. Mais je suis étonné qu'aucune des deux n'ait remarqué la somnolence de l'autre.

— Elles étaient en train de boire du vin, précisa papa.

— Ah, fit oncle Sidney comme si cela réglait la question.

Ma tante écarquilla les yeux.

— Lucy était en train de boire ? J'ai vraiment du mal à le croire.

Moi aussi. Le seul moment où j'avais vu ma mère boire, c'était pendant le déjeuner de Noël où elle prenait un verre de vin qu'elle finissait rarement.

Quelqu'un tira la chasse d'eau dans les toilettes. La porte s'ouvrit et Kipper apparut, encore en pyjama – avec son chapeau sur la tête. Sans dire un mot, il nous fixa. Puis il vint se mettre à côté de papa.

Tante Mildred prit son sac et ses gants sur le comptoir.

— Maintenant, nous allons à Forest Lawn choisir le cercueil...

Sa voix se brisa. Elle hésita un moment avant de continuer.

— Nous allons prendre toutes les dispositions. Ne vous inquiétez pas pour les frais. Sidney et moi, nous réglerons tout.

— Ce n'est pas nécessaire, objecta papa en soupirant.

— Nous le souhaitons, répondit oncle Sidney doucement.

Tandis qu'ils discutaient des décisions à prendre pour l'enterrement, je m'efforçais de démêler la confusion de toutes ces questions sans réponse. Pourquoi maman et Marlene se trouvaient-elles sur un voilier ? D'après le message laissé par maman, elles devaient jouer aux cartes hier soir. Avait-elle menti ? J'avais toujours cru que maman était comme Kipper – incapable de mentir. Je réfléchis à ce qu'avait dit oncle Sidney. Savoir que ma mère n'avait pas souffert, qu'elle s'était simplement endormie, aurait dû me réconforter. Mais ce n'était pas le cas.

Je fermai les yeux en tentant de me représenter son visage. Impossible.

— Je ne vois plus son visage ! criai-je, affolée, à Frankie.

Les yeux brouillés de larmes, je me tournai frénétiquement vers papa.

— Je veux aller la voir.

Ma tante posa la main sur mon épaule.

— Je ne crois pas que ce soit une bonne idée, mon trésor. À la maison, nous sortirons les albums et tu pourras regarder toutes les photos de ta maman.

— Non !

Je me libérai d'une secousse pour rejoindre papa.

— Je ne me souviens plus de son visage. Je veux la voir avant qu'elle parte au ciel.

— Moi aussi, je veux voir maman, intervint Kipper, la lèvre inférieure tremblante.

Tante Mildred l'ignora. Elle jeta un œil noir à mon père.

— Tu n'as pas l'intention de souscrire à cela ?

— Ce n'est peut-être pas une mauvaise idée, déclara Frankie.

— C'est idiot. Cette enfant est bien assez traumatisée comme cela.

— Eh bien, à dire vrai, intervint Sidney, rien ne prouve que le fait de voir...

— Non, gémit tante Mildred.

Papa leva la main.

— Stop, dit-il doucement, presque d'un air d'excuse.

Attirant Kipper à lui, son regard passa de mon frère à moi.

— Vous ne pouvez pas voir votre mère aujourd'hui, mais peut-être demain. Ou bien à l'enterrement, vous la verrez pour lui dire au revoir.

— Howard ! s'écria tante Mildred. Je ne peux pas croire que tu envisages pareille chose. Et tout de même, tu n'as pas l'intention de les emmener à la cérémonie ?

— Bien sûr que si ! répliqua-t-il. Il s'agit de leur mère.

— Le gamin ? Tu veux emmener le gamin ? Excuse-moi, Howard, mais réfléchis un peu. Il ne va faire que brailler pendant tout le service.

— Si on ne peut pas pleurer à un enterrement, rétorqua papa, alors je me demande où on peut le faire.

Peu de temps après que la Volvo de tante Mildred eut quitté le bord du trottoir, on frappa à la porte. Papa alla répondre et trouva Mme Manson sous le porche.

— Lucy est là ? demanda-t-elle sans se soucier de dissimuler qu'elle voulait regarder par-dessus l'épaule de papa ce qui se passait dans la maison.

Papa ne lui répondit pas et ce fut Frankie qui se chargea d'elle.

Durant le reste de la journée, des amis et des voisins qui, pour la plupart, étaient à l'évidence inconnus de papa, entrèrent et sortirent sans discontinuer de la maison. Ils apportaient ragoûts et quatre-quarts en témoignant avec nervosité toute leur compassion.

8

Une fois, maman avait fait le compte de la population qui vivait dans les vingt-trois maisons de notre quartier. À l'exception de celle des Fenwick, à côté de la nôtre, toutes les maisons de la rue avaient été construites par le gouvernement après la guerre pour loger les familles des soldats revenus des combats. Pour avoir droit à ces logements subventionnés, il fallait avoir au moins deux enfants. Selon les chiffres de maman, qui n'incluaient pas Frankie parce que, d'après elle, il était difficile de le compter encore parmi les enfants, soixante-six gamins vivaient dans Barclay Street. Pourtant, toute la journée, il régna un silence étrange. Bien que la pluie eût cessé, il n'y eut aucune partie de hockey ou de baseball, contrairement à d'habitude. Personne ne sauta à la corde ni ne joua à la marelle sur le trottoir. Même le square avec son aire de jeux de l'autre côté de la rue était vide. Kipper excepté.

Quand toutes les femmes du quartier furent rentrées chez elles, après avoir laissé leur mari au salon avec papa, je m'assis sous le porche. Adossée à la rambarde, j'observais Kipper qui enroulait la balançoire sur elle-même avant de la laisser tournoyer. Au bout d'un moment, la porte de la maison à côté du square s'ouvrit et M. Manson sortit. Il traversa la rue dans la lumière crépusculaire portant une bouteille enveloppée dans un sac en papier brun.

Il me montra le square d'un signe de tête.

— Un bon moyen de se donner le vertige, commenta-t-il.

Je me levai pour le faire entrer dans la maison où il rejoignit les autres hommes installés dans le salon sombre où je n'avais plus mes repères.

Dans la cuisine, Frankie, penché devant le réfrigérateur ouvert, l'air perplexe, tentait d'y caser des monceaux de nourriture. Il releva la tête en m'entendant entrer et j'allai m'asseoir au bout de la table.

— Tu as mangé ? s'enquit-il.

Le mélange des odeurs des différents plats préparés par nos voisins me soulevait le cœur. Ou peut-être était-ce parce que je venais de remarquer que la bouteille de whisky n'était plus en haut du frigo.

— Je n'ai pas faim.

Le regard de Frankie suivit le mien. Sa mâchoire se durcit. Il fourra le dernier plat dans le frigo, comme s'il plaçait en force l'ultime pièce d'un puzzle, et referma la porte avant qu'il tombe.

— Il faut manger, déclara-t-il sans conviction.

Avant que j'aie eu le temps de répliquer, nous avons vu tous deux Dora Fenwick traverser la pelouse. Danny, son fils, la suivait, visiblement embarrassé.

Mme Fenwick était la meilleure amie de maman. Danny et elle vivaient dans la vieille ferme voisine, avec la grand-mère. J'avais le même âge que Danny, nous avions grandi ensemble et jusqu'à l'été dernier nous étions très proches.

Ils montèrent l'escalier et Frankie alla leur ouvrir la porte. Mme Fenwick, les yeux gonflés, eut l'air surpris puis elle entra. Danny, tête basse, resta à traîner sous le porche. Je voyais la peau de son crâne sous la coupe en brosse tandis qu'il fixait ses pieds à travers ses nouvelles lunettes à grosse monture façon Buddy Holly.

— Spaghettis aux boulettes, annonça Dora Fenwick avec un sourire forcé.

Elle posa encore un autre plat sur le comptoir, attira mon frère dans ses bras et le serra contre elle, en lui murmurant quelque chose à l'oreille.

— Merci, marmonna Frankie avant de reculer en toussant. Je vais chercher papa.

Elle hocha la tête. Lissant avec nervosité ses courts cheveux noirs derrière l'oreille, elle se tourna vers moi. Elle dut sentir que, si jamais elle me prenait dans ses bras, je m'effondrerais. Gardant ses distances, elle saisit un mouchoir en papier dans la manche de son pull-over et s'en tamponna les yeux.

— Tu entres, mon chéri ? proposa-t-elle alors à Danny.

Celui-ci remonta ses lunettes sur son nez et secoua la tête.

— J'attends ici. Tu viens dehors ? ajouta-t-il, me prenant au dépourvu.

Je me levai. Papa entra dans la pièce juste à ce moment-là. Mme Fenwick et lui s'embrassèrent gauchement puis se séparèrent.

— J'ai tant de peine, Howard, dit-elle en acceptant la chaise qu'il lui offrait. Puis-je faire quelque chose ?

— Non. Non, affirma papa en se passant les doigts dans les cheveux. Je crois que sa sœur va réussir à prendre les choses en main.

Elle hocha la tête d'un air compréhensif.

— Je ne peux pas y croire. Hier et aujourd'hui, j'étais au travail toute la journée.

Elle se moucha et papa s'assit sur le siège que je venais d'abandonner.

— Ma mère a dit que Lucy... (Elle hésita une seconde puis reprit :) Elle a dit que Lucy est passée me voir hier matin. Mais, ajouta-t-elle avec un rire étranglé, vu l'état de la mémoire de maman en ce moment, il peut aussi bien s'agir de la semaine dernière.

À l'entendre parler de ce qu'avait fait maman hier, une étrange chaleur m'envahit. Rien que d'entendre prononcer son nom était déjà douloureux. Je me glissai dehors en laissant la porte de la cuisine ouverte et je m'assis sur les marches. Sans rien dire, Danny vint me rejoindre. Dans la rue, on n'entendait que le grincement de la balançoire de Kipper.

Dans la cuisine, Dora se moucha encore une fois. Après quelques instants de silence, papa s'éclaircit la gorge.

— Y avait-il quelque chose qui la tracassait, Dora ? demanda-t-il à voix si basse que je dus tendre l'oreille. Paraissait-elle perturbée ces derniers temps ?

Je me redressai. Perturbée ? Maman ? Était-ce la raison pour laquelle elle était dans la salle de bains hier matin ? Pour laquelle elle était allée voir Marlene ?

Danny s'agita à côté de moi.

— Allons plutôt au square, chuchota-t-il.

Je secouai la tête tandis qu'à l'intérieur sa mère assurait papa que, de ce qu'elle en savait, rien d'inhabituel ne tracassait maman.

Brusquement, ce fut une évidence. C'était peut-être ma faute. Elle avait sans doute compris que Kipper commençait à me peser.

Quelqu'un frappa à la porte d'entrée, de l'autre côté de la maison.

— Je m'en vais, dit Dora dont la chaise racla le carrelage. Appelle-moi si je peux t'aider en quoi que ce soit.

Papa lui ouvrit la porte de la cuisine. En les voyant sortir, Danny se leva d'un bond. Le regard de sa mère s'adoucit en nous voyant.

— Veux-tu venir dormir à la maison ce soir, Ethie ? proposa-t-elle.

Surprise, je jetai un regard à Danny. Il était impassible. Lorsque nous étions plus jeunes, lorsque nous étions amis, la maison des Fenwick était un second foyer pour Kipper et moi. Nous y avions très souvent dormi le week-end et les nuits d'été.

— Si cela te convient, Howard ? ajouta Mme Fenwick.

Papa hocha la tête.

— Si elle le souhaite.

Il paraissait soulagé, me sembla-t-il.

— Kipper aussi ? demandai-je.

— Bien sûr, Kipper aussi, répondit la mère de Danny en souriant.

Je montai chercher nos pyjamas. J'évitai le salon en redescendant parce que je n'avais toujours pas compris ce que Frankie avait voulu dire quand je lui avais demandé pourquoi ces hommes restaient simplement assis là avec papa en silence.

— Ce sont tous des vétérans, avait-il expliqué avec un haussement d'épaules. Je pense que le lien qui les unit est au-delà des mots.

9

2 novembre 1941 : Port d'Honolulu, Hawaï

Howard n'avait jamais rien vu de pareil. Coincé contre la rambarde du bateau, il se serrait épaule contre épaule avec les autres soldats qui se bousculaient pour ne rien rater. Juste en dessous, sur les ponts inférieurs, des têtes et des bras s'agitaient, dépassant de bâbord. Les acclamations des troupes couvraient presque totalement la musique des ukulélés accompagnant les filles à la peau couleur bronze qui dansaient le *hula* sur le quai. Des pièces et des billets de banque, assortis parfois d'un paquet de cigarettes, pleuvaient sur les danseuses. Un garçon vêtu d'une chemise rouge à fleurs courait partout pour ramasser ces cadeaux qu'il jetait dans une grande coupe en bois.

L'air marin était imprégné de l'odeur exotique des épais leis d'orchidées des danseuses. Leurs seins ronds reposaient dans des noix de coco polies et leurs longues chevelures noires ondulaient au même rythme que leurs jupes végétales. La grâce fluide de leurs bras et de leurs hanches était si sensuelle que le besoin de Lucy se fit soudain douloureux.

Gêné par cette érection, Howard s'appuya davantage contre la rambarde. Comme les autres soldats, il n'était vêtu que d'un short, celui de son nouvel uniforme, et d'un maillot de corps à manches courtes. Les troupes avaient pour ordre de ne porter aucun insigne les identifiant comme Canadiens. Cela lui paraissait sensé. L'Empire britannique était en guerre contre l'Allemagne, après tout, et même si l'infanterie canadienne ne participait pas encore aux combats, les déploiements de forces devaient demeurer top secrets. Ils étaient consignés à bord le temps de s'approvisionner en carburant.

— Tu ne vas pas donner un petit quelque chose à ces filles ? le taquina Gordy en lui allongeant un coup de coude avant de lancer une autre pièce de cinquante cents.

— Une jolie frimousse, tu ne résistes pas, hein ! s'exclama Howard. Moi, je suis un homme marié, tu t'en souviens ? Il faut que je ménage mon argent…

— Allez, vieux radin ! Cinquante cents.

Howard fouilla dans sa poche, en sortit sa monnaie et lança quelques pièces.

— Voilà. Tu es content ?

— T'inquiète pas, se moqua Gordy, je le dirai pas à Lucy.

— T'as intérêt, répondit Howard en riant.

Il ne plaisantait qu'à moitié. Avec le temps, il en était venu à la conclusion que provoquer la jalousie de Lucy était une mauvaise idée. Il ne se voyait pas en train de lui expliquer qu'il avait lancé de l'argent à des beautés aux hanches ondulantes.

Il prit le paquet de cigarettes roulé dans sa manche. Même s'il ne fumait pas, il acceptait les rations distribuées au compte-gouttes par l'armée. Il avait grandi avec l'idée qu'on ne refuse jamais ce qu'on vous offre : on ne sait pas quand ça s'avérera utile. Par désœuvrement, il avait déjà fumé une ou deux cigarettes mais il ne se voyait pas accroché à ces trucs qui sentaient si mauvais.

Il jeta le paquet sur le quai. Lorsque la chemise rouge se précipita pour le récupérer, Howard vit que ce n'était pas un gamin mais un homme. Il enfouit les cigarettes dans sa poche

et leva les yeux avec un simulacre de salut. Howard effleura
son front du bout des doigts.

Danse et musique hawaïennes continuèrent jusqu'à ce que
les moteurs vrombissent et qu'on largue les amarres. Au premier mugissement de la sirène, les danseuses enlevèrent leurs
leis pour les lancer vers les mains tendues. Howard réussit à
en attraper un. Il sourit et fit un signe à la fille qui le lui avait
envoyée. « Lance-le dans l'eau en partant ! cria-t-elle. Ça te
fera revenir. »

Dans l'enthousiasme du moment, Howard lui adressa un
baiser.

— Waouh ! s'exclama Gordy en regardant d'abord la fille,
ensuite le lei. Pas sûr de pouvoir cacher cette petite bricole à
Lucy.

Il haussa un sourcil puis tendit la main pour toucher les
orchidées violettes et blanches.

— D'un autre côté…, reprit-il.

Howard mit la guirlande hors de sa portée.

— Oh non, pas question, objecta-t-il avec un petit sourire
narquois. Pas question que tu me manipules pour que je te
la donne.

— Quoi ? Tu ne veux pas que ton meilleur pote revienne
ici ?

Howard accrocha les fleurs à son cou.

— Trouves-en une pour toi, répliqua-t-il.

Mais le bateau quittait le quai. Les filles continuaient à faire
de grands signes mais déjà, on ne les distinguait plus très bien.
Howard et Gordy fendirent la foule pour se diriger vers
l'arrière. Ils s'assirent sur le casier métallique sous les tourelles
à canon. Encadré par des remorqueurs, le bâtiment avançait
lentement et passa à quelques mètres d'un cargo japonais.
Connaissant les préoccupations guerrières du nouveau Premier ministre du Japon, connaissant également la tension

croissante entre les États-Unis et le Japon, Howard devina
que les passagers qui s'entassaient sur les ponts du *Lisbon Maru*
devaient être des citoyens japonais rentrant chez eux.

Un groupe de soldats s'approcha de la rambarde pour
observer le navire japonais que longeait l'*Awatea*. Brusquement, un jeune homme tira ses paupières vers le haut pour
en faire deux fentes. « Père japonais. » Il les tira vers le bas.
« Mère chinoise. » Puis, les tirant dans des directions opposées,
il ricana : « Pauvre bébé. » Les passagers du *Lisbon Maru* ne
pouvaient pas entendre ce qu'il disait mais la grossièreté des
gestes était évidente.

— Seigneur ! s'écria Gordy en se levant d'un bond.

Plus gêné que choqué par la blague enfantine, Howard saisit
son ami par le bras pour le ramener en arrière. Il avait déjà
vu Gordy se battre pour moins que ça.

— Ce n'est qu'un gamin, dit-il.

Le soldat leur sourit puis s'éloigna.

Gordy se calma.

— Tout le monde sait que certains types ont menti sur
leur âge, déclara-t-il, mais nom de Dieu, comment un officier
recruteur a-t-il pu croire que ce morveux avait plus de seize
ans ?

Howard haussa les épaules. Il jeta un coup d'œil au *Lisbon
Maru* juste au moment où, à bord, un homme abaissait son
appareil photo. Leurs regards se croisèrent. Même de loin, la
haine brûlant dans les yeux du Japonais était indiscutable.
Howard se détourna en frissonnant. Une fois de plus, la vue
de la flotte américaine alignée dans Pearl Harbor l'emplit de
crainte. Il lui vint à l'esprit que l'*Awatea* – comme l'homme
sur le quai – était bien petit à côté de ces bateaux de guerre
et ces destroyers menaçants.

Dès qu'ils furent sortis du port, les remorqueurs larguèrent
les amarres pour faire demi-tour. L'*Awatea* et son escorte, le

Prince Robert, mirent le cap à l'ouest. Howard se pencha par-dessus le bastingage pour lancer son lei dans l'eau. Observer la guirlande de fleurs disparaître dans l'écume du sillage ne fit rien pour dissiper son appréhension croissante.

Deux heures plus tard, tout le monde fut convoqué sur le pont.

— J'imagine que nous allons enfin connaître notre destination, dit Gordy tandis qu'ils attendaient.

Durant les cinq derniers jours passés en mer, les rumeurs étaient allées bon train : de Singapour jusqu'à l'Inde en passant même par les combats dans les déserts d'Afrique. Vu les uniformes tropicaux qu'on leur avait distribués, Howard estimait toutes ces destinations possibles. Mais, dominant le bruit du vent et le grondement du moteur, le brigadier Lawson leur annonça du haut de la passerelle que leur devoir allait être de « défendre le Gibraltar du Pacifique ».

Sa voix crépitait dans les haut-parleurs du bateau.

— Soldats, nous sommes en route pour renforcer la garnison britannique dans la colonie de Hong Kong.

Des grognements se firent entendre parmi les grenadiers. Howard comprenait très bien leur réaction. Beaucoup de ces hommes expérimentés venaient d'achever quinze mois de faction à la Jamaïque et agir les démangeait. Lui, ça lui était égal. Il s'était enrôlé parce que son pays était en guerre. Il irait là où on lui dirait d'aller. C'était aussi simple que cela. Cependant, secrètement, il devait bien s'avouer que, en grande partie, il avait été poussé par une vision adolescente de l'appel de l'aventure. Maintenant que, apparemment, l'occasion de faire ses preuves au combat était perdue, il se retrouvait écartelé entre la déception et le soulagement.

Cette nuit-là, le bateau passa au black-out. Les hublots voilés restèrent fermés. Gêné par la chaleur et l'atmosphère fétide des quartiers confinés, Howard décrocha son hamac et

l'emporta sur le pont où il s'aperçut qu'ils étaient nombreux
à avoir eu la même idée. Il retourna à l'arrière et s'installa
sous les canons. Il s'allongea, heureux – et étonné – de ne pas
être en proie au mal de mer, contrairement à d'autres. Il était
agréable de sentir le vent secouer son hamac et il s'enfonça
dans le sommeil, bercé par les vagues qui s'écrasaient contre
la coque tandis que l'*Awatea* avançait plein ouest sur l'océan
éclairé par la lune.

Sous les ordres de Lawson l'entraînement continua durant
la traversée du Pacifique. Des heures durant, les soldats travaillaient par roulement sur les ponts surpeuplés, enchaînant
les exercices depuis le maniement du mortier et du Brengun
jusqu'au nettoyage des armes. Cela ne dérangeait pas Howard.
Ainsi le temps passait plus vite.

Le reste des journées était occupé par des débriefings sur ce
qui les attendait à Hong Kong. Les officiers se succédaient,
abordant tous les sujets, de l'histoire de la colonie aux maladies
tropicales – y compris les maladies vénériennes. Ils transmet-
taient des rapports des services secrets britanniques sur la nature
du soldat japonais – rapports qui considéraient comme quantité
négligeable les quatre ou cinq mille soldats de l'armée impériale
rassemblés le long de la frontière du territoire de Hong Kong.

Au Canada, Howard avait vu dans la presse les caricatures
montrant des Japonais à dents de lapin tremblant derrière leurs
grosses lunettes. Il pensait à l'homme sur le pont du *Lisbon
Maru*, à la haine sur ses traits, et il n'était pas convaincu.
Apparemment, le brigadier Lawson ne l'était pas davantage,
se disait-il en l'écoutant prévenir ses hommes de ne pas sous-
estimer les soldats de l'armée impériale.

Malgré l'entraînement quotidien exigé par le brigadier tant
qu'ils étaient en mer, certaines recrues trouvaient encore le

soir l'énergie de participer aux parties de poker illégales orga-
nisées dans une des réserves du pont inférieur. Les hommes
entraient et sortaient au gré de leur porte-monnaie. Les premiers soirs, Howard descendit regarder Gordy jouer. Des
sommes d'argent importantes changeaient de mains et il se
demanda si des querelles allaient éclater mais chacun paraissait
prendre pertes et gains avec sérénité.

— Eh, tu vas la faire c'te partie, oui ou non, Wheathead ?
railla un Royal Rifle un soir où Howard se tenait derrière
Gordy.

Les cheveux décolorés par le soleil de Howard lui avaient
valu ce surnom – « Tête-de-Foin » – parmi les grenadiers.
Mais prononcé avec l'accent français, il ne sut plus très bien
si c'était une offense ou un compliment. Il observa le Qué-
bécois souriant puis sortit un billet de dix dollars. Il le lâcha
avec une pointe de regret mais se dit que leur camaraderie de
soldats valait bien l'argent qu'il risquait de perdre. Tout était
bon pour alléger l'ennui des longues soirées.

Douze jours plus tard, lorsque le bateau entra dans le port
de Manille aux Philippines, Howard était plus riche de cinq
cents dollars et fumait une douzaine de cigarettes par jour.

À l'instar des autres soldats, il commençait à ne plus tenir
en place. Ça faisait dix-sept jours qu'ils n'avaient pas mis pied
à terre. Mais, comme à Hawaï, ils furent consignés à bord.
Au bout de quelques heures, une fois ravitaillés en carburant,
ils ressortirent du port, escortés par le croiseur britannique
HMS Danae.

— Mais pourquoi avons-nous brusquement besoin d'une
deuxième escorte, hein ? se demanda Gordy à voix haute ce
soir-là, en jetant sa première mise dans le pot.

Les autres joueurs de poker commencèrent à spéculer sur
la probabilité d'une guerre avec le Japon.

— Ce serait le pompon ! railla un Royal Rifle en ajoutant sa mise.

Mais beaucoup étaient persuadés qu'il leur faudrait se battre à leur arrivée à Hong Kong, dès qu'ils auraient mis pied à terre. Cette simple perspective semblait les réjouir, remarqua Howard.

Tandis que le débat s'animait, lui continuait à s'interroger sur les cales vides. Le matériel militaire n'était pas encore arrivé à Vancouver lorsque l'*Awatea* avait levé l'ancre et était sorti de l'English Bay le matin qui avait suivi l'embryon de mutinerie. À bord, la rumeur courait que les moyens de transport et les armes avaient été chargés sur un cargo, parti seulement quelques jours plus tard. Howard espérait que c'était vrai.

Le 16 novembre, au petit matin, vingt et un jours après s'être embarqués sur l'*Awatea* à Vancouver, Howard et Gordy, accoudés au bastingage, contemplèrent la masse sombre de l'horizon se transformer en terre.

— Voilà Hong Kong, mon pote, déclara Howard. Le bonheur ou l'enfer. On ne va pas tarder à le savoir.

Ils atteignirent la colonie au moment où les rayons du soleil levant éclairaient la montagne et les collines tout du long des seize kilomètres de l'île. Lorsqu'ils pénétrèrent dans le port, entre l'île et le continent, ils virent des centaines de sampans danser sur l'eau. Howard s'étonna qu'il n'y ait aucune collision mais les étranges embarcations avec leurs voiles rectangulaires savaient se faufiler avec adresse. Les occupants de ces bateaux bondés regardaient passer l'*Awatea* et ses passagers d'un air indifférent.

— Regarde-moi ça, s'exclama Howard en montrant les toits des somptueuses demeures qu'on apercevait au milieu de la végétation luxuriante.

— Qui aurait cru que deux bouseux comme nous allaient se retrouver au paradis ? dit Gordy en riant.

En approchant, Howard remarqua ce qui semblait être des milliers de cabanes entassées les unes sur les autres le long des rives et des quais de l'île ainsi que du continent. Ces abris précaires, construits de bric et de broc, tôle ondulée, bambou et papier – un bon petit vent aurait suffi pour les emporter – formaient un contraste saisissant avec l'opulence des demeures sur les collines.

Quand l'*Awatea* accosta sur le continent, il fut accueilli par des avions décrivant des cercles dans le ciel.

— J'espère bien que ce n'est pas la totalité des forces aériennes, lança Howard en regardant ces quatre avions à hélice vétustes.

Sur le quai, des représentants de la garnison britannique attendaient au garde-à-vous dans le soleil matinal. Ce qui fit siffler Howard.

— Heureusement que ces gars-là sont de notre côté, glissa-t-il en montrant un régiment d'Indiens.

Pas un muscle ne tressaillait, pas un œil ne cillait chez ces hommes de haute taille, au visage sombre. Howard n'aurait pu imaginer soldats plus royaux, plus farouches, tous bâtis sur le même modèle, même stature, même position, vêtus d'uniformes kaki bien repassés et de turbans ocre.

On descendit les passerelles de l'*Awatea*. Sur le quai, un orchestre militaire entama *Rule Britannia* et Howard observa le général de division Christopher Maltby, commandant britannique de la garnison de Hong Kong, et ses officiers qui montaient à bord. En uniforme tropical et armés de pied en cap, les troupes canadiennes, la Force C, – certains, comme Howard et Gordy, n'avaient reçu leurs armes que la veille au soir – attendaient impatiemment sur le pont tandis que leurs chefs discutaient avec les officiers britanniques dans le salon du bateau.

— Une parade militaire, ça plaît aux Anglais, affirma Gordy. Et là, les gars, on va pouvoir leur en offrir une.

Howard, lui aussi, était soulagé à l'idée de rejoindre leurs nouveaux quartiers équipés de vrais fusils et de baïonnettes plutôt que ces armes en bois avec lesquelles ils s'étaient entraînés au Canada.

Bizarrement, les hommes avaient encore pour ordre d'ôter tout insigne ou galon susceptibles de les faire reconnaître comme appartenant à l'armée canadienne. Alors qu'ils attendaient de pouvoir débarquer, l'orchestre entonna *The Maple Leaf Forever* et, dans la foule qui grossissait, on entendit crier : « Bienvenue aux Canadiens ! » Bravo pour la discrétion, pensa Howard.

À midi, au son des cornemuses du Royal Scots, les troupes commencèrent à débarquer. Howard n'était pas du tout sûr d'avoir dans les veines, mélangé à la sauce Heinz 57, du sang écossais mais un frisson patriotique s'empara de lui à l'appel des cornemuses. Il rejoignit sa compagnie rassemblée sur le quai du continent. Encouragé par les cris de la foule et avec l'étrange sensation que la terre bougeait sous ses pieds, Howard força ses jambes encore au rythme de la mer à marcher du même pas que celles de ses camarades.

Dans la chaleur humide de l'après-midi, la procession se dirigea vers l'artère principale de Kowloon. En parcourant les trois kilomètres qui les séparaient de leurs nouveaux quartiers, Howard jeta des coups d'œil dans les rues latérales sombres. Un chaos désordonné de bâtiments délabrés, hauts de trois ou quatre étages, avec des façades couvertes d'enseignes chinoises et d'échafaudages en bambou, s'étendait aussi loin que portait le regard. Les trottoirs étroits grouillaient de gens qui se bousculaient devant des éventaires de nourriture, des cages en osier où gloussaient des poulets et couinaient des cochons. Des odeurs de cuisine étranges, que la graisse rance et des épices inconnues rendaient âcres, assaillaient les narines de Howard. Pourtant, il y avait quelque chose d'irrésistible dans cette ville débordante d'activité. Il se sentit soudain électrisé, un mélange d'excitation et d'appréhension.

Tout au long du chemin, des coolies torse nu qui tiraient des rickshaws se faufilaient adroitement dans les brèches du défilé en décochant des sourires aux soldats en marche. De vieilles femmes, courbées sous des perches en bambou chargées de lourds paniers, attendaient, stoïques, de pouvoir passer. Des badauds et des commerçants asiatiques observaient depuis des trottoirs et des magasins les hordes de Blancs qui agitaient des drapeaux anglais en poussant des cris de bienvenue. Howard remarqua bien quelques Orientaux qui les ignoraient ou les examinaient à la dérobée mais la plupart paraissaient enchantés de voir surgir du renfort pour les dix mille hommes de troupe qui composaient actuellement la garnison.

Grâce aux conférences entendues à bord, Howard savait que la population de la petite colonie atteignait presque les deux millions, avec l'afflux des réfugiés chinois qui fuyaient les Japonais. Mais, tandis que les colons les escortaient à grands cris jusqu'aux portes du camp de Sham Shui Po, il se demanda quelle différence pourraient faire deux mille hommes supplémentaires.

10

La fille apparut pour la première fois le lundi matin. Chez les Fenwick, le lit dans la chambre d'amis, à l'étage, se trouvait tout à côté de la fenêtre. Sans même lever la tête de l'oreiller, je voyais parfaitement Barclay Street. La rue était si étroite que, s'il y avait une voiture garée de chaque côté, il restait à peine assez de place pour qu'une troisième passe au milieu. Les maisons, tassées les unes contre les autres, se ressemblaient toutes mise à part leur couleur – maman disait toujours que le gouvernement n'avait sans doute eu à sa disposition que trois teintes. D'un bout à l'autre de la rue, il y avait la même alternance : marron, vert, gris. Seule se distinguait la vieille ferme des Fenwick, passée à la chaux, construite au milieu d'un terrain clos à la végétation désordonnée. Une pelouse pelée comme un tapis s'étendait devant les autres, interrompue seulement par le bitume du trottoir qui menait à des porches identiques et par les balançoires du square de l'autre côté de la rue.

Le petit square n'en était pas vraiment un mais plutôt un vaste espace de pelouse entre la maison des Manson et celle de mon amie Ardith. Des années auparavant, quelques pères du quartier s'étaient unis pour installer un portique de balançoires et un toboggan. Presque plus personne ne s'en servait à présent, en dehors des quelques bébés qu'il restait encore et parfois Kipper. Nous autres organisions les jeux de notre enfance dans la rue.

Le reflet du soleil matinal dans les vitres des Manson me fit plisser les yeux. La lumière dure m'aveugla momentanément mais j'eus le temps de voir Mme Manson aux aguets. Elle aussi surveillait le square – et la fille toute seule devant les balançoires. Même si elle n'avait pas été étrangère, je l'aurais remarquée. Ses vêtements, un corsage blanc rentré dans une jupe plissée sombre, paraissaient trop guindés pour une journée d'été. Ses cheveux d'un noir d'ébène étaient coupés au carré et une frange sombre tombait jusqu'à ses yeux en amande. Elle était orientale – japonaise ou chinoise. Je ne savais pas faire la différence. Il n'y avait pas de familles orientales dans notre quartier. Les seuls Chinois que je connaissais, c'étaient les propriétaires de l'épicerie dans Victoria Drive et M. Fong, le marchand de légumes.

Quelques années auparavant, presque tout ce dont nous avions besoin nous était livré à domicile. Le laitier passait tous les deux jours. Le marchand de légumes et le boulanger Mc Gavin venaient une fois par semaine. Quand nous étions plus jeunes, pendant la journée ne circulaient que des camions de livraison. Si nous étions en train de jouer dans la rue, nous nous rangions sur le côté, indignés de cette interruption.

Le marchand de légumes passait le mercredi. Je n'avais jamais vu quelqu'un aussi âgé que M. Fong. Il n'était pas bavard mais le sourire de ses yeux sombres s'intensifiait lorsque, descendant de sa cabine, il nous voyait, Kipper et moi, en train de l'attendre avec la liste de maman. Nous grimpions derrière lui les marches qui menaient dans son camion. J'adorais l'odeur chaude de terre, de légumes et de fruits qui montait des casiers de bois. M. Fong nous tendait des paniers d'osier qu'il remplissait avec la commande. De temps en temps, il nous glissait une banane tachetée dans la poche.

L'été de mes sept ans, son camion arriva un jour en cahotant alors que nous étions en train de jouer au milieu de la rue. Mon amie Ardith et moi, nous tenions chacune l'extrémité de deux longues cordes à sauter tandis qu'une rangée de filles attendaient leur tour pour entrer dans le jeu au rythme de la chanson que nous entonnions en chœur. À l'approche de M. Fong, tout le monde, en râlant, monta sur le trottoir, les mains sur les hanches. Le camion s'arrêta dans un vrombissement devant chez nous, la portière s'ouvrit et le marchand descendit lentement du siège.

Tandis qu'il se dirigeait vers l'arrière de son véhicule, je sentis un mouvement d'impatience de l'autre côté des cordes et, obéissante, je redescendis sur la chaussée. Le jeu reprit. Dès les premiers mots de la comptine, je vis le petit sourire narquois sur les lèvres d'Ardith, le défi dans son regard quand elle fredonna : « Chinetoque-toc-toc-toc, Chinetoque-toc-toc-toc… »

C'était une comptine que nous chantions souvent mais pour la première fois, je liais les paroles à M. Fong. Pourtant, elles tombèrent de mes lèvres comme de celles des autres.

> Chinetoque-toc-toc-toc,
> Gonflé à bloc,
> Ne tient pas le choc
> Parce qu'il débloque…

M. Fong s'arrêta sur les marches de son camion et attendit la fin de la ritournelle. Puis il fit volte-face. Nos regards se croisèrent. Je vis sa tristesse et je m'empourprai. Mais il était trop tard. Je détournai le regard.

Tout le reste de l'été, je restai à l'intérieur chaque fois qu'il vint faire ses livraisons. Peu de temps après, on construisit un grand supermarché quelques pâtés de maisons plus loin et, l'une après l'autre, les livraisons à domicile disparurent. Plus de cinq ans après, je me sentais encore rouge de honte en repensant à cette journée. Je me demandai si ma mère l'avait jamais su. J'espérais que non.

Mon menton se mit à trembler à l'évocation de maman.

— Tu descends ? s'enquit Danny, de l'autre côté de la porte.

— Oui, répondis-je, mais je demeurai pelotonnée sous les couvertures tandis que le bruit de ses pas s'éloignait.

Il me laissait tranquille. Exactement comme la veille au soir. Une fois que je fus chez lui, je crois qu'il fut soulagé de me voir monter directement dans la chambre d'amis. Je m'étais mise au lit tandis qu'il emmenait Kipper faire une partie de jeu de l'oie dans sa chambre. Lorsque Mme Fenwick avait passé la tête par la porte, j'avais fait mine de dormir mais pourtant, j'avais l'impression que, plus jamais, je ne serais capable de dormir ou de rire. J'étais restée couchée dans l'obscurité, irritée contre Danny et Kipper chaque fois qu'un éclat de rire étouffé me parvenait de l'autre côté du palier.

Danny était un des rares enfants du quartier à ne jamais se moquer de mon frère. Et apparemment, à l'époque où nous étions inséparables, lui et moi, devoir le traîner en permanence ne le dérangeait pas. Et puis un jour, l'été dernier, en coupant à travers les fourrés pour rentrer de la piscine, j'avais cédé à la curiosité et au défi de Danny qui était prêt à me montrer le « sien » si je lui montrais le « mien ».

Après, je fis jurer le secret à Kipper. Mais j'aurais dû m'en douter. À peine arrivés à la maison, lorsque maman nous demanda si nous avions passé une bonne journée, il bafouilla :

— Je peux rien dire. J'ai promis à Ethie.

Maman me prit à part.

— N'oblige pas ton frère à rompre sa promesse, dit-elle.

Sa réaction fut moins dramatique que je ne l'avais prévu. Il était normal d'être curieux mais pour le moment, mieux valait garder pour soi ses parties intimes. J'ignore si elle en parla à la mère de Danny mais à partir de ce jour il m'évita.

Je jetai un nouveau coup d'œil sur la fille dans le square. En soupirant, je me redressai et rejetai mes couvertures. Kipper était déjà levé. Lorsque je l'avais entendu descendre, j'étais restée au lit. J'aurais aimé y rester éternellement. Hier soir, je ne voulais surtout pas m'endormir ; ce matin, je ne voulais plus me lever.

À contrecœur, je m'habillai. En bas, je pénétrai dans le gigantesque salon. La grand-mère de Danny était assise dans l'ombre, les yeux dans le vide, la tête ailleurs – comme mon père mais son absence était due au grand âge. Je lui adressai un gentil salut mais elle ne réagit pas.

Dans la cuisine, Kipper était installé au comptoir, avec un tablier par-dessus son jean et son T-shirt, le chapeau repoussé sur la nuque. Il me fit un sourire plein de fierté en trempant une tranche de pain dans un bol rempli d'œufs battus.

— Qui a faim ? s'enquit Dora Fenwick, au fourneau.

Elle jeta un morceau de pain perdu bien doré sur une assiette puis s'approcha pour permettre à Kipper de transférer une nouvelle tranche dégoulinante dans sa poêle grésillante.

La culpabilité me submergea quand je me rendis compte que j'avais bel et bien faim.

— Non merci, marmonnai-je.

Je quittai la cuisine pour aller dans la salle de bains.

Une fois lavée, je pris une brosse et tentai de discipliner mes cheveux. Les soies s'emmêlèrent dans mes boucles serrées. Plus je tirais, pire c'était. La brosse toujours accrochée sur la tête, je m'effondrai dans un coin, les genoux entre les bras et je me mis à sangloter tout en me berçant d'avant en arrière.

Qui allait me coiffer désormais ? Qui allait nous faire à manger ? S'occuper de Kipper ? Qui allait s'occuper de nous ?

— Ethie ? appela la mère de Danny de l'autre côté de la porte. Je peux entrer, chérie ?

Je déchirai une poignée de papier hygiénique pour me moucher puis j'ouvris la porte.

Mme Fenwick entra et referma la porte derrière elle. Elle m'aida à me relever puis me fit asseoir sur le rebord de la baignoire. Elle s'installa à côté de moi et entreprit de récupérer la brosse en douceur. J'essayai de rester tranquille pendant qu'elle se démenait.

— Ça fait très mal, non ? demanda-t-elle au bout de quelques instants.

J'avalai difficilement ma salive puis hochai la tête. Elle ne parlait pas de mes cheveux. La douleur était intérieure, là où j'étais meurtrie et ulcérée. Cette douleur avait envahi mon ventre la veille et, le soir, alors que je voulais résister au sommeil, elle pesait comme une pierre brûlante. Comment dormir ou manger alors que ma mère ne pourrait plus jamais faire ni l'un ni l'autre ?

Plus jamais. Impossible à imaginer. Jamais c'est pour l'éternité. Amen. Une pensée qui embrasa mon ventre. Alors, comment aurais-je pu avoir faim ?

— J'aimerais pouvoir te dire que tout ira bien, déclara Mme Fenwick. J'aimerais pouvoir faire disparaître ta souffrance. Mais c'est impossible. Elle demeurera éternellement en toi mais un jour, elle se retirera dans un autre endroit de ton cœur, un endroit plus résistant, et ce sera moins lourd à porter. Jusqu'à ce moment, je suis là si tu as besoin de moi.

Je ne pouvais croire qu'un jour la douleur disparaîtrait. Mais je ravalai mes larmes tandis que Mme Fenwick me brossait les cheveux, en commençant par le bas pour remonter doucement.

— Tout à l'heure, je te ferai des tresses plaquées, proposa-t-elle.

Elle me tapota le genou et se leva.

— Et il n'y a rien de mal à avoir faim, ajouta-t-elle.

Après le petit déjeuner, elle me lava la tête dans la cuisine. Tandis qu'elle me shampouinait le crâne, je regardais par la fenêtre au-dessus de l'évier. La fille que j'avais vue plus tôt dans la journée était toujours plantée au même endroit dans le square, les yeux fixés sur notre maison. Curieuse, je me demandai si elle n'était pas raide dingue de Frankie. Il y avait toujours des filles qui lui téléphonaient ou qui venaient sonner à la porte. Peut-être était-elle en train de l'observer.

Était-il déjà debout ? Et papa ? Brusquement, j'étais impatiente de rentrer chez moi.

Une demi-heure plus tard, j'examinai dans le miroir mes cheveux tressés. Ces derniers temps, j'avais évité de laisser maman me faire des nattes parce que je détestais m'entendre dire que je ressemblais à Fifi Brindacier. Je touchai les tresses encore humides. J'aimais bien la façon dont elles étaient proprement collées sur mon crâne avant de tomber sur mes épaules au lieu de pointer toutes raides comme faisaient les nattes folles de maman.

— Merci, murmurai-je. On ferait bien d'y aller maintenant, Kipper.

En attendant qu'il lace ses tennis, je sortis sous le porche. Hier, Barclay Street était déserte. Ce matin quelques enfants s'étaient aventurés dehors. Plus bas dans la rue Wayne et Rob Ellis décrivaient lentement des huit sur leurs vélos. Debra Martin et Ardith Price jouaient avec une balle de hockey sur le trottoir.

Danny sortit et resta près de la porte. Il avait beaucoup changé au cours de l'année écoulée. Il était maintenant plus grand que moi. Avec sa nouvelle coupe en brosse plate sur le dessus et ses lunettes à la Buddy Holly, je parie qu'il se trouvait sans aucun doute formidable. Et je n'étais que… eh bien je n'étais qu'une fille.

Il loucha, une vieille habitude que même ses lunettes fantaisie ne lui avaient pas fait perdre.

— T'as envie… euh… de te balader, aujourd'hui ? demanda-t-il en remontant sa grosse monture sur son nez.

— Non, répondis-je en descendant les marches.

Sa mère l'avait sans doute obligé à poser cette question.

— On va voir maman aujourd'hui ? souffla Kipper derrière moi, qui essayait de ne pas se faire semer.

— Je sais pas.

Le rire des enfants qui jouaient dans la rue s'interrompit en nous voyant sortir de chez Danny. Je quittai le trottoir pour éviter Ardith et Debra. Deux jours auparavant, nous étions amies, Ardith et moi. Aujourd'hui, j'avais l'impression que je lui faisais peur.

Kipper s'arrêta juste derrière elle.

— Salut, Ardith, dit-il.

Elle saisit la balle en caoutchouc dur et la serra contre elle. Elle marmonna un vague salut, tenta de me sourire mais c'était plutôt un rictus.

— Tu vas à l'école biblique aujourd'hui ? s'enquit-elle.

— Non, répliquai-je. Et toi ?

— Je sais pas… Peut-être.

— D'accord. À plus tard.

— Salut, Wayne ! cria Kipper.

— Salut ! répondit Wayne qui se concentra pour braquer son vélo dans l'autre sens.

— On va voir notre maman aujourd'hui. Avant qu'elle parte au bradis.

Wayne mit pied à terre pour arrêter son vélo.

— Oui, j'ai entendu dire, je… euh… je suis désolé, bégaya-t-il.

Il ne regardait ni Kipper ni moi mais un point entre les deux.

Je pris mon frère par la main et l'entraînai.

— Je t'ai dit que je ne savais pas si nous allions la voir ou pas – et c'est le paradis. Paradis ! Pas bradis.

— Pardon, Ethie, s'excusa Kipper en reniflant, dangereusement au bord des larmes. Bradis, répéta-t-il. Bradis.

Il me regarda, quêtant mon approbation.

Regrettant déjà de m'être fâchée contre lui, je tentai de lui sourire.

— C'est bien, lui dis-je.

Avant d'entrer dans notre jardin, je me retournai pour regarder le square.

La fille n'était plus là.

11

Si j'y avais vraiment réfléchi sur le moment, j'en serais peut-être arrivée à la conclusion que, indirectement, Kipper était responsable de tout ce qui était arrivé. Sans lui, maman n'aurait jamais connu Marlene. L'année où j'entrai en primaire, maman menait encore son combat perdu d'avance contre ce qu'elle appelait « ces esprits fermés » qui empêchaient Kipper de fréquenter l'école. Elle se mit à faire elle-même son instruction. La première semaine de septembre, cette année-là, ils allèrent acheter du matériel artistique et revinrent avec, pour Kipper, des pinceaux et de la peinture et, pour maman, un travail dans le magasin de fournitures artistiques de Marlene sur Granville Street. C'était parfait parce que Kipper pouvait l'accompagner. Pendant qu'elle travaillait à la boutique, il passait ses journées dans l'atelier avec les étudiants en art de Marlene.

J'aimais bien Marlene Telford. Elle refusait de nous laisser l'appeler Mme Telford, insistant pour que nous utilisions son prénom, Kipper et moi. À plusieurs reprises, lorsque maman ne parvenait pas à trouver quelqu'un pour nous garder le mercredi soir, elle nous avait emmenés dans l'appartement du West End, près de Stanley Park. Nous nous installions à la table de la cuisine, moi avec mon travail scolaire et Kipper avec ses couleurs, tandis que les femmes jouaient aux cartes dans le salon. Toutes les amies de Marlene connaissaient mon frère du magasin et elles étaient toujours aux petits soins pour lui, elles l'embrassaient et elles lui pinçaient la joue en l'appelant leur beau Picasso.

Elles étaient tellement différentes de notre mère. Alors que maman portait toujours une robe pour sortir ou pour aller travailler, elles s'habillaient de pantalons ou de longues jupes flottantes avec des grandes chemises. Et contrairement à maman, qui n'aurait jamais franchi le seuil de la porte sans rouge à lèvres et fard à joues, aucune d'elles n'était maquillée.

Frankie traitait Marlene de beatnik. J'ignorais ce que cela signifiait mais je savais qu'il l'aimait bien, lui aussi. Contrairement à tante Mildred. Chaque fois que celle-ci parlait de Marlene, elle disait « l'amie bohème de Lucy ».

— Elle porte l'anticonformisme comme on porte un vêtement, l'entendis-je un jour dire à maman, et pourtant son mari est un gros marchand d'art. Facile de se montrer critique par rapport au système quand on est riches.

Maman avait ri.

— Marlene, c'est Marlene. C'est une des personnes les plus authentiques que je connaisse.

— Authentique ? avait répété tante Mildred avec un reniflement plein de mépris. Tu vas voir, tu vas te retrouver habillée tout en noir, collants et col roulé, à hanter les bistrots en récitant des vers de Jack Kerouac.

— Mmm, ça semble sublime ! l'avait raillée maman et même tante Mildred avait dû sourire.

L'édition dominicale du *Daily Province* était sous le porche lorsque je revins avec Kipper de chez Danny. La photographie d'une Marilyn souriante posant en maillot de bain occupait la moitié de la première page. La légende disait : « La mort de la star, un mystère. »

Je m'emparai du journal et le feuilletai, à la recherche de quelque chose sur ma mère. Kipper s'affala sur la première marche et regarda tomber à mes pieds les pages rejetées. Je faillis le rater mais page douze, en bas, le nom de ma mère me sauta aux yeux dans un petit article.

« *L'OXYDE DE CARBONE FAIT DEUX VICTIMES*
La police municipale confirme la mort accidentelle de deux femmes de Vancouver, Lucy June Coulter et Marlene Agnes Telford. Leurs corps ont été découverts dimanche matin à l'aube à bord d'un voilier dans Coal Harbour. On pense que la mort a été causée par un empoisonnement à l'oxyde de carbone. On n'a pas pu joindre le propriétaire du bateau, Jeremy Telford, patron des Telford Galleries et époux de l'une des victimes. »

Marlene Telford ? J'avais entendu les conversations la veille – je me souvenais même de papa disant « elles » au pluriel – mais je n'avais pas encore fait le rapprochement. Le soir, j'étais restée éveillée à chercher quelqu'un, ou quelque chose, à blâmer, et c'était tombé sur Marlene. Après tout, c'était le voilier de son mari. Alors que ma cervelle, engourdie par cette nouvelle information, enregistrait le fait qu'elle était également morte, la porte d'entrée s'ouvrit à la volée et Frankie surgit, louchant dans la lumière du matin. Les yeux rouges et gonflés, il avait l'air de ne pas avoir dormi de la nuit. Il jeta un regard sur les feuilles éparpillées par terre.

— Je vois que tu as déjà lu le journal, remarqua-t-il.

Il se pencha pour m'aider à ramasser les pages éparses. Notre chat Ginger sortit à son tour, la queue dressée. Kipper l'attrapa au passage et enfouit son visage dans son pelage.

— T'as faim ? demanda-t-il en se relevant pour l'emporter dans la maison.

Mes deux frères rentrèrent et je les suivis. Je m'arrêtai net en voyant papa couché sur le canapé du salon sous la couverture grise d'habitude rangée dans le placard à linge. Choquée, je cherchai Frankie des yeux mais il était déjà dans la cuisine ; le dos tourné, il posait le journal en désordre sur la table.

Kipper alla remplir la gamelle du chat puis sortit l'animal et sa nourriture dans le jardin. Je m'assis en face de Frankie.

— Pourquoi papa dort-il sur le canapé ? chuchotai-je.

— Il ne supporte sans doute pas la chambre vide, répondit Frankie en haussant les épaules et en se concentrant sur les feuilles à remettre en ordre.

— Frankie ? Tu crois que... euh... tu crois que maman était fâchée après moi, que c'est ma... faute ? bredouillai-je.

Frankie laissa tomber les pages qu'il tenait.

— Non ! Bien sûr que non, répondit-il en scrutant mon visage. Pourquoi tu penses une chose pareille ?

— Papa a dit... il a dit qu'elle était fâchée à propos de quelque chose. J'ai pensé... j'ai pensé que, peut-être, c'était parce que j'emmenais plus Kipper partout avec moi...

Les sanglots qui montaient dans ma gorge m'empêchèrent de continuer.

— Ethie, non.

Il s'agenouilla pour se trouver à la même hauteur que moi.

— Maman, reprit-il, maman est... était... très fière de toi. Et de Kipper. Ce qui s'est passé n'a rien à voir avec vous deux. C'est juste un accident épouvantable.

Il m'ouvrit les bras et je me jetai dedans.

— Mais pourquoi était-elle sur un bateau avec Marlene ? murmurai-je dans sa chemise, déjà trempée par mes larmes.

— Elle avait peut-être besoin d'une pause, d'un peu d'intimité avec une amie. Je ne sais pas. Nous ne le saurons probablement jamais, dit-il en soupirant. Et chercher à deviner, ça ne peut que nous rendre fous.

À ce moment-là, par-dessus son épaule, je vis entrer tante Mildred. Son regard s'adoucit en nous voyant enlacés dans la cuisine. Elle se tourna vers le salon.

— Howard ! souffla-t-elle.

Frankie me lâcha et se releva. Il entra dans l'autre pièce au moment où papa repoussait sa couverture. Il portait les mêmes vêtements que la veille. L'air égaré, il posa les pieds par terre et se redressa lentement.

Tante Mildred fit claquer sa langue.

— Regardez-moi cet endroit ! dit-elle en examinant la pièce.

La vaisselle et les verres de la veille étaient éparpillés partout. La table basse était jonchée de cendriers débordant de mégots et de bouteilles d'alcool vides.

— Qu'en dirait votre mère ? commenta-t-elle avant de se diriger vers la cuisine.

— Elle en dirait qu'elle nous manque, répliqua Frankie derrière elle.

Les épaules de tante Mildred s'affaissèrent. Elle prit une profonde inspiration puis ouvrit la fenêtre.

— Ça pue ici, marmonna-t-elle.

Je remarquai enfin la vaisselle sale qui débordait dans l'évier. Je me précipitai pour la laver.

— Qui t'a coiffée ? demanda tante Mildred.

Je m'empourprai, muette de culpabilité à l'idée d'avoir laissé Mme Fenwick me faire des tresses. D'avoir passé la nuit chez elle. D'avoir pris un petit déjeuner.

Kipper entra par la porte de la cuisine.

— C'est la mère de Danny, annonça-t-il avant d'ajouter avec fierté : Et on a fait du pain perdu.

Ginger, le chat, sauta de ses bras, traversa la pièce et, le dos rond, vint s'enrouler autour de la jambe de notre tante.

Tante Mildred poussa un cri et bondit en arrière.

— Du balai ! siffla-t-elle en se débarrassant de Ginger sans douceur.

Kipper intercepta le chat en fuite avant d'aller dans le salon. Tante Mildred pinça les lèvres. Elle posa son sac sur une chaise puis me rejoignit à l'évier où elle commença à regrouper les verres sales.

Frankie vint derrière elle.

— Je t'en prie, tante Mildred, dit-il d'une voix polie mais ferme, nous allons nettoyer.

— Mais je veux seulement...

Elle reposa la vaisselle dans l'évier et se tourna vers lui.

— Écoute, déclara-t-elle, laissons déjà passer les quelques jours à venir. L'enterrement est prévu pour jeudi. Je suis venue choisir une tenue pour votre mère.

— Nous pouvons nous occuper de cela, insista Frankie.

Le dos droit, elle alla récupérer son sac.

— Je reviendrai demain à dix heures, annonça-t-elle. J'emmènerai Ethie acheter des vêtements convenables pour la cérémonie puisque votre père insiste pour qu'elle y aille.

Elle braqua son regard sur le salon.

— Mais, reprit-elle, je commence à croire que votre père n'est nullement en état de prendre des décisions.

Frankie la raccompagna jusqu'à la porte.

— Si l'un de vous a besoin de quelque chose, ajouta-t-elle, faites donc une liste que je prendrai demain.

Frankie l'embrassa sur la joue.

— On va se débrouiller, tante Mildred.

Mais, alors qu'il cherchait à la rassurer, j'entendais le mensonge dans sa voix trop neutre et je me rendis compte qu'il n'y croyait pas lui-même. Pas plus que moi. Comment pourrions-nous jamais nous débrouiller, à présent ?

Une fois tante Mildred partie, papa s'assit sur le bord du canapé, la tête dans les mains, se massant les tempes. Il paraissait plus petit, rétréci, comme si un énorme morceau de lui avait disparu avec notre mère – et il ne restait plus grand-chose. Je repensai aux paroles de notre tante. Qu'avait-elle voulu dire en affirmant que papa n'était pas en état de prendre des décisions ? En vérité, l'argent mis à part, c'était toujours maman qui prenait les décisions dans la vie quotidienne de la famille, maman qui arrondissait les angles. À voir mon père assis là, à moitié ailleurs, une vague de panique me submergea. Sans la présence de notre mère pour le soutenir, allait-il s'enfoncer encore plus profondément dans le silence de son monde ?

Kipper vint le rejoindre sur le canapé. Caressant Ginger d'une main, il tapota l'épaule de papa de l'autre. Venu de très loin monta un petit bruit – comme une bouilloire qui siffle. Le bruit s'amplifia et je finis par reconnaître la plainte aiguë, semblable au cri d'un animal, qui s'échappait régulièrement du ventre de mon père.

— Un souvenir de la guerre tapi au fond de son intestin, avait dit ma mère un jour alors qu'il était en proie à une de ces crises.

Il réussit à se lever et fila vers la salle de bains.

— J'ai fait du café, cria Frankie.

Je nettoyais la cuisinière quand il vint prendre la cafetière sur le feu. S'efforçant de contrôler le tremblement de ses mains, il se versa une tasse de café noir épais avant de s'installer sur une chaise au bout de la table.

Devant l'évier, Kipper avait les bras jusqu'aux coudes dans l'eau mousseuse.

— On est en train de faire le ménage, annonça-t-il.

— Oui, je vois, répondit papa en essayant de sourire.

Il but une gorgée de café et tressaillit.

— Désolé, c'est la première fois que je fais du café, dit Frankie en essuyant la table.

— J'ai connu pire, répliqua papa en prenant une nouvelle gorgée pour le prouver.

Il reposa sa tasse et saisit un paquet de cigarettes sur le rebord de la fenêtre.

Frankie fit glisser un cendrier propre sur la table et s'assit en face de lui.

— Papa ? interrogea-t-il en passant d'un air absent le torchon sur la même tache invisible. Tu as entendu ce qu'a dit tante Mildred à propos... de... euh... une tenue pour maman ?

— Non.

— Elle voulait en choisir une. Je lui ai dit qu'on s'en chargerait.

— Ouais, réagit papa. Ce n'est pas à votre tante de prendre cette décision.

Il tira intensément sur sa cigarette. Tandis que la fumée s'échappait lentement de ses lèvres, il déclara tranquillement, les yeux fixés sur la fenêtre :

— On va prendre sa robe verte.

Frankie attendit un petit moment. Puis, secouant la tête, il se leva, prit un torchon à côté de l'évier et entreprit d'essuyer la vaisselle. Tante Mildred avait raison sur un point. Il fallait laisser passer les quelques jours à venir. Nous engourdir l'esprit et avancer. Si quelqu'un connaissait la bonne méthode, c'était bien notre père : il était passé maître dans l'art de franchir en somnambule les obstacles de la vie. Mais maman avait toujours été là pour lui aplanir le chemin.

De toute la journée, il ne quitta pas la fenêtre des yeux pendant que mes frères et moi, nous nettoyions la maison dans un silence obstiné. Une fois la vaisselle rangée, je fis les poussières partout tandis que Frankie et Kipper tondaient la pelouse. Dans la soirée, alors que j'étais montée dans ma chambre, j'entendis Frankie sortir et la maison me parut encore plus vide. Je me glissai dans mon lit ; l'air sentait fort le citron et le vinaigre. J'inspirai profondément, dans l'espoir que l'odeur du produit de nettoyage de maman la ramènerait dans ma tête. Mais je ne parvenais toujours pas à revoir ses traits. Je pleurai le nez dans l'oreiller jusqu'à ce que j'entende la respiration spongieuse de Kipper. Je relevai la tête et, la vue brouillée, je l'aperçus à côté de mon lit, sa poitrine bombée se soulevant à chacune de ses respirations rauques.

— Où est ton inhalateur ? lui demandai-je en m'essuyant le visage.

Il prit laborieusement son souffle, fouilla dans sa poche et l'en sortit. Il le mit dans sa bouche, appuya dessus d'une main et de l'autre, brandit quelque chose. Tout en expirant, il laissa échapper :

— Pour que tu retrouves sa tête.

Rien n'échappait à Kipper. La veille, il m'avait entendue me plaindre que je ne me rappelais plus le visage de maman et il était là avec une photo d'elle. Reconnaissante, je me redressai et la pris. Tandis qu'il inspirait son médicament, j'examinai le cliché de maman et Kipper pris dans la boutique de Marlene.

Kipper repartit dans sa chambre et je glissai la photo sous mon oreiller ; je m'endormis avec le sourire de maman tout frais dans mon esprit. Le lendemain, mardi, je m'éveillai tard, oubliant un bref instant que tout avait changé ; je dus à nouveau subir le supplice de retrouver la mémoire. De me souvenir que plus jamais je ne reverrais maman, sauf en photo.

La porte de la salle de bains se ferma bruyamment en bas, rompant le silence de la maison. Je me levai. Dans le salon, la couverture et l'oreiller de papa traînaient encore sur le canapé vide. Des bruits d'eau venaient de la salle de bains. Dans la cuisine, la cafetière se trouvait sur le comptoir avec du café moulu renversé à côté. J'ouvris le réfrigérateur et contemplai les étagères surchargées de plats étrangers. Je n'avais pas faim. Je refermai la porte. Je m'assis au bout de la table et regardai par la fenêtre, pile au moment où la voiture de tante Mildred apparaissait en haut de la rue.

Les courses ! J'étais censée faire des achats avec elle aujourd'hui. Je bondis sur mes pieds, non sans jeter un coup d'œil au square, de l'autre côté de la rue. La fille que j'avais vue la veille près des balançoires était au même endroit et elle regardait notre maison. Lorsque la voiture de ma tante vint se garer le long du trottoir, elle quitta le square.

Derrière moi, la porte de la salle de bains s'ouvrit et mon père entra dans la cuisine. Le visage couleur de cendre, il s'approcha de la fenêtre pour scruter l'extérieur, l'air hagard comme s'il avait vu un fantôme.

12

17 novembre 1941 : Camp de Sham Shui Po
à Kowloon

Elle s'appelait Feng Shun-ling. Howard la vit pour la première fois le lendemain de son arrivée à Hong Kong. Gêné par
l'immobilité de son lit après toutes ces nuits passées en bateau,
gêné aussi par des démangeaisons suspectes qui l'avaient réveillé
en plein milieu de la nuit, il se leva de bonne heure. Dehors,
dans la solitude glacée qui précédait l'aurore, il alluma sa première cigarette de la journée. On entendait quelque part dans
le port résonner la cloche d'une balise isolée.

Appuyé contre la clôture, il scruta la baie. Au milieu des
bancs de brouillard, les bateaux de pêche s'apprêtaient à partir
en mer, leurs lumières clignotant. En contrebas, la laisse de vase
était jonchée de débris abandonnés par la marée. Une odeur
saumâtre d'algues et de décomposition flottait dans l'air
humide. Tirant sur sa cigarette, il entendit derrière lui des bruits
de pas. Il fit volte-face et vit deux vieilles femmes, très voûtées,
avancer d'un pas traînant sur la route, de l'autre côté de la
clôture. Fasciné, il observa leur lente progression ; elles marchaient sur des pieds tellement minuscules qu'on avait du mal
à croire qu'ils puissent soutenir le plus frêle des corps. Derrière
elles, d'autres silhouettes sombres surgirent du brouillard.

Elles venaient de toutes les directions, procession silencieuse et dépenaillée d'hommes, de femmes et d'enfants. Lorsqu'ils atteignaient les rives de la baie, sans se soucier des rouleaux de barbelés qui leur barraient la route, ils se faufilaient par des brèches invisibles et disparaissaient.

Sur les traits creusés de ceux qui passaient près de la clôture, Howard reconnut le désespoir de la faim. Et chez beaucoup, l'indifférence de la résignation. Quelques-uns lancèrent des regards de convoitise sur la cigarette qu'il fumait. D'instinct, il sortit le paquet de sa poche puis se rendit compte à quel point il était inutile de vouloir leur offrir les quelques cigarettes qui lui restaient. Ils étaient vraiment trop nombreux. Honteux de sa richesse face à cette pauvreté flagrante, il laissa tomber la sienne, sans la terminer, et l'écrasa sous son talon.

Ne souhaitant pas jouer les intrus, il fit un pas en arrière. Ce fut alors qu'il vit les filles.

Elles avançaient bras dessus bras dessous. La plus jeune, guidée par la plus âgée, marchait lentement, tête basse, comme fascinée par le tissu noir de ses chaussures. Un homme, chargé d'un outil rudimentaire ressemblant à une pelle, les escortait d'un air protecteur. Le trio approchait de l'endroit où se trouvait Howard et la plus jeune des filles l'aperçut. Elle poussa un cri de surprise puis se cacha dans l'épaule de sa compagne en s'accrochant à elle. L'aînée tourna son visage ovale pour examiner Howard sans détour.

Ses grands yeux bruns étaient si sombres qu'on les aurait dits d'un noir d'ébène dans la lumière du matin ; aussi foncés que ses cheveux, attachés en chignon serré sur sa longue nuque pâle, rehaussant la beauté inattendue de son visage. Comme ses compagnons, elle était vêtue d'une tunique grise et d'un pantalon ample. Les vêtements informes ne dissimulaient en rien les angles aigus d'un corps émacié ; pourtant, ses joues rondes et ses lèvres pleines narguaient les ravages de la faim.

Elle soutint le regard de Howard pendant quelques instants, puis ses paupières, frangées de cils, papillotèrent. Elle attira l'autre jeune fille encore plus près et la serra contre elle en lui murmurant des paroles apaisantes.

Au bout de la route, elle se fraya avec souplesse un passage au milieu des rouleaux de fil de fer et, comme par magie, se retrouva de l'autre côté. Puis elle aida les autres – qui, Howard en était maintenant convaincu, étaient son père et sa sœur – à franchir l'obstacle.

Il savait qu'il jouait les voyeurs mais il ne pouvait pas s'en empêcher.

Comme si elle sentait son regard scrutateur, la fille se retourna. Pris en flagrant délit de voyeurisme, Howard se sentit coupable d'observer ainsi la souffrance nue de ses yeux sombres ; elle finit par suivre sa famille le long d'un chemin invisible.

Quelques minutes plus tard, ils réapparurent sur les laisses de vase, en dessous. Ôtant leurs chaussures en tissu, ils les nouèrent ensemble pour les porter autour du cou et marchèrent pieds nus, dépassant les foules qui écumaient déjà les berges. Dès qu'ils se furent éloignés, les filles pataugèrent dans les flaques peu profondes laissées par la marée, triant les algues du bout d'un bâton qu'elles avaient ramassé en chemin. De temps à autre, la plus âgée des deux se penchait, ramassait quelque chose qu'elle fourrait, avec des poignées d'algues, dans le sac en tissu que portait la plus jeune sur son dos.

Non loin de là, l'homme avançait à pas lents, s'arrêtant régulièrement pour sonder le sable avec sa pelle. Lorsqu'il se mit soudain à creuser – avec une rapidité qui stupéfia Howard – les deux filles se précipitèrent pour l'aider. Elles s'accroupirent l'une en face de l'autre et, à mains nues, déblayèrent le sable jusqu'à ce que l'homme se penche pour ramasser une insaisissable palourde. Ils enfouirent leur trésor dans le sac et continuèrent leurs recherches.

Sur les étendues plates libérées par la marée, ils étaient nombreux à faire la même chose. Cette armée de pilleurs ne laissait rien dans son sillage, sauf les traces de leurs pieds qui marquaient le sable lisse et la vase.

Howard ne quittait pas des yeux la plus grande des deux filles. Même de loin, on la repérait facilement. Malgré ses vêtements informes, on voyait qu'elle avait une façon de se mouvoir bien à elle. Contrairement à ceux qui couraient dans tous les sens pliés en deux comme s'ils craignaient de rater une bonne prise, elle marchait d'un air résolu. La tête baissée, les yeux au sol, elle avançait d'une démarche royale, la démarche de quelqu'un habitué à une vie meilleure.

— Qu'est-ce que tu regardes ?

Gordy arracha Howard à sa rêverie. Il montra la plage d'un mouvement de tête.

— On dirait qu'ils meurent de faim.

Gordy alluma une cigarette et ils demeurèrent silencieux. Ils avaient tous deux connu la faim pendant la Grande Dépression, pourtant ils avaient du mal à imaginer qu'on pût être assez démuni pour considérer les algues comme un moyen de subsistance. Howard finit par partir. Sur des jambes que le souvenir du tangage faisait encore trembler, il se dirigea vers le mess.

— Howie, attends ! Avant d'aller manger, il faut que tu voies ça, cria Gordy en désignant leur cantonnement.

Howard haussa les épaules et l'accompagna jusqu'à leur baraquement. Il n'y avait aucune raison de se presser. Les troupes fraîchement débarquées étaient consignées au camp pour la journée.

À l'intérieur, les soldats s'agitaient, certains en fort petite tenue.

— Regarde-moi ça ! s'exclama Gordy en indiquant les lits de camp militaires enveloppés de moustiquaires au bout de leur rangée.

Howard reconnut deux soldats anglais rencontrés la veille au soir. Peter et Dick – impossible de retrouver leurs noms – étaient couchés en sous-vêtements, les yeux clos comme s'ils dormaient encore, tandis que des Orientaux rasaient leurs visages couverts de mousse. La veille au soir, les deux mitrailleurs du Middlesex Regiment s'étaient vantés, auprès de leurs nouveaux compagnons de chambrée, des domestiques asiatiques qui venaient tous les matins. Pour deux dollars de Hong Kong par semaine, l'équivalent d'environ soixante cents canadiens, ils accomplissaient toutes sortes de tâches depuis nettoyer les uniformes jusqu'à cirer les godillots, faire les lits et jouer les barbiers. Howard frissonna en les observant manier le rasoir avec dextérité. Ce n'était pas demain la veille qu'il laisserait une autre main que la sienne approcher de sa gorge ainsi armée.

— On dirait que vous menez une vraie vie de pacha ici, remarqua-t-il. Ça ressemble plus à une colonie de vacances qu'à un campement militaire.

— Ouais, des congés payés au paradis, mon pote, répondit le nommé Peter, d'un ton volontairement sarcastique. Hong Kong, merde alors ! Les gars, vous feriez bien d'enregistrer ce que tout le monde sait déjà – pas question d'action pour cette mission. Mais pas question de médailles non plus !

Ces scénarios n'avaient rien pour déplaire à Howard. Mais il n'avait nulle envie d'avouer ce qu'il pensait, surtout ici où il cohabitait avec deux cents grenadiers qui rongeaient leur frein en rêvant de se battre. Cependant, quelque chose dans cette existence pleine d'insouciance le mettait mal à l'aise.

— Vous ne croyez pas que les Japonais vont attaquer ? demanda-t-il.

Dick prit la serviette des mains de son barbier et essuya les restes de savon sur ses joues.

— Tu parles, pas la moindre chance !

Il s'assit sur le bord de son lit tandis que son domestique s'éloignait d'un pas traînant.

— Ce serait comme attaquer la totalité de l'Empire britannique, continua Dick. En plus, les Japonais ont une sacrée mauvaise vue. Ils peuvent pas se battre la nuit et leurs pilotes sont trop myopes pour lâcher les bombes au bon endroit. Ces petits salopards jaunes n'oseraient pas venir chercher la bagarre !

Il se leva pour enfiler son short.

— On les surveille de près, on les observe à la jumelle près de la frontière. Une bande de miteux qui traînent dans leur camp l'air à moitié endormis et aussi affamés que les réfugiés. Non, c'est pas eux qui vont nous causer des ennuis…, conclut-il.

Son domestique revint avec un plateau chargé. Dick prit une tasse de thé qu'il leva à l'adresse des grenadiers à moitié habillés qui l'observaient, bouche bée.

— N'empêche, cette affectation a quelques avantages. Mieux vaut en profiter tant que c'est possible, hein ?

Au petit déjeuner, les deux soldats anglais s'installèrent à la table du mess en face de Howard et Gordy. En les écoutant plaisanter, Howard se sentit immédiatement en affinité avec eux. Comme Gordy et lui, c'était des paysans et des copains d'enfance. Ils s'étaient enrôlés ensemble, eux aussi, bien décidés à faire partie du même régiment. Cependant, contrairement à Howard et Gordy, qui n'avaient aucune ressemblance physique, les soldats Peter Young et Dick Baxter avaient l'air d'être frères. Tous deux assez minces, ils ne mesuraient pas plus d'un mètre soixante-dix. Même leurs coiffures étaient identiques, bien dégagées derrière les oreilles avec des mèches longues sur le dessus. La seule différence, c'était la couleur : Peter était blond foncé et Dick roux carotte, en harmonie avec les taches de son dont son visage de lutin était criblé.

— Ça, c'est un peu la plaie ! dit-il à Howard qui grattait inconsciemment un bouton qu'il avait sur le bras. Ces petites bestioles doivent adorer le goût du sang canuck[1] tout frais.

Tout en mangeant, ils conseillèrent à leurs compagnons de table de démonter leur lit de camp pour enduire le cadre métallique de kérosène.

— Pendant que ça sèche, suspendez vos matelas au soleil, dit Peter en mâchant sa saucisse. Les punaises détestent la lumière et la chaleur.

La marée recouvrait lentement les étendues de vase quand ils revinrent du mess. Tout ce qui n'était pas encore immergé était parfaitement propre, le sable humide et satiné brillant dans le soleil levant.

En arrivant à leur baraquement, Gordy se pencha pour se gratter l'arrière du mollet.

— Allons voir à l'intendance s'il y a encore du kérosène, avant que tout soit distribué.

Au moment où il se redressait, Howard aperçut la famille qu'il avait déjà vue à l'aube apparaître sur la berge, derrière leurs baraquements. Il entendit Gordy reprendre son souffle avant de se tourner, hypnotisé, vers la clôture. Les mains posées sur le piquet, il lança :

— Salut ! Parlez anglais ?

La plus jeune des filles recula pour se cacher dans l'épaule de sa sœur. Avec un regard méprisant, le père leur fit presser l'allure.

---

1. Terme d'argot pour désigner les Canadiens.

— Attendez ! cria Gordy. Je veux juste discuter…

Sa voix se perdit en les voyant battre en retraite.

— T'inquiète pas, mon pote, le rassura Peter en l'entourant de son bras. En ville, il y a tout un tas de pépées qui meurent d'envie de tailler une petite bavette avec toi.

Il lui fit un clin d'œil.

— Sans parler d'autres services. Venez avec nous ce soir. Dicky et moi, on va vous montrer les ficelles, à vous les gars de la colonie. Pas besoin de courir après les réfugiées pour passer du bon temps à Hong Kong.

Consigné dans son cantonnement depuis la veille au soir, Howard, comme presque tout le régiment, était impatient de profiter de sa première permission de quatre heures pour découvrir la ville. Dans la chaleur lourde de ce début de soirée, il fit son premier trajet en rickshaw. Gordy et lui se tassèrent au fond du truc qui paraissait dangereusement prêt à verser, tandis qu'un coolie aux pieds nus hissait les longs manches de bois sur ses hanches et partait au trot dans la circulation dense. Devant, Peter et Dick faisaient la même chose.

Howard se mit à rire en voyant d'autres soldats de la base pousser leur conducteur à foncer dans Nathan Road. Les coolies souriants accéléraient l'allure, se frayant adroitement un chemin au milieu des voitures, des bus et des vélos, indifférents aux coups d'avertisseur et aux cris de colère. Tandis qu'ils filaient, Gordy se pencha en avant et promit à leur conducteur de doubler le prix s'il dépassait le rickshaw devant eux. Lorsqu'ils arrivèrent les premiers devant le changeur, il donna vingt-cinq cents à l'homme.

— Ne fais pas l'idiot, le réprimanda Peter en descendant de son rickshaw. Ça vaut dix cents.

— Vingt-cinq, ça fait pas grand-chose, rétorqua Howard en faisant signe au conducteur de partir.

— N'empêche, t'arranges pas nos affaires. Avec nos livres, on n'a pas le même taux de change que vos foutus dollars canadiens.

— Allez, ça va, mon pote, intervint Gordy. C'est pas la mer à boire.

— C'est le tarif auquel ils sont habitués.

— D'accord, d'accord, tempéra Howard. Allons changer de l'argent et on vous offre une bière.

— Oui, et ça vaut dix cents, ça aussi. Pas question de payer davantage.

— Très bien, répliqua Howard en riant et en tirant Gordy à l'intérieur. On n'est pas ici pour chambouler l'économie de Hong Kong.

Ils ressortirent quelques instants plus tard, tout sourire devant le tas d'argent qu'ils avaient obtenu en changeant leurs gains au poker.

— Cachez tout ça, conseilla Dick. Il y a des pickpockets et des voleurs partout. Et pas de problème, les gars, vous pouvez nous payer une bière !

Même répartis dans toutes les poches de son uniforme et glissés dans les bandes molletières au-dessus de ses godillots, les rouleaux de billets de Howard faisaient saillie. Il sentit pour la première fois de sa vie le pouvoir enivrant de la richesse, amoindri cependant par la peur de la perdre. Suivant leurs guides autoproclamés à travers un labyrinthe de ruelles et de rues, il ne cessait de vérifier ses poches.

La prospère vie nocturne de la colonie ne ressemblait à rien de ce qu'il avait connu. Même Winnipeg, qui l'avait beaucoup impressionné la première fois que ses parents l'y avaient emmené quand il était enfant, n'était rien comparé à cela. Des néons, avec des caractères chinois ou anglais, brillaient au-dessus des devantures sombres. Si Kowloon leur avait paru exotique lorsqu'ils l'avaient traversée la veille, cette ville,

comme n'importe quelle autre la nuit, offrait un aspect plus
minable. Les rues transversales pavées grouillaient encore de
gens qui se déplaçaient à l'aveuglette dans toutes les directions,
indifférents aux mendiants accroupis qui tendaient la main.
Dans les rigoles des ruelles étroites, les égouts coulaient à ciel
ouvert. L'odeur des épices se mêlait à la puanteur de la pourriture. Des corps endormis – qu'Howard avait d'abord pris
pour des paquets de vêtements abandonnés – étaient recroquevillés dans l'obscurité. Des femmes aux cheveux noirs et
luisants se tenaient sur le pas de leurs portes.

— Eh, tu veux faire la fête, so'dat ? Du bonheur, que du
bonheur !

La psalmodie des propositions escortait le quatuor.

— Cinquante cents le petit moment. Un dollar le grand.

— Pas ce soir, ma chérie, s'exclama Peter en adressant un
clin d'œil à Howard et Gordy. Inutile de prendre des risques.
Il y a un gars au Sun Sun Café. Si ce genre de choses vous
intéresse, vous pouvez vous choisir une jolie petite poule bien
propre dans le catalogue qu'il propose. Toutes auscultées par
un médecin militaire d'excellente réputation – et ne répétez
pas que je vous l'ai dit.

— Je suis marié, annonça Howard.

— Eh bien, pas moi, rétorqua Gordy en riant.

Après une soirée à courir les pubs et à se remplir la panse
de bière à dix cents, ils arrivèrent au Sun Sun Café et au
dancing. En haut, la salle était remplie de filles exotiques,
eurasiennes et asiatiques, à dix cents la danse ; elles dansaient
avec les marins et les soldats ou entre elles. D'autres, assises
à des tables bondées, riaient aux éclats ; d'autres, encore,
étaient au bar. Des robes de soie aux couleurs vives, fendues
sur la cuisse, laissaient voir des jambes d'ivoire dans différentes
positions. Des dragons brodés montaient à l'assaut de cols
mandarin jusqu'aux visages poudrés et maquillés.

La salle obscurcie de fumée sentait la bière renversée, l'encens et la sueur de trop de corps entassés. Une musique tonitruante sortait du jukebox Wurlitzer installé dans un coin. Par-dessus le vacarme, des hommes en uniforme s'efforçaient d'attirer l'attention des filles et de leurs camarades. À l'extrémité du bar, un groupe d'hommes d'affaires bien habillés, des Blancs et des Asiatiques, restaient entre eux, se démarquant de la clientèle militaire.

Dans le sillage de leurs nouveaux copains, Howard et Gordy se frayèrent un chemin sur la piste encombrée. Une fois leurs bières servies, les quatre hommes s'adossèrent au bar pour observer le spectacle.

Gordy dit quelque chose mais ses paroles se perdirent dans le vacarme.

— Quoi ? demanda Howard en portant la main à son oreille.

— Aucune de ces dames ne supporte la comparaison avec cette petite poupée chinoise qu'on a vue ce matin devant le camp, cria Gordy.

Si Howard n'approuvait pas totalement la façon dont son ami s'exprimait, il partageait son avis.

Le lendemain matin, lorsque Howard se réveilla, le lit de Gordy était vide et déjà fait. Il avait une petite idée de l'endroit où trouver son ami. Il se leva et s'habilla. À part les billets cachés dans ses chaussures et ceux qui étaient enfoncés dans ses bandes molletières, il laissa le gros de sa fortune en dollars de Hong Kong dans son barda, à l'intérieur de son casier. Content d'échapper à la puanteur du kérosène qui collait aux lits métalliques, il rejoignit Gordy à la clôture. Ils restèrent là à fumer en observant les glaneurs des plages occupés à fouiller la vase.

Tard dans la nuit, la gravité de la situation des réfugiés leur était apparue dans toute son horreur. Au moment où ils quittaient le Sun Sun Café, un gros camion s'était arrêté quelques mètres plus loin en grondant. « La patrouille de la mort », avait murmuré Dick quand deux hommes avaient sauté de la cabine. La bouche et le nez dissimulés derrière des tissus noirs, les hommes avaient ramassé ce que Howard avait pris pour un paquet de vêtements abandonnés dans la ruelle. Ils l'avaient hissé et jeté à l'arrière du camion où il avait atterri avant de glisser le long d'une pile impressionnante de corps sans vie. Ce ne fut qu'à ce moment-là que Howard comprit que la puanteur obstinée qui flottait sous les odeurs exotiques de la ville, cette pourriture nauséabonde, c'était l'odeur de la mort.

Il la sentait encore là où il était.

Laissant Gordy à la clôture, il se rendit au mess. Son appétit s'était envolé mais il but une tasse de café. Avant de partir, il prit les trois œufs durs de son plateau et les fourra dans sa poche.

Lorsqu'il revint au baraquement, la marée montante chassait les glaneurs de la vase. Gordy, toujours posté au même endroit, observait les réfugiés qui revenaient lorsque Howard le rejoignit. Ils faillirent la rater. Après s'être glissée sous le grillage, la famille était restée carrément de l'autre côté de la route. Gordy ne les repéra que lorsqu'ils furent passés.

— Attendez ! Attendez ! cria-t-il.

Il tendit la main de l'autre côté de la barrière. Il tenait trois barres chocolatées Hershey.

— Regardez ! Chocolat. Cadeau.

Les filles accélérèrent l'allure mais leur père ralentit. Gordy se mit à courir le long de la clôture jusqu'à les dépasser. Il brandit à nouveau les barres en criant.

— Regardez. Du chocolat pour vous. Je vous en prie, prenez-le.

L'homme s'arrêta. Encouragé, Gordy tendit l'autre main.

— Je m'appelle Gordy Veronick, enchanté de vous connaître, s'exclama-t-il avec un sourire auquel, selon Howard, il était impossible de résister, même pour un esprit méfiant.

L'homme s'approcha et, à la grande surprise de Howard, serra la main de Gordy.

— Je m'appelle Feng-Guo-ren, dit-il en anglais, prenant encore Howard au dépourvu. Merci de votre cadeau.

Il saisit le chocolat et rattrapa ses filles.

— Non ! Attendez ! s'écria Gordy. Je veux vous parler ! Je veux demander à votre fille...

Vaincu, il regarda la famille filer.

— Bon Dieu, je voulais juste l'inviter à aller au cinéma.

Howard lui lança les œufs. Gordy sourit, les attrapa et se mit à courir pour rejoindre la famille ; restant à leur hauteur, il leur tendit les œufs jusqu'à l'angle de la clôture.

Alors que Howard était certain que le père ne céderait pas, il s'arrêta à nouveau. Laissant ses filles de l'autre côté de la route, il s'avança vers la clôture. Une conversation animée, que Howard ne pouvait pas entendre, se poursuivit pendant quelques minutes. Finalement, les œufs changèrent de mains. L'homme repartit vers ses filles. Il dit quelques mots brefs à l'aînée qui vint à la barrière. Il y eut encore un autre dialogue rapide entre Gordy et elle ; elle hocha la tête et alla retrouver sa sœur et son père.

Gordy les regarda disparaître sans bouger. Puis, les mains dans les poches, les épaules voûtées, la tête basse, il se dirigea vers les baraquements.

Howard lui courut après.

— Alors ? Elle a accepté d'aller au cinéma avec toi ? demanda-t-il en s'efforçant de gommer toute trace d'envie dans sa voix.

Gordy hocha la tête. Sans rien dire, ce qui ne lui ressemblait pas, il continua à marcher.

— Eh bien, euh... c'est très bien, dit Howard en s'adressant à son dos.

Gordy s'arrêta puis se retourna ; tout son visage reflétait l'indignation.

— Seigneur, Howie, lâcha-t-il. Il me l'a vendue. Mais putain, tu peux y croire ? Il m'a vendu les services de sa fille pour trois dollars de Hong Kong par semaine !

13

Le jeudi après-midi, je revins de bonne heure de notre sortie courses avec tante Mildred. Elle prit les sacs posés sur la banquette arrière de sa voiture pendant que je me précipitais à la porte. L'air chaud de l'été sentait l'herbe fraîchement coupée et les œillets de poète qui s'épanouissaient sous nos fenêtres. La pierre brûlante retomba lourdement au fond de mon ventre dès que je respirai le parfum des fleurs préférées de maman.

Dans la cuisine, Frankie, appuyé contre le mur, nous tournait le dos et téléphonait en parlant tout bas. Kipper était installé avec ses pots de peinture et son matériel étalés devant lui. Il leva les yeux de son travail et me vit.

— Ethie ! cria-t-il.

Il abandonna son pinceau, se leva d'un bond, me prit dans ses bras et nicha sa tête au creux de mon épaule.

— Tu m'as manqué !

— Où est ton père ? s'enquit tante Mildred en soupirant.

Frankie se retourna pour désigner le salon. Il savait que la question ne s'adressait pas à Kipper. Elle n'avait pratiquement aucun échange direct avec lui. La plupart du temps, elle parlait de lui comme s'il n'était pas là. Ce qui mettait notre mère hors d'elle.

— On ne parle pas de Kipper comme s'il était ailleurs, répétait-elle chaque fois que quelqu'un commettait cette erreur devant elle.

Mais avec tante Mildred, cette remarque restait lettre morte. Si jamais elle s'adressait à lui, c'était généralement pour le critiquer. La semaine dernière encore, il se trouvait avec maman sous le porche au moment où sa sœur partait.

— Ferme la bouche, Christopher, avait dit tante Mildred après avoir embrassé maman. On dirait que tu t'apprêtes à gober les mouches.

Il lui avait souri.

— C'est parce que ma langue est plus grosse que celle des autres gens, avait-il répondu avec cette franchise qui n'appartenait qu'à lui. Et, avait-il ajouté fièrement, j'ai un chromo-some supplémentaire.

Maman avait ri.

— Eh bien, là, tu es en train de te vanter, avait-elle dit en l'entourant de son bras.

Tout ce qu'elle apprenait sur la trisomie 21, maman le transmettait, à nous et surtout à Kipper. Elle voulait qu'il soit « armé » d'informations, comme elle disait, et à voir son sourire ce jour-là alors que ma tante partait vexée, elle considérait que sa technique avait payé. Plus tard dans la soirée, je l'entendis raconter à papa comment la vérité avait été gagnante dans cet accrochage avec sa sœur.

Notre mère ne prétendait jamais que Kipper était comme tout le monde. Elle voulait qu'il connaisse sa différence. Non pas ses limites, soulignait-elle, simplement sa différence. Quand il eut l'âge d'entrer à l'école primaire, elle refusa les excuses de l'administration qui aurait voulu lui barrer l'accès au système scolaire. De 1954 à 1958, chaque fois qu'elle tenta de l'inscrire, elle eut droit à des réponses évasives. Le conseil d'école se défaussait sur le directeur ; et le directeur se défaussait sur les enseignants.

— Il ne saura jamais lire ni écrire, répétaient les professeurs l'un après l'autre. Avec lui nous ferons simplement de la garderie. C'est injuste par rapport aux autres enfants de la classe.

Leur décision était prise depuis belle lurette, les accusait maman sans relâche. Ils étaient fermés, encore plus que les portes de l'école, vis-à-vis de Kipper. Fermés à la possibilité, disait-elle, que les autres enfants aient quelque chose à apprendre de lui.

C'est maman qui se chargea de son instruction et, à eux deux, ils prouvèrent que les autres avaient tort. À l'âge de dix ans, Kipper savait lire, certes pas couramment, mais il déchiffrait beaucoup de mots. Il écrivait en majuscules. Mais son fort, c'était la peinture. Il peignait essentiellement des maisons, de toutes formes et de toutes tailles. Les maisons de notre quartier étaient peut-être identiques mais dans les aquarelles aux couleurs vives de Kipper, chacune ressemblait à la famille qui habitait dedans. À les regarder, on les aurait crues prêtes à respirer, en particulier la nôtre avec ses deux étages. Les fenêtres du salon et de la cuisine, de chaque côté de la porte d'entrée, étaient comme des yeux sous le front que formait le toit pentu. La porte avec les trois marches du porche évoquait une bouche et les fenêtres ouvertes à l'étage des oreilles. Il peignait notre demeure de couleurs variées, au gré des saisons et de son humeur. Marlene, qui adorait son travail, encadrait tous ses tableaux et en avait choisi plusieurs pour sa dernière exposition. On en avait même vendu deux. Pour célébrer l'événement, Kipper avait insisté pour nous emmener tous au King's Drive Inn dans Kingsway manger des hamburgers et boire des milkshakes, le menu préféré de notre père en dehors des sandwiches à la sardine.

Kipper peignait sans relâche. Marlene encadrait sans relâche. L'espace commençait à manquer sur les murs. Un de ses tableaux représentant la maison dans des nuances de rose était même accroché au-dessus de mon lit. Tante Mildred ne faisait jamais aucune allusion à ces œuvres qui décoraient la maison et elle ne prêta aucune attention au tableau que mon frère était en train de réaliser avant d'aller rejoindre papa dans le salon.

Je demeurai dans la cuisine et je regardai par-dessus l'épaule de Kipper. Je fus étonnée de découvrir non pas les prémices d'une nouvelle maison mais un ciel d'un bleu éclatant rempli d'une multitude de nuages aux formes diverses.

— Qu'est-ce que c'est ? Où est la maison ?

— Maman bit pus dans une maison maintenant, déclarat-il d'un ton qui dénotait qu'il s'efforçait d'être courageux. Elle bit au bradis.

Ma gorge se serra et je déglutis avec difficulté, ravalant par la même occasion l'envie de corriger sa prononciation.

J'entendis alors ma tante dire à papa qu'elle allait emporter la tenue de maman pour l'enterrement. Frankie l'entendit aussi. Il mit rapidement fin à sa conversation téléphonique et sortit de la cuisine à grands pas. Je me déplaçai pour observer ce qui se passait dans le salon. Ma tante, debout à côté de la télévision, les bras croisés, attendait une réponse de papa affalé sur sa chaise. Il ouvrit la bouche, puis la referma quand Frankie vint se mettre à côté de lui.

— Nous allons nous occuper de cela, tante Mildred, affirma Frankie.

— Mais…

— J'étais justement au téléphone avec Forest Lawn, l'interrompit-il. Le coroner va nous la rendre.

Il me vit alors en train de les observer.

— Papa et moi, reprit-il, nous irons voir les pompes funèbres demain. Nous prendrons tout ce qu'il faut.

— Très bien. Dites-moi seulement quand vous y allez et je vous y rejoindrai.

— Merci, répondit Frankie. Mais je crois que nous devons d'abord y aller seuls.

— Ah bon, je... euh... je..., bafouilla-t-elle avant de remarquer ma présence, elle aussi. Ethie, monte donc tes nouveaux vêtements dans ta chambre, m'ordonna-t-elle en me tendant les sacs. Et emmène ton frère avec toi. Il faut que je discute avec votre père.

Déçu d'être arraché à sa peinture, Kipper monta lourdement derrière moi. Dans ma chambre, je jetai les sacs dans un coin.

— Des babies, voilà ce qu'elle m'a acheté, me lamentai-je. Des chaussures de bébé avec des chaussettes en dentelle ! Et des gants blancs !

Kipper resta là à regarder les sacs.

— Je les mettrai pas !

Je fis la moue et me jetai en travers du lit.

Et puis, aussi clairement que si elle avait été dans la pièce, j'entendis la voix de ma mère.

« Le petit oiseau va venir te crotter sur la lèvre ! »

Je cessai de grimacer. La dernière fois que je l'avais entendue utiliser cette expression idiote, c'était la semaine passée lorsque j'avais perdu une de mes chaussures préférées au Trout Lake. Le petit lac marécageux n'était qu'à dix minutes de voiture de chez nous. Maman nous y emmenait souvent pour nous rafraîchir pendant l'été. Nous y étions allés la veille du jour où il s'était mis à pleuvoir. En revenant nous allonger après être allés nager, ma serviette et une chaussure avaient disparu. Je m'étais mise à pleurer la tennis perdue et ma mère m'avait consolée. J'adorais ces tennis à carreaux avec des lacets jaunes,

les seules chaussures que je possédais, à part une paire de
vieilles espadrilles. Mais nous avions eu beau ratisser l'endroit,
nous n'avions rien trouvé nulle part. Tandis que nous rem-
ballions nos affaires pour rentrer, maman me conseilla de
laisser la chaussure restante sur l'étagère des vestiaires.

— Pourquoi ?

— Celui qui a pris l'autre la trouvera peut-être. Inutile que
deux personnes se baladent chacune avec une seule chaussure.

J'avais boudé pendant tout le trajet de retour. Et voilà que
j'entendais encore maman qui essayait de me dérider avec ses
menaces de crotte d'oiseau. En l'occurrence, ce n'était pas
maman : Kipper se moquait de moi avec les mots de maman.
Je roulai sur moi-même ; il souriait. Je me redressai pour
mettre la main dans ma poche. Puis, tandis que les adultes
discutaient sans faire de bruit en bas, assis près de Kipper au
bout du lit, je contemplai la photo de notre mère.

Durant les jours qui précédèrent l'enterrement, je conservai
ce cliché sur moi ; chaque fois que je commençais à oublier
ses traits, je le sortais. Pourtant, quoi que je fasse, où que je
sois, je ne pensais qu'à l'absence de ma mère. Sans elle, notre
maison était étrangement calme. Tous ceux qui passaient
apporter de quoi manger ou rendre visite à papa parlaient à
voix basse ou chuchotaient. Même le téléphone, qui sonnait
toutes les trois minutes, paraissait plus discret. Je n'arrêtai pas
de faire le ménage, m'efforçant de garder la maison propre
parce que je craignais de voir à nouveau surgir tante Mildred
inopinément, prête à se fâcher contre notre père.

Kipper devait raisonner de la même façon. Le mercredi en
fin d'après-midi, veille de l'enterrement, alors que j'étais dans
la cuisine en train de récurer un de ces innombrables plats
pour le rendre aux voisins, je l'entendis pousser un cri. Mon
père se précipita vers le sous-sol. Je ne l'avais jamais vu se
déplacer aussi vite. Ouvrant la porte à la volée, il dévala

l'escalier, Frankie et moi sur ses talons. Nous nous sommes arrêtés pile au milieu. Kipper, les bras couverts de mousse et l'air affolé, se tenait debout dans un océan d'eau savonneuse. À côté, la machine à laver soufflait et sifflait, en lâchant des tourbillons de vagues blanches. Le sol et la première marche de l'escalier étaient déjà submergés. Des flocons de mousse flottaient dans l'air ; un gros avait atterri sur le chapeau de Kipper et faisait comme un pompon. Derrière lui, installé sur le rebord de la fenêtre, Ginger surveillait la scène.

Frankie se précipita pour débrancher la machine à laver, papa et moi derrière lui. Pataugeant dans une mer de mousse, papa réprima une toux qui se transforma en fou rire. De l'autre côté de la machine, Frankie était hilare. Le regard de Kipper passait de l'un à l'autre et son expression affolée se transforma en sourire.

— Oups ! lâcha-t-il. Trop de bulles.

Papa et Frankie éclatèrent d'un rire hystérique. D'abord perplexe, je restai muette jusqu'à ce que Kipper me balance un grand paquet de mousse. Ensuite, on se lança dans une bagarre à grands coups d'eau savonneuse tandis que les larmes ruisselaient sur nos joues.

On finit par se calmer et, sans quitter nos vêtements trempés et savonneux, on entreprit d'éponger. Tandis que nous travaillions, Kipper nous expliqua qu'il avait voulu aider en lavant le linge.

— Quelle quantité de lessive as-tu mise ? s'enquit Frankie.

Kipper désigna l'étagère au-dessus de la machine à laver où il y avait encore un gros paquet de lessive Tide.

— Une, dit-il fièrement. C'est ce que j'ai lu sur le carton.

— Une dose ? demanda Frankie.

— Oh ! s'exclama Kipper, prenant soudain conscience de ce qu'il avait fait. Une boîte.

Le nettoyage des bêtises bien intentionnées mais brouillonnes de Kipper se révéla amusant. Sans doute parce que cela nous donnait l'occasion d'agir ensemble, de penser à autre chose qu'à maman. Je suis persuadée qu'une bonne partie de nos larmes de rire, nous les versions pour elle, mais pendant ce temps, nous oubliions plus ou moins notre chagrin.

Et puis tante Mildred apparut en haut de l'escalier et vint tout gâcher.

14

— Voilà exactement contre quoi je t'avais mis en garde, déclara Mildred au dos de Howard occupé à se rincer les mains sous le robinet de l'évier, dans la cuisine. Comment vas-tu pouvoir t'occuper de ces enfants quand tu seras retourné au travail ?

… Alors que tu n'y parviens pas quand tu es chez toi. Il compléta la phrase sous-entendue aussi clairement que si elle l'avait prononcée à voix haute. Il s'essuya les mains sur un torchon et se retourna pour lui faire face. Arc-boutée contre la table, sa belle-sœur serrait son sac entre ses bras repliés. Cette femme ne s'asseyait-elle donc jamais quand elle venait chez eux ?

— Ce n'est que du savon, répliqua-t-il en soupirant.

— Pour aujourd'hui. La prochaine fois, ce sera le feu ou…

Elle continua à égrener la litanie des tragédies qui pouvaient survenir à cause d'une fraction de seconde d'inattention. Ses paroles se fondirent en un bourdonnement tandis que le regard de Howard s'égarait derrière elle.

Depuis la veille, il ne cessait de surveiller la rue, cherchant si la vision fantôme qu'il avait vue le matin dans le square allait réapparaître. Une vision qui ne pouvait pas être réelle. Était-il la proie d'hallucinations ? Ou ses cauchemars le rattrapaient-ils en plein jour ? Il n'y avait pas assez d'alcool dans le monde pour noyer ses remords.

— Tu m'écoutes, Howard ?

La voix stridente de sa belle-sœur vint briser le fil de ses pensées.

Il se força à la regarder, à faire le point sur son visage.

— Tu m'as entendue ? répéta-t-elle. Je t'ai demandé quels étaient tes projets ?

— Je ne sais pas, répondit-il lentement.

Il ne savait plus rien, plus rien du tout. Son esprit n'était qu'un fouillis de questions et d'images confuses, réelles et imaginaires.

— Eh bien, il va falloir commencer à y réfléchir – et sans tarder.

Tandis qu'elle parlait, une douleur sourde s'infiltra entre les omoplates de Howard. Une douleur qui remonta le long de la colonne vertébrale jusqu'à la nuque. Elle explosa sous son crâne, fulgurant nuage champignon. De leur propre chef, ses mains vinrent frotter ses tempes battantes tandis qu'il fixait le linoléum jaune du sol. D'en bas, on entendit soudain l'aboiement bref du rire de Kipper, suivi de la réponse étouffée d'Ethie. La porte du sous-sol s'ouvrit et se referma. Howard leva la tête et demanda calmement :

— Faut-il vraiment en discuter maintenant ?

Mildred décroisa les bras et fit passer son sac de l'autre côté.

— Je ne veux pas insister là-dessus alors que ma sœur n'est pas encore enterrée, mais te souviens-tu seulement de ce dont nous avons parlé hier ? As-tu réfléchi à ma proposition ?

Howard s'en souvenait. Il savait ce qu'elle voulait.

— Il faut vraiment que tu y réfléchisses, Howard. Elle est presque adolescente, une jeune femme. Qui va la guider pour traverser ces années ? Qui va lui acheter son premier soutien-gorge ? Lui parler des changements dans son corps ? Toi ? Frankie ?

Et Christopher ? reprit-elle, sans attendre sa réponse. Il y a des institutions pour les gens comme lui, des établissements, des internats, où on saura s'occuper de lui, garantir sa sécurité. Vraiment, cela aurait dû être fait depuis belle lurette. Mais maintenant que Lucy n'est plus là… Eh bien, il n'y a vraiment plus le choix.

— Nous allons nous débrouiller, affirma Frankie en entrant dans la cuisine.

— Et comment ferez-vous ?

La voix de Mildred s'adoucit nettement en s'adressant à son neveu.

— Pour les quelques semaines à venir, papa va prendre des vacances et après, je prendrai les miennes, expliqua Frankie. Ensuite, on verra. Peut-être qu'on travaillera à la scierie dans des équipes à horaires alternés, je ne sais pas encore, mais on se débrouillera de toute façon.

— Et tu vas renoncer à tes cours du soir ?

— Pour l'instant.

— Howard, vas-tu laisser sans réagir ton fils faire une chose pareille, au nom d'un malvenu sentiment de loyauté ? s'écria-t-elle. Vas-tu continuer à le laisser refuser notre proposition de payer ses frais universitaires ? Ou veux-tu qu'il travaille le reste de son existence dans une scierie ?

— Ce n'est pas la décision de papa, l'interrompit Frankie d'une voix lourde d'avertissement.

— Howard, il fait un sacrifice qui n'a aucun sens, insista Mildred. Si Ethie vivait avec nous, si Christopher était dans une institution, Frankie n'aurait plus aucune raison de se retrouver coincé. Notre proposition tient toujours. Tout ce qu'il faut, c'est un mot venant de ta part.

Howard secoua la tête pour essayer de se remettre les idées en place ; bizarrement, en dépit de sa brutalité, le raisonnement de sa belle-sœur n'était pas complètement idiot.

— Laisse-nous du temps, déclara-t-il d'une voix pleine de lassitude. Je vais réfléchir à tout cela. Nous en discuterons. Mais pas maintenant.

— D'accord, céda Mildred avant de sortir de son sac une enveloppe en papier kraft. Voilà des renseignements sur des internats et des établissements en ville, ajouta-t-elle en posant l'enveloppe sur la table. Et cela…, reprit-elle en fouillant à nouveau dans son sac. Sidney a réussi à se procurer par piston une copie du rapport du coroner.

Elle regarda l'enveloppe blanche.

— Il n'a pas voulu que je l'ouvre. Il est d'avis que c'est à vous de décider si vous souhaitez nous faire part de ce qui est écrit. J'espère bien que vous le ferez, conclut-elle en la tendant à contrecœur.

Comme Howard ne faisait pas mine de s'en saisir, elle la posa sur l'enveloppe kraft.

— Quand vous serez prêts, dit-elle.

Frankie, après avoir fermé la porte derrière elle, se tourna vers Howard.

— Tu n'as pas l'intention…

Howard avait la bouche sèche. Il déglutit.

— Je sais pas, marmonna-t-il. Je sais vraiment pas.

Il ramassa les deux enveloppes. Les tenant par le bord comme si elles risquaient de le brûler, il sortit de la cuisine.

Derrière lui, Frankie jura entre ses dents.

Dans l'entrée, Howard se raidit devant la porte de sa chambre. Chaque fois qu'il devait y entrer, il était en proie à la même douleur torturante. Il ne s'était toujours pas résolu à dormir dans leur lit. Inspirant profondément, il ouvrit la porte. À l'intérieur, des grains de poussière dansaient dans le soleil qui passait à travers l'interstice des rideaux. Quelqu'un avait fait le lit, mais les affaires de Lucy étaient toujours éparpillées dans la pièce et l'air encore imprégné de son parfum.

Comme s'il était en train d'avancer sur un champ de mines, Howard s'approcha de la commode et ouvrit le tiroir du haut. Il laissa tomber les enveloppes sur les autres papiers qu'il conservait là et referma. La main posée sur la poignée, il s'immobilisa avant de changer d'avis. Il rouvrit le tiroir, en retira l'enveloppe kraft, celle qui contenait les renseignements sur les internats. Sans l'ouvrir, il la déchira en deux, ainsi que son contenu, puis encore en deux avant de tout remettre dans le tiroir.

Il prit l'enveloppe blanche. Il la retourna, hésita un moment puis l'ouvrit et avec précaution, sortit le rapport du coroner. Les bruits étouffés de la maison et le tic-tac du réveil disparurent peu à peu tandis qu'il lisait et relisait le document en essayant de comprendre le jargon technique.

Il n'y avait aucune surprise. C'était conforme à ce que la police soupçonnait. Le coroner concluait ainsi : « Mort accidentelle due à un chauffage au kérosène défectueux dont la mauvaise combustion a entraîné une production de monoxyde de carbone... » Une seule chose, dans le rapport, lui avait sauté aux yeux. « La quantité d'alcool contenu dans le sang de la victime était tellement élevée que celle-ci était sans doute inconsciente au moment de la mort. »

Même si le rapport correspondait à ce qu'il attendait, il n'était pas prêt à encaisser le coup brutal provoqué par ce langage impersonnel. Lucy soûle ? C'était inconcevable. Tête basse, il s'écroula sur le petit tabouret. Il ferma les yeux et appuya ses paumes dessus. Quand il les ôta, malgré sa vue brouillée, il remarqua quelque chose qui dépassait du dernier tiroir de la coiffeuse de Lucy. Il se pencha pour attraper ce bout de papier et le contempla jusqu'à comprendre ce que c'était. Lentement, il ouvrit le tiroir en grand. À l'intérieur, il y avait une boîte à chaussures à moitié renversée. Une bonne partie de son contenu, un fouillis de coupures de journaux identiques à celle qu'il tenait à la main, était répandu sur les fournitures de papeterie proprement rangées au fond du tiroir. Il en saisit une poignée. C'était typique de Lucy. Elle avait l'habitude – une habitude qui tournait à l'obsession – de découper des articles dans la presse quotidienne pour les partager avec quiconque susceptible d'être intéressé. Presque tous les soirs, Howard héritait des rubriques trouées du *Daily Province* si elle le lisait avant lui. Mais ces coupures-là n'étaient pas récentes. Jaunies par le temps, elles étaient devenues friables. Il les reposa, en prit une autre poignée qu'il feuilleta. Elles dataient toutes de la guerre. Pourquoi ne les avait-il jamais vues ? Pourquoi s'était-elle cramponnée ainsi à un passé qu'il s'efforçait d'oublier ? Avait-elle conservé ces articles durant tout ce temps dans l'attente d'un jour qui, désormais, ne viendrait jamais ? D'un jour où il aurait été capable de partager ces années perdues ?

Elle savait. Bien sûr qu'elle savait qu'il lui était revenu porteur de quelque chose d'infiniment plus terrible que ces parasites latents dans ses entrailles. Pourtant, durant toutes ces années, elle n'avait jamais insisté, elle n'avait jamais demandé ce qui s'était passé là-bas. Il ferma les yeux. Seigneur, mais pourquoi ne lui avait-il pas dit la vérité ?

La porte de la chambre s'ouvrit.

— Papa ? appela Ethie.

Il sursauta violemment, quelque chose lui échappa des mains ; il fourra le reste dans le tiroir en se penchant pour ramasser ce qu'il avait laissé tomber. Avant de mettre ce papier avec les autres et de refermer le tiroir, il remarqua que ce n'était pas une coupure de presse mais un télégramme jauni. Un télégramme, daté de vingt et un ans plus tôt, qui annonçait qu'il était bien arrivé à Hong Kong.

15

19 novembre 1941 : Hong Kong

```
19 NOVEMBRE 1941 17 : 46
MME LUCY COULTER
455 VINE STREET
VANCOUVER BC
CANADA


ARRIVÉ SAIN ET SAUF. LETTRE SUIT.
AVEC TOUT MON AMOUR.

HOWARD
```

Howard relut le message trop court. Ils étaient autorisés à télégraphier chez eux mais il y avait des restrictions. Il signa au dos et le tendit à l'employé qui le prit avec un bref signe de tête avant de passer au soldat suivant, tout aussi inquiet.

Devant le bureau des télégrammes, Gordy s'impatientait en se balançant inconsciemment d'un pied sur l'autre.

Howard dévala les marches.

— C'est fait ! annonça-t-il en remarquant que son compagnon paraissait soulagé.

Un peu plus tôt, Gordy l'avait pris au dépourvu lorsqu'il lui avait demandé de l'accompagner le soir.

— Je vous ai assez suivis, Lucy et toi, affirma-t-il comme s'il s'agissait d'une dette à régler.

Derrière cette insistance, Howard capta une nuance suppliante. Gordy nerveux à l'idée d'un rendez-vous avec une fille ? Il aurait refusé d'y croire s'il n'en avait été témoin de ses propres yeux. Il avait du mal à reconnaître son copain d'enfance. Rien à voir avec le gars impétueux et sûr de lui avec qui il avait grandi. Enfants, ils étaient inséparables jusqu'à ce qu'il commence à sortir avec Lucy. À son tour de découvrir l'effet que cela faisait d'être celui qui tient la chandelle.

Ils se joignirent au flot régulier des piétons qui marchaient en direction de l'embarcadère de Kowloon. Au bout de Nathan Road, ils traversèrent au pas de course la large avenue, esquivant les autobus et autres véhicules qui roulaient dans un concert d'avertisseurs. Dans un coin de sa tête, Howard se demandait même si la fille allait venir. Son père avait peut-être accepté le chocolat et les œufs avec l'intention de disparaître avec ses enfants dans la nature, après avoir empoché les trois dollars de Gordy. Ce qui aurait été aisément compréhensible.

Howard n'avait pu s'empêcher de demander à Gordy pourquoi il avait accepté ce rendez-vous, alors que l'idée de ce père vendant les services de sa fille l'indignait.

— Tu crois quand même pas que je vais laisser n'importe quel minable lui mettre le grappin dessus ?

Mais, durant tout le reste de la journée, Howard avait senti la grande nervosité de son ami.

Saisi d'appréhension en approchant de la queue des passagers qui attendaient le *Star ferry*, Howard éprouva un élan de compassion à l'égard de Gordy. Mais elle était là, à côté des tourniquets. Elle attendait, tête haute et bras croisés sur une version plus propre de la tenue qu'elle portait sur les laisses de vase. Ses cheveux, cependant, n'étaient pas attachés et leur cascade d'ébène encadrait l'ovale de son visage aux yeux sombres. Elle eut l'air brièvement surpris – une expression fugace – en les voyant s'avancer vers elle. Howard se demanda si c'était sa présence qui l'étonnait mais elle n'en souffla mot quand ils la rejoignirent.

Gordy lui présenta Howard en se dandinant encore d'un pied sur l'autre. La jeune fille le salua d'un signe de tête. Elle ne réagit pas lorsque Gordy leva la main puis la baissa, manifestement indécis : devait-il lui offrir son bras ou la prendre par la main ? Retrouvant un peu d'aisance, il lui fit franchir le tourniquet en la tenant par les épaules.

Le ferry s'éloigna du quai en grinçant et ils suivirent le flot des passagers vers les bancs de bois. Quand ils furent assis, Howard s'aperçut qu'il n'y avait pas d'autres Blancs sur le pont inférieur bondé. Il nota également qu'il y avait des femmes debout. Gordy et lui se relevèrent en même temps pour céder leurs places. Shun-ling les suivit et ils se faufilèrent contre le bastingage. Troublé par la promiscuité des corps, surtout celui de la jeune fille – elle était coincée entre Gordy et lui –, Howard préféra contempler l'animation du port.

De l'autre côté de l'eau, les rayons du soleil mourant disparaissaient derrière la silhouette des montagnes qui surplombaient la mer. Les sommets sombres se découpaient sur le ciel cramoisi, dominant les falaises et les côtes abruptes qui formaient l'île de Hong Kong.

Shun-ling dit quelque chose, sa voix douce se perdit dans les vibrations du moteur et l'intense circulation de bateaux.

— Pardon ?

Gordy se pencha davantage vers elle.

— Port Odorant, répéta-t-elle par-dessus le vacarme.

Les deux soldats haussèrent les sourcils. L'odeur des eaux boueuses rappelait à Howard celle du compost rance.

— Signification chinoise de Hong Kong, expliqua Shun-ling. Port Odorant.

Elle désigna la montagne qui s'élevait au-dessus de la ville de Victoria brillamment illuminée.

— Prendre tram jusqu'à sommet, reprit-elle. Vue magnifique.

Mis à part son salut pour le moins réservé lorsque Gordy l'avait présenté, Howard n'avait pas encore entendu le son de sa voix. Il s'approcha pour ne rien rater de ses paroles mélodieuses tandis qu'elle nommait les petites îles et désignait quelques points de repère.

Voir Shun-ling dans le rôle de guide calma la nervosité de Gordy.

— Vous êtes de Hong Kong ? demanda-t-il. Je veux dire, vous êtes née ici ?

— Non. Nous habitions petit village près Nankin.

Elle se tut un moment puis ajouta :

— Jusqu'à arrivée Japonais…

Ses derniers mots se perdirent dans le vent. Ni Gordy ni Howard ne lui demandèrent de répéter. Elle demeura silencieuse pendant le reste du trajet.

Si Kowloon était déjà animée, la ville de Victoria, tassée sur la côte de l'île, débordait de vie. Le claquement des innombrables sandales de bois sur les planches du quai rivalisait avec le bourdonnement de la circulation et les cris des conducteurs de rickshaws interpellant dans un mauvais anglais les clients potentiels. Le parfum du bois de santal et de l'encens se mêlait à l'odeur du port. L'œil et l'oreille aux aguets pour ne rien rater, Howard descendait la rue fourmillante de monde tout en se disant que, chez lui, deux soldats escortant une jeune beauté chinoise auraient pu causer quelques remous ou, du moins, attirer l'attention d'un certain nombre de gens. Ici, ils passaient inaperçus, partie intégrante de cette foule dense dont chaussées et trottoirs étaient saturés.

Il se mit à rédiger une lettre dans sa tête. « Imagine deux millions de gens, Lucy ! Plus du double de la population du Manitoba ! » C'était difficile à croire et plus encore à décrire. D'un côté, Hong Kong était une parfaite métropole cosmopolite avec des immeubles et des magasins d'un modernisme impressionnant, comme il n'en avait jamais vu. De l'autre, des temples anciens aux toits recourbés s'entassaient à côté de terriers de lapin à la structure précaire. Et partout, dans les rues surpeuplées et les ruelles sombres, grouillaient les mendiants.

Au premier coin de rue, une vieille femme accroupie tendait la main. Howard s'arrêta et prit de la monnaie dans sa poche. Les pièces disparurent dans une manche en loques. Brusquement, d'autres doigts squelettiques s'enfoncèrent dans la chair de son bras, tirant sur son uniforme. Une foule grandissante, suppliant avec des mots qu'il n'y avait pas besoin de traduire, se pressait contre lui et le cernait, cherchant à attirer son attention. Un Anglais qui passait asséna aux mendiants insistants un bon coup de journal roulé.

— Ne les encouragez pas, espèce de crétin ! aboya-t-il, sinon nous serons tous assiégés.

Gordy et Shun-ling entraînèrent Howard et ils se faufilèrent de l'autre côté de la rue dans les embouteillages de la circulation.

— Si vous faire aumône, dit Shun-ling dès qu'ils furent à l'abri, mieux laisser faire moi. Donner et personne voit.

Howard hocha la tête. L'incident l'avait laissé tremblant et honteux. Cela ne faisait certainement pas partie des anecdotes qu'il souhaitait raconter dans ses lettres. Durant la Dépression, les gens connaissaient la faim mais tout le temps où il avait vécu à Winnipeg, il n'avait jamais rien vu de comparable au désespoir qui se lisait dans les yeux de ces mendiants. Pas plus qu'il n'avait vu de vitrines comme celles qu'ils longeaient au pas de course, étalant sans vergogne des marchandises de luxe à portée de main de ceux qui mouraient de faim.

Devant le Harbour Hotel, un photographe de rue, son appareil monté sur un tripode, prenait des photos des passants. Eh bien, voilà au moins une chose comme chez nous, pensa Howard. Dès qu'ils eurent atteint le champ de l'objectif, Howard saisit le bras de Gordy par-dessus l'épaule de Shun-ling pour le rapprocher et sourit à l'appareil. La lumière du flash s'éteignit et il prit le ticket numéroté de la main tendue du photographe. Qu'est-ce qui avait bien pu le pousser à faire une chose pareille ? Sa récente rencontre avec les mendiants ? Ou peut-être le souvenir de Lucy, Gordy et lui sautant sur un photographe de rue dans le centre de Winnipeg le jour où on leur avait remis leur uniforme. De toute façon, le jeu en valait la chandelle : il donna le ticket à Gordy et fut récompensé par un timide sourire de Shun-ling. Le premier qu'il ait vu.

— Maintenant, dit Gordy en empochant le ticket, le dîner. Où allons-nous manger ?

Il s'arrêta devant un hôtel.

— Ici ? demanda-t-il à Shun-ling.

Elle secoua la tête et continua à marcher. Howard jeta un œil dans le restaurant brillamment illuminé. Ils étaient peut-être invisibles dans la rue mais s'ils entraient tous les trois dans cette salle à manger animée, tous les regards convergeraient vers eux. Des hommes en smoking blanc et des officiers en tenue de cérémonie étaient assis devant des tables recouvertes de nappes en compagnie de dames vêtues de leurs plus beaux atours. Shun-ling, avec sa pauvre robe, faisait bel et bien partie des nécessiteux.

Elle quitta la grande rue pour s'enfoncer dans une ruelle transversale, les deux hommes sur ses talons. Dans le clair-obscur, ils parcoururent un labyrinthe de passages étroits et Shun-ling finit par s'arrêter devant une boutique. Examinant les rangées de canards rôtis pendus dans la lumière jaune de la vitrine, elle dit :

— Ça, bon.

Ils trouvèrent une table libre au fond du restaurant bondé. Howard s'assit et examina la salle enfumée. À nouveau, Gordy et lui étaient les seuls Blancs. Dans le vacarme des conversations étrangères et le cliquetis des baguettes, les serveurs se faufilaient entre les tables en balançant d'énormes plateaux chargés de nourriture au-dessus de leur tête. Gordy jeta un coup d'œil sur la table voisine couverte d'un nombre impressionnant de plats inconnus et demanda à Shun-ling de commander.

Le serveur arriva et posa sur la table une théière blanche et des verres. Shun-ling et lui échangèrent quelques mots rapides et il redisparut. Elle versa le thé fumant. Comme, à l'évidence, personne d'autre n'allait lancer la conversation, Howard dit :

— Vous parlez très bien anglais, Shun-ling. Où l'avez-vous appris ?

— Mon père. Lui professeur.

— Et votre sœur ? Parle-t-elle aussi bien anglais ? s'enquit-il.

— Ma sœur, Shun-qin, ne parle pas, répondit-elle en fixant ses mains posées sur ses genoux.

— Elle ne parle pas anglais ?

Elle releva la tête et leurs regards se croisèrent.

— Ni anglais. Ni chinois. Elle ne parle pas.

— Oh. Vous voulez dire qu'elle est muette, intervint Gordy. Elle ne peut pas parler.

Shun-ling se tourna vers lui.

— Non. Elle peut parler. Mais elle ne parle pas. Ma sœur ne parle pas. Depuis Japonais envahir notre village.

Howard vit la souffrance noyer ses yeux sombres. Il se souvint d'un article qu'il avait lu dans le magazine *Life* à propos de la terreur qui régnait durant le siège de Nankin, en 1937. Que la violence décrite dans ce récit s'incarnât dans une jeune fille assise à côté de lui ne faisait que rendre ces atrocités plus insupportables. Il ne sut comment réagir. Shun-ling se remit à étudier ses mains jusqu'à ce que le serveur apporte trois assiettes et trois paires de baguettes avant de repartir à toute allure.

— Si je dois manger avec ces trucs, je vais mourir de faim, dit Gordy.

Howard fit la grimace.

— Je apprendre vous, proposa Shun-ling.

Lorsque les plats arrivèrent, elle saisit la main droite de Gordy de ses longs doigts effilés et plaça avec délicatesse les baguettes dans la bonne position. Avec des mouvements si précis, si fluides que Howard avait l'impression que ses mains n'avaient pas d'os, elle amena avec compétence son ami à piocher un morceau blanc et glissant dans la sauce grise du premier plat. Il releva lentement la main. Elle relâcha sa prise.

— Chose qui nage, expliqua-t-elle tandis qu'il réussissait à transporter la nourriture jusqu'à sa bouche avec un sourire triomphant.

Prenant ses propres baguettes, elle les utilisa pour désigner chacun des plats, moins identifiables l'un que l'autre.

— Chose qui rampe et chose qui vole.

Howard devait la croire sur parole. Cela ne lui donnait aucune indication supplémentaire sur ce qu'il mangeait – désirait-il vraiment le savoir ? –, mais de toute façon, chaque bouchée parfumée valait bien mieux que la nourriture du mess.

Tandis qu'avec Gordy, ils rivalisaient dans la maîtrise de ces encombrantes baguettes, Shun-ling observait leurs progrès avec une ombre de sourire. Elle mangeait lentement, mâchant chaque morceau avec délicatesse. Howard remarqua que, sur les trois morceaux qu'elle prenait dans chaque plat, elle n'en mangeait qu'un seul. Il croisa le regard de Gordy par-dessus la tête de la jeune fille et, par un accord tacite, ils se servirent tous deux moins généreusement. À la fin du repas, il restait plus de la moitié des plats. Le serveur réapparut pour débarrasser et adressa quelques mots à Shun-ling. Lorsqu'il revint avec l'addition, il posa une boîte enveloppée de papier brun devant elle.

Dehors, ils suivirent les indications de Peter et Dick pour se rendre à l'Empress Theatre.

— Drôlement chouette ! remarqua Gordy en voyant l'élégant fronton. Rien à envier à Hollywood.

Ils trouvèrent trois places côte à côte au balcon. Une odeur de gingembre et d'huile de sésame s'échappait du paquet que Shun-ling avait posé sur ses genoux tandis que passaient les actualités sur « L'Angleterre en guerre ». En voyant les images noir et blanc des bombardiers qui survolaient la Manche, Howard se demanda si ses frères avaient déjà été envoyés en Europe.

Le grand film, *Les Raisins de la colère*, commença et Henry Fonda apparut sur l'écran.

— Il ressemble à Howard, hein ? chuchota Gordy.

Il répéta tellement de fois cette phrase que quelqu'un derrière finit par lui intimer l'ordre de se taire.

Après la séance, dans le flot des spectateurs qui sortaient de la salle, plusieurs femmes dévisagèrent Howard en chuchotant.

— Tu vois ? Je te l'avais dit, tu lui ressembles, déclara Gordy en lui allongeant un coup de coude dans les côtes.

Même si Lucy avait souvent insisté sur cette ressemblance, elle échappait complètement à Howard, mis à part, peut-être, le nez et la mâchoire carrée. Mal à l'aise, il s'éloigna de l'affiche où Henry Fonda, grandeur nature, posait dans le rôle du jeune métayer idéaliste, Tom Joad, contemplant le ciel avec toute la souffrance du monde dans ses yeux bleus.

Shun-ling observa l'affiche, son regard passant plusieurs fois de Howard au visage de l'acteur.

— C'est les yeux, affirma-t-elle. Vous avez mêmes yeux. Yeux gentils.

Elle effleura à peine son bras, une caresse aussi légère qu'une plume, envolée avant même de se poser mais, alors qu'ils se dirigeaient vers l'embarcadère du ferry, il en sentit la chaleur irradier jusqu'à l'épaule.

Tout le long du port, un marché nocturne s'était installé sur les planches de bois ; on y trouvait de tout, depuis les éventails en papier jusqu'aux robes de soie. Soldats et marins, ainsi que des civils anglais et asiatiques, déambulaient au milieu des éventaires, inspectant les marchandises et discutant en mauvais anglais. Howard ne put s'empêcher de comparer l'atmosphère de carnaval qui régnait dans la ville avec Londres dévasté tel qu'il l'avait vu aux actualités. Ici, ni couvre-feu ni rationnement alimentaire.

Brusquement, Gordy cessa d'avancer.

— Excusez-moi vous deux, déclara-t-il, mais il faut que j'aille là où le roi va tout seul. Trop de thé.

Il fit un geste en direction d'un hôtel proche et les quitta.

Howard et Shun-ling se promenèrent au milieu des étalages en attendant son retour. Un des marchands leur proposa une robe rouge brodée.

— Achetez pour votre amie ! cria-t-il.

— Elle n'est pas..., commença Howard puis il s'aperçut que Shun-ling le regardait.

Ses yeux sombres pétillaient de gaieté. Il se mit à rire.

— Shun-ling, dit-il, aidez-moi à choisir quelque chose pour ma femme.

— Oh... vous êtes marié.

Elle s'approcha de l'éventaire pour examiner les vêtements de soie pliés.

Howard se demanda si la déception qu'il avait perçue dans la voix douce était un effet de son imagination. Il prit un *cheongsam* orange sophistiqué.

— Et ça ? demanda-t-il.

— Mauvaise couleur, objecta Shun-ling. Trop excentrique.

— Oh, je crois que Lucy aurait pu la porter.

Howard replia la robe et la reposa.

Shun-ling tripotait le col mandarin d'une robe à motif fleuri bleu et blanc.

— Celle-là beaucoup moins, commenta le marchand. (Il regarda Howard et ajouta :) Même bleu que vous yeux.

Shun-ling caressait le coton.

— Celle-là mieux. Porter davantage.

— Et celle-là ? s'enquit Howard en sortant une robe de soie verte de la pile.

Il la déplia.

Tandis que Shun-ling marchandait le prix, Gordy revint.

— Pour Lucy, expliqua Howard en lui montrant la robe.

— Je la vois très bien se pavaner à Winnipeg dans cette petite bricole, déclara Gordy.

Tandis que le marchand glissait l'achat de Howard dans un sac en papier, Gordy prit le *cheongsam* orange. Il demanda à Shun-ling si elle aimerait qu'il le lui offre. Le visage de la jeune fille se ferma.

— Vous voulez que je sois fille de joie ?

— Non. Oh, non non, attendez, répondit Gordy en reposant la robe. Je voulais seulement vous offrir quelque chose de joli.

Il lui toucha gauchement l'épaule.

— Écoutez, bafouilla-t-il, je veux que vous ne soyez rien du tout. Je n'ai pas besoin que vous ciriez mes chaussures, que vous me rasiez ou que vous laviez mon linge. Vous ne devez rien faire du tout. On est amis, c'est tout. D'accord ?

Derrière elle, Howard montra l'étalage d'un signe de tête.

— Alors, celle-là ? embraya Gordy en prenant la robe de coton bleu et blanc indiquée par Howard. Permettrez-vous à un ami de vous l'offrir ?

Elle jeta à la robe un regard plein d'envie puis hocha la tête.

Une fois de retour à Kowloon, elle tenta de dissuader Gordy de la ramener chez elle, en lui disant que sa sœur avait peur de tous les hommes, leur père excepté.

— Je ne risque rien, dit-elle. On ne peut rien me voler, si ce n'est cela.

À la façon dont elle s'accrochait aux paquets contenant sa robe et les restes de nourriture, Howard était bien sûr que personne n'aurait pu les lui arracher des mains.

Mais Gordy insistait. Il n'entrerait pas dans la maison, « mais il faut au moins que je vous raccompagne jusqu'à votre porte. Si je vous laisse toute seule dans ces rues, je ne fermerai pas l'œil de la nuit. »

Howard les quitta dans Nathan Road. Plutôt que de héler un rickshaw, il parcourut à pied les quelques kilomètres qui le séparaient du camp, le sac contenant la robe de Lucy coincé sous son bras. Une fois aux baraquements, il s'assit dehors sur les marches et alluma une cigarette. En soufflant l'allumette, il remarqua un homme accroupi dans l'ombre du bâtiment. Il le reconnut : c'était un des domestiques qui avaient rasé les soldats le matin même. Attendait-il là toute la nuit ?

Howard lui tendit son paquet de cigarettes. Souriant, l'homme s'approcha, en prit une et la mit entre ses lèvres.

Howard la lui alluma puis lui fit signe de s'asseoir à côté de lui. Il voulait lui poser quelques questions mais l'autre secoua la tête. Il ne parlait pas anglais. Ils fumèrent en silence. Howard contemplait le ciel scintillant d'étoiles. Il pensait à Lucy qui se trouvait sous les mêmes étoiles puis il se rendit compte que, chez lui, il faisait jour. Quelle heure pouvait-il être ? Que pouvait-elle faire ? Il sortit son carnet de sa poche et prit la photographie qu'il y avait glissée. Il l'étudia pendant quelques instants puis la montra à son compagnon.

— Ma femme, dit-il avec fierté.

— Ah !

L'homme hocha la tête, le langage universel de l'admiration.

— Nous sommes amoureux depuis l'enfance, expliqua Howard.

— Am… am…

Il tenta de reproduire les sons mais sans succès.

— Oui, amoureux depuis l'enfance, répéta Howard au visage souriant de la photo.

Sa Lucy. Elle était tout pour lui.

— Je suis un sacré veinard, s'exclama-t-il, plus pour lui-même que pour son compagnon.

Seigneur, comme elle lui manquait.

Alors, pourquoi sentait-il encore son bras brûler, là où Shun-ling l'avait touché ?

16

Ce matin-là, le soleil n'aurait jamais dû briller. À l'évidence, le monde entier aurait dû pleurer. De lourdes gouttes de pluie auraient dû tremper la terre, rebondir sur les trottoirs, glisser sur les vitres comme d'interminables larmes. Mais le soleil entrait à flots dans le salon. À dix heures, la maison était déjà étouffante et l'air épaissi par la chaleur estivale. Dehors, des nuages blancs et floconneux, aussi peu menaçants que ceux des dessins de Kipper, flottaient dans un ciel d'un bleu limpide. Le bruit des arroseuses de nos voisins, qui n'étaient pas synchronisées, pénétrait par les fenêtres ouvertes du salon en même temps qu'une odeur d'herbe humide et d'asphalte cuit par le soleil. Les odeurs de l'été. Des odeurs qui, généralement, signifiaient que les gamins du quartier jouaient dehors. Je jetai un œil dans la rue déserte. Où étaient-ils tous ? Ils se cachaient probablement chez eux pour ne pas nous voir partir à l'enterrement de maman.

J'attendais sur le canapé l'arrivée de mon oncle et de ma tante. Ma colère contre le soleil débordait pour inclure tout et tout le monde. J'étais fâchée contre ma tante qui m'obligeait à porter ces idiotes de chaussures blanches à brides et ces vêtements bêtes, fâchée contre tous les gamins de la rue qui avaient encore une mère et fâchée contre Jésus à qui je n'ouvrirais désormais plus jamais mon cœur. Mais surtout, surtout, j'étais fâchée contre moi-même : si je n'étais pas allée à l'école biblique samedi dernier, si j'étais restée à la maison, maman ne serait peut-être pas sortie.

À côté de moi, Kipper tripotait son chapeau. Les manches de sa veste étaient un peu courtes et ses chaussettes blanches dépassaient de son pantalon, mais le costume que maman lui avait acheté pour l'exposition était encore comme neuf. Il enfonça son chapeau sur son front puis haussa les sourcils pour le faire remonter, un tic qu'il avait lorsqu'il était nerveux.

— Arrête ! ordonnai-je.

J'allongeai un coup de pied dans le canapé et regardai papa pour voir sa réaction. Il était affalé sur une chaise, vêtu du costume que Frankie lui avait magiquement déniché. À voir l'expression de son visage, je regrettai instantanément mon accès de colère. Mais mon père ne s'intéressait ni à Kipper en train d'ajuster son chapeau ni à mes talons qui frappaient le canapé : il fixait mes mains.

— Pas de gants, dit-il dans un murmure étranglé. Enlève-les, s'il te plaît, Ethie.

Soulagée, j'ôtai les gants blancs achetés par ma tante et les fourrai entre deux coussins.

Le front luisant de sueur, mon père tambourinait des doigts sur l'accoudoir du fauteuil. Frankie cessa d'arpenter la pièce. Il prit un mouchoir dans sa poche et le tendit à papa.

J'avais toujours considéré mon frère Frankie comme un adulte. Le protecteur de papa. Le meilleur ami de maman. Je ne l'avais jamais imaginé autrement, une version plus jeune de notre père. La version des vieilles photographies d'avant-guerre. Mais, tandis qu'il se remettait à arpenter la pièce, son menton se mit à trembler et je vis l'enfant qu'il avait été autrefois.

— Tu es vraiment très beau, lâchai-je.

Je me sentis idiote. Il devait avoir sacrément l'habitude d'entendre ce genre de compliments, mais pas de la part de sa petite sœur. Et pas le jour de l'enterrement de sa mère.

Il releva un côté de sa bouche dans une esquisse de sourire qui ressemblait plutôt à une grimace. Il se pencha pour me caresser la joue, un geste si doux et si inattendu que mes yeux se remplirent de larmes.

— Merci, sœurette, dit-il.

Je mordis l'intérieur de mes joues en roulant des yeux, une tactique qui, d'après maman, permettait d'éviter des larmes indésirables. Mais l'une d'elles s'échappa tout de même. Je me levai d'un bond pour examiner encore une fois la rue inondée de soleil.

L'odeur des œillets de poète montait du parterre sous la fenêtre. Et avec ce parfum vint une vision de maman à genoux dans le jardin en train de cueillir des fleurs. Elle plonge son nez dans le bouquet coloré, prend une profonde inspiration et me l'offre. « As-tu jamais senti odeur plus divine, Ethie ? »

Depuis que Kipper m'avait donné la photo de maman lundi, j'étais passée d'une phase où je ne pouvais retrouver les traits de son visage à une autre où je la voyais partout. Si j'entrais dans la salle de bains, elle se reflétait dans le miroir de l'armoire à pharmacie. Elle avance les lèvres et applique une couche de rouge rubis, penche la tête légèrement, sourit du résultat puis, avec des gestes exagérés, en met sur les miennes.

Lorsque Kipper était entré dans le salon vêtu de son costume, je l'avais vue lui arranger son nœud papillon comme elle l'avait fait avant qu'ils aillent à l'exposition de Marlene vendre ses tableaux. Elle resserre le nœud papillon, le redresse et déclare en souriant : « Beau jeune homme, elles vont toutes succomber ! ».

Au début de la matinée, alors que Mme Fenwick me tressait les cheveux, j'avais imaginé ma mère présente. Elle sourit et tend la main pour enrouler une mèche de cheveux sur mon front. « Il était une petite fille qui avait une petite boucle… »

Et, en regardant par la fenêtre, je vis maman debout, un pied sur la marche de la voiture garée le long du trottoir. Je clignai des yeux et notre vieille Hudson verte fut à nouveau vide et seule dans la rue.

Même si elle affirmait toujours avoir acheté cette voiture pour papa, en réalité, c'était la sienne. Et c'était, d'après Frankie, la raison pour laquelle tante Mildred avait insisté pour venir nous chercher en limousine.

— Elle est pétrifiée à l'idée de nous voir débarquer dans la « voiture de gangster » de maman.

La voiture de gangster de maman. C'était ainsi qu'il l'avait surnommée le jour même où elle avait ramené l'Hudson verte de 1947 – essentiellement à cause de la réaction horrifiée de tante Mildred en apprenant l'endroit où elle l'avait achetée.

J'avais neuf ans le jour où maman repéra l'annonce d'une vente aux enchères organisée par la police dans le *Daily Province*. Elle avait découpé l'article pour le poser sous le nez de papa le soir même, à l'heure du dîner.

L'argent était un sujet sensible pour papa. C'était la seule chose à laquelle il paraissait prêter attention dans la vie quotidienne. À chaque paie, il passait un week-end pénible à préparer des enveloppes blanches pour régler les factures mensuelles. Toute allusion à l'argent semblait le faire souffrir.

— Une vieille manie, qui remonte à la Dépression, marmonnait maman.

Mais, généralement, elle évitait d'aborder les sujets financiers. Sauf quand il s'agissait du problème de la voiture familiale. Notre père insistait pour dire que cela ne le dérangeait nullement d'aller travailler en bus et qu'une automobile était un luxe dont on pouvait se passer.

Nous n'étions pas la seule famille de Barclay Street à ne pas posséder de voiture mais lorsque maman tomba sur l'article annonçant la vente aux enchères, ce fut, d'après elle, le signe que l'heure avait sonné. Elle commença à travailler papa au corps. Elle ne se laissa nullement décontenancer par son manque de réaction. Tous les soirs de cette semaine-là, elle lui rappela la vente à venir, inventant des histoires d'enchères de plus en plus délirantes. Lorsque papa lui annonça qu'il ne pouvait pas se permettre de prendre sa journée, elle répondit qu'il n'y avait pas de problème : elle irait toute seule.

— Une femme aux enchères de la police ? avait-il répliqué en haussant les sourcils.

— Et pourquoi pas ? avait-elle riposté.

— Exact. Pourquoi pas ? admit-il avec une ombre de sourire, avant d'ajouter : Sauf que nous n'en avons pas les moyens.

Il eut beau répéter qu'il était fauché, elle fit la sourde oreille : il y avait des affaires à faire et elle avait bien l'intention de participer. Le matin de la vente, avant de partir travailler, papa ouvrit son portefeuille pour lui montrer qu'il ne contenait qu'un seul billet de vingt dollars. Elle le lui arracha sans lui laisser le temps de dire quoi que ce fût.

Assise sur son lit, je l'ai regardée s'habiller. Elle a mis des bas de soie qu'elle a fixés à un porte-jarretelles effiloché en glissant une pièce de monnaie dans une des jarretelles pour remplacer l'attache manquante. Après avoir examiné son placard, elle en a sorti un cintre rembourré en me faisant un clin d'œil.

— Une robe exceptionnelle pour une occasion exceptionnelle, déclara-t-elle.

Ses bas étaient peut-être filés et tenaient avec une pièce de monnaie mais, quand je l'ai vue enfiler cette robe vert clair, j'ai compris que l'affaire était sérieuse.

Dans la bruine du petit matin, Kipper, maman et moi, pelotonnés sous un parapluie noir tordu, nous sommes partis prendre le bus dans Victoria Drive. Je me souviens de l'entrepôt de Water Street entièrement dans des tons noir et blanc. Une lumière grise entrait par les grandes portes coulissantes. Des ampoules nues pendaient du plafond au bout de longs fils, leur éclat blanc absorbé par les murs noirs et le sol de béton taché de graisse. Ça sentait l'huile et la poussière. Et les hommes. Comme prévu par mon père, il n'y avait pas d'autre femme.

Kipper et moi, nous sommes restés dans le sillage de maman quand elle s'est jointe à la foule qui examinait les voitures. Elle faisait le tour de chacune comme si elle savait quoi chercher. Elle ouvrait les portières pour inspecter l'intérieur, donnait des coups de pied dans les pneus et, si le capot était levé, scrutait le moteur. Elle ne prêtait aucune attention aux regards pleins de curiosité ni aux coups d'œil intéressés. Elle faisait mine d'ignorer qu'elle était la seule femme présente et en plus la seule avec des enfants en remorque.

Son inspection terminée, nous sommes allés nous mettre au fond. Tandis que nous attendions le démarrage des enchères, elle décida de nous distraire en nous faisant deviner le métier exercé par ces hommes autour de nous. « Vendeurs de voitures », murmura-t-elle en désignant quelques groupes compacts qui comparaient leurs notes. Des jeunes gens inquiets qui s'efforçaient d'avoir l'air à l'aise, c'était « des garçons à la recherche de leur toute première voiture » et des plus vieux en costume qui consultaient leur montre avec nervosité, « des hommes d'affaires qui avaient volé une matinée de travail pour suivre les enchères ». Selon maman, depuis les enseignants près de leurs sous jusqu'aux collectionneurs d'antiquités, toutes les professions étaient représentées. Les ouvriers en combinaison grise et les policiers en uniforme bleu étaient

faciles à repérer. Tous les hommes, quels qu'ils fussent, faisaient comme si elle n'était pas là. Pourtant, je remarquai
maints regards dérobés tandis qu'elle nous chuchotait à l'oreille
ses hypothèses.

Lorsque les aiguilles de la pendule murale derrière sa cage
grillagée indiquèrent exactement dix heures, la foule se divisa.
Le commissaire priseur s'approcha de la première voiture. Il
prit le carton numéroté sur le pare-brise et, la main sur le
capot, démarra la vente. Les enchères commencèrent à cent
dollars. En pensant à l'unique billet de vingt que maman avait
pris dans le portefeuille de papa, je sentis que c'était fichu.

Sans me laisser le temps de comprendre, le commissaire-
priseur abattit sa main sur le capot de la voiture.

— Vendue ! cria-t-il. Pour cent soixante-quinze dollars !

Il passa à la suivante. Une fois encore, la litanie des mots
sortit à flot continu de sa bouche jusqu'à ce qu'il reprît sa
respiration pour annoncer : « Vendue ! » Voiture après voiture, il procéda de la même façon.

Plus il avançait, plus les enchères montaient. Si les prix
surprenaient maman, elle ne le manifestait nullement et attendait calmement. Puis il arriva à l'Hudson 1947 vert foncé. La
berline poussiéreuse était sûrement la plus vieille voiture de
l'entrepôt et celle qu'elle avait examinée avec le plus d'attention. Lorsque le commissaire-priseur posa la main sur la
courbe de l'aile, maman passa à l'action. Elle nous attrapa
chacun par une main, Kipper et moi, et se fraya un chemin
dans la foule jusqu'à se faufiler devant pour être juste sous le
nez du commissaire-priseur. Entourée de ses deux enfants
comme d'une armure, elle attendit, prête à la bagarre.

Personne ne réagit à l'ouverture de l'enchère à cinquante
dollars. Prenant son souffle, le commissaire-priseur dit :

— Ai-je-entendu-quarante-qui-offre-quarante-dollars ?

— Cinq dollars ! cria ma mère.

Des rires, d'abord isolés, finirent par gagner tout l'entrepôt. Même le commissaire-priseur ne put retenir un petit sourire. Ignorant son enchère, il répéta son appel à quarante dollars. Une deuxième voix intervint :

— Dix !

Les derniers ricanements cessèrent. Les têtes se tournèrent pour repérer l'auteur de cette sur-enchère. Je suivis le regard du commissaire-priseur : c'était un des vendeurs de voitures, adossé au mur, un cure-dents pendant entre ses lèvres, son feutre gris repoussé en arrière. Apparemment indifférent à la progression de l'enchère, il était concentré sur le carnet qu'il tenait à la main.

Je regardai maman. Elle aussi avait repéré son rival. Le fixant résolument de ses yeux plissés, elle annonça :

— Je propose onze dollars.

Cette fois, personne ne rit. L'entrepôt tout entier demeurait silencieux, comme retenant son souffle. Le vendeur de voitures releva paresseusement la tête. Son regard traversa la salle jusqu'à l'endroit où se trouvait ma mère, dans toute sa gloire provocante. Leurs yeux se croisèrent. Il l'examina de haut en bas, le cure-dents se baladant lentement d'un côté à l'autre de sa bouche.

— Douze, la défia-t-il.

— Treize, riposta-t-elle aussi sec.

Comme s'ils étaient tous les deux seuls dans la salle, comme s'il avait tout le temps du monde, l'adversaire de maman l'observait fixement.

— Une fois ! psalmodia le commissaire-priseur.

Lancés dans un duel de regards au finish, pas plus maman que le vendeur de voitures ne tressaillirent.

— Deux fois !

Le dos droit et le menton levé, maman ne cligna même pas des yeux.

Sans la lâcher du regard, le vendeur de voitures dressa son stylo. Les coins de sa bouche se relevèrent dans un fantôme de sourire. Il s'amusait. Le commissaire-priseur avait arrêté les enchères, attendant la décision de l'homme. Celui-ci, toujours accroché au regard de maman, toucha le bord de son chapeau de deux doigts et la salua d'une brève inclinaison de tête. Lentement, il se tourna vers le commissaire-priseur en secouant la tête.

Une main s'abattit sur le capot.

— Vendue pour treize dollars à la dame en vert !

Tous les regards convergèrent vers maman lorsqu'elle s'avança d'un air triomphant pour récupérer son ticket. Et tout le monde vit – comment aurait-il pu en être autrement ? – la pièce de monnaie tomber entre ses pieds. Horrifiée, je contemplais les cinq centimes de sa jarretelle rebondir bruyamment sur le ciment et rouler par terre.

Maman avait toujours dit que, même si on n'avait qu'un penny en poche, il fallait marcher comme si on possédait un million de dollars. Et c'est exactement ce qu'elle fit quand sa pièce roula jusqu'aux pieds du vendeur de voitures effaré. La tête haute, elle prit le reçu que lui tendait le commissaire-priseur puis revint vers nous.

— Eh bien, déclara-t-elle, nous allons maintenant laisser ces messieurs continuer leurs affaires réservées aux messieurs.

Elle nous prit chacun par une main et, fendant la foule, se dirigea vers le fond de la salle pour payer sa nouvelle voiture. Avant que la vente recommence, on entendit encore pendant quelques secondes des bruits de pas, de toux et des raclements de gorge.

Mais maman n'en avait pas encore fini. Quand elle eut payé, on l'informa qu'elle devait enlever le véhicule dès que la vente serait terminée. Elle n'avait jamais conduit de sa vie ; il fut donc arrangé que quelqu'un garerait la voiture dans la rue jusqu'à ce que papa puisse venir la récupérer. Un jeune policier monta dedans et tourna la clé. Rien ne se produisit. Il pompa sur l'accélérateur et tourna de nouveau la clé. Rien. Il descendit et, avec maman qui regardait par-dessus son épaule, ouvrit le capot. La voiture n'avait pas de batterie.

Comme une poule qui a pris la pluie et dont les plumes sont tout ébouriffées, maman se dirigea résolument vers le comptoir, indignée à l'idée que la « fine fleur » de Vancouver pût vendre une voiture sans batterie à une femme innocente. Même si la règle était que les voitures se vendaient « dans l'état où elles étaient ». Maman discuta, récrimina, leur fit honte. Elle provoqua un tel ramdam qu'on lui fournit une nouvelle batterie qui coûta à la police de Vancouver quinze dollars, soit deux dollars de plus que le prix de la voiture, comme elle s'empressait toujours de le faire remarquer chaque fois qu'elle racontait l'histoire.

Triomphante, elle s'assit au volant après avoir téléphoné à sa sœur, tandis que Kipper et moi nous sautions sur la banquette arrière, soulevant des nuages de poussière des coussins.

Tante Mildred arriva, plus gênée qu'impressionnée par l'acquisition de maman.

— Pour l'amour du ciel, Lucy, si tu avais besoin d'une voiture, pourquoi ne nous as-tu pas demandé de te prêter de l'argent pour en acheter une convenable ? Qui sait où celle-là a traîné ?

Mais notre tante n'avait pas fini de s'indigner. Un journaliste du *Daily Province* avait assisté à la vente aux enchères. Le lendemain, une photo de maman le pied posé sur la marche de sa voiture à treize dollars, semblable à quelque chasseresse aussi belle qu'échevelée piétinant sa proie, parut dans le journal.

— Lucy ! gémit tante Mildred. Comment as-tu pu faire une chose pareille ?

Mais maman était fière de son achat et elle adorait raconter comment elle s'était rendue à la vente aux enchères de la police avec un billet de vingt dollars, comment elle y avait acheté une voiture pour papa et comment elle avait rapporté de la monnaie. À chaque récit, l'histoire s'embellissait. Elle disait toujours que, si elle avait fait une aussi bonne affaire, c'était parce qu'elle avait surenchéri en face des vendeurs de voitures. Elle jouait l'innocence lorsque papa, pour l'asticoter, affirmait que cela avait peut-être un rapport avec l'effet qu'elle avait produit sur les hommes présents à ces enchères. Je soupçonnais qu'il n'avait pas tort parce que j'avais vu le regard qu'elle avait décoché au vendeur de voitures, un regard capable de figer sur place les enfants turbulents et les hommes adultes, un regard « n'ajoutez-pas-un-mot-de-plus-c'est-inutile ». Un défi de même nature pouvait se lire aussi dans les regards hostiles et glacés dont la gratifia l'armée d'hommes debout derrière elle.

Quand Frankie commença à travailler à la scierie, la première chose qu'il s'acheta, ce fut une Studebaker d'occasion. Elle était plus récente que l'Hudson mais, d'après maman, elle avait beaucoup moins d'allure. Frankie n'était pas d'accord : les filles trouvaient très sexy son coupé bleu en forme d'obus. Papa finit par aller travailler avec lui et maman apprit à conduire pour pouvoir utiliser l'Hudson. Frankie et papa passaient leur temps à la rafistoler.

— Elle tient avec des promesses et des bouts de ficelle, se moquait Frankie. Un jour ou l'autre, elle va rendre son dernier soupir et ce sera fini.

Mais elle était encore là, garée dans la rue comme si elle attendait que maman saute dedans pour l'emmener ailleurs.

Une limousine noire vint s'arrêter derrière.
— Les voilà ! annonçai-je, le cœur battant.

Même si c'était moi qui avais insisté pour assister à l'enterrement, brusquement, j'avais peur.

— Il faut que j'aille faire pipi.

Kipper se précipita aux toilettes.

La portière de la limousine s'ouvrit, oncle Sidney et tante Mildred descendirent.

Je les observai qui s'avançaient vers la maison. Ma tante ne portait que du noir, sa robe, son chapeau, ses chaussures et même ses bas.

Frankie ouvrit la porte avant qu'ils frappent. Papa réussit à s'arracher à son siège et j'allai me mettre à côté de lui.

— Nous sommes tous prêts ? demanda tante Mildred de derrière la voilette noire qui couvrait son visage.

— Prêt ! répondit Kipper qui entra en s'essuyant les mains sur son pantalon.

Ma tante haussa les sourcils derrière sa voilette en le voyant débarquer dans le salon mais elle ne dit rien et nous fit signe d'y aller. Comme des prisonniers condamnés, nous sortîmes à la file dans le soleil brûlant. En voyant Kipper sous le porche, tante Mildred lui ordonna sèchement :

— Retire ce ridicule chapeau.

Perplexe, Kipper s'y accrocha à pleine main, me jeta un regard désespéré et ses yeux se remplirent de larmes.

La poitrine traversée par un éclair brûlant, je sus exactement comment aurait réagi ma mère en pareille occasion. Et ce qu'elle aurait attendu de moi. Carrant les épaules, j'entourai Kipper d'un bras protecteur.

— Tout va bien, dis-je en le faisant avancer. Garde-le. Il va le porter, affirmai-je en passant devant ma tante. C'est maman qui lui a donné ce chapeau.

17

Il me fallut bien des années pour comprendre que la mort n'était pas une inconnue pour mon père. Il n'était que trop familier de sa réalité crue. Il connaissait son allure, ses bruits, son odeur. Il avait perdu ses deux parents avant même d'avoir vingt ans. Il était devenu un homme dès la première explosion sur le champ de bataille, lorsque son casque s'était trouvé couvert de chair, d'os et de sang.

Et lorsqu'il était revenu de guerre pour apprendre la mort de ses trois frères, il avait compris que la souffrance ne désarme pas, longtemps après que la Faucheuse a revendiqué sa proie. Ils avaient tous disparu dans des missions de bombardement de l'autre côté de la Manche, moins de six mois après leur arrivée en Angleterre.

Oui, la mort lui était familière. Pourtant, même Frankie devait se souvenir de lui tête basse à l'arrière de la limousine alors que nous allions à l'enterrement de notre mère ; il craignait que, atteint de plein fouet par ce coup inattendu, notre père ne parvienne jamais à remonter la pente.

La mémoire est souvent inconstante, elle fonctionne par à-coups, au mieux elle reste dans le flou. Mais le souvenir que je garde de cette journée n'est que trop clair. Dans la voiture, l'odeur de renfermé du cuir épaississait l'atmosphère. Les sièges brun rouille, la même couleur que le blouson d'aviateur de mon père, étaient fendillés et passés, non par la pluie mais plutôt par les larmes de milliers de gens en deuil. Cette odeur animale devait me rappeler à jamais le trajet de chez nous au cimetière de Forest Lawn.

J'étais serrée entre mon père et mes frères. En face de nous, tante Mildred et oncle Sidney étaient assis aux deux extrémités d'une banquette de cuir identique. Nous roulions en silence, perdus chacun dans nos pensées tandis que la limousine descendait lentement Kingsway. Je regardais par la fenêtre en me demandant comment le monde pouvait avoir l'air aussi normal.

La circulation autour de nous ralentit pour laisser passer la voiture noire des pompes funèbres avec son chargement d'affligés. « Soulagés que ce ne soit pas eux, que ce ne soit pas leur tour. » Je me souvenais que maman avait une fois fait cette remarque tout en se rangeant avec les autres véhicules pour laisser la voie libre à un cortège funéraire.

On dépassa Boundary Road et la végétation dense de Central Park. Je pris conscience que je ne marcherais plus jamais dans ces allées en l'écoutant raconter comment la fille de la prairie en elle serait toujours écrasée par la splendeur de ces immenses arbres en pleine ville. Tout, absolument tout, était lié à maman. Comment le monde pouvait-il continuer à tourner sans elle ?

Trop vite, on fut dans Royal Oak Avenue pour franchir les imposantes grilles en fer forgé du cimetière. On suivit le chemin étroit qui sinuait entre de vastes étendues marquées de pierres tombales réparties sur la pelouse soigneusement entretenue. La mâchoire de papa, assis à côté de moi, se crispa en voyant une tombe solitaire entourée de couronnes de fleurs et d'un tas de terre.

La chapelle se trouvait sur le plus haut tertre, à côté du parking bondé. Nous fîmes halte juste devant l'escalier de marbre. Personne ne bougea avant que le chauffeur sorte nous ouvrir la portière. Une fois dehors, alors que nous tentions de nous accoutumer à la violente lumière du jour, je crois que nous étions tous assez perdus. Mais tante Mildred reprit ses esprits et nous fit monter les marches.

À l'intérieur, le parfum lourd des lys envahissait le hall. Kipper regarda autour de lui.

— C'est une église, dit-il en ôtant son chapeau qu'il garda contre son cœur.

Nous restions groupés tous les quatre tandis qu'un flot de voisins, d'amis et d'inconnus se déversait dans la chapelle déjà pleine. Certains touchaient au passage le bras ou l'épaule de papa, en murmurant quelques paroles de réconfort. Un homme vint nous emmener, avec tante Mildred et oncle Sidney, jusque dans une salle mal éclairée à l'autre bout de la chapelle. Un grand panneau vitré masqué par de simples rideaux gris nous séparait du reste de l'assistance et du cercueil disparaissant sous les fleurs.

Je m'écroulai sur le banc en tapisserie à côté de papa. Kipper s'assit de l'autre côté, tapotant d'une main le genou de papa, l'autre cramponnée à son chapeau. Frankie prit place à côté de moi, droit comme un i, regardant fixement devant lui. Je me collai contre lui, comme si je pouvais m'enfouir en lui.

On entendait les gens se moucher et renifler dans la chapelle. Je jetai un œil par la fente du rideau par-dessus les fleurs. La salle était pleine, tous les sièges étaient occupés et beaucoup de gens étaient debout au fond. Sur le premier banc, je reconnus Mme Manson, avec son mari et ses enfants. Derrière eux, j'aperçus le visage d'autres voisins. Les Price, les Black et les Johnson. Ardith, Mary, Susie. Tout Barclay Street était là. Mais les autres ? Il y en avait tellement. J'identifiai quelques dames de la boutique de Marlene, avec leurs vêtements excentriques. Parmi elles, je repérai le visage sillonné de larmes de Dora Fenwick, avec Danny assis à côté d'elle.

La douce musique de l'orgue, que je venais seulement de remarquer, se tut. Derrière son pupitre en bois, le pasteur, un inconnu, s'éclaircit la voix. Depuis combien de temps était-il là ? Il se mit à parler. Je me débranchai de cette voix étrangère qui disait des choses qui n'avaient rien à voir avec ma mère. Le sermon prit fin et la musique recommença. Quelques voix courageuses se joignirent à celle du pasteur lorsqu'il entonna *À la croix du calvaire...*

Après l'hymne, il y eut un moment de silence, rompu par une nouvelle tournée de toux et de mouchages.

— L'hymne suivant était un des préférés de Lucy Coulter, annonça le pasteur. Numéro quatre-vingt-sept dans votre livre de cantiques.

Comment pouvait-il savoir quel était l'hymne préféré de maman ? Qui avait bien pu le lui dire ? Tante Mildred ? Papa ? Mais papa le savait-il seulement ?

Tout le monde se mit à chercher l'hymne dans un bruit de pages tournées. Frankie hocha la tête en entendant les premières mesures de l'orgue. Puis Kipper se leva d'un bond. Marchant sur place, il entonna *En avant, soldats du Christ,* sa voix puissante résonnant dans la petite salle. Je me levai, ainsi que Frankie, pour chanter avec lui. Lorsque oncle Sidney nous rejoignit, tante Mildred s'enfonça dans son siège, la tête entre les mains. Papa, lui, regardait fixement devant lui un endroit que nul ne pouvait voir.

Après le chœur final, une fois tout le monde à nouveau assis, le pasteur annonça que la famille souhaitait s'exprimer. Sortant une feuille de papier pliée de sa poche de poitrine, Frankie se pencha en avant.

— Papa ! souffla-t-il.

Devant son absence de réaction, il passa devant moi pour pousser le bras de papa avec la feuille.

— Le poème, chuchota-t-il.

Mais notre père était parti loin, là où il n'entendait plus rien. Frankie soupira et se leva. Après avoir lancé un dernier coup d'œil à papa, il carra les épaules puis s'avança. Le pasteur recula pour lui laisser la place au pupitre.

— Ce n'est pas facile, commença Frankie en lissant la feuille, mais j'ai une promesse à tenir. (Sa voix se brisa, il déglutit avec difficulté.) Tous ceux qui connaissaient notre mère savaient qu'elle aimait la poésie. La poésie sous toutes ses formes. La bonne et la mauvaise, la sérieuse et la légère. Elle savait aussi bien réciter du Byron que de l'Ogden Nash ou une simple comptine pour enfants au moment le plus opportun, ou le moins opportun.

Des petits rires approbateurs s'élevèrent des bancs et il y eut des hochements de tête.

— Elle aimait particulièrement ce poème de William Wordsworth, entre autres parce qu'il y avait son prénom dedans. Maman n'a jamais nié qu'elle était vaniteuse, ajouta-t-il avec un demi-sourire avant de laisser le temps aux murmures de se calmer. Elle avait exprimé le désir que… (Il jeta un coup d'œil à papa)… qu'un jour on le lise à son enterrement. Aucun d'entre nous n'avait jamais imaginé que ce jour fût si proche.

Il serra les mâchoires en clignant des paupières à plusieurs reprises.

— Avant d'accéder à sa demande, j'aimerais dire que, si le sermon d'aujourd'hui était plein de sincérité, poursuivit-il en se tournant vers le pasteur avec un sourire d'excuse, ce n'était pas de ma mère qu'il parlait. Il n'évoquait pas la femme forte et fougueuse toujours prête à se battre pour défendre ses convictions, ses enfants et son mari. C'est… c'était une femme dont le caractère ardent était à l'image de sa chevelure rousse, une femme qui aimait un bon mélo et l'émission *Reconnaissez cette chanson*, même si elle n'avait strictement aucune oreille. Une femme qui jouait au poker et non au bridge.

Il leva les yeux vers le ciel en murmurant « pardon, maman » puis il s'éclaircit la gorge.

— Elle encourageait ses enfants à être les meilleurs possibles, persuadée qu'il n'existait pas de gens « ordinaires » parce que tout le monde, avait-elle coutume de dire, était extraordinaire à sa manière.

Il prit une profonde inspiration avant de continuer.

— Pour vous tous rassemblés, elle représentait bien des choses, j'en suis persuadé. Elle n'était peut-être pas une ménagère hors pair ni même une cuisinière d'exception, mais Dieu le sait, ses enfants le savent, elle était une mère parfaite.

La tête basse, il lissa à nouveau son papier.

— Ce poème est pour elle.

Puis, d'une voix claire et forte, il se mit à lire :

Lucy habitait une vallée
Que les monts enfermaient,
Sa grâce croissait isolée
Et peu de cœurs l'aimaient.

Violette qui sous la mousse
Fuit à moitié les yeux !
Première étoile qui luit, douce
Et seule dans les cieux.

Bien peu l'admiraient, fraîche et forte,
Sa mort fit peu d'émoi.
Hélas ! tout, depuis que Lucy est morte,
Tout est changé pour moi.[1]

---

1. Traduction d'Emile Legouis (1928), légèrement remaniée. (*NdT*).

Il laissa le silence s'installer puis releva la tête et ajouta :

— Le vers « Et peu de cœurs l'aimaient » n'a aucun sens rapporté à notre mère car tous ceux qui la connaissaient l'aimaient. Eh oui, quelle différence, quelle énorme différence son absence va faire pour nous !

Il replia soigneusement sa feuille de papier et, après l'avoir rangée dans sa poche, quitta l'estrade.

Dehors, la foule défila devant nous alors que j'étais entre Frankie et Kipper. Les commentaires sur sa beauté me mettaient en colère. Ces gens ne connaissaient-ils donc pas du tout ma mère ?

— Exactement comme Marilyn Monroe, chuchota une femme à sa voisine. Quel gâchis !

Je levai les yeux vers mon père mais il n'avait pas entendu. Une fois de plus, même si son corps était présent, lui était ailleurs.

Puis il se produisit quelque chose d'étrange. Son regard s'anima. Secouant la tête comme s'il ne croyait pas à ce qu'il voyait, papa fit un pas en direction de deux hommes qui venaient vers lui. Ils m'étaient tous deux inconnus. Ils étaient vêtus de vestes bleues identiques mais la manche du plus petit était épinglée à la hauteur du coude, là où aurait dû être son bras droit. Le plus grand tendit la main à papa.

— Ken Campbell, le salua papa dans un murmure rauque.

— Nous avons appris la mort de Lucy dans le journal de la légion, dit l'homme en prenant la main de papa dans les siennes. Nous sommes venus, évidemment.

18

20 novembre 1941 : Hong Kong

— Je crois que Lawson cherche à nous tuer, gémit Ken Campbell en se jetant, les jambes écartées, sur le lit de camp à côté de celui de Howard.

Le cadre métallique trembla sous l'assaut de son mètre quatre-vingt-dix.

Howard ôta son casque et sourit à l'opérateur radio. La taille et la corpulence de son camarade, grenadier comme lui, formaient un contraste complet avec son visage de chérubin, encore couvert de poussière. Mais il n'y avait absolument rien d'enfantin chez le soldat Campbell. Howard avait vu l'ampleur de sa force au cours de la journée de manœuvres et il était content d'être dans la même section que lui.

— Notre commandant ne pense sûrement pas que ces Japs se rassemblent le long de la frontière pour organiser une soirée feu de camp, dit Howard en déboutonnant son uniforme taché de sueur.

— C'est un piège, rétorqua de son lit où il sirotait du thé, Peter Young, le mitrailleur anglais. Si jamais il devait y avoir une invasion – et putain, c'est vraiment peu probable ! – d'après le major Maltby, ce serait une attaque navale.

La plupart des soldats anglais qui entendaient cette conversation marmonnèrent leur approbation. Certains Canadiens, cependant, soutenaient le point de vue de leur propre commandant qui affirmait que l'attaque viendrait principalement par la terre, du nord. Très tôt dans la matinée, le brigadier Lawson avait annoncé qu'ils commenceraient d'emblée à se familiariser avec le terrain, aussi bien l'île que le continent. L'entraînement allait être intense, promit-il aux troupes, mais quiconque ayant l'énergie nécessaire à la fin de la journée pourrait s'apercevoir que le régime des laissez-passer nocturnes était très libéral.

La première journée de manœuvres avait laissé Howard avec des muscles douloureux. Pourtant, en dépit de la fatigue accumulée à force d'escalader ces pentes ardues sous un soleil de plomb, il fut incapable de résister lorsque Gordy lui proposa à nouveau de passer la soirée avec Shun-ling et lui.

— Eh, Campbell, cria Gordy en se dirigeant vers les douches, viens avec nous au Sun Sun ce soir.

— Non, répondit Ken en se relevant. Je vais au cinéma avec Black et Richards. Je suis marié, tu sais.

Shun-ling les attendait aux portes du camp, vêtue de la robe à fleurs. L'air timidement contente d'elle, elle rougit en baissant les yeux quand elle les vit arriver.

— Waouh, mazette ! s'exclama Gordy avec un sifflement approbateur. Vous allez être la plus jolie fille de toute la boîte.

— Aller d'abord à Kowloon, s'il vous plaît ? Après, à Peak ? demanda-t-elle en relevant les paupières.

— Nous sommes à votre disposition, répondit-il en riant et en levant les bras en signe de reddition.

Le rickshaw de Howard suivit le leur, se faufilant malgré la circulation le long de ruelles pavées vers des quartiers plus anciens, loin de l'animation des commerces. Dans les petites rues sombres, des bannières en tissu étaient pendues au-dessus des portes des magasins de curiosités et des fumeries, les caractères peints en noir ondulant au plus léger souffle d'air. Du linge était étendu aux fenêtres ouvertes et aux balcons délabrés où des familles entières cherchaient à échapper à la chaleur de cette fin d'après-midi. Des enfants aux cheveux noirs étaient assis entre les barreaux, les jambes pendantes, tandis que leurs parents, affalés sur des chaises en osier, s'éventaient. Sur un balcon bondé, quatre étages plus haut, un groupe d'adolescents s'appuyaient sur une balustrade qui paraissait prête à s'effondrer sous leur poids. Ils firent de grands saluts aux « sol'ats » qui passaient en dessous dans leurs rickshaws et se mirent à pouffer derrière leurs mains lorsque Howard leur rendit leurs saluts.

Il était très surpris des réactions amicales des Chinois. Partout où ils allaient, ils étaient accueillis avec enthousiasme, traités en héros venus protéger la colonie. Il espérait qu'ils seraient à la hauteur de la situation.

Les rickshaws ralentirent et s'arrêtèrent devant une boutique étroite. Dès qu'ils eurent touché leur argent, les conducteurs repartirent dans l'autre sens et furent avalés par la nuit. Dans la vitrine, une enseigne « Ordonnances » nimba d'orange le profil de Shun-ling.

Une cloche tinta lorsque la porte s'ouvrit. L'intérieur de la boutique ressemblait à une version miniature du drugstore du beau-père de Howard, là-bas au Canada. Il reconnut de nombreux produits familiers sur les étagères chargées, depuis l'aspirine Bayer jusqu'aux tuyaux en caoutchouc pour les lavements. Mais l'homme qui verrouillait la vitrine en verre derrière le comptoir ne ressemblait nullement au père de Lucy. Au lieu de la veste blanche du pharmacien, il portait une robe noire qui traînait jusqu'à terre. Il était coiffé d'une petite toque en satin assorti et une interminable tresse en sortait comme une corde.

Il fourra la clé quelque part dans les plis de sa robe puis fit volte-face. Son visage s'éclaira d'un sourire.

— Feng Shun-ling ! s'exclama-t-il.

— Ah Sam.

Elle le salua d'une inclinaison de tête et ils bavardèrent en chinois pendant quelques instants.

Elle lui présenta Howard et Gordy qu'il examina d'un œil approbateur. Il accueillit chacun d'un léger signe de tête, les bras croisés, les mains cachées dans ses grandes manches.

Shun-ling continuait à parler. Lorsqu'elle se tut, le commerçant hocha la tête.

— Je vois, dit-il. Ce qu'il vous faut, messieurs, ce n'est pas là que vous le trouverez.

Il rejeta d'un geste de la main les remèdes occidentaux et sortit de derrière son comptoir.

— Pour combattre cette calamité, le *Cimex lectularius*, ces vilaines petites bêtes nocturnes, les compétences de l'apothicaire sont indispensables, déclara-t-il.

Non seulement il s'exprimait à la perfection mais en plus, il avait un accent anglais. Il leur fit signe de le suivre dans un dédale d'étagères. Sa longue natte ondulait au rythme de ses pas tandis qu'il continuait à expliquer le fléau des punaises par-dessus son épaule. Derrière lui, Howard lança à Gordy un regard interrogatif, se demandant s'il avait informé Shun-ling de leur problème. Son ami secoua la tête en signe de dénégation et haussa les épaules.

Dans un coin sombre, Ah Sam releva un rideau de bambou pour laisser apparaître un mur de minuscules tiroirs de bois, chacun gravé d'un symbole différent. Sur les étagères au-dessus, une multitude de flacons et de pots en verre contenaient des poudres et des feuilles sèches, des herbes et des racines, des cuisses de grenouille fripées, des lézards déshydratés et des morceaux d'animal non identifiables.

— Comment se porte votre honorable père, Shun-ling ? demanda Ah Sam en prenant un pot de poudre verte.

Il en fit glisser avec adresse une toute petite quantité dans deux fioles d'huile.

— Il va bien, je vous remercie.

— Pourquoi ne vient-il plus me voir ? Nos parties d'échecs me manquent. Ainsi que, ajouta-t-il en riant, nos débats philosophiques.

— Mon père est très occupé.

Ah Sam haussa un sourcil presque invisible mais ne fit aucun commentaire. Il boucha les deux fioles puis, prenant une bougie allumée sur le comptoir, fit couler de la cire dessus.

— Et votre sœur ? s'enquit-il en posant les flacons pour laisser à la cire le temps de durcir.

— Shun-qin est toujours dans le même état.

Il alla chercher sous le comptoir une boîte métallique de la taille d'un livre. Il l'enveloppa dans une feuille de papier brun.

— Pour sa gorge, précisa-t-il en la nouant avec un bout de ficelle. Ce remède ne lui rendra peut-être pas la parole mais qui sait ? Si elle y croit ? Et, ajouta-t-il avec un clin d'œil que Howard trouva presque comique, il a goût de bonbon.

— Je suis désolée, dit Shun-ling en baissant les yeux. Je n'ai pas d'argent.

— Non, non, ma chère enfant. C'est un cadeau. Ayez la bonté de l'accepter.

— Merci, Ah Sam. Une fois de plus, nous sommes vos débiteurs.

— Oh pff, fit-il en enveloppant les fioles. Ce n'est rien. Votre visite m'a fait grand plaisir. Transmettez mes salutations à votre père.

Il tendit les paquets à Howard et Gordy.

— Vieille médecine chinoise, expliqua-t-il, redevenu sérieux. Cela marche. Une seule application suffira pour soulager vos démangeaisons et après les bestioles vous laisseront en paix.

Il accepta sans hésiter leur argent ; une somme inférieure à deux dollars, d'après Howard. Une excellente affaire si cela devait mettre fin à ces démangeaisons insupportables.

Le pharmacien s'inclina lorsque Howard le remercia.

— Je vous en prie.

— Mais pourquoi vous parlez comme un Engliche ? s'enquit Gordy.

— Eh bien, mon cher monsieur, répliqua Ah Sam en le regardant avec un sourire indulgent qui excusait la grossièreté de la question tout en la réprimandant gentiment, je suis un « Engliche », comme vous l'avez si bien dit. Je suis né à Londres. J'ai fait mes études à Oxford. Une fois pharmacien, je me suis installé à Hong Kong qui, monsieur, est également britannique.

— Oh... je..., bafouilla Gordy, je voulais seulement... euh... les vêtements... le...

— C'est excellent pour le commerce, vous ne trouvez pas ? Un Chinois en costume traditionnel ? C'est une nouveauté qui plaît autant aux Asiatiques qu'aux Européens, déclara-t-il, les bras tendus, en faisant onduler les plis de sa robe de soie.

Tandis que le funiculaire montait lentement à l'assaut de la pente raide du Peak, Howard interrogea Shun-ling sur Ah Sam.

— Nous faisons connaissance première fois nous venons Hong Kong, il y a trois ans, répondit-elle, le regard tourné vers la végétation luxuriante qui poussait à portée de main, de l'autre côté de la vitre. Après nous avons fui les Japonais.

En l'écoutant, Howard prit brutalement conscience que, tant qu'ils étaient dans la boutique, elle s'exprimait dans un anglais parfait. Et à nouveau, elle était revenue au pidgin. Il lui vint à l'esprit que, comme le pharmacien, Shun-ling jouait son rôle, celui d'une subalterne.

Et pourquoi pas ? Elle avait confiance en Ah Sam. Elle n'avait aucune raison de faire confiance au premier venu qui avait acheté sa compagnie.

— Ma sœur besoin médicaments, continua-t-elle. Gens du nord ont dit nous que Ah Sam aidera. Lui pas trop cher. Essaie tout le temps de donner gratuit à nous. Mais mon père homme fier. Ah Sam, mon père, deux intellectuels. Aiment parler tous les deux. Ah Sam parfois trouver travail interprétation pour mon père. Plus maintenant. Mon père trop fier pour retourner le voir. Refuse son ami voie comme il est descendu bas.

Howard ne put s'empêcher de s'étonner devant une si étrange culture. Trop fier pour accepter la charité de la part d'un ami mais pas trop fier pour vendre sa fille à un étranger ?

Le dancing saturé de fumée au-dessus du Sun Sun Café était tellement bondé qu'on ne pouvait s'y tenir que debout. Dominant le vacarme des conversations, le son métallique de l'orchestre de Glen Miller interprétant *The Nearness of You* sortait du Wurlitzer placé dans un coin. Sur la piste, les danseuses tarifées se collaient contre leurs partenaires en uniforme, leur visage maquillé scrutant la salle à la recherche du client suivant.

Howard laissa Gordy et Shun-ling près du juke-box et se fraya un chemin dans la foule pour chercher à boire. Repérant la touffe de cheveux roux de Dick Baxter, il se glissa entre Peter et lui au bar.

— Salut, les gars, dit-il s'efforçant, en vain, d'imiter l'accent anglais. Trois bières, cria-t-il au barman en élevant la voix pour se faire entendre. Et deux autres pour mes amis ici présents, ajouta-t-il avant de s'adosser contre le bar.

— T'as tout raté ! dit Peter.

Tandis qu'ils attendaient leurs consommations, les deux mitrailleurs lui fournirent quelques explications.

— On a eu droit à une petite bagarre entre les Anglais et les Canadiens, raconta Dick. Il y a eu échange de coups de poing mais tout est arrangé maintenant.

— Que s'est-il passé ?

Dick haussa les épaules.

— Apparemment, certains de nos gars en avaient assez de vous voir, vous les colons, jeter l'argent par les fenêtres comme si demain n'existait pas.

— Oh, ils s'amusent, c'est tout, répliqua Howard.

Il sortit une poignée de monnaie de sa poche et compta ce qu'il devait.

— Ils sont comme des gosses dans un magasin de bonbons, déclara-t-il en prenant les bières que le serveur glissait vers lui.

— Eh bien, il faudrait peut-être leur conseiller de mettre la pédale douce, rétorqua Peter en saisissant la chope dégoulinante que lui tendait Howard. Ça râle beaucoup dans nos rangs. La rumeur dit que vous, les gars, vous n'avez apporté strictement aucun matériel avec vous.

Il leva sa chope et regarda Howard par-dessus la mousse.

— Que vous comptez sur la garnison pour pratiquement tout, ajouta-t-il avec une nuance de défi dans la voix.

— Tout ça va s'arranger dès que notre navire ravitailleur arrivera, répondit Howard en offrant une bière à Dick. Il est en route.

— Putain, il y a drôlement intérêt, renchérit Dick en buvant une gorgée avant de s'essuyer la lèvre supérieure. Nous n'avons déjà pas assez de munitions et de matériel pour nous, et maintenant, les mecs, voilà que vous débarquez avec des poches profondes et les mains vides. Sans vouloir te vexer, mon pote, on est nombreux à se demander à quoi vous allez bien servir !

— À quoi on va bien servir quand ? répéta Howard. Quand les invisibles Japonais vont enfin se manifester ?

— T'inquiète, le rassura Peter en souriant et en tapant Howard dans le dos. Dicky et moi, on te fait marcher. Je vais te dire, ajouta-t-il en faisant un clin d'œil à son ami. Si y en a un des deux qui se manifeste – ton bateau ou les Japs – nous, on paie une bière.

— D'accord ! acquiesça Howard en riant.

Tout en tenant les trois chopes restantes en équilibre pour se frayer un chemin dans la foule, il se prit à espérer qu'il avait raison et que le matériel allait vraiment arriver bientôt. Aujourd'hui, l'armée britannique avait prêté des Bren Gun Carriers à quelques veinards, mais aucune de ces chenillettes n'avait trouvé le chemin de son propre régiment. Au cours des manœuvres, Gordy et lui avaient dû se relayer pour transporter les armes d'une position à l'autre. Et comme si elles ne pesaient pas déjà suffisamment lourd en elles-mêmes, le terrain pentu était mortel. Une fois de plus, Howard avait été content des mois passés à Winnipeg à livrer des pains de glace. N'empêche, en se faufilant au milieu des danseurs pour rejoindre Gordy et Shun-ling, il sentait que, à la suite des exercices du jour, il avait des courbatures à l'arrière des cuisses.

En fin de soirée, alors qu'ils étaient rentrés au camp, il s'assit sur son lit pour écrire à Lucy. Pas question de parler des exercices à répétition, du creusement des tranchées et des manœuvres sur le terrain. Il tenta plutôt de décrire la vie si animée de la ville. Il raconta leur excursion en funiculaire jusqu'au sommet du Peak, bien au-dessus de l'île.

Un wagon de train qui escalade une montagne terriblement pentue !
À travers la jungle et au-dessus des toits de maisons grandes comme des

palais ! Tu te rends compte, Lucy ? C'est comme se retrouver au sommet du monde. Je pouvais même distinguer les lumières des jonques dans le port. Des familles entières vivent dans ces drôles de bateaux et certains ne mettent jamais pied à terre pendant toute leur vie, à ce qu'on nous a dit.

Tout ce que je vois ici, je le vois à travers ton regard. Cela te plairait-il ? Je pense que oui. Tu serais sans doute très étonnée par certaines choses. J'ai bien peur que nous, les gars, on se balade par ici avec les yeux exorbités. Apparemment, le passe-temps principal, ce sont les achats. Je t'ai acheté une robe chinoise en soie verte. Ne t'inquiète pas, ça vaut pratiquement rien ici.

Tout le monde fume ; même les plus pauvres trouvent de quoi s'acheter des cigarettes. J'ai un aveu à te faire, Lucy. Je m'y suis mis moi aussi. Accroché aux rations militaires de cigarettes gratuites, j'arrêterai en rentrant chez nous.

Je suis devenu plus ou moins copain avec un Asiatique, un barbier qui vient raser des soldats anglais le matin. Je partage mes cigarettes avec lui quand je reviens au cantonnement le soir. Aujourd'hui, je lui ai rapporté une bière. Il ne parle pas un mot d'anglais mais on s'assoit devant les baraquements et on admire ta photo comme deux lycéens malades d'amour.

Il ne fit aucune allusion aux centaines de milliers de réfugiés dont la ville était bourrée, aucune allusion au fossé profond entre les très riches et les très pauvres – Lucy aurait détesté entendre parler de tout cela. Il ne dit mot des corps balancés à l'arrière des camions par les patrouilles de la mort. Et il omit de raconter la rencontre avec Ah Sam, à quel point il avait été attiré par cet homme, produit de deux cultures. L'espace d'un instant, dans la petite boutique, il avait été tenté de partager avec lui son rêve de devenir lui-même pharmacien mais il avait finalement gardé cela pour lui. Il raconterait tout cela à Lucy en rentrant au pays.

Pas plus qu'il ne mentionna l'idée qui l'avait frappé alors qu'il se trouvait au sommet du Peak, dominant la mer de Chine méridionale. C'était une vue à couper le souffle qui perdit soudain tout attrait lorsqu'il s'interrogea : « Si le brigadier Lawson avait raison, si une invasion venue du nord les repoussait sur l'île, où iraient-ils, une fois arrivés là ? »

19

C'est Frankie qui me découvrit. Éblouie par la lumière qui entrait à flots dans le placard, je le vis debout devant moi, la veste de costume de papa sur le bras.

— Salut, Ethie ! s'exclama-t-il comme s'il était tout à fait normal de me trouver assise par terre au fond du placard de maman en train de respirer un de ses chemisiers.

L'odeur musquée de sa transpiration et de son parfum s'était échappée en même temps que l'obscurité.

Frankie attrapa un cintre au-dessus de ma tête.

— Qu'est-ce que tu fais là ? demanda-t-il.

— Rien, répondis-je en serrant mes genoux dans mes bras.

— Ah. Je vois, dit-il en accrochant la veste de papa. Plusieurs de tes amis sont dehors, ajouta-t-il en ôtant la sienne. Pourquoi ne vas-tu pas leur dire bonjour ?

Je secouai la tête. C'étaient eux que je fuyais. Eux et tous les voisins rassemblés dans notre maison. J'avais bien vu comment ils me regardaient pendant l'enterrement. Désormais, je serais la fille dont la mère avait été mise au fond d'un trou.

— Je ne veux pas les voir, marmonnai-je.

Frankie accrocha sa veste et desserra son étroit nœud de cravate.

— D'accord, dit-il en retroussant ses manches de chemise. Mais tu dois étouffer là-dedans. Au moins, sors voir Kipper, il te cherche. Il est dans le square, précisa-t-il en me tendant la main.

Je le suivis hors de la chambre. Dans l'entrée, une fille, coiffée à la Sandra Dee avec une chevelure blonde crêpée, était assise sur la première marche, le menton dans les mains. Elle se leva d'un bond en nous voyant. De grands yeux de biche, lourdement soulignés de noir, observaient Frankie avec une expression identique à celle de Kipper quand il se plantait sur le trottoir, sa batte de hockey à la main, avec l'espoir que les autres enfants l'inviteraient à jouer avec eux.

Frankie lui chuchota quelque chose à l'oreille. J'étais désolée pour elle jusqu'à ce que je la voie s'avachir à nouveau contre le mur en faisant la moue, les lèvres gonflées. Maman aurait fait ses choux gras de cette mimique forcée. Je lâchai la main de Frankie, l'abandonnant à cette fille grognon, et me frayai un chemin dans l'entrée encombrée.

Tout le monde s'efforçait de discuter tranquillement, comme si le fait de se taire, de laisser le silence prendre possession des lieux risquait de révéler à quel point la maison était désormais vide. J'étais escortée par le bourdonnement des voix. En dépit des fenêtres ouvertes, l'air demeurait étouffant car les pièces de la maison étaient trop petites pour contenir tant de gens.

Dans la cuisine, les femmes de Barclay Street, vêtues de robes en coton noir identiques – beaucoup portaient encore les drôles de petits chapeaux noirs qu'elles avaient pendant l'enterrement – étaient installées autour de la table. La semaine précédente, la conversation tournait autour de la pluie. Aujourd'hui, elles parlaient de la chaleur étouffante. Comment pouvaient-elles rester là à fumer et bavarder, comme s'il s'agissait du petit café hebdomadaire qu'organisait maman ? Comme si sa chaise vide était la seule différence.

Les autres femmes, certaines que je reconnaissais et d'autres pas, s'activaient autour des plats chargés de nourriture posés sur toutes les surfaces disponibles. Dora Fenwick était en train de remuer une carafe de citronnade près de l'évier. Elle leva les yeux au moment où je me faufilai entre deux dames.

— Ah, te voilà, Ethie. Tu veux de la citronnade ? Ou du thé glacé ?

Je haussai les épaules.

— Danny est rentré à la maison avec ma mère, dit-elle en me tendant le verre qu'elle m'avait versé. Si tu allais le rejoindre ?

Je pris la citronnade sans relever sa proposition. Je n'avais aucune envie de voir Danny et son regard compatissant, pas plus que sa grand-mère, qui peut-être se souviendrait de mon nom.

Les conversations cessèrent autour de la table. Je les sentais hésiter derrière moi, comme une volée d'oiseaux noirs, épiant le moindre de mes mouvements, prêtes à se jeter sur moi pour me consoler. Si quelqu'un s'avisait encore de me demander « Comment ça va, ma chérie ? » ou tentait de m'embrasser, j'étais sûre de me mettre à crier. Pourquoi fallait-il qu'elles soient là ? Pourquoi ne rentraient-elles pas chez elles, comme l'avaient fait mon oncle et ma tante ?

Dora Fenwick se pencha pour repousser une mèche sur mon front.

— As-tu faim ? demanda-t-elle.

Une boule m'obstrua la gorge je sentis la caresse de ses doigts. Je secouai la tête et sortis de la pièce.

Dans l'entrée, Frankie, appuyé contre le mur, discutait avec la même fille à la moue prononcée. Sa dernière conquête, sans doute. Combien de temps cela allait-il durer ? Une fois, alors qu'il avait largué une fille que maman appréciait particulièrement, elle l'avait accusé d'être un vrai mufle.

— C'est pas ma faute si les dames me trouvent irrésistible, avait rétorqué Frankie en riant.

— Tu sais, avait répondu maman en levant les yeux au ciel, à une époque, ton père avait la grosse tête à cause de son physique, lui aussi. Il a commencé à se prendre pour un tombeur quand nous étions encore adolescents. Mais j'ai mis bon ordre à tout cela. Quand tu rencontreras la femme de ta vie, tu succomberas comme tout le monde.

En souriant, Frankie l'avait embrassée sur la joue puis avait quitté la cuisine en fredonnant qu'il cherchait une fille comme celle que son cher vieux papa avait épousée. Au passage, il m'avait fait un clin d'œil en disant :

— Qui pourra jamais être à la hauteur ?

Sûrement pas cette fille à la Sandra Dee.

Je lui collai le verre de citronnade dans la main. Elle l'accepta sans que ses yeux alourdis de mascara quittent le visage de Frank. Elle le porta à ses lèvres puis s'interrompit en me voyant là.

— Oh, c'est Eva, non ? s'enquit-elle d'une voix suave.

— Ethie, la corrigea Frankie.

— Ethie. Je suis vraiment navrée pour ta mère, roucoula-t-elle en s'avançant.

Je m'échappai d'un bond et filai au salon. Un nuage de fumée de cigarettes flottait au-dessus de la tête des hommes regroupés là. À travers une brèche dans la foule, j'aperçus mon père affalé au bord de sa chaise, les coudes sur les genoux. Comme un épouvantail qui aurait perdu son rembourrage, il contemplait le verre qu'il tenait dans ses mains jointes tandis que les deux hommes assis sur le canapé, penchés vers lui, étaient plongés dans leur conversation. Contrairement au reste de l'assistance — tous les présents avaient tombé la veste et retroussé leurs manches de chemise —, les deux inconnus qui avaient assisté à l'enterrement portaient encore veste et cravate.

Je me glissai vers papa.

— J'ignorais que tu t'étais fixé à Vancouver, Howard, déclara l'homme qui paraissait grand, même assis. Pourquoi n'as-tu jamais pris contact...

Il s'interrompit en me voyant.

— Bonjour.

Je m'installai sur l'accoudoir du fauteuil de papa. Il tourna la tête avec un sourire forcé.

— Elle ressemble à la photo que tu gardais toujours sur toi, nota l'homme. Le portrait tout craché de sa mère, non ?

— Oui, chuchota papa en me tapotant le genou.

L'homme à qui il manquait un bras s'éclaircit la gorge.

— Dis donc, tu savais que le soldat Ken Campbell est devenu le docteur Ken Campbell ?

Le regard de papa passa de l'un à l'autre ; ce changement de sujet était manifestement un soulagement pour lui.

— Je l'ignorais, mais je ne suis pas autrement surpris, répondit-il.

Le médecin fit un demi-sourire à papa.

— Et toi, Howard, as-tu fait finalement des études de pharmacie après la guerre ?

— Non. Je suis entré comme apprenti dans une scierie. Et toi, Jack ? demanda papa au manchot. Tu vis à Vancouver ?

— Ouais, je suis allé travailler dans les conserveries de poisson. Quand le patron de la boîte a appris les épreuves que j'avais traversées, il m'a offert un emploi à vie. (Il leva son verre.) Même si mon bras a fini là-bas bouffé par les vers parce qu'un politicien trop mou était incapable de dire non à notre mère l'Angleterre, fulmina-t-il en louchant sur son verre avec un rire amer, je suis encore capable d'appuyer sur des putains de boutons.

Après avoir avalé cul sec le reste de son verre, il croisa mon regard.

— Oups, désolé, dit-il. Il faut excuser ma façon de parler, petite demoiselle.

Mon père, apparemment, ne remarqua ni le langage grossier de l'homme ni mon ricanement nerveux. Il leva son propre verre presque vide. Et je sentis les effluves du liquide ambré. Tandis que mon père avalait ce qui restait de ce thé glacé qui n'était pas du thé glacé, le manchot se pencha maladroitement sur le côté. De sa main gauche, il sortit une petite flasque de sa poche. Frankie entra dans le salon au moment où le manchot remplissait le verre de papa. Frankie s'arrêta net. Ses traits se durcirent. Il fit demi-tour et quitta la maison, sa copine sur ses talons.

Je me tournai vers mon père et je vis ce qu'avait vu Frankie : le vide qui séparait mon père du monde était en train de s'agrandir.

Je n'avais pas pleuré de la journée. Ni dans la limousine ni pendant l'enterrement. Lorsqu'ils descendirent le cercueil de ma mère dans le trou, lorsque la poignée de terre jetée par le pasteur s'éparpilla sur le bois ciré, provoquant les sanglots de Dora Fenwick, je ne versai pas une larme. Pourtant j'étais triste et j'aurais volontiers pleuré mais je n'y parvenais pas. Mes larmes étaient coincées quelque part derrière mon chagrin. Mais lorsque mon père avala son verre d'un trait, la peur de le voir disparaître complètement dans ce vide fit voler ce chagrin en éclats. Quittant l'accoudoir de son fauteuil, je sortis précipitamment de la maison.

Debout sous le porche, la vue brouillée, je tentai de me concentrer sur le square de l'autre côté de la rue. Frankie avait ses copines. Papa avait son whisky. J'avais Kipper.

— Tu la connais ? demanda une voix derrière moi.

Je m'essuyai le visage en hâte et je me retournai : Irene Manson, les bras croisés, appuyée contre le chambranle, m'observait derrière ses lunettes noires et brillantes.

— Qui ça ?

— La Chinoise, dit-elle en montrant l'autre côté de la rue. Celle qui est dans le square en train de discuter avec Kipper.

20

Je ne comprendrai jamais vraiment pourquoi je mentis à Mme Manson. Peut-être à cause de tous les enfants du quartier assis sur notre pelouse et sur les marches du porche ; mal à l'aise, ils s'agitaient dans leurs habits du dimanche en évitant mon regard. Peut-être parce que j'avais envie de les fuir, de la fuir, de fuir notre maison et toutes ces voix chuchotantes. Ou peut-être simplement parce que, sur le coup, je croyais lui dire la vérité.

— Je me pose cette question parce que je l'ai déjà vue, déclara Irene Manson en voyant que je ne réagissais pas d'emblée.

Elle alluma une cigarette sans me quitter du regard.

— Elle vient généralement le matin, reprit-elle en soufflant la fumée en biais. Elle débarque et elle se plante là, à observer votre maison.

La même fille que j'avais vue lundi et mardi ? Je fis volte-face au moment où une silhouette sortait du square et remontait la rue. Je regardai plus attentivement. C'était bel et bien la même fille.

— C'est seulement quelqu'un qui craque pour Frankie, dis-je en lâchant ce bobard par-dessus mon épaule avant de passer entre Ardith et Debra assises sur les marches de notre porche.

Ignorant leurs saluts, je descendis sur le trottoir où j'attendis impatiemment que deux voitures se faufilent dans l'espace étroit que laissaient les véhicules garés des deux côtés de la rue. Dès que la voie fut libre, je fonçai. Kipper était tout seul près des balançoires et il faisait des signes à la fille qui partait comme s'il s'agissait d'une vieille amie.

— Qui était-ce ? demandai-je.

— Chépa.

— De quoi te parlait-elle ?

— De maman.

— De maman ! criai-je. Qu'est-ce qu'elle disait ?

— Elle voulait savoir où elle était.

— Qu'est-ce que tu lui as dit ?

Je posai la question mais je savais exactement ce qu'il lui avait raconté.

— Bradis. Je lui ai dit que maman était au bradis.

En haut de la rue, la fille disparut dans le virage.

J'examinai notre maison, les silhouettes aux fenêtres, Mme Manson qui rentrait à l'intérieur. Les enfants dispersés sous le porche et sur la pelouse, qui, manifestement, auraient préféré se retrouver n'importe où ailleurs – à l'image de ce que je ressentais moi-même.

— Suivons-la, décidai-je en saisissant Kipper par le bras.

Même au mieux de sa forme, Kipper avançait toujours pesamment, les pieds comme du plomb. Il avait toujours du mal à se maintenir à ma hauteur à cause de cette démarche lente et déhanchée. Mais là, il n'essayait même pas. Il ne cessait de se retourner.

Je m'arrêtai.

— Je refuse de rentrer tant qu'ils ne seront pas tous partis, déclarai-je en reprenant son bras. Viens, le pressai-je, ça va être l'aventure.

— D'accord, Ethie.

Parvenus à l'angle de la rue, nous vîmes que la fille était deux pâtés de maisons plus loin. Nous la suivîmes de loin jusqu'à Victoria Drive où elle attendit l'autobus.

J'attirai Kipper derrière l'abribus.

— Tu as de l'argent ? chuchotai-je.

Souriant, il ôta son chapeau et le retourna. De ses doigts épais, il fouilla le ruban et en sortit une pièce d'un dollar en argent.

— Waouh ! Où as-tu trouvé ça ?

— Quand j'ai vendu mes peintures, répondit-il fièrement. Je le garde pour une occasion particulière.

— Eh bien, c'est une occasion particulière. On va prendre le bus.

— D'accord, c'est bien, acquiesça-t-il juste au moment où arrivait le bus de Hastings Street.

Les portes s'ouvrirent ; la foule monta en ordre. J'attendis que la fille soit passée et poussai Kipper en avant. Nous étions les derniers passagers et les portes se refermèrent derrière nous avec un soupir mécanique. Kipper tendit son dollar au conducteur qui le lança dans la boîte en verre. Je récupérai la monnaie qui tomba en cliquetant dans le plateau métallique et la donnai à Kipper.

— Avancez vers le fond, ordonna le conducteur.

Le bus redémarra. Je m'assis avec Kipper sur la première banquette libre. Faisant mine de regarder par la fenêtre, je surveillai la fille du coin de l'œil. Elle était installée derrière l'issue de secours. Dès que le bus se glissa dans la circulation, je me mis dans le sens de la marche.

— Qu'est-ce qu'elle a dit d'autre ? chuchotai-je à Kipper, occupé à trier les pièces sur la paume de sa main.

— Elle a dit qu'elle était désolée, répondit-il en fronçant les sourcils dans un effort de concentration.

Le bus dépassa Kingsway puis Broadway. À chaque arrêt, je vérifiais qu'elle ne descendait pas. Mais Victoria Drive devint Commercial Drive et elle restait toujours là, à regarder par la fenêtre.

Je connaissais ce trajet. Avant que maman sache conduire, c'était le bus que nous prenions pour aller en ville. En dépassant le virage du Trout Lake, je ravalai maladroitement mes sanglots en me souvenant de la façon dont elle m'avait consolée le jour où j'avais perdu les chaussures que je croyais si importantes.

Dans Hastings Street, nous sommes passés devant le magasin de l'Armée du salut – le Sally Ann, comme l'appelait maman quand elle m'y emmenait choisir des vêtements pour l'école. Il y en avait un sur Victoria Drive mais elle refusait d'acheter mes vêtements si près de la maison pour ne pas me faire courir le risque de débarquer en cours vêtue des vieilles nippes d'une camarade de classe.

Dans Main Street, le bus s'arrêta à un feu rouge. En voyant le musée à l'angle de la rue, je ne pus m'empêcher de penser au jour où nous y étions allés avec maman au printemps dernier. Je repoussai le souvenir de la momie dans sa vitrine au deuxième étage.

Le feu passa au vert. Le bus continua jusqu'à l'arrêt devant les magasins de l'armée et de la marine. N'y avait-il donc que quelques semaines que j'avais aidé maman à fouiller dans les bacs de soutiens-gorge à vingt-neuf cents jusqu'à ce qu'elle en sorte triomphalement un à sa taille ?

Elle était partout. Sauf avec nous. Pourquoi nous avait-elle abandonnés ?

Je me rencognai dans mon siège, en me demandant ce que je fabriquais dans ce bus, pourquoi je suivais cette fille. Qu'est-ce que j'espérais apprendre ? N'empêche, lorsque Kipper me donna un coup sur l'épaule en me montrant la fille qui filait sur le trottoir encombré, je me levai d'un bond et me précipitai vers les portes. Avec un soupir énervé, le conducteur abaissa à nouveau la manette qui commandait leur ouverture pour nous laisser descendre, Kipper et moi.

Dans le centre-ville, les rues sentaient le sucre brûlé et le café moulu. Mon ventre se mit à gronder tandis que nous nous faufilions entre les piétons sur le trottoir encombré.

On rattrapa la fille au carrefour, où elle attendait pour traverser Hastings Street. Je retins Kipper en arrière puis l'entraînai dans le flot de gens. J'étais à peu près sûre de savoir où elle allait.

Chinatown. Un des endroits préférés de maman. Elle adorait flâner dans les boutiques exotiques, manger dans les restaurants animés ou regarder les fêtes qui se déroulaient dans les rues. Je me souvenais de la première fois où elle nous avait emmenés pour le Nouvel An chinois. Kipper et moi, nous étions terrifiés par le bruit des tambours et des pétards dans les rues surpeuplées. Nous nous cachions dans les jupons de maman en voyant surgir l'énorme dragon déchaîné jusqu'à ce que Frankie nous montre les jambes humaines qui dépassaient du costume à franges rouge et jaune. Dans mon souvenir papa ne nous avait jamais accompagnés.

Nous avons suivi la fille dans les rues grouillantes de monde jusqu'au moment où les grands immeubles ont cédé la place aux petites boutiques regroupées sous des auvents colorés dont la majorité était peinte de caractères chinois rouges ou dorés. L'odeur de graisse chaude alliée à la vue des canards cuits pendus dans les vitrines de restaurant, sous une lumière jaune, ne firent qu'accentuer les grondements de mon ventre.

Devant nous, la fille entra dans une épicerie, au bout d'un pâté de maisons. Je retins Kipper un petit moment puis le poussai vers les casiers de fruits et légumes alignés sur le trottoir. Nous examinâmes ce qui se passait à l'intérieur. La fille était en train de discuter avec un homme en tablier blanc. Il lui tendit une orange.

— J'ai faim, gémit Kipper.

— Chut ! On trouvera quelque chose tout à l'heure, chuchotai-je.

— Tout à l'heure quand ?

— Quand nous saurons où elle va.

— Mais pourquoi ? demanda-t-il, les sourcils froncés. Pourquoi on la suit ?

Au même moment, la fille ressortit et s'enfonça dans la ruelle à côté de la boutique.

— Y a qu'à faire semblant qu'on est des espions sur la piste de l'ennemi, dis-je en lui emboîtant le pas.

— Mais c'est pas une ennemie. Elle est gentille, rétorqua Kipper derrière moi.

— On fait semblant, d'accord ?

Je jetai un œil dans la ruelle. Elle avait disparu.

— Viens, dis-je en faisant signe à Kipper d'avancer.

— Le bonhomme lui a bonné une orange gratuite, déclara-t-il en traînant les pieds et en essayant de regarder à l'intérieur de la boutique. C'est peut-être M. Fong. Peut-être qu'il nous en donnerait une à nous aussi.

— Ce n'est pas M. Fong.

Tout le long du magasin courait une palissade de bois noircie par les intempéries. Nous allâmes jusqu'au bout pour jeter un œil derrière. Elle n'était pas là non plus. Nous l'avions perdue.

J'étais là à me demander quoi faire quand je remarquai les buissons de mûres sauvages qui poussaient contre les planches. Devant ces baies appétissantes, il me fut impossible de nier plus longtemps ma faim. Je glissai ma main entre les ronces pour en cueillir une poignée. Kipper en fit autant, les fourrant droit dans sa bouche. Il se faufila dans une brèche entre les buissons.

— Oh, jolie, admira-t-il.

— Quoi donc ?

Je m'approchai pour voir ce qu'il regardait.

— Une petite maison.

Il recula pour me laisser voir. Je jetai un œil dans l'interstice. Il avait raison. Dans la cour derrière le magasin, il y avait une petite bâtisse, guère plus grande qu'une maison pour enfants. Une version miniature des temples chinois que j'avais vus dans les livres. La peinture rouge était passée, le toit incliné formait un damier de tuiles cassées ou manquantes. Les avant-toits recourbés avaient dû être jolis autrefois, mais maintenant, il ne restait plus que des traces de peinture dorée. Cependant, aux yeux de Kipper, c'était magnifique.

— C'est quoi comme maison ? demanda-t-il.

Avant que j'aie pu répondre, la fille monta l'escalier sur l'arrière du magasin. Elle grimpa les dernières marches donnant sur un second palier, elle ouvrit une porte et elle se glissa à l'intérieur. Elle doit vivre là, pensai-je.

Brusquement, mon excitation retomba. Le jeu était terminé. Je cueillis encore quelques poignées de mûres.

— Allons-y, dis-je en m'essuyant les mains sur ma robe. On va s'acheter une orange.

Kipper fourra les dernières mûres dans sa bouche tachée de jus et nous revînmes dans la rue pour examiner les oranges bien empilées dans le casier devant le magasin. J'en choisis une et je m'apprêtais à entrer pour la payer lorsque je vis la fille derrière le comptoir, en train de nouer son tablier.

Kipper la vit, lui aussi.

— Elle travaille ici ! cria-t-il.

La fille leva la tête. Je rejetai l'orange dans le casier, saisis la chemise de Kipper à pleine main et fonçai en le traînant derrière moi.

Deux pâtés de maisons plus loin, je m'arrêtai et attendis qu'il trouve son inhalateur au fond de sa poche de pantalon.

— Pourquoi…, siffla-t-il entre deux bouffées, on n'est pas allés la voir ?

Je n'aurais su répondre à cette question. J'ignorais pourquoi et je regrettais déjà de ne pas l'avoir fait.

Il aspira encore une dose de son inhalateur avant de proposer :

— Retournons-y.

Je regardai la rue. J'avais envie de rentrer à la maison. Peut-être seraient-ils tous partis le temps qu'on arrive. Ce que j'avais dit à Mme Manson était sans doute vrai. Encore une fille qui s'était amourachée de mon grand frère.

Nous fîmes halte au premier marchand de fruits. Après avoir vérifié que Kipper avait encore deux pièces de dix cents pour le trajet de retour, j'achetai une orange. Je la pelai tandis que nous prenions un raccourci par Victory Square pour aller à l'arrêt de bus de Hastings Street. Je connaissais ce petit parc au centre de Vancouver grâce aux cérémonies commémoratives auxquelles papa et maman nous emmenaient au mois de novembre. Tous les ans, à la fin de la messe, mon père déposait son coquelicot au pied du cénotaphe de granit, au milieu du parc. En passant devant, nous vîmes un homme vêtu de vieux vêtements sales affalé contre la pierre grise. Je détournai le regard mais Kipper s'arrêta brusquement.

— Il dort dehors ! s'exclama-t-il, étonné.

L'homme ouvrit les yeux et nous gratifia d'un sourire aux dents noircies.

— Salut, le môme ! dit-il d'une voix pâteuse. T'as pas un petit sou pour un vieux soldat ?

Kipper fouilla dans sa poche. Je l'entraînai en m'accrochant à sa main jusqu'à l'arrêt d'autobus. Pendant que nous attendions, je lui donnai le reste de l'orange ; l'ivrogne couché par terre m'avait ôté l'appétit.

Le bus arriva et je réclamai à Kipper le reste de monnaie.

Il fourra le dernier quartier dans sa bouche, s'essuya les mains sur sa chemise – ajoutant des taches d'orange aux traînées de mûres – puis chercha dans sa poche. Et n'y trouva rien. Il fouilla dans les autres, les retourna.

— Y en a plus ! cria-t-il au bord des larmes.

— Impossible !

Je tâtai ses poches, même celle de sa chemise. Mais il avait raison : la monnaie dont nous avions besoin pour le trajet en bus avait disparu.

— Retournons chercher l'argent, Ethie.

Je pensai à l'ivrogne sur le trottoir. Les pièces avaient dû tomber à ce moment-là. Il n'y avait plus aucune chance de les retrouver.

— C'est bel et bien perdu, dis-je, résignée. Il va falloir qu'on marche. Ce n'est pas si loin que ça.

Mais, en fait, c'était loin. J'ignore combien d'heures il fallut marcher dans les rues tandis que le soleil se couchait. À Kingsway, le crépuscule tombait. Et au moment où nous avons tourné dans la Cinquante et unième Avenue pour rejoindre laborieusement notre rue, les lumières brillaient dans le noir. Les arrosages automatiques cliquetaient sur les pelouses et l'air nocturne embaumait l'herbe humide et les fleurs.

Durant tout le trajet de retour, Kipper ne se plaignit pas une seule fois, alors qu'il devait être aussi épuisé et affamé que moi. Lorsque son souffle devenait rauque, il tirait sur son inhalateur. Tous les quatre ou cinq pâtés de maisons, il répétait : « Pardon, Ethie. Pardon. » Il était tellement malheureux qu'il m'était impossible de rester fâchée contre lui. Je fus quand même très soulagée d'arriver enfin à Barclay Street.

Toutes les voitures garées plus tôt dans la journée étaient parties et la maison plongée dans l'obscurité. La fenêtre du salon n'était même pas éclairée par la lueur vacillante de la télévision. On traversa la pelouse et je jetai un coup d'œil derrière la maison. La Studebaker de Frankie n'était pas là. Il devait être encore avec sa petite amie. Ou alors il était parti à notre recherche. Papa et lui devaient se faire du souci. Ils avaient peut-être prévenu la police et tout le monde ratissait les environs.

Les fenêtres du salon étaient grandes ouvertes, la porte entrebâillée. La maison était silencieuse. Vide ? On se glissa à l'intérieur et j'appuyai sur l'interrupteur. L'entrée fut inondée de lumière et je vis papa avachi sur son siège exactement dans la position où nous l'avions laissé. Il ouvrit les yeux. Il nous regarda en essayant de reprendre ses esprits puis il se redressa. Repoussant les cheveux de son front, il s'enquit d'une voix endormie :

— Oh, vous êtes encore debout, vous deux ?

Il n'avait même pas remarqué notre absence.

21

Des gants blancs désincarnés flottaient dans les ténèbres. Lumineux, ils effectuaient une danse macabre au-dessus de Howard, dont la vue était brouillée. Luttant contre les liens invisibles qui le retenaient captif, il savait qu'il n'échapperait pas à la scène d'horreur écarlate qui allait suivre. Des cris déchirants montèrent dans sa gorge, le réveillant brutalement. Il se retrouva assis tout droit sur le canapé, se débattant contre cette terreur qui s'évanouissait tandis que les supplications mouraient sur ses lèvres.

— Papa ?

Une main lui toucha l'épaule.

— Papa, c'est moi, Frankie.

Couvert de sueur froide, le cœur battant, Howard inspira l'air fétide. Cherchant à clarifier son esprit embrumé, il se concentra sur les ombres devant lui. La silhouette de son fils, éclairée à contre-jour par les réverbères allumés devant la fenêtre du salon, se précisa. Et la vérité dans toute sa crudité le ramena d'un coup à la réalité.

— Ce vieux canapé cabossé ne doit pas être très confortable, dit doucement Frankie.

— J'ai connu pire.

Il s'attendait à se voir contredit, à être gentiment poussé vers son lit mais Frankie quitta la pièce. Il revint quelques instants plus tard avec un oreiller, une couverture et le peignoir écossais de Howard. Il les posa au bout du canapé et lui souhaita bonne nuit. Sur le seuil, il se retourna.

— Tu vas t'en sortir, papa ? demanda-t-il.

Howard espérait que l'obscurité masquait le tremblement de ses mains tandis qu'il se battait avec les boutons de sa chemise.

— Oui, affirma-t-il. Bonne nuit, fiston.

Sans se presser, il finit de se déshabiller, enfila son peignoir et se recoucha. Mais il garda les yeux grands ouverts, terrifié à l'idée de se rendormir, terrifié à l'idée de se retrouver face aux visions atroces tapies derrière ses paupières. Et le cauchemar récurrent dont, sans Lucy pour le rattraper, il risquait bien de ne jamais sortir. Cependant, éveillé, il s'enfonçait sans pouvoir résister dans les souvenirs obsédants provoqués par sa mort atroce. Et par la réapparition des deux vétérans de Hong Kong. En particulier Ken Campbell.

22

6 décembre 1941 : Île de Hong Kong

Au balcon de la salle de cinéma plongée dans l'obscurité, Howard, comme les autres, protesta lorsque le film fut interrompu par une série de parasites. Sur l'écran, le personnage-titre, le sergent York[1], était partagé entre le désir de se battre pour son pays et ses convictions religieuses. Mais les mots qui sortirent des haut-parleurs ne correspondaient pas du tout aux mouvements des lèvres de Gary Cooper.

— Attention, à tous les soldats et les marins. Cette annonce annule toutes les permissions et les sauf-conduits. Je répète, tous les sauf-conduits sont annulés. Les soldats doivent retourner à leurs bases et les marins à bord de leurs bateaux. Exécution immédiate.

— Eh bien, nous y voilà, commenta Ken Campbell en se levant.

Howard se faufila dans la rangée de sièges, s'excusant chaque fois qu'il cognait les genoux de ceux qui restaient voir le film. Dans tout le cinéma, les protestations fusaient en entendant le message qui se répétait.

— En plein milieu du putain de spectacle !

---

1. *Le Sergent York*, film de Howard Hawkes (1941).

— Les Japs ont dû se manifester !

— On va être dans la mouise d'ici demain matin !

— Oh ! C'est encore des manœuvres. On va pas s'affoler...

— Ouais, c'est quoi ce bazar ? s'exclama le soldat au bout du rang en refusant de bouger pour laisser passer Howard. On peut au moins rester jusqu'à la fin du film !

— Vous êtes sourd, soldat ? « Exécution immédiate », ça veut dire maintenant ! Dégagez ! aboya la silhouette imposante derrière Howard, ce qui fit aussitôt détaler l'homme dans l'allée.

Howard se mit à rire.

— Heùreusement qu'il fait trop sombre pour qu'on voie ton grade, Ken. Ou ta tronche. Personne n'accepterait d'ordres d'une pareille bouille de bébé.

— Mais ils sont réceptifs à ma voix radiophonique !

Ken éclata d'un rire tonitruant tandis qu'ils rejoignaient la foule qui sortait. Sur l'écran, le champion du tir au dindon, Alvin York, était parvenu à la conclusion que certaines causes méritaient qu'on se batte pour elles.

Durant le trajet en ferry qui le ramenait à Kowloon, Howard se demanda si Ken avait raison. Y était-on ? Était-il sur le point de découvrir, comme le sergent York pendant la Grande Guerre, qu'il est facile de tuer s'il s'agit d'empêcher un plus vaste massacre ? Ces manœuvres des trois dernières semaines, propres à vérifier les ardeurs, allaient-elles prouver leur utilité ou s'agissait-il encore d'un nouvel exercice ?

Howard observa les soldats sur le pont inférieur du Star ferry. Certains, comme Ken Campbell, étaient appuyés au bastingage, perdus dans leurs pensées, tandis que le bateau se dirigeait lentement vers le débarcadère de Kowloon. D'autres alternaient entre se plaindre de la permission perdue et se lancer dans des hypothèses folles sur les perspectives d'actions. On n'avait aucun mal à identifier le côté bravache de la jeunesse tempéré par la probabilité de la guerre. Howard aussi sentait le sang circuler plus vite dans ses veines à l'idée d'être mis à l'épreuve, de découvrir ses réactions face au danger. Et, en contradiction avec ces idées héroïques, le frisson de la peur dans toute sa réalité.

À Sham Shui Po, le colonel Sutcliffe conseilla aux hommes de s'offrir une bonne nuit de repos mais les laissa dans l'ignorance.

Couché, incapable de dormir, Howard pensait à Gordy. Tôt le matin, il avait quitté le camp avec une permission pour le week-end. Savait-il que toutes les permissions avaient été supprimées ? Ce soir, il devait se trouvait quelque part dans Victoria en compagnie de Shun-ling.

Durant les trois dernières semaines, Gordy – qui avait toujours juré qu'aucune fille ne parviendrait jamais à lui passer la corde au cou – avait consacré tout son temps libre à Shun-ling. Déjà étonné de la rapidité avec laquelle son ami était tombé amoureux, Howard avait été effaré en apprenant qu'il allait louer un appartement sur l'île pour Shun-ling et sa famille.

— Tu n'irais pas un peu trop vite en besogne ? avait-il glissé.

— Eh, mêle-toi de tes oignons ! avait rétorqué Gordy. Que je sache, tu m'as pas demandé la permission d'épouser Lucy !

Il souriait mais Howard avait bien perçu le ton coupant de sa repartie.

Après un silence tendu, il avait ajouté :

— Tu n'imagines pas dans quoi ils vivent, Howie.

D'une voix redevenue normale, il s'était mis à décrire la cabane de tôle ondulée qu'ils considéraient comme leur foyer.

— Tu laisserais même pas un clébard dormir dans ce taudis d'une pièce.

Avec l'aide de Peter et de Dick, qui l'avaient traité de « sacré cinglé » pour se charger des misères d'une famille entière, il avait trouvé un appartement dans le district de Wanchai. Ce matin, Shun-ling et lui avaient pris le ferry pour préparer les lieux. Le père et la sœur de la jeune fille ne devaient emménager que le lundi matin, lorsque Gordy serait retourné au camp.

Toute la semaine, Howard avait passé ses soirées en ville avec Ken Campbell.

— Nous, les vieux époux, il faut qu'on se serre les coudes, disait-il en manière d'excuse pour éviter de rester avec le couple.

Mais la vérité, c'était que la compagnie de Gordy et de Shun-ling était devenue perturbante. Passer du temps avec eux rendait l'absence de Lucy encore plus pénible. Et il ne parvenait pas à oublier ce qui était arrivé le samedi précédent.

Cet après-midi-là, il avait erré tout seul dans les ruelles de Kowloon. Il voulait retrouver le chemin de la boutique de Ah Sam, ignorant si elle serait ouverte le week-end car, sur les instances de Ken Campbell, il voulait acheter de la potion anti-punaises. Un bon prétexte pour rendre visite au pharmacien.

La clochette tinta au-dessus de la porte lorsqu'il entra.

— Bonjour, Ah Sam, lança Howard à l'homme derrière le comptoir. Vous vous souvenez de moi ?

Le visage impassible, Ah Sam avait haussé les épaules.

— Pour moi, vous êtes tous pareils.

— Je... euh..., avait commencé à bafouiller Howard.

Mais Ah Sam avait levé la main.

— Je plaisantais, monsieur, dit-il avec un sourire qui plissa son visage rond. Je me souviens évidemment des deux amis canadiens de Feng Shun-ling. Comment vont ces piqûres d'insectes ?

Soulagé, Howard sourit lui aussi.

— Très bien. Je veux dire, c'est fini. Je suis venu acheter un autre flacon de ce remède pour un ami.

Ah Sam l'emmena au fond du magasin où il rassembla les ingrédients.

— J'ose espérer que vous traitez ma chère amie Feng Shun-ling avec respect, messieurs.

— Bien sûr, répliqua Howard, interloqué.

— C'est une jeune femme exceptionnelle, déclara Ah Sam en se concentrant sur sa tâche. Je suis certain que vous comprenez les épreuves terribles que sa famille et elle ont traversées.

Tout en versant adroitement de la poudre verte dans le minuscule flacon, il raconta à Howard que Shun-ling et son père avaient été coincés dans l'enceinte de l'université lorsque les Japonais avaient envahi Nankin.

— Ils se sont retrouvés en zone de sécurité – un endroit protégé au milieu de la ville organisé par les ressortissants étrangers. Les Allemands.

Il releva la tête et la pencha.

— Ironique, n'est-ce pas ? reprit-il. Sauvés par la swastika !

Sans attendre de réponse, il continua :

— Ils ont été témoins du massacre en direct. Des foules entières de civils sans armes qui cherchaient à fuir ont été mitraillées, des enfants assassinés, des femmes violées et écartelées, tout cela sous leurs yeux.

Il secoua la tête puis reprit :

— Feng Guo-ren, le père de Shun-ling, m'a raconté que deux importants gradés japonais s'étaient effectivement lancés dans un pari « amical » sur lequel parviendrait à tuer le plus de civils au fil de l'épée.

Howard écoutait sans en croire ses oreilles Ah Sam lui expliquer comment on alignait les victimes pour les massacrer.

— Vieux, jeunes, ça ne faisait pas de différence, seul le corps comptait, expliqua-t-il en versant de la cire fondue sur le bouchon de la fiole. Après, on a affiché dans la ville les photos des officiers encore vêtus de leurs uniformes ensanglantés, avec leurs scores. Un employé de la Croix-Rouge a rapporté qu'un des gradés s'était plaint amèrement parce qu'il avait abîmé son épée en coupant un homme en deux.

Il se tut. Un silence sinistre tomba dans la pièce. Ah Sam posa le flacon sur le comptoir pour laisser la cire durcir.

— Au bout d'une semaine, reprit-il, le père de Shun-ling a payé deux soldats de Tchang Kaï-chek en déroute pour qu'ils les emmènent avec eux. Ils ont fui en pleine nuit par un égout qui passait sous l'enceinte de la ville. Ils ont marché jusqu'à leur village où ils ont vu que tout avait été pillé et incendié. Ils ont eu beaucoup de mal à retrouver leur propre maison brûlée jusqu'aux fondations. Au milieu des ruines, ils ont découvert le corps carbonisé du petit frère de Shun-ling, qui avait deux ans. Il avait été éventré. Leur mère était dehors, son corps nu mutilé.

Howard ravala la bile qui montait du fond de sa gorge.

— Sa sœur ?

— Elle en a réchappé en se cachant au fond de la fosse aux choux. Un des soldats japonais avait eu pitié d'elle et l'avait épargnée. Quand était venu son tour de la violer, il l'avait enfouie sous les choux en fermentation. Elle est restée là pendant des jours, avec les rats qui grouillaient, jusqu'à ce que son père et Shun-ling la trouvent, à peine vivante. Depuis, la pauvre petite n'a pas prononcé un mot.

Encore sous le choc quand il avait rejoint Gordy et Shunling un peu plus tard dans la soirée, Howard ne parvenait pas à se libérer des images atroces qu'avait fait naître le récit de Ah Sam. Savoir que Shun-ling et sa famille avaient enduré la réalité bestiale de ces visions lui donnait envie de protéger la jeune fille.

Au Sun Sun, il s'était installé au bar avec Gordy et elle. Lorsque le barman s'était tourné vers eux, Shun-ling, surprise, s'était recroquevillée, terrifiée.

— Guizie ! avait-elle chuchoté. Japonais !

Howard et Gordy l'avaient escortée dans l'escalier, toute tremblante, et ils étaient sortis.

Maintenant, tout en fixant l'obscurité et en attendant que le matin et Gordy arrivent, Howard ne pouvait s'empêcher de se souvenir que c'était à son bras que Shun-ling s'était agrippée quand elle avait voulu quitter le bar. Et du regard noir que lui avait lancé Gordy quand il s'en était aperçu.

À midi le lendemain, tous les soldats, les marins et les volontaires se trouvaient à leur poste de combat. Plus ou moins. Gordy n'était pas rentré.

À l'extrémité sud-ouest de l'île, dans une tranchée donnant sur la mer de Chine méridionale, Howard était adossé contre une paroi faite de sacs de sable. En tenue de combat, il avait réparti ce qui restait de ses dollars de Hong Kong un peu partout dans son uniforme. Au cas où. La photo de Lucy était rangée entre les feuilles de son carnet, dans sa poche de poitrine. Il était prêt. Mais à quoi ?

Deux cents mètres plus bas, sur la route étroite qui faisait le tour de l'île, tout était apparemment comme d'habitude. Au cours de la journée, on vit passer de temps en temps une voiture civile ainsi que d'insouciants habitants à pied ou à bicyclette. Même le petit cerf qui parcourait les pentes à la recherche d'insaisissables touffes d'herbe les ignorait. En début d'après-midi, un couple d'Anglais d'un certain âge suivit le sentier, portant un panier de pique-nique.

À quelques mètres de Howard, Ken Campbell se dressa dans la tranchée.

— Eh ! messieurs-dames, cria-t-il de loin, c'est peut-être pas le jour idéal pour pique-niquer !

En dessous, l'homme s'arrêta et, s'appuyant sur sa canne, s'abrita les yeux du soleil.

— Et pourquoi ça, si je puis me permettre ? Nous pique-niquons dans ces collines tous les dimanches.

— Vous n'êtes pas au courant ? Toute la colonie est en état d'alerte. Je filerais à la maison si j'étais vous. L'attaque peut se déclencher à tout moment.

— Ridicule ! Les Japonais n'oseraient jamais défier l'Empire britannique.

Sidéré, Howard regarda le couple quitter le chemin et descendre jusqu'à une saillie rocheuse sur laquelle ils étalèrent leur couverture. La femme ouvrit un parasol et ils prirent leur thé en profitant du soleil de l'après-midi. Le temps était idéal. Des étourneaux à col noir descendaient en piqué attraper les miettes qu'on leur lançait et la mer étincelait sous un ciel d'un bleu parfait. Cependant, Howard ne put s'empêcher de remarquer que, comme s'ils savaient qu'il se préparait quelque chose, la flottille de jonques, de sampans et de bateaux de pêche qui, généralement, dansait sur les eaux, s'était évaporée.

Deux heures plus tard, le couple se leva, rassembla ses affaires et partit. Howard ne pouvait qu'admirer cette tranquille détermination alors qu'il sentait la sueur ruisseler dans sa nuque.

Dans la touffeur de l'après-midi, les rumeurs contradictoires allaient bon train dans les tranchées.

On avait repéré l'armada japonaise dans la mer de Chine méridionale, se dirigeant vers Hong Kong.

Inutile de s'inquiéter : les deux navires de guerre, le *Prince of Wales* et le *Repulse*, orgueil de la marine britannique, étaient en route.

L'armée japonaise regroupée à la frontière ne cessait de grossir ; le nombre de soldats augmentait à chaque heure. À cinq heures du soir, officieusement, on en annonçait quarante mille.

Inutile de s'inquiéter : l'armée de Tchang Kaï-chek arrivait par derrière.

La totalité du matériel manquant avait été détourné vers l'Europe.

Mon cul qu'ils vont pas risquer de perdre leur précieux matériel ! Je me demande ce que ça peut bien signifier pour nous ?

Les blagues qui s'échangeaient dans les tranchées allégeaient un peu l'ennui qui gagnait à force de contempler une mer vide. Cependant, à la tombée du jour, Howard décida de ne plus prêter attention à la moindre rumeur de conflit. Il ne croirait que ce qu'il verrait de ses propres yeux et justement Gordy était en train de sauter de l'arrière d'un camion de ravitaillement. Il enjamba le fossé et, tête baissée, fonça sur la colline comme un taureau pour se glisser à côté de Howard dans la tranchée.

— Content que tu aies pu passer !

— Ouais, j'avais pas vraiment le choix, hein ?

Howard fut surpris du ton inhabituellement cassant de son ami, mais il ne dit rien.

Le camion de ravitaillement apportait le repas du soir. Gordy ne toucha ni à ses biscuits ni à son corned-beef. Debout, accoudé à la tranchée, il contemplait la mer qui s'obscurcissait.

— Pendant le trajet en ferry, nous avons entendu dire que des civils japonais ont disparu ce week-end.

Il se tourna vers Howard, le visage creusé d'inquiétude.

— Les réfugiés sont affolés, reprit-il. Shun-ling aussi.

Étant donné son histoire, cela n'avait rien de surprenant. Il se demanda ce que Gordy savait exactement mais s'abstint de poser la question.

Gordy dévissa sa gourde, but une longue gorgée puis s'essuya les lèvres d'un revers de main.

— C'est le chaos à Kowloon, reprit-il. En descendant du ferry, on a dû jouer des coudes dans la foule des réfugiés qui essayaient de gagner l'île. À la minute où on a réussi à s'en sortir, Shun-ling s'est précipitée pour retrouver son père et sa sœur. Elle ne voulait pas que je l'accompagne mais je l'ai suivie quand même. J'ai attendu d'être sûr qu'ils étaient bien à bord du ferry avant de retourner au camp prendre mes affaires. Et les commentaires de ce type de l'armée à propos de mon retard, je m'en fiche comme d'une guigne.

— Tu n'as rien manqué.

Gordy s'accroupit dans la tranchée et sortit un paquet de cigarettes froissé de sa manche. Il en offrit une à Howard, en silence. Les mains en coupe, il alluma les deux, puis se rassit et leurs regards se croisèrent.

— Tu sais, j'ai mobilisé toutes mes forces pour revenir, Howie, chuchota-t-il. Je suis pas un déserteur. Oui, j'ai peur. Mais j'ai pas peur de me battre ni même de mourir. J'ai peur de ce qui pourrait leur arriver à elle et à sa famille si les Japonais attaquaient.

— Ils n'attaqueront peut-être pas, suggéra Howard d'un ton qu'il espérait convaincu. Ce sera peut-être une fausse alerte. Demain soir à la même heure, on sera peut-être de retour au cinéma.

À sept heures le lendemain matin, Howard tenta de localiser l'origine d'un vrombissement indubitable, celui d'avions volant haut. Le ciel était encore vide mais, d'après le bruit, des douzaines d'appareils devaient approcher. Des renforts ?

Le bourdonnement se transforma en plainte stridente et synchronisée, celle d'une escadrille qui perdait rapidement de l'altitude. Quelques instants plus tard, un feu roulant d'explosions sur le continent noya son bref espoir.

— Seigneur, ils sont en train de bombarder la base ! cria-t-il en secouant Gordy pour le réveiller.

Le hurlement des sirènes de la défense passive suivi de l'explosion des tirs antiaériens venaient de la direction du terrain d'aviation de Kai Tak. Avec le reste de la troupe, Howard et Gordy étaient accroupis, impuissants au fond de leur tranchée, incapables de voir, incapables d'aider tandis que tout près de là, de l'autre côté de l'eau, la dévastation faisait rage. Moins de dix minutes plus tard, les avions firent demi-tour. À l'est, des nuages de fumée noire montèrent à l'assaut du ciel. Howard jeta un coup d'œil dans la tranchée et croisa le regard de Ken Campbell. Il était blême. Sans lâcher le récepteur radio, il cria :

— Pearl Harbor a été attaqué il y a six heures…

Il fut interrompu par le vrombissement d'un avion volant à basse altitude.

L'avion de chasse solitaire, un Zero, passa droit au-dessus de leurs têtes, et le crépitement des tirs de mitraillette atteignit les oreilles de Howard au moment où les balles hachaient littéralement la colline, soulevant la poussière qui retombait en pluie dans les tranchées. Il vit le rond rouge sang sur le bout des ailes une seconde avant qu'il heurtât le sol. Le doute n'était plus permis. Ils étaient en guerre contre le Japon.

Deux jours plus tard, ils se trouvaient au fond de la même tranchée et la guerre ne leur parvenait que comme un grondement lointain et par des rapports radio. La situation n'était pas bonne à terre. Comme l'avait prévu le brigadier Lawson, l'invasion par voie de terre était venue essentiellement du nord.

La ligne Gin Drinkers, défendue par les Royal Scots et les brigades indiennes, les Punjabis et les Rajputs, avait été enfoncée. La robuste ligne de défense, longue de dix-sept kilomètres et courant d'ouest en est, à moins de quinze kilomètres au nord de Kowloon, aurait dû normalement tenir pendant des semaines. Dans les tranchées, les rapports ne provoquaient plus guère de répliques spirituelles. Il y avait mort d'hommes. Le mercredi, l'inquiétude de Gordy pour Shun-ling était patente : affalé au fond de la tranchée, il avait le front ruisselant de sueur.

— Nom de Dieu, j'apprécierais vraiment un de ces pains de glace que nous livrions à Winnipeg, dit Howard pour tenter de dérider son ami.

Celui-ci demeura silencieux.

— Tu te souviens des gamins qui volaient les débris de glace à l'arrière de notre break et qui s'enfuyaient comme s'ils avaient récupéré un trésor ? insista-t-il. Ils croyaient vraiment être riches, non ?

Brusquement, un camion surgit sur la route et s'arrêta en dessous d'eux. Un sergent en descendit, cherchant des volontaires. On déployait la Compagnie D sur le continent pour soutenir les Royal Scots qui, ayant souffert de lourdes pertes, se retiraient dans l'île. Howard et Gordy s'arrachèrent de la tranchée et foncèrent en bas de la colline sans attendre la fin du discours. Ken Campbell avançait d'un pas pesant quelques mètres devant eux.

Sur le continent, Kowloon était en flammes et c'était le chaos total. En débarquant du ferry, leur camion fut submergé par une marée de civils fous de terreur qui tentaient encore de s'échapper vers l'île. Des policiers en uniforme, tapant de-ci de-là dans la foule, dégagèrent le camion qui put avancer très lentement. En passant devant Sham Shui Po, ils virent des pillards lourdement chargés s'échapper du camp mis à sac. Howard sentit un pincement de regret en pensant à la robe de soie verte destinée à Lucy qu'il avait laissée dans son casier – elle avait sûrement disparu. Il aurait dû l'envoyer.

Une fois déployée aux lisières de la ville, la compagnie de Howard et Gordy passa la nuit sur le terrain de polo tandis que des explosions intermittentes de bombes et de tirs de mortier illuminaient le ciel saturé de fumée.

Le lendemain matin, en assurant la retraite des Scots, Howard aperçut l'ennemi pour la première fois. Lorsque la multitude de soldats japonais, le visage noirci et l'air farouchement déterminé, surgit en criant « Banzaï-aï-aï ! », il put goûter à l'action. Un goût qu'il trouva amer. Accroupi dos à dos avec Gordy sur le seuil affaissé d'un bâtiment bombardé, il lança sa première grenade. Puis une deuxième. Aucune des deux n'éclata.

— Nom de Dieu, jura-t-il, on pourrait aussi bien lancer des pierres !

Quelques instants plus tard, ils se relevèrent pour courir derrière les Royal Scots épuisés. Tout en tirant à l'aveuglette, ils battirent précipitamment en retraite avec le reste des grenadiers, les guerriers japonais sur leurs talons.

Debout sur le pont du ferry qui s'éloignait, le cœur battant à cent à l'heure, Howard observa l'arrière-garde ; composée des unités de l'Inde orientale, elle lutta pied à pied contre les Japonais qui grouillaient dans les rues et sur les docks de Kowloon.

— Pas grand-chose à voir avec les petits bonshommes myopes dont on nous avait parlé, haleta Ken Campbell à côté de lui.

Un Royal Scot aux yeux fous, assis contre la rambarde, parlait tout seul avec véhémence.

— Seigneur ! Il en venait de plus en plus ! répétait-il. Putains de cinglés suicidaires ! Les premiers se sont jetés sur les barricades de barbelés et les suivants les ont piétinés, en se servant de leurs corps comme d'un pont – on pouvait pas les descendre assez vite. Dès qu'il y en avait un qui tombait, y en avait dix qui prenaient sa place !

23

Durant les jours qui suivirent l'enterrement de ma mère, la première chose que je faisais en me réveillant, c'était jeter un œil au square de l'autre côté de la rue. La fille n'y était jamais. Mais, tous les matins, je trouvais mon père assis à la table de la cuisine, son visage pas rasé encore plus gris à la lumière du jour. Le samedi, je compris que, lui aussi, il regardait le square. Une idée dont je me débarrassai aussi vite qu'elle me traversa l'esprit. Cela n'avait aucun sens. Ce qui en avait, en revanche, c'étaient les bouteilles de whisky vides dans les poubelles.

« Howard n'a jamais raté un seul jour de travail à cause de la boisson », je me souvenais avoir entendu maman dire cela d'un ton résolu lors d'une conversation avec ma tante.

En réponse, tante Mildred avait posé un flacon de pilules sur la table.

— Mets-en donc une dans son café tous les matins, avait-elle enjoint. Il se sentira très mal dès qu'il essayera de boire la moindre goutte d'alcool.

— Vraiment, Mildred ! Tu dis parfois des bêtises plus grosses que toi ! s'était exclamée maman. Howard n'a rien d'un alcoolique.

— Ah oui ?

— La guerre a été une épreuve très difficile.

— Comme pour beaucoup d'hommes.

— Boire de temps en temps, c'est sa manière d'affronter cela, avait riposté maman en ignorant la remarque de sa sœur. C'est inoffensif.

— Ah oui ?

Tante Mildred laissa son regard errer dans la pièce, sur notre foyer spartiate.

— Au moins, il ne me bat pas, répliqua maman, indignée du sous-entendu. Pas plus qu'il ne finit dans la rue au milieu de la nuit à se bagarrer avec ses fils, comme certains de nos voisins. Et si tu crois que je vais rendre mon Howie malade en glissant des pilules dans son café, tu es vraiment folle.

Plantée sur le seuil de la cuisine ce samedi matin, j'observais les mains tremblantes de papa en train de boire un café et je me posais des questions sur la confiance inébranlable de ma mère. La nuit précédente, ses cris d'angoisse m'avaient réveillée. À moitié endormie, j'avais attendu que la voix maternelle l'arrache aux tourments qui le tenaient entre leurs griffes. Je m'étais brutalement réveillée, terrassée par l'idée qu'elle ne ferait plus jamais cela et que quelqu'un d'autre devait s'en charger. Je bondis hors de mon lit et j'étais déjà au milieu de l'escalier lorsque j'entendis la voix de Frankie. Longtemps après que le cauchemar de papa fut fini, longtemps après que mon frère fut remonté dans sa chambre, alors que le salon était redevenu silencieux, j'étais restée éveillée, aux aguets, me préparant à prendre la place de ma mère.

Ce samedi matin, il était à nouveau affalé devant la table de la cuisine, à regarder fixement par la fenêtre. En face de lui, Kipper avait installé ses couleurs. Vêtu d'une vieille chemise de Frankie, il se concentrait sur les pots alignés devant lui. Ses mains et ses joues étaient couvertes de taches de peinture et une traînée jaune décorait le lobe épais de son oreille gauche. Le bout de sa langue dépassant d'un coin de la bouche, il mélangeait les couleurs, indifférent, tout comme papa, à ce qui pouvait se passer autour de lui.

Je l'observai qui donnait de petits coups de pinceau aux différents pots jusqu'à obtenir un beau rouge vif. Alors qu'il commençait son travail lent et méticuleux, une mouche se posa sur la table. Elle se promenait entre la toile de Kipper et la main de papa. Je m'emparai du chasse-mouches accroché près du poêle et je m'approchai doucement. D'un mouvement de poignet, je la virai de la table. Papa tourna la tête et je perçus sur ses traits son habituelle expression lointaine.

Je m'étais souvent demandé ce que mon père voyait dans cette fraction de seconde avant de se reprendre. Où se trouvait-il lorsque ses yeux étaient ainsi vitreux ? Voyait-il ce qu'il y avait devant lui et devait-il s'obliger à revenir de là où il était parti ? Souhaitait-il même revenir ?

Son regard suivit la chute de la mouche puis il releva la tête.

— Merci, Ethie, dit-il.

Je me sentis soudain fière de reprendre la mission de maman : débarrasser notre maison des mouches que mon père détestait.

Arraché à sa transe, papa remarqua Kipper occupé à peindre. Le pinceau bougeait avec lenteur, il remplissait les contours avec sa peinture rouge vif.

— Qu'est-ce que tu peins, Kipper ? s'enquit papa.

Je me figeai.

— Une petite maison.

— Où as-tu déjà vu une maison pareille ?

La sonnerie aiguë du téléphone me fit sursauter. Chez nous, le téléphone, c'était le domaine de maman. Lorsqu'il sonnait, c'était presque toujours une de ses amies. Elle pouvait rester à bavarder pendant des heures, le récepteur collé à l'oreille. Ces derniers temps, lorsque le téléphone sonnait, c'était soit tante Mildred soit quelqu'un qui venait d'apprendre la mort de maman et qui appelait pour dire combien il était désolé.

Frankie était devenu le répondeur officiel. Mais Frankie était encore au fond de son lit, à l'étage.

Papa et moi, nous contemplions le téléphone mural comme si c'était un serpent. Finalement, Kipper se leva et alla décrocher.

— Allô, dit-il avant d'écouter le correspondant à l'autre bout du fil. Oui, il est ici, monsieur Telford.

Il tendit l'appareil à papa qui le regarda comme s'il risquait de se faire mordre.

— Oui ? répondit-il en tenant l'appareil à quelques centimètres de son oreille.

J'entendis M. Telford dire quelque chose à propos des œuvres de Kipper dans la boutique. Tandis que papa écoutait, Frankie descendit. Il passa la tête dans la cuisine avant de se rendre dans la salle de bains.

Soudain pressée de dissimuler l'œuvre de Kipper, je repensai à une idée que j'avais eue le matin même en m'habillant.

— Allons ramasser des bouteilles de soda vides ! proposai-je en m'efforçant d'avoir l'air excité pour que Kipper le soit également. On va se faire un peu d'argent pour aider papa, ajoutai-je à son oreille.

— D'ac !

Kipper se leva d'un bond et essuya son pinceau sur un chiffon.

— Si on en a assez, on pourra peut-être aller au ciné *drive-in*.

— Oui, c'est une bonne idée, répondis-je en enroulant la peinture représentant la maison avec un toit rouge et recourbé. On va ranger ça dans ma chambre.

Je ne voulais surtout pas expliquer pourquoi nous étions allés jusqu'à Chinatown l'autre jour. Papa n'avait peut-être pas du tout idée que nos expéditions dépassaient largement le cadre des balades en centre-ville, mais Frankie, lui, le savait parfaitement.

24

Je compris très tôt le pouvoir de l'argent. Ou, plus exactement, du manque d'argent.

— Il reste trop de mois à la fin de l'argent, plaisanta maman un jour où elle manquait de crème pour le café du matin de ses amies. Si le loup n'est pas tout à fait à la porte, il rôde quelque part dans le quartier, ajouta-t-elle avec un entrain forcé.

À présent, sans ce qu'elle gagnait, alors que papa et Frankie ne travaillaient plus depuis plus d'une semaine, et d'après les bribes de conversation que j'avais surprises entre ma tante et eux, j'avais peur que l'argent ne devînt un problème encore plus envahissant. En quittant la maison avec Kipper, j'étais convaincue que, si je parvenais à en rapporter un peu, cela relâcherait la pression sur papa et peut-être, mais seulement peut-être, l'empêcherait de couler encore davantage.

Le vieux chariot rouillé de Kipper – une des roues tenait avec un fil de fer enroulé autour de l'axe – cahotait en cliquetant derrière nous tandis que nous avancions le long des chemins poussiéreux au-dessus de Marine Drive. Chaussés de bottes en caoutchouc, nous donnions des coups de pied dans les mauvaises herbes à la recherche de bouteilles abandonnées dans les fossés. À l'heure du déjeuner, le chariot était déjà plein.

Nous avons porté cette première cargaison chez l'épicier de Victoria Drive. Nous avons attendu sur les lattes de bois que la minuscule dame chinoise, dont le visage était tellement ridé qu'on distinguait difficilement ses yeux, compte les bouteilles. Kipper fixait intensément les bonbons à un penny dans les bocaux en verre posés sur le comptoir.

— Vingt-sept bouteilles, annonça la vieille dame. À deux cents chacune, cinquante-quatre cents.

Elle ouvrit le tiroir-caisse et me tendit l'argent. Devant l'expression de Kipper, elle demanda :

— Peut-être quelques bonbons ?

— Non, répondit-il en lui souriant avec fierté. Nous économisons pour notre papa.

Nous sommes remontés en haut de la colline. Kipper, qui suçait un bonbon, avait la bouche et les lèvres noires ; l'épicière nous en avait donné un à chacun.

Avec cinquante-quatre cents, on n'aidait rien ni personne. Rien que pour entrer au *drive-in* de la Cascade, ça coûtait deux dollars – si papa acceptait de nous y emmener. Je ne savais pas du tout quel film on jouait ce soir. En vérité, je n'avais pas vraiment envie d'y aller mais j'aimais bien l'idée de Kipper : faire quelque chose, n'importe quoi, avec notre père.

À chaque pas, mes bottes devenaient plus lourdes et plus chaudes. Au sommet, nous avons dépassé notre rue pour aller sur les chantiers des maisons en construction.

— Viens, dis-je en tournant dans une allée de gravier. On va voir si les ouvriers ont laissé des bouteilles.

Les maisons inachevées des deux côtés de la rue étaient silencieuses, abandonnées pour le week-end. Le soleil de l'après-midi tapait sur les charpentes apparentes. L'air chaud sentait le bois frais et le béton en train de sécher. Ignorant l'écriteau « Passage interdit », j'explorai la première cour, laissant Kipper dans la rue avec le chariot.

— Qu'est-ce que ça veut dire, con-con-treven… ? cria-t-il derrière moi.

Je me retournai pour regarder le panneau qu'il avait tant de mal à déchiffrer.

— Contrevenants. Cela signifie que celui qui sera surpris en train de voler du matériel de construction ira en prison. Mais nous ne sommes pas en train de voler. Les vieilles bouteilles de soda ne les intéressent pas.

Je fis le tour des matériaux de construction stockés dans la cour. Au milieu des papiers cirés froissés et des trognons de pomme pourris abandonnés par les ouvriers, je découvris une bouteille d'Orange Crush. On sentait encore l'odeur piquante du soda tandis que je l'essuyais en vérifiant qu'elle n'était ni fêlée ni ébréchée.

Passant d'une cour à l'autre, je découvris au moins une ou deux bouteilles vides dans chaque chantier. À certains endroits, elles étaient alignées proprement comme si elles nous attendaient. À côté d'un tas de bois, je tombai sur une bouteille de whisky vide. Laide et inutile. Je la jetai dans un trou noir, satisfaite de l'entendre s'écraser sur les murs de ciment.

En revenant vers la rue les bras chargés, je vis un grand chariot de bois à côté du nôtre. Deux garçons encadraient Kipper. L'un était penché sur notre chariot, des bouteilles de soda serrées contre sa poitrine. Ils nous volent nos bouteilles ! Je lâchai les miennes pour me jeter sur le garçon, que je fis tomber. Les bouteilles qu'il tenait volèrent dans toutes les directions.

— C'est quoi, ce bazar ? rugit-il tandis que je le bourrais de coups de poings en le griffant.

— Ethie, arrête ! cria Kipper.

Quelqu'un me saisit par derrière.

— Du calme, Ethie !

C'était Danny Fenwick.

— Nous étions seulement en train de donner des bouteilles à Kipper, se défendit-il en me repoussant.

— Purée ! jura l'autre garçon en se relevant d'un bond. T'es cinglée !

Il s'épousseta avant de s'éloigner dans la rue.

— Et garde ces satanées bouteilles, cria-t-il. On dirait que t'en as vraiment besoin.

Danny lui courut après et lui expliqua calmement quelque chose. Je savais ce qu'il était en train de lui raconter.

L'expression de l'autre garçon changea et il me lança un coup d'œil.

— Désolé, dit-il juste assez fort pour que je l'entende.

— Oui. Moi aussi.

Je donnai un coup de pied dans la poussière. Je ne voulais pas de sa compassion. Ni de ses bouteilles.

— Viens, Kipper ! On y va, l'appelai-je en attrapant la poignée du chariot.

Danny revint en hâte et commença à ramasser les bouteilles éparpillées dans la rue.

— Il n'avait aucune mauvaise intention, affirma-t-il en les mettant dans le chariot. Nous sommes en train de construire un fort près du golf. Pourquoi vous viendriez pas le voir, tous les deux ?

— Non, décréta Kipper en montrant les matériaux de construction dans le chariot en bois. Je crois que t'es un con-con-contrevenant.

— À cause de ça ? s'exclama Danny en riant. Non ! C'est juste des vieux clous tordus et des morceaux de bois que les ouvriers nous laissent. Comme les bouteilles.

C'était une chose que j'avais toujours aimée chez Danny. La façon dont il s'adressait de façon directe à mon frère.

— Qu'est-ce que t'en dis, alors ? lui demanda-t-il à nouveau. Tu viens voir notre fort ?

Kipper accepta la proposition pour nous deux.

Autour de notre quartier, les zones de végétation et de marais rétrécissaient sans cesse. Remplacées par de nouvelles rues bordées de nouvelles maisons. Mais il y avait encore des hectares de brousse autour du terrain de golf de Fraserview. Le fort de Danny était caché dans les arbres au-dessus de Marine Drive. Pour l'atteindre il fallait escalader une échelle de corde.

Je passai le reste de l'après-midi avec Kipper et Danny. Comme autrefois. Nous avons fait une grande promenade dans les bois en pataugeant dans la crique qui sentait le moisi pour attraper des grenouilles, en déterrant des trognons de choux puants avec lesquels nous nous sommes bombardés. Nous avons crié dans les nouveaux tuyaux d'égouts en béton en écoutant nos voix nous revenir en écho. Danny et moi avons rampé dans l'un d'eux en faisant semblant d'être des soldats en train de nous planquer pour échapper à l'ennemi. Quand il a fait trop noir pour y voir, nous sommes ressortis retrouver Kipper qui avait refusé de nous accompagner. Assis à l'entrée du tuyau, il dessinait une maison dans la vase du bout d'un bâton. Une maison avec des avant-toits recourbés. Il avait cette maison chinoise en tête. J'avais espéré qu'entretemps il l'aurait oubliée.

Ensuite, nous sommes allés nous promener sur le terrain de golf où Danny nous a montré comment chercher des balles dans l'herbe haute le long des passages. Ce n'était guère différent de la chasse aux bouteilles de soda mais, lorsque nous avons apporté les balles sur le parking, les golfeurs nous ont payé infiniment plus cher.

Kipper était un négociateur hors pair. D'après Danny, c'était parce qu'il suffisait de regarder une seule fois son visage honnête pour savoir qu'il n'avait pas couru les greens pour les voler, comme faisaient certains gamins. Tout excitée, je me suis dit que nous avions trouvé une autre manière de gagner de l'argent.

Nous sommes arrivés à la maison au moment où Frankie partait à ses cours du soir. Il a froncé le nez devant l'odeur de vase et de trognons de choux accrochée à nos vêtements et nous a demandé où nous avions traîné toute la journée. Kipper lui a expliqué que nous avions collecté les bouteilles de soda et les balles de golf.

— Bon plan ! a commenté Frankie en apprenant que nous allions demander à papa de nous emmener au *drive-in*. Mais vous feriez bien de changer de vêtements avant de vous asseoir dans la même voiture que lui.

Après avoir mis la table du dîner, j'ai posé douze dollars devant l'assiette de papa.

— Qu'est-ce que c'est ? a-t-il demandé en s'asseyant.

— C'est pour toi, p'pa, a annoncé Kipper, rayonnant.

Tout en mangeant, nous lui avons raconté à tour de rôle comment nous l'avions gagné, cet argent.

— Et Kipper a pensé que peut-être, on pourrait en prendre un peu pour aller au *drive-in* ce soir, ai-je ajouté.

Papa a regardé la pile de pièces et de billets d'un dollar froissés.

— Lorsque j'avais votre âge, il fallait plus d'un mois de distribution du *Star Weekly* pour gagner ce genre de somme, a-t-il dit en secouant la tête.

Distribuer un journal.

— Kipper et moi, on pourrait peut-être distribuer un journal, nous aussi ?

— Peut-être, a répondu papa.

Son regard a vacillé vers le haut du réfrigérateur tandis qu'il faisait glisser l'argent sur la table.

Mon cœur s'est serré. Pas de *drive-in* ce soir.

— Mais gardez ça, les gamins ! Vous l'avez gagné, a-t-il déclaré en posant sa fourchette. Eh bien, a-t-il ajouté en se levant, qu'est-ce que vous attendez ? On fait la vaisselle et on y va !

Ce soir-là, nous ne sommes pas allés au *drive-in* de la Cascade. Quand papa a vu dans le journal qu'on donnait *Jugement à Nuremberg*, il a préféré nous emmener au *drive-in* du New Westminster où on jouait *Du silence et des ombres*.

Aucun d'entre nous n'a profité de la fin du film. Nous nous sommes assoupis sur la banquette avant de l'Hudson. Durant le trajet de retour, pelotonnée entre mon père et Kipper, j'ai fait semblant de continuer à dormir. J'ai laissé papa me porter dans ma chambre et me mettre au lit sans ouvrir les yeux. En sentant qu'il me bordait après m'avoir embrassée sur le front, je me suis prise à espérer que, peut-être, cela allait marcher, que, peut-être, si j'y mettais toutes mes forces, j'allais réussir à lui faire comprendre à quel point nous avions besoin de lui. Avant de sombrer dans le sommeil, je me suis souvenu de ce qu'avait dit Mme Fenwick. Elle avait raison. La tristesse et la douleur ne disparaissaient pas mais il n'y avait rien de mal à être heureuse d'aller au cinéma avec mon père et mon frère, rien de mal à aimer de nouveau jouer avec les amis.

Papa avait dû lui aussi avancer dans ses réflexions. Pour la première fois depuis la mort de maman, il a passé la nuit dans leur lit.

25

13 décembre 1941 : Île de Hong Kong

Howard resserra la mince couverture militaire autour de ses épaules. Gordy et lui avaient été envoyés dans ce blockhaus en béton dominant la mer de Chine méridionale après leur retour du continent. En dehors de quelques écorchures bénignes et autres blessures superficielles, la compagnie s'en était sortie à peu près indemne. Tous présents à l'appel. Sauf le soldat John A. Gray. Howard s'efforça en vain de mettre un visage sur le nom du garçon de ferme du Manitoba.

Il frissonna. Leur blockhaus était encore humide de la bruine de la veille au soir. En dépit de la chaleur de l'après-midi, il avait froid.

— Mais, putain, qu'est-ce qu'on fiche ici ? explosa Gordy pour la énième fois de la journée.

Pas plus que précédemment, il n'attendait une quelconque réponse à sa question.

Il n'y avait pas à discuter de la situation. De Kowloon leur parvenaient des bruits terrifiants, des cris inhumains d'une violence telle qu'on les entendait de l'autre côté de l'étroit bras de mer qui séparait l'île du continent. Ils savaient tous deux ce que ces hurlements signifiaient.

Après avoir évacué dans l'île l'ensemble des forces de la garnison, les Japonais – qui, sur le continent, contrôlaient les stations de radio de la colonie – avaient déclaré par la voie des ondes que toutes les Chinoises étaient des prostituées. Sous-entendu, elles avaient moins de valeur qu'un animal. Le speaker établit clairement que les soldats vainqueurs pouvaient traiter à leur guise ces femmes, considérées comme butin de guerre.

Gordy se prit la tête à deux mains. Il se boucha les oreilles pour ne plus entendre les hurlements au loin.

— Seigneur ! C'est insupportable !

Il se balança d'avant en arrière, injuriant les Japonais, Dieu, celui qui avait envoyé son régiment ici. Tout à coup, il se leva d'un bond et fonça vers la sortie.

— Je peux pas rester ici à rien foutre ! cria-t-il soudain en luttant contre Howard qui cherchait à le retenir par le bras. Putain, on sert à rien !

La terre sous leurs pieds se mit soudain à trembler. Au même moment, venant du nord, on entendit une série d'explosions et un barrage de tirs d'artillerie. Victoria était à nouveau bombardée. Gordy s'affaissa puis se laissa glisser à terre, accablé.

Howard examina le terrain en pente qui descendait jusqu'à la route étroite et la côte découpée. La roche était nue, depuis longtemps nettoyée de tout ce qui pouvait alimenter un feu. Même le plus petit des soldats japonais n'aurait pu y trouver de quoi se planquer. De toute façon, qu'est-ce qu'ils surveillaient là ? Les Japonais n'étaient pas sur l'île. Alors ?

Une unité de mitrailleurs du Middlesex qui était passée quelques heures plus tôt leur avait donné les dernières nouvelles. Repérant Peter Young sur le Bren-gun Carrier et le visage criblé de taches de rousseur de Dick Baxter qui marchait à côté, Howard avait dévalé la pente jusqu'à la route. La chenillette avait ralenti et s'était arrêtée.

— Eh, salut ! Voilà les Canucks ! s'était exclamé Peter avec un grand sourire. Qu'est-ce que vous fichez là, les gars ?

— Apparemment, y a un Engliche qu'a pas pu renoncer à l'idée que l'invasion viendrait de la mer.

— Pff ! Y a vraiment peu de chances maintenant ! Les Japs nous aboient au cul. Ils croient qu'ils ont déjà gagné ce putain de truc. Ce matin, ils nous ont envoyé une délégation du continent. Les gars tenaient une banderole où était écrit « Peace Mission ».

Peter eut un reniflement de mépris.

— Ils nous donnaient l'occasion de nous rendre. Sympa de leur part, non ?

— Et la réponse ?

— On leur a dit d'aller se faire foutre, évidemment, répliqua Dick.

— Là, on va garder la passe Lye Mun, expliqua Peter en emballant le moteur de sa chenillette. Cette passe de huit cents mètres de large est sûrement l'endroit par lequel les Japs vont essayer de traverser. Pourquoi vous viendriez pas avec nous, les gars ?

— On peut pas quitter notre poste.

— À votre guise.

La chenillette bondit en avant.

— Mais ici, vous serez pas dans l'action, cria Peter par dessus son épaule.

— Et on gagnera pas de médailles non plus ! répondit Howard.

— T'es au courant, pour nos bateaux de guerre ? demanda Dick en s'éloignant à reculons. Le *Prince of Wales* et le *Repulse* ont coulé tous les deux au large des côtes de Malaisie.

Howard en resta bouche bée. Les deux navires disparus ? Il remonta la colline d'un pas pesant, accablé. Il n'y avait plus aucun espoir de renfort venu de la mer. Marinant à présent dans le soleil de l'après-midi qui se faufilait par l'étroite ouverture, il était tenaillé par la faim. Ils n'avaient pas eu de repas chaud depuis trois jours. Ils avaient épuisé la veille leurs dernières rations – des biscuits secs. Il commençait à se demander si le chef de leur unité ne les avait pas oubliés, Gordy et lui. Tout en surveillant la route dans l'attente du camion de ravitaillement, il lui fallait bien s'avouer qu'il avait été tenté de suivre les mitrailleurs. Tout plutôt que de rester des heures durant dans ce blockhaus écroulé à contempler une colline désertique. Et la mer, la mer vide, d'où, il le savait – Gordy, Lawson, tout le monde le savait à l'exception du major Maltby –, l'invasion ne viendrait jamais. N'empêche, les ordres étaient les ordres. Il resterait là jusqu'à ce que les poules aient des dents, s'il le fallait. Jusqu'à ce qu'il reçoive l'ordre de son chef de troupe d'abandonner son poste. Un ordre qu'il implorait de recevoir. Ce n'était pas qu'il fût impatient de se retrouver au cœur de la mêlée. Il n'avait nullement le désir d'être héroïque. Il entendait au loin les hurlements des tirs de mortier, il percevait la secousse des explosions, il sentait dans le vent l'odeur âcre de la fumée et de la cordite. Il savait à quel point tout cela était réel. Mais, comme Gordy, il trouvait frustrant de rester là, inutile, sans rien faire.

Six heures plus tard, leurs rations arrivèrent avec l'ordre de bouger. On les transféra à la faveur de l'obscurité mais, à l'aube, ils se retrouvèrent dans un bunker identique avec une vue différente sur la mer.

Les bombardements intensifs venus du continent continuèrent toute la journée et la nuit suivante. Les sirènes de raids aériens et de fin d'alerte hurlaient par intermittence tandis que Gordy et lui ne faisaient rien sinon passer d'un poste à l'autre.

Finalement, partis faire leur rapport au quartier général de la brigade dans Wong Nei Chong Road, dans le centre de l'île, ils retrouvèrent leur section le matin du 17 décembre. À travers un rideau de pluie, Howard reconnut Ken Campbell – le matériel radio gonflant sa cape imperméable – qui marchait devant eux. Ils se précipitèrent pour le rattraper.

— C'est le désordre organisé, marmonna Ken, le visage strié de pluie. On n'est pas plus tôt stationnés quelque part que quelqu'un envoie un autre plan par radio. On donne des ordres, on les annule. Je commence vraiment à me demander si on sait ce qu'on fait…

— Oui, nous aussi, approuva Howard.

Mais au moins, ils avançaient. Vers le nord, vers Victoria. Gordy était manifestement soulagé. Ils passèrent la nuit aplatis au fond d'un fossé. Howard était impatient d'atteindre le quartier général de la brigade. Le brigadier Lawson était là-bas. Il saurait remettre la situation d'aplomb.

Le lendemain, à l'aube, l'unité de Howard cernait la gorge de Wong Nei Chong. Fatigués, affamés, ils brûlaient leurs dernières réserves. La veille au soir, les Japonais avaient envahi l'île – ils grouillaient littéralement. Exactement comme l'avait prévu Peter Young, profitant de l'obscurité, ils avaient franchi l'étroite passe de Lye Mun. Désormais tous les hommes de la section savaient qu'ils pouvaient se retrouver à combattre au corps à corps avant la fin de la journée.

L'angoisse du lendemain n'empêchait plus Howard de dormir. Au cours de ces derniers jours ponctués de bombardements incessants et de manœuvres constantes qui n'avaient mené nulle part, il avait appris à récupérer en profitant d'un silence, d'une pause dans les hurlements permanents des tirs. Il avait cessé de sursauter à chaque balle, à chaque tir de mortier, il avait cessé de penser au fait d'avoir à ôter la vie à un autre être humain. En couvrant la retraite des Royal Scots sur le continent, il avait vu tomber son premier soldat ennemi, une fraction de seconde après avoir visé et appuyé sur la détente. Contrairement au sergent York, il s'aperçut qu'il était incapable de tuer comme on abat une dinde. Il s'agissait d'une personne, après tout. Cependant, avant de se concentrer sur le suivant, Howard avait ressenti un certain soulagement à l'idée d'avoir déjà supprimé un Japonais.

Ils se firent attaquer à moins de deux kilomètres du quartier général de la brigade. Les rafales de mitraillette dispersèrent les troupes. Howard se jeta au fond d'un fossé en entendant le sifflement suraigu d'un mortier. Cramponné à son arme – ne lâchez jamais votre arme –, il se coucha, le visage enfoui dans le sol humide pendant que pleuvaient sur lui de la terre et des débris de pierre. Et quelque chose d'autre. Quelque chose de doux. Des gouttes lourdes comme de la pluie tombaient sur son casque, sur son dos. Il ramena sa main et examina la bouillie rouge qui tachait ses doigts. Il les essuya frénétiquement sur son pantalon.

Où est Gordy ? Il se tourna dans tous les sens, fouillant furieusement le sol autour de lui, avec les mains, avec les yeux.

— Gordy ! cria-t-il.

Il souleva la tête pour jeter un œil. Là, juste au-dessus de lui, le soldat Veronick se tenait figé sous une avalanche de tirs, en train de contempler un cratère tout frais ouvert quelques mètres plus loin sur la route.

— Gordy ! Couche-toi !

Mais Gordy resta debout, à marmonner quelque chose d'inintelligible au milieu du crépitement de la mitraille. Howard avança en rampant, se redressa, saisit son ami par la taille et le tira à lui. Il l'entraîna dans le fossé et se coucha sur lui tandis qu'une nouvelle explosion déclenchait une pluie de débris. Résistant aux mouvements désordonnés de Gordy, il se tourna vers Ken Campbell qui se battait un peu plus loin avec la radio sans fil qu'il finit par frapper du plat de la main.

— Tir de mortier venant du nord, cria-t-il au chef de section.

Le nord. Seigneur Jésus ! Comment les Japs pouvaient-ils être déjà au nord ?

Sous lui, Gordy protestait avec énergie.

Une heure durant, cloués au sol, les hommes tirèrent à l'aveuglette sur un ennemi invisible. Puis, aussi brutalement qu'ils avaient commencé, les tirs cessèrent. Prudemment, l'un après l'autre, les grenadiers se redressèrent et, accroupis au fond du fossé, firent l'inventaire. Deux hommes avaient disparu.

— Johnson et Maxwell, marmonna Gordy. Ils étaient là... et puis plus rien. Il n'y avait plus qu'un trou dans la route.

Un des godillots de Gordy attira l'œil de Howard.

— Ton pied ?

Hébété, Gordy baissa la tête. Sa chaussure droite était béante au niveau de la semelle et on voyait sa chaussette de laine trempée de sang.

— J'ai dû prendre un éclat d'obus. Bizarre, je ne sens rien.

— Il y a un poste de secours un peu plus haut, dit le chef de section en indiquant la direction d'où ils étaient venus. Première route à droite. Emmenez-le là-bas.

— Je vais bien, monsieur, protesta Gordy.

— Allez-y ! Tout de suite. C'est un ordre !

Les deux soldats sortirent comme ils purent du fossé. Courbé en deux, Howard traîna derrière lui son ami qui boitait, s'attendant à prendre une pluie de balles. Mais le silence régnait et ils se jetèrent dans le fossé de l'autre côté de la route. Pendant un moment qui leur parut des heures, ils rampèrent au fond avant de se décider à marcher à découvert.

L'ambulance criblée de balles qui bloquait la route étroite fut le premier signe annonciateur de l'horreur à venir. À l'intérieur, le chauffeur punjabi était affalé sur le volant, le visage emporté. Secoués, Howard et Gordy contournèrent le véhicule mais d'autres cadavres les attendaient de l'autre côté ; tous semblaient avoir rampé vers leur mort, tendus vers des secours qui ne viendraient pas. En contrebas de la route, le ravin était encombré d'un amas de corps emmêlés.

— Leur montrez pas que vous boitez, dit quelqu'un derrière eux.

Gordy et Howard firent volte-face, l'arme à l'épaule, prêts à tirer.

De l'autre côté de la route, une pile de corps oscilla. Un soldat en uniforme kaki en sortit. Couvert de poussière et de sang séché, un pansement en lambeaux autour de la tête, il tenta de se dégager en s'aidant du bras gauche.

— Soldat Jack Dell, se présenta-t-il. Royal Rifles.

Howard abaissa son arme.

— Nom de Dieu, que s'est-il passé ici ?

— Un massacre. Rien d'autre qu'un putain de massacre, cracha le Terre-Neuvien. Ils veulent pas de prisonniers. Toutes les excuses sont bonnes pour nous tuer.

Il montra un arbre non loin de là. Il fallut un moment à Howard pour comprendre que la forme pendue aux branches était un cadavre attaché par les pieds.

— Passé au fil de la baïonnette rien que pour s'amuser, dit Jack Dell en cherchant à s'asseoir. Les blessés, tous tués jusqu'au dernier. Les infirmières, les toubibs, tous disparus, emmenés Dieu sait où. J'ai fait le mort sous les cadavres de mes camarades. Ils m'ont raté – enfin presque, ajouta-t-il en montrant son bras droit ensanglanté. J'ai pris un coup de baïonnette.

Tendant la main, Howard remit sur ses pieds le soldat qui ne paraissait pas peser bien lourd. Jack Dell mesurait moins d'un mètre soixante-dix.

Howard se tourna vers Gordy.

— Va avec lui et retournez sur la côte. Trouvez un autre poste de secours. Moi, je vais rejoindre notre unité.

— Foutaises ! répondirent-ils en chœur.

— Je n'ai aucun problème à part cette écorchure sur le front, ajouta le Terre-Neuvien. Et je n'ai rien au bras, reprit-il en agitant les doigts. Il me faut seulement un pansement. Je peux encore m'en servir pour tirer sur les Japs.

— Ouais. Et qui t'a promu au grade de sergent ? gronda Gordy. Je marche parfaitement bien.

Et, pour le prouver, il remonta sur la route, en s'appuyant sur son talon.

Ce soir-là, ils retrouvèrent le reste de la compagnie. Trop tard. Le quartier général de la brigade était tombé. Lawson était mort, abattu alors qu'il menait ses hommes à l'attaque. Les Japonais avaient pris le contrôle de Wong Nei Chong Road. L'île était coupée en deux.

Contournant le massacre considérable autour du bunker, sur la route et les collines alentour, l'unité de Howard fonça, profitant de l'obscurité de la nuit. Une fois sur les pentes est du mont Nicholson, ils s'arrêtèrent juste à temps pour entendre une voix impassible sortir de la radio de Ken Campbell :

— À toutes les forces militaires de Hong Kong. Mark Young, le gouverneur de Hong Kong, est en train de vous parler. L'heure a sonné de marcher contre l'ennemi. L'Empire a les yeux braqués sur nous. Soyez forts. Soyez résolus et faites votre devoir.

— Qu'est-ce qu'il croit donc qu'on a fait, ce con ? maugréa Jack Dell.

Le lendemain soir, après une journée de combats intensifs, Howard avait perdu toute notion du temps. Les heures étaient devenues des minutes. Le matin, le commandant de section avait envoyé d'office Jack Dell à l'hôpital Saint Stephen. Il refusait toute discussion. Gordy, échappant à son examen attentif, avait été renvoyé avec Howard à Middle Gap, pour tenter de reprendre Wong Nei Chang Road.

Dépassés en nombre, sous-équipés et manquant d'entraînement, ils se retrouvaient pilonnés par les Japonais rompus au combat. Au cours des dernières heures, Howard avait été témoin de plus d'actes d'héroïsme qu'il souhaitait en voir dans toute sa vie, sans compter tous ceux dont il avait entendu le récit. Le sergent-major Osborne, un grenadier, avait péri en étouffant une grenade dégoupillée pour sauver ses hommes. Le soldat Jack Williams était mort en cherchant à mettre à l'abri un de ses camarades blessés. Le soldat Aubrey Flagg s'était jeté volontairement dans un piège mortel, armé de deux Colts, pour sauver une Anglaise et ses deux filles d'un groupe de renégats japonais. Même la mascotte du Royal Rifles, l'énorme terre-neuve noir qui s'appelait Gander, avait sauvé son unité en se précipitant dans la mêlée pour rapporter une grenade qui avait atterri à leurs pieds. Il s'était enfui avec la grenade dans la gueule et s'était retrouvé pulvérisé jusqu'au ciel. Il y avait des héros partout, Howard en était persuadé mais, comme la plupart de ses camarades, il s'efforçait seulement de rester en vie.

Il regarda Gordy assis sur la colline à côté de lui, profondément endormi. C'était quelque chose, là encore, cet ami si courageux qui refusait de boiter alors qu'il avait dû desserrer son lacet pour soulager son pied enflé. Il fonctionnait à l'adrénaline pure. Mais combien de temps allait-il tenir le coup ?

Dans la lumière qui précédait l'aube, son unité se préparait à reculer sur ces mêmes pentes gravies avec tant de peine la veille. Un groupe de Hong Kong Volunteers était coincé en dessous dans un bunker en béton. L'unité d'Howard, en pleine débandade, comprenant moins de trente hommes et une seule mitraillette Vickers, allait tenter de les sauver. Couverts par les mitrailleurs, ils entamèrent leur descente.

Ils étaient déjà à mi-chemin lorsque Howard aperçut le reflet métallique des baïonnettes et entendit les cris de guerre à vous figer le sang montant de la vague noire qui envahissait la colline. Il se laissa tomber à terre. Sortant une grenade de sa ceinture, il la dégoupilla d'un coup de dents et la lança avant de lever son arme pour viser les Japonais menaçants. Une rafale de balles venue de la Vickers siffla au-dessus de sa tête et l'ennemi recula. Un véhicule blindé surgit sur la route, faisant feu de toutes ses armes. Le Middlesex anglais ! Les Japonais étaient pris en étau, les grenadiers les repoussant par en haut, le véhicule blindé les talonnant à l'arrière. Howard et Gordy, avec ce qui restait de leur troupe, chargèrent à flanc de colline, balançant des grenades et tirant dans les rangs de l'ennemi encerclé. Brusquement, ils furent submergés latéralement par une deuxième vague de Japonais, soutenus par un intense tir de mortier. Le blindé fut touché. Howard se laissa rouler derrière une butte, Gordy le suivant de près. Sur leur droite, le lit d'un ruisseau asséché longeait la pente. Howard le désigna d'un geste. Gordy acquiesça. Ils se redressèrent et plongèrent en roulant. Rampant sur les coudes, ils reprirent leur lente descente.

L'odeur trop familière de cordite mélangée à celle de la terre fraîchement retournée emplit les narines de Howard ; la vision inattendue d'un champ de blé tout juste labouré au Manitoba surgit dans son esprit. Il releva la tête pour examiner les alentours.

Le toit du bunker recouvert d'herbe dans lequel les Hong Kong Volunteers étaient enfermés se trouvait juste en dessous.

Sur la route, jonchée de victimes des deux bords, un canon japonais était pointé directement sur la porte du bunker. Surgi de nulle part, un casque apparut au bord du toit. Une silhouette sombre se hissa et rampa jusqu'au tuyau d'aération. Elle se redressa, c'était un soldat japonais ; d'un mouvement rapide, il saisit une grenade à sa ceinture, la dégoupilla et se pencha au-dessus du tuyau.

Sans réfléchir, Howard bondit, saisit le Japonais par derrière et l'envoya, lui et sa grenade, de l'autre côté du bunker.

La violence de la déflagration le projeta en arrière. Bras et jambes écartés, il s'envola. Il atterrit face contre terre et son arme lui sauta des mains. Les oreilles bourdonnantes, les yeux brûlants, il chercha son fusil à tâtons. Heureusement, il sentit la crosse sous sa main et roula sur le dos en la serrant contre sa poitrine.

Au-dessus, dans l'innocent ciel du matin, les dernières étoiles brillaient sur un monde devenu fou. Il eut une vision de Lucy, une vision si claire qu'il distinguait même les taches de rousseur éparpillées sur son nez, la blancheur de ses dents lorsqu'elle lui souriait. Le moment était donc venu. La mort l'attendait là, au tournant de l'aube. S'il devait mourir, il mourrait en combattant, à l'image du brigadier Lawson. Il rassembla ses forces pour se lever, pour se remettre sur pieds et foncer vers le destin, quel qu'il fût, qui l'attendait.

Il vit le reflet de l'acier, il sentit le poids sur sa poitrine avant de distinguer un soldat japonais à califourchon sur lui, l'obligeant à rester couché de la pointe de sa baïonnette. Il se pencha, arracha l'arme des mains de Howard et l'envoya au loin. Il prit son élan en souriant, prêt à enfoncer sa baïonnette.

— Teiryuu !

L'ordre aboyé arrêta la baïonnette en pleine course. Le soldat se raidit et laissa tomber son arme. Howard tourna la tête vers la voix. Sur la route, il y avait un officier japonais, les pieds écartés. Derrière lui, des soldats vociférant, faisaient sortir en troupeau les Hong Kong Volunteers du bunker. L'officier gonfla la poitrine puis regarda Howard.

— Alors, nous nous retrouvons, mon ami, dit-il.

Howard se releva lentement ; il examina l'uniforme immaculé, l'étoile et le ruban rouge sur le képi de l'officier, le sabre pendant du ceinturon de cuir. Il lui fallut un petit moment pour comprendre que cet officier japonais, qui s'exprimait dans un anglais parfait, n'était autre que le petit barbier avec lequel, des siècles auparavant, il avait partagé bière et cigarettes devant les baraquements de Sham Shui Po.

Le bruit des combats continua alors qu'ils marchaient en désordre vers Victoria. Cependant, pour Howard et ce qui restait de son unité, la bataille était terminée. Ils étaient maintenant prisonniers de guerre. Mais ils étaient vivants, grâce à l'officier qui avait épargné la vie de Howard. Durant cette marche forcée vers le nord, ils virent l'étendue de cette boucherie gratuite : des soldats anglais et canadiens qu'on laissait pourrir en tas au fond des fossés, la plupart les bras liés dans le dos avec du fil de fer. Les victimes n'étaient pas seulement militaires. La route était jonchée de corps décomposés de civils, dont des femmes et des enfants. Dans les faubourgs de Victoria, ils tombèrent sur le cadavre d'une jeune femme qui avait été tellement maltraitée et mutilée que Howard dut détourner le regard.

— Barbares ! cria Gordy au garde qui lorgnait le corps dénudé. Vous êtes qu'une bande de barbares !

Il prit un coup de crosse sur la tête. Howard, attaché à lui par du fil de téléphone, vacilla en même temps.

— La ferme ! grogna quelqu'un dans le groupe en débandade. Ces types nous tueront à la première occasion.

— N'attire pas l'attention sur toi, chuchota Howard en redressant Gordy. Appuie-toi contre moi.

Ils reprirent leur marche vacillante.

Il était impossible de concilier ce carnage aveugle avec la gentillesse inattendue que manifestaient parfois leurs gardiens, sans raison. Des soldats susceptibles de vous allonger à terre d'un coup de crosse se retrouvaient à offrir un peu d'eau de leur gourde ou à glisser en douce quelque chose à manger à un prisonnier.

Et puis, il y avait l'officier à qui Howard devait la vie.

Après le siège du bunker, les Hong Kong Volunteers, ainsi que les Canadiens vaincus, furent alignés, fouillés et dépouillés du moindre objet de valeur. La montre de Howard, les dollars de Hong Kong répartis dans les poches de son uniforme et son alliance furent confisqués vite fait. La mort dans l'âme, il vit son carnet jeté à terre. Le barbier devenu officier s'avança alors, se pencha et le ramassa. Il se redressa, ouvrit le carnet et en ôta la photo de Lucy.

— Amour d'enfance, dit-il en souriant à Howard.

Puis il chercha dans sa veste d'uniforme son propre carnet. Il l'ouvrit, en sortit une photographie similaire et la tendit à Howard.

Sur la photographie sépia, une jeune femme brune souriait avec une modestie affectée.

— Très jolie, se força à commenter Howard.

— Oui, répondit l'officier d'une voix à peine audible.

Il rendit son carnet à Howard, avec la photo de Lucy, puis il s'éloigna. Howard ne devait plus le revoir.

Épuisés, sales et affamés, les prisonniers atteignirent Victoria deux jours après avoir été capturés. Sous un dais de fumée noire, ils défilèrent dans les rues bondées derrière les officiers japonais juchés sur de fringants étalons. La ville avait été pulvérisée : les chaussées étaient encombrées de bus et de voitures calcinés. Le port était un cimetière de navires à moitié coulés, de ferries et de réservoirs à essence en feu. À chaque pas, on piétinait des débris de verre. L'emblème du Soleil levant pendait aux façades des immeubles bombardés et grêlés. Partout se déployaient des banderoles arborant le même signe. Et sur les trottoirs, des civils chinois terrifiés portant sur le bras des bandanas ornés du même cercle de sang, criaient en chœur et en mauvais anglais : « L'Asie aux Asiatiques ! L'Asie aux Asiatiques ! »

Gordy et Howard scrutaient frénétiquement la mer de visages. Mais il y en avait tant. Leur défilé prit fin à North Point, l'ancien camp de réfugiés, où on les fit entrer.

Le camp avait été mis à sac, pillé de tout ce qu'il contenait. Il ne restait plus un seul lit métallique, plus une seule couverture, plus un seul matelas dans aucune des baraques en ruines. Pire encore, il n'y avait plus de latrines. Howard et les autres prisonniers passèrent la nuit entassés sur quelques châlits de bois et sur le sol de béton nu. Le lendemain, beaucoup se mirent à tourner en rond, épaule contre épaule, fouillant le moindre centimètre carré de terrain à la recherche de quelque chose de comestible. D'autres restaient assis sans bouger, avec le regard vide des vaincus. Certains se racontaient mutuellement les épreuves qu'ils avaient traversées. Nombreux étaient ceux qui pleuraient des camarades perdus. Pour la plupart, les Japonais ne leur prêtaient aucune attention. Quelques gardiens crevant d'ennui ne cessaient de les railler parce qu'ils s'étaient rendus. Accepter d'être capturés plutôt que de mourir glorieusement sur le champ de bataille ou se tuer était un signe de lâcheté.

De nouveaux prisonniers, anglais et canadiens, débarquaient toutes les heures. Howard poussa un soupir de soulagement en voyant Ken Campbell, délesté de son casque et de sa radio, franchir les portes du camp ce soir-là. Crasseux et paraissant peser dix kilos de moins, il rejoignit Howard à la clôture et lui apprit qu'une compagnie de Royal Rifles et de Hong Kong Volunteers continuait à se battre à Stanley, dos à la mer, offrant une ultime résistance.

Peu de temps après l'arrivée des Rajputs survivants, un convoi d'officiers japonais vint inspecter le camp. Vêtus d'uniformes de cérémonie et gantés de blanc, ils se déplaçaient dans des voitures ouvertes, comme des personnages royaux. L'un d'eux descendit pour parader de l'autre côté du grillage.

— Vous êtes des Asiatiques, comme nous, déclara-t-il aux troupes de l'Inde orientale. Serrons-nous la main. Unissez-vous à nous pour la victoire. Rejoignez-nous dans notre combat pour l'Asie aux Asiatiques. Nous devons montrer notre unité au monde entier.

Les Rajputs restèrent assis par terre, dans l'enceinte du camp, les jambes croisées, silencieux, tandis que se déversaient sur eux des propositions d'amitié et la promesse d'un monde libéré de la suprématie blanche. Les appels à s'enrôler pour la cause japonaise demeurèrent lettre morte.

Les officiers finirent par s'énerver. On apporta des mitraillettes qu'on installa sur des trépieds, braquées sur le camp.

— Le ralliement ou la mort ! cria un officier en brandissant son épée.

Les Rajputs, qui venaient de se battre comme des lions pendant dix-sept jours d'affilée, se levèrent comme un seul homme. Howard, la gorge serrée, les regarda marcher jusqu'au grillage. En silence, les fiers guerriers déchirèrent leurs chemises et poussèrent en avant leur poitrine dénudée.

Le camp tout entier retint son souffle. Howard se raccrochait aux bruits familiers, le vent sur l'eau et les cris des mouettes. Pas un muscle ne tressaillit. De chaque côté du grillage, les adversaires tenaient bon. Les Japonais finirent par cligner des yeux. L'officier cracha un ordre en japonais. Les mitraillettes reculèrent.

Les jours qui suivirent, les Japonais ignorèrent leurs prisonniers.

Howard passait la plus grande partie de ses journées à se battre contre les mouches tenaces qui torturaient tout le monde. Seule la pluie apportait un certain soulagement. Dès qu'elle cessait, cependant, les mouches revenaient, grouillant en nuages sombres au-dessus des tas de crottin abandonnés par les chevaux et les mules de l'armée japonaise. À l'extérieur du camp, des tapis noirs et grouillants enveloppaient les corps en décomposition, animaux et humains. Sans pitié, elles envahissaient la moindre parcelle de peau nue, se glissaient sous les vêtements, dans tous les orifices, dans les plaies ouvertes. Il régnait dans le camp une puanteur insupportable. Les hommes étaient tous malades.

Puis, le jour de Noël, on apprit que le gouverneur Mark Young avait signé la capitulation de la colonie. C'était officiellement terminé. Dans l'après-midi, un camion s'arrêta aux portes du camp et déversa trois sacs de riz en toile brune par terre.

— Joyeux Noël, railla Ken Campbell en en hissant un sur son épaule.

Trois sacs pour nourrir des milliers d'hommes.

Quelques heures plus tard, Howard assis par terre, adossé à un des poteaux du grillage, regardait la poignée de riz à moitié cuit dans son casque. Il pensait à la vieille femme à l'extérieur du camp qui, la veille, cherchait des grains de riz non digérés dans le crottin de cheval séché. N'empêche, il fallait bien manger. Lentement, lentement.

Gordy avala sa ration en deux bouchées et continua à fixer la grande route de l'autre côté du grillage. Il attendait Shunling. Howard se surprit à prier pour qu'elle ne s'approche pas du camp. Il avait vu ce que les Japonais pouvaient faire à une femme sans défense.

Si les Japonais détestaient les prisonniers, ils semblaient détester les Chinois encore plus. Certains gardiens tiraient à l'aveuglette sur le premier qui s'aventurait trop près, vieux ou jeune, homme ou femme, rien que pour le plaisir. Leurs supérieurs, s'ils s'en apercevaient, ne disaient rien. La vieille femme affamée à l'extérieur du camp avait payé de sa vie les quelques grains de riz couverts de crottin. Les gardiens l'avaient laissée s'approcher puis lui avaient tiré dans les jambes ; ensuite, alors qu'elle tentait de s'enfuir en rampant, ils avaient pris son corps pour cible tout en s'esclaffant.

Gordy posa son casque par terre, à côté de lui.

— Elle était vierge, déclara-t-il sans quitter la route des yeux.

— Quoi ?

— Shun-ling.

Sidéré par cette confidence inattendue, par l'intimité de cette phrase, Howard resta sans voix.

— Je ne m'y attendais pas…, continua Gordy en cherchant ses mots. Euh, je pensais… je sais pas. Je pensais que, puisque son père l'avait vendue…

Il s'interrompit.

— Je n'avais pas l'intention de le faire, reprit-il. Ça s'est passé comme ça. Elle était reconnaissante. Enfin je le crois. Je ne suis pas fier de moi, conclut-il en secouant la tête.

Howard demeura silencieux, s'efforçant d'ignorer la brûlure dans ses entrailles ; une brûlure qui n'avait rien à voir avec la faim.

— Seigneur. J'ai des sentiments pour elle, Howie. Rien à voir avec les autres filles. Ce n'est ni de la pitié ni de la concupiscence, même pas simplement du désir. C'est quelque chose de plus.

Il avala péniblement sa salive.

— Je sais, reprit-il, ça fait moins d'un mois mais je pense à… euh… la ramener chez nous. Lui demander de m'épouser, tu comprends.

La chaleur dans le ventre d'Howard gagna sa poitrine.

— Tu en es sûr ?

Gordy releva la tête.

— Oui, j'en suis sûr, gronda-t-il. Je n'ai jamais été aussi sûr de quelque chose.

Dans son regard, il y avait un défi tacite. Howard s'obligea à soutenir ce regard.

— Ah, parfait ! Alors, c'est formidable !

— Ouais, formidable, répéta Gordy. Sauf que maintenant, je ne la reverrai sans doute jamais.

En dépit du chaos qui régnait des deux côtés de la clôture, en dépit de l'ambivalence de ses sentiments, Howard réussit à parler.

— Bien sûr que si, affirma-t-il d'un ton rassurant. Quand tout cela sera terminé, tu iras à Victoria et tu la trouveras qui t'attendra dans cet appartement.

— Ouais. Quand tout cela sera terminé. D'accord.

— Évidemment.

Même à ses propres oreilles, les paroles de Howard sonnaient faux.

— Les Américains sont avec nous maintenant. Ce n'est plus qu'une question de temps.

26

Papa essaya. Il essaya vraiment. Le lendemain du jour où nous étions allés au cinéma *drive-in*, il se leva de bonne heure. Lorsqu'on descendit, Kipper et moi, il buvait un café dans la cuisine, le journal du dimanche étalé devant lui.

— Marée basse ce matin, annonça-t-il. Qu'est-ce que vous diriez d'aller passer la journée à Birch Bay ?

Quelques secondes de silence surpris suivirent sa question.

— Oh oui ! dis-je d'une voix délibérément calme, comme si toute démonstration d'excitation risquait de pulvériser cette possibilité.

Kipper, lui, n'avait pas pareille crainte.

— Ouais ! cria-t-il en claquant dans ses mains, puis il alla taper sur l'épaule de papa en s'exclamant : C'est bien, papa !

Papa lui sourit puis se tourna vers Frankie qui faisait frire du bacon.

— Et toi, Frankie ?

Frankie ne dit rien pendant un temps interminable. Il finit par lâcher : « Oui. D'accord. » Mais sa voix, comme la mienne, demeurait prudente. Ce n'était pas faute d'aimer Birch Bay – tout le monde dans la famille, et surtout papa, adorait la petite station balnéaire américaine de l'autre côté de la frontière. Dès que maman avait acheté l'Hudson, on l'avait souvent vu le dimanche quand il faisait beau vérifier les horaires des marées dans le journal. Si c'était marée basse, on partait pour la journée pêcher les crabes de Dungeness sur le sable mouillé. Imaginer aller là-bas sans maman était difficile. Préparer le pique-nique sans elle parut bizarre. Kipper et moi beurrions le pain pour les sandwiches – beurre de cacahuètes et confiture pour nous, saucisse fumée et moutarde pour Frankie et pour papa, évidemment, ses bien-aimées sardines. En observant Kipper étaler le beurre de cacahuètes, je ne pus m'empêcher de noter la facilité avec laquelle il s'était habitué à l'absence de maman. À quel point il paraissait l'accepter comme partie intégrante de nos vies. Je me demandai même s'il se rendait compte qu'il ne la reverrait jamais. Savait-il seulement ce que « jamais » signifiait ? Maman disait toujours que, pour peu qu'on lui en laisse le temps, Kipper comprenait tout, résolvait tout et, laissé à lui-même, aurait toujours la bonne réaction.

— Il possède une sagesse au-delà du savoir, affirmait-elle.

Comme s'il avait lu dans mes pensées, Kipper me regarda. Son visage large se fendit d'un sourire de guingois.

— Je crois qu'au bradis maman est contente qu'on aille à la plage, déclara-t-il en refermant son sandwich par une tranche de pain.

Je remarquai le faux entrain dans la voix de papa lorsqu'on s'entassa tous dans la Studebaker de Frankie. Mais durant le trajet, alors qu'il discutait avec Kipper du festin de crabes que nous allions faire, on avait l'impression qu'il était réellement avec nous.

Le trajet jusqu'à Washington prit moins d'une heure. Franchir la frontière des États-Unis à la Peace Arch provoqua les habituels cris de joie de Kipper. Une fois installés à la dernière table de pique-nique de la plage, on escalada les rochers couverts de bernaches pour pêcher dans les flaques peu profondes laissées par la marée. Chaque fois que nous arrachions des algues un de ces énormes crabes rouges, Frankie ou papa l'attrapait par derrière. Évitant les gigantesques pinces, ils lançaient le butin frétillant dans un seau tandis que Kipper et moi, nous poussions des cris enthousiastes.

L'après-midi, bien calés dans nos chambres à air, on se laissa porter par la marée montante. En sortant de l'eau, j'étalai ma serviette sur le sable pour m'étendre à plat ventre. Pendant le pique-nique, Frankie avait annoncé à papa qu'il retournait à la scierie le lendemain.

— Dans l'équipe de nuit, précisa-t-il.

La dernière chose dont je me souviens avant de sombrer dans le sommeil, c'était de les entendre dire qu'il fallait trouver quelqu'un pour venir à la maison quand papa reprendrait son travail.

En me réveillant, je les entendis discuter du coup de téléphone de M. Telford.

— Quel homme étrange, commentait Frankie. S'inquiéter de la vente des tableaux de Kipper alors que sa femme... (Il hésita.) À pareil moment.

— Chacun se débrouille comme il peut, sans doute, répliqua posément papa.

J'ouvris un œil : il contemplait la baie, mais il n'avait pas son expression habituelle.

— Je crois que cet appel téléphonique était une excuse pour mettre les choses à plat, déclara-t-il au bout d'un moment. Il se sent peut-être coupable parce que c'était son bateau, son chauffe-eau déficient, je ne sais pas. Mais il prétend qu'il ignorait totalement qu'elles allaient venir là, et que, lorsque Marlene avait pris son carnet de croquis après l'appel de Lucy, il avait cru qu'elles allaient à la boutique.

Il se passa la main sur le visage puis poussa un soupir.

— Il m'a raconté que Lucy avait demandé à Marlene de faire son portrait, reprit-il. Une surprise pour moi. Il a proposé de me donner les esquisses qu'il avait trouvées...

Il croisa mon regard et se tut.

Plus tard, alors que le soleil descendait, on s'installa dans la chaude lumière du feu de camp pour déguster la chair des crabes fraîchement cuits. Une situation aussi normale qu'il était possible avec la douleur de nos cœurs meurtris. Je surveillais papa du coin de l'œil, m'attendant à le voir glisser dans son monde. Je remarquai que Frankie l'observait lui aussi avec circonspection. Mais papa demeurait présent et ne buvait rien d'autre que du Coca-Cola.

Il maintint le cap pendant plusieurs jours. Et puis, le mercredi après-midi, Dora Fenwick lui apporta le message laissé par maman.

27

— Je ne cherchais pas à la cacher, affirma Mme Fenwick. Je ne l'ai trouvée qu'hier soir.

Elle examina l'enveloppe qu'elle tenait à la main.

— Dans la boîte à sucre, ajouta-t-elle. L'état de la mémoire de maman empire tous les jours.

Elle suivit papa dans la cuisine, mais refusa la chaise qu'il lui offrait.

— Je ne reste pas. Je voulais seulement te donner ça.

Elle jeta un coup d'œil vers moi, occupée à essuyer la vaisselle.

Je connaissais ce regard. Il signifiait qu'elle ne parlerait pas de ce qui la tracassait tant que je serais dans la pièce. Je posai le torchon et sortis sous le porche. Par la fenêtre entrouverte, je les voyais, papa et elle, debout près de la table.

— J'ai longuement hésité : fallait-il ou pas te donner cette lettre ? dit-elle en tournant et retournant l'enveloppe entre ses doigts. J'ignore si cela va te faire du bien ou du mal, mais j'ai décidé que tu devais l'avoir.

Elle la tendit à papa avec beaucoup de réticence.

Il avala péniblement sa salive. Dans son cou, une veine battait.

— Elle...

La voix de Dora Fenwick se brisa.

— Lucy, reprit-elle, l'a laissée à ma mère ce samedi-là. Elle ne lui faisait sans doute pas confiance pour se souvenir de me prévenir qu'elle était passée.

Elle tripotait les manches de son pull comme si elle ne savait plus quoi faire de ses mains maintenant qu'elles étaient vides.

— Je te laisse maintenant.

Elle se dirigea vers la porte de la cuisine puis s'arrêta pour faire de nouveau face à papa.

— La veille, nous avions remarqué la petite dans le square alors que nous prenions le café, déclara-t-elle, et nous nous étions demandé ce qu'elle faisait là sous la pluie mais, avant de lire cette lettre, je n'y avais plus repensé.

— La petite ? interrogea papa en relevant brusquement la tête.

— Lis la lettre, murmura-t-elle. Lucy avait besoin d'une amie ce jour-là. Si seulement j'avais été chez moi.

La porte se referma et papa s'effondra sur une chaise. Il sortit la feuille de papier pliée de l'enveloppe et l'étala sur la table, les mains tremblantes. Les tremblements remontèrent le long de ses bras et gagnèrent tout son corps tandis qu'il lisait.

— Oh mon Dieu, j'aurais dû lui dire la vérité il y a des années.

Mais Mme Fenwick était déjà repartie. Dès qu'elle eut traversé la pelouse, je rentrai dans la cuisine.

— Papa ?

Je dus l'appeler trois fois de suite avant qu'il relève la tête. Il replia la feuille et, sans dire un mot, se leva et quitta la pièce. Quelques instants plus tard, j'entendis la porte de sa chambre se fermer. Lorsque Frankie l'appela pour le dîner, il prit place à table avec nous mais toucha à peine à son assiette de ragoût réchauffé.

Après le repas, papa et Kipper s'installèrent devant la télévision et Frankie sortit pour la soirée. J'attendis que sa voiture fût sortie de la cour. Puis je me rendis dans la chambre de papa. Je refermai doucement la porte derrière moi, marchai sur la pointe des pieds jusqu'à sa commode et fouillai dans ses tiroirs. L'enveloppe que lui avait donnée Mme Fenwick ne se trouvait nulle part. Je me mis à fouiller dans les tiroirs de maman. Elle n'y était pas non plus – il n'y avait plus rien sauf quelques-unes de ses vieilles coupures de journaux. Curieuse, j'en détachai une. C'était un article extrait d'un ancien numéro du *Daily Province*.

> ## LES CANADIENS SUR LE FRONT À HONG KONG
> ### *Après l'attaque des Japonais, le territoire au cœur des combats*
>
> *Ottawa, 8 décembre 1941 – Les troupes canadiennes en garnison à Hong Kong se trouvent désormais en pleine zone de conflit puisque le Canada a déclaré la guerre au Japon et que les combats ont commencé dans le Pacifique Ouest...*
> *Une dépêche de Londres, selon laquelle il est probable que les Japonais aient déjà attaqué « certaines possessions britanniques » et qui mentionne Hong Kong parmi « les endroits attaqués », n'a fait que renforcer le fait que la zone où sont postés les Canadiens se trouve en pleins combats. Le nom des unités concernées n'a pas été divulgué.*

Pourquoi avait-elle conservé cet article ?

Je passai rapidement en revue les autres coupures de presse, m'arrêtant pour examiner une photo sous un gros titre pâli : « Hong Kong envoie les premiers Canadiens au combat. » Les visages sérieux des soldats posant devant l'objectif étaient ceux d'inconnus.

Je parcourus l'article.

10 décembre – Correspondant de guerre canadien
Les forces canadiennes de Chine suscitent l'envie. Aujourd'hui,
les troupes canadiennes en Angleterre suivent les rapports de près
pour avoir des nouvelles de leurs camarades stationnés à Hong Kong.
« Les veinards ! » entend-on de tous côtés.

« Et penser que si j'étais resté avec mon vieux régiment, je serais
à Hong Kong aujourd'hui », a déclaré un colonel de 1ʳᵉ division de
Winnipeg débarqué en Angleterre avec le premier contingent il y a
deux ans. Ils vont donner du fil à retordre à ces Japs. »

En remettant la coupure de presse dans le tiroir, j'aperçus
le télégramme jaune et passé. Je lus le court message, adressé
à maman chez tante Mildred, Vine Street.

Hong Kong ? Mon père était allé à Hong Kong ? Je ne
comprenais plus rien. Je m'assis sur le tabouret. Même si mon
père n'en parlait strictement jamais, je savais qu'il avait fait
la guerre mais j'ignorais qu'il était allé à Hong Kong. Je pensai
brusquement à la petite Chinoise dans le square. Avait-elle
quelque chose à voir avec mon père ? Venait-elle de Hong
Kong ? L'avait-elle connu quand il y était ? Non. Elle était
bien trop jeune. Dans ma cervelle, un fouillis de questions
m'assaillaient dans tous les sens.

Perplexe, je refermai tout et allai m'asseoir sous le porche.
À la télévision, la voix de Timmy demandant à Lassie de
rentrer passait par la fenêtre ouverte du salon tandis que je
contemplais le square de l'autre côté de la rue.

Un groupe d'enfants jouaient à la balle au prisonnier dans
la lumière du crépuscule. Leurs rires résonnaient dans la nuit
chaude de l'été. Ardith me fit signe de venir les rejoindre. Je
secouai la tête. De temps à autre, venue des porches et des
maisons, on entendait la voix mélodieuse d'une mère rappelant ses enfants. La pierre brûlante du chagrin encore au fond

de ma poitrine s'alourdit à l'idée que je n'entendrais plus jamais cet appel familier.

Je demeurai assise, le menton dans la main, jusqu'à ce que Danny Fenwick apparût sur notre pelouse. Il s'installa sur une marche, plus bas que moi, adossé à la balustrade. Le ciel s'obscurcissait. J'essayai de rester attentive tandis qu'il racontait des banalités – la rentrée scolaire dans deux semaines, sa nouvelle bicyclette –, mais, comme papa, j'avais la tête ailleurs. Il n'insista pas et on resta là, en silence, à observer le jeu qui continuait à la lumière des réverbères.

— Tu savais que ma mère était venue chez toi voir la tienne ce samedi-là… le jour où elle est morte ? demandai-je.

— Non, dit-il en remontant nerveusement ses lunettes sur son nez. Non, je ne savais pas.

— Bon, tu as déjà vu une fille, une Chinoise, par ici ?

Je désignai le square d'un signe de tête.

— Ah oui, plusieurs fois. Et même un matin où il pleuvait à verse.

— Qu'est-ce qu'elle faisait ?

— Elle restait là, comme ça. Je croyais qu'elle attendait quelqu'un jusqu'à ce que je la voie…

Il s'interrompit brusquement.

— Quoi ? Tu la vois faire quoi ? Quel jour ?

— Rien.

— Quoi ? répétai-je en l'attrapant par l'épaule.

— Bon Dieu, Ethie, je voulais pas…

— Dis-le moi. Je t'en prie.

— Eh bien… euh, je l'ai vue sous ton porche ce… euh… ce matin-là… en train de discuter avec ta mère.

À ce moment-là, Mme Fenwick appela Danny d'une voix retentissante. Il se leva.

— Faut que j'y aille, dit-il en fourrant ses mains au fond de ses poches.

Il fit quelques pas puis se retourna et marmonna quelque chose.

— Comment ?

— J'ai demandé si tu voulais revenir au fort dans l'arbre avec moi demain ?

— Oh… euh non, déclinai-je en tentant de m'arracher un sourire mais sachant que c'était un échec. Merci, mais pas demain.

Demain, je retournais au centre-ville. J'allais enfin découvrir quel rapport il y avait entre cette fille et ma famille.

28

1ᵉʳ janvier 1942 : Hong Kong, camp de North Point

Le groupe chargé de l'ensevelissement quitta le camp à l'aube. Une fumée grise montait des bûchers funéraires japonais tandis qu'ils approchaient du champ de bataille jonché de cadavres. Tant de morts. Des deux côtés. Howard planta sa pelle dans le sol. Puis il enleva sa chemise et s'enveloppa le visage dedans. Le tissu maculé par la sueur et les combats n'était guère efficace pour atténuer la puanteur asphyxiante – une puanteur si épaisse que l'air était devenu opaque –, mais du moins, il empêchait les mouches de s'introduire dans sa bouche et ses narines.

La terre humide cédait facilement, s'ouvrant volontiers pour recevoir son dû.

L'espace d'une seconde, l'odeur innocente du sol détrempé par la pluie allégea la pestilence environnante. Lui revint le souvenir-éclair d'une rue de Vancouver sous la pluie. Un peu plus de deux mois auparavant, Lucy et lui étaient-ils vraiment ensemble sur la pelouse mouillée devant chez Mildred ? C'était dans une autre vie. Dans un autre monde – un monde raisonnable. Existait-il encore ? En ce moment même, Lucy marchait-elle dans cette rue ou était-elle couchée dans cette maison, inquiète de ne pas savoir s'il était mort ou vivant ?

Je vais bien, Lucy. Je vais bien. À chaque pelletée de terre, il répétait silencieusement ce message pour que, porté par le vent, il traverse l'océan et parvienne jusqu'au cœur de Lucy. Je vais bien, Lucy.

Lorsque le trou fut assez large et profond, les soldats, deux par deux, s'attelèrent à l'épouvantable tâche d'entasser leurs camarades morts dans ce tombeau collectif. Howard se pencha sur le premier corps. Il déglutit, bloquant la nausée provoquée par la bile qui montait du fond de sa gorge, et ôta doucement la plaque d'identité du cadavre boursouflé. Quelqu'un cria : « Teiryuu ! » Stop.

Howard prit un coup de crosse sur la tête et tomba à genoux sous le choc. La plaque lui fut arrachée des mains et lancée au fond du trou. Les oreilles bourdonnantes, il entendit une dispute éclater entre les gardes hurlants et les prisonniers fous de colère qui tentaient de sauver les plaques d'identité.

Howard s'obligea à se remettre debout. Au cours des dernières semaines, il avait compris que leurs geôliers ne suivaient les règles que si elles leur convenaient. La veille encore, après qu'un officier anglais avait demandé que ses hommes soient traités de façon plus humaine, il avait été passé à tabac par un garde du camp qui avait craché en mauvais anglais : « Japon pas signé Convention Genève. » La vie des prisonniers ne tenait qu'à la magnanimité de l'Empereur ; ce qui signifiait, se disait Howard, qu'ils devaient présenter une utilité quelconque – une monnaie d'échange, des otages, qui pouvait le savoir ?

En tout cas, il était évident que les gardes étaient bien décidés à les démoraliser et les déshumaniser par tous les moyens possibles. Et quel meilleur moyen que de leur prendre leurs noms ?

Il se remit à la tâche. Ignorant le harcèlement des ordres incessants, ignorant les coups de crosse, ignorant l'odeur de

la mort, ignorant son ventre qui criait famine, il se concentra
sur la plaque d'identité du corps suivant.

— Souvenez-vous des noms ! cria-t-il. Souvenez-vous des
noms !

L'appel fut entendu et passa d'homme en homme tandis
qu'ils inhumaient leurs frères. Souvenez-vous des noms.

Bujold… Lebel… McGrath… Chalmers…

De retour au camp, Howard aperçut le colonel Sutcliffe
dans la section réservée aux officiers. Il semblait avoir vieilli
de quarante ans en deux semaines et ses épaules jadis carrées
s'affaissaient davantage à chaque nom de disparu.

Durant les semaines qui suivirent, à chaque appel, à chaque
interminable séance de garde-à-vous sous le soleil de l'après-
midi, Howard ne cessait de répéter silencieusement les noms
des soldats tombés. Ce mantra interne aidait à estomper les
voix, les visages, la présence de ses geôliers, renforçant sa
détermination à ne pas laisser de place pour leurs noms à eux
dans sa tête.

18 janvier 1942 : … Doyle… Main… Slaughter…

Impossible de retenir la totalité des noms mais il en mémo-
risait le plus possible. Durant la journée, il n'y avait pas grand-
chose d'autre à faire si ce n'était penser à la nourriture et il
refusait catégoriquement de tomber dans ce piège. Il classait
de tête par ordre alphabétique une liste qui ne cessait de
s'allonger, répétant l'exercice en silence dès qu'il était tout seul
— même pendant qu'il vidait ses entrailles hurlantes. Les mouches avaient amené la dysenterie. Personne n'était épargné.

Howard sauta sur la digue de l'autre côté de la palissade —
le seul endroit possible où se soulager, tout au fond du camp.
Il accrocha sa ceinture à un poteau de la clôture pour conserver
son équilibre et s'accroupit. Il s'efforçait de ne pas regarder
en bas l'eau qui venait lécher les rochers couverts de vase.

Chaque vague apportait son lot d'horreurs nouvelles – des cadavres boursouflés et des membres humains flottant au milieu d'autres détritus.

Il remonta son pantalon. Malgré lui, ses yeux se dirigèrent vers le bas. Il se figea. Dans l'eau, juste à l'aplomb, il y avait une jambe humaine. Une longue bande molletière traînait derrière le mollet dénudé, flottant comme un point d'interrogation à partir du brodequin, toujours lacé. Un pied droit. En hâte, Howard se décrocha de la clôture. Il avait besoin d'un grand bâton pour repêcher la chaussure qui remplacerait avantageusement celle de Gordy. Avançant frénétiquement jusqu'au bord de la digue, il essaya de soulever une des planches.

— Laisse tomber ! D'ici quelques heures, y en aura un nouveau qui quittera le Mouroir. Une fois partis, ils n'ont plus besoin de chaussures…

Howard fit volte-face pour voir qui avait parlé mais il n'y avait personne. Ces mots sortaient directement de sa tête. Il s'effondra par terre. Mais à quoi pensait-il ? Un brodequin alourdi d'eau ? La faim et l'inquiétude que lui inspirait Gordy le faisaient délirer.

L'état de la jambe de Gordy avait bien empiré. Il ne pouvait plus prendre appui dessus. Tous les matins, Howard l'aidait à clopiner dehors pour monter la garde près de la clôture. Il refusait de retourner à l'infirmerie. Howard pouvait difficilement le lui reprocher. Il l'avait accompagné la première semaine dans l'entrepôt reconverti afin que le médecin libère le pied enflé de la grosse chaussure. « Rien d'étonnant à ce que ce lieu soit surnommé le " Mouroir " », avait-il pensé en regardant le médecin nettoyer la plaie et l'envelopper dans des pansements usagés. Guère plus qu'un baraquement au fond du camp, « l'hôpital » n'était ni plus propre ni plus hygiénique que les autres bâtiments en ruine du camp de North Point.

Il y avait maintenant plus de six mille prisonniers entassés dans des baraques prévues pour loger trois cents réfugiés. L'hôpital était à l'avenant ; peu adapté à un homme en bonne santé, c'était une catastrophe pour les malades et les blessés. Ils gisaient sur des lits de fortune et des civières posées à même le sol de béton maculé de sang et de crasse, protégés par des couvertures trop légères ou par rien du tout, soignés par des médecins militaires et des bénévoles débordés qui n'avaient pas grand-chose à offrir en dehors de leur compassion et de leurs faux espoirs. Une vision obsédante à laquelle Howard fut aussi soulagé que Gordy d'échapper.

Si les prisonniers redoutaient cet hôpital de fortune, ce n'était pas seulement à cause des conditions sanitaires. Howard, comme la totalité du camp, était au courant du carnage qui avait eu lieu à l'hôpital militaire de Saint Stephen. Jack Dell s'était démené pour prévenir tout le monde. Il s'y était fait amputer d'un bras deux jours avant le débarquement des Japonais, la veille de Noël. Ayant déjà survécu à un massacre, il savait à quoi s'attendre. Dès que les Japonais envahirent l'escalier et les salles, il roula au bas de son lit et alla se cacher derrière une pile de linge. Il resta là durant tout le carnage. Maintenant, il arpentait le camp en racontant à qui voulait l'entendre comment les malades et les blessés avaient été tués par balles ou à coups de baïonnette.

— Le sang coulait tellement à flots qu'il ruisselait sur les marches d'escalier. Une fois tous les soldats liquidés, les Japonais, déchaînés, se sont mis à violer et assassiner les infirmières et les religieuses.

D'après lui, l'interminable orgie de destruction sanglante avait duré jusqu'au lendemain. Soixante-dix soldats anglais et canadiens périrent, ainsi que vingt-cinq membres du personnel de l'hôpital. Jack Dell et les quelques autres survivants furent obligés de les incinérer. Et, comme lors des inhumations qui avaient suivi la capitulation, il leur fut interdit de récupérer les plaques d'identité. Lorsque les officiers japonais débarquèrent sur les lieux du massacre et apprirent de la bouche d'un médecin hystérique ce qui s'était passé, ils exécutèrent les coupables sur place, en promettant que ces impardonnables atrocités ne se reproduiraient plus. Mais qui pouvait encore croire à ce qu'ils disaient ? Certainement pas les prisonniers, qui souffraient déjà de malnutrition et qui, chaque jour, assistaient, impuissants, à la mort de leurs amis et de leurs camarades.

Cependant, comme le pied et la jambe de Gordy ne cessaient d'enfler sous les pansements noircis, Howard le suppliait de retourner à l'hôpital. Celui-ci refusait. Il ne voulait qu'une seule chose : se poster à la barrière du camp.

Howard harcelait les médecins pour obtenir des médicaments qui n'existaient pas. « Trouve-lui seulement une meilleure alimentation », tel était l'unique conseil qu'ils pouvaient offrir.

La nourriture – deux misérables rations de riz moisi souvent couvert d'asticots et de crottes de souris – devenait l'événement autour duquel s'articulait toute la journée. De temps en temps, les prisonniers recevaient en plus des gamelles de légumes puants, qui se révélaient être des épluchures en décomposition mélangées à de l'herbe et des algues. Howard espérait que la « saloperie verte », comme l'appelaient les prisonniers, renforçait un peu la valeur nutritive des maigres portions. Il faisait la queue deux fois par jour, raclant la moitié de sa propre ration dans le casque de Gordy avant de le lui apporter, mais son corpulent ami perdait du poids à vue d'œil, encore plus rapidement que les autres prisonniers, et le rouge profond de l'infection grimpait à l'assaut de sa cuisse.

Durant la deuxième semaine de février, sur l'insistance de Howard, Ken Campbell amena un médecin du camp au chevet de Gordy.

— Il va falloir s'en débarrasser, déclara le médecin après avoir examiné la jambe. Amenez-le dans les baraquements sanitaires.

— Pas question qu'ils me coupent la jambe, grommela Gordy dès que le médecin fut parti.

Ken, un des rares courageux qui avaient accepté de travailler comme garçon de salle dans l'hôpital de fortune, refusa de l'écouter.

— Il n'y a pas le choix, riposta-t-il. C'est ta jambe ou ta vie.

— Je prends le risque, s'entêta Gordy en s'efforçant de se mettre debout.

— Et qu'est-ce que je suis censé raconter à Shun-ling quand ce sera cuit ? Que tu es mort parce que tu avais peur ? Que ça t'était bien égal de ne jamais la revoir mais que tu voulais garder ton corps intact ?

On lui coupa la jambe en dessous du genou. Ken réussit à convaincre un des gardes les plus amicaux de leur fournir un petit flacon de chloroforme. Mais Howard ne savait vraiment pas comment Gordy avait pu supporter ça. À l'extérieur, même en se bouchant les oreilles, il entendait encore ses cris étouffés tandis que les médecins l'opéraient dans des conditions absolument primaires. Les jours suivants, il resta dans le baraquement pour soigner son ami, dormant par terre à côté de lui. Dès que Gordy parvint à tenir sur sa jambe valide, ils quittèrent le Mouroir en clopinant.

Dès lors, prendre soin de Gordy devint l'objectif prioritaire de Howard. Il dénicha un bidon d'huile d'arachide pour lui éviter d'avoir à marcher jusqu'à la digue ; il l'aidait à s'accroupir dessus devant leur baraque. Il arracha deux planches à la cloison du fond pour lui fabriquer une paire de béquilles. Et tous les matins, il allait avec lui jusqu'à la barrière ; ils s'asseyaient dans l'ombre du corps de garde et surveillaient la route qui passait devant le camp.

Au fil des mois, les conditions de vie à North Point ne firent qu'empirer. Dans la journée, il n'y avait aucun moyen de fuir le soleil torride. Les nuits étaient étonnamment froides. De nombreux prisonniers n'avaient pour tout lit que des planches nues ou le sol de béton ; ils dormaient donc serrés à trois ou quatre et se relayaient pour être au milieu et récupérer un peu de chaleur.

— Quand on rentrera chez nous, tu raconteras à Lucy que j'ai bien chauffé ton lit, plaisantait un Gordy frissonnant, calé entre Ken et Howard. Dis-lui que j'ai tenu ma promesse : je me suis bien occupé de toi.

— Tu lui diras toi-même.

Les punaises sévissaient, en dépit de l'absence de couvertures. Avec les poux et les puces, elles torturaient ceux qui souffraient déjà le martyre. Heureux que Gordy, Ken et lui soient encore miraculeusement préservés de cette plaie, Howard regardait ses malheureux compagnons devenir fous à force de se gratter. Il se demandait combien de temps allaient encore durer les effets de la potion magique de Ah Sam.

Lieutenant-colonel J. L. R. Sutcliffe. Le 7 avril, Howard ajouta ce nom à sa liste mentale. Le béribéri et l'anémie avaient eu raison du colonel. Mais Howard était persuadé qu'il avait lâché prise, que voir périr tant de « ses gars » avait fini par lui briser le cœur. Il participa à la cérémonie au cours de laquelle on l'enterra dans le cimetière de fortune à l'extérieur du camp. Ils avaient cessé de jouer le *Last Post*. Un dernier adieu trop déchirant. Plus rien ne venait signaler les tombes. Dès qu'on plantait une croix en bois, les réfugiés venaient la nuit chaparder ce bon combustible. Ils rouvraient les tombes pour y voler les pauvres suaires. Les prisonniers, à la longue, cessèrent d'envelopper les corps. La nuit, les vivants manquaient déjà de chaleur.

On était à la fin avril et Howard, posté à la clôture, observait les régiments anglais qui partaient sur le continent, pour Camp Argyle et Sham Shui Po. Soudain, parmi les milliers de soldats dépenaillés qui défilaient devant lui, il aperçut Peter Young et Dick Baxter. Leurs cheveux avaient poussé et leurs uniformes débraillés pendaient sur leurs corps amaigris, mais les mitrailleurs du Middlesex réussissaient encore à porter beau. Soulagé de voir qu'ils avaient tous deux survécu, Howard les interpella.

— Eh, vous vouliez de l'action ! Vous avez été servis, non ?

Peter s'arrêta et scruta la foule massée près de la barrière. Il sourit quand son regard croisa celui de Howard.

— Ouais, on attend toujours les médailles !

Il prit un coup de crosse dans les côtes. Projeté en avant, il cria :

— Les Canucks, on vous retrouve au Sun Sun quand tout sera terminé ! C'est pas pour rien qu'on nous surnomme les durs à cuire !

— Ce sera votre tour de payer la tournée ! cria Howard à son tour.

Les gardiens les plus sadiques partirent en même temps que les Anglais. Le pire d'entre eux était un petit homme au visage pincé qui se pavanait dans le camp comme un coq nain. Cette pose affectée de duelliste convaincu aurait paru comique à Howard si la cruauté de l'homme n'avait pas été si implacable. Il se tenait souvent à l'entrée du camp où, à force de faux sourires et d'offres de nourriture, il attirait les jeunes filles des environs pour les violenter dans le corps de garde. Leurs hurlements étaient une torture pour Gordy et Howard.

Si prendre plaisir à la souffrance des autres représentait l'essence du mal, alors Howard estimait qu'elle était incarnée dans ce garde que les prisonniers avaient surnommé Satan. Tard le soir, il se cachait au fond du camp pour guetter les malheureux qui venaient à la digue se soulager. Sans leur en laisser le temps, il surgissait en leur ordonnant de s'incliner devant lui. Il les forçait à se pencher encore et encore, de plus en plus bas, tout en les piquant de la pointe de sa baïonnette. Quand ils finissaient par se souiller, il s'esclaffait. Il avait l'habitude d'aspirer l'air entre ses dents de devant écartées et, comme le grelot d'un chat, ce bruit avertissait tout le monde. Howard, en même temps que le reste du camp, poussa un soupir de soulagement lorsqu'il partit avec les Anglais.

Brusquement, une fois les prisonniers anglais transférés, la surpopulation diminua à North Point. La vie du camp s'organisa et Howard était convaincu de ce qu'il affirmait à Gordy : leur liberté n'était qu'une affaire de mois. Malheureusement, la nourriture ne subit aucune amélioration et la moindre récrimination provoquait raclée ou nouvelle réduction des portions. Mais l'espoir était là. Howard prit conscience de la présence d'une radio de contrebande cachée entre les montants du mur d'une des baraques. Le moral remontait quand le bouche à oreille transmettait d'authentiques nouvelles – plutôt que la propagande diffusée par les Japonais.

La rumeur courait, chargée d'espoir, que la situation allait bientôt s'arranger ; mais désormais, ils ne croyaient plus qu'aux Américains. Plus personne ne faisait allusion à l'armée fantôme de Tchang Kaï-chek.

En mai, les prisonniers furent autorisés pour la première fois à écrire chez eux, vingt-cinq malheureux mots sur une mince feuille de papier pelure. Il n'y avait aucun moyen de savoir si cette lettre partirait jamais mais cela faisait du bien de griffonner ce message positif, d'imaginer la joie de Lucy en reconnaissant son écriture. « Ma Lucy chérie, tu me manques. Je pense à toi tous les jours. Tout va bien. Bon moral.

Bien traité. Je t'aime pour toujours, Howard. » Mentir de la sorte ne lui donnait aucune culpabilité.

Peu de temps après avoir bénéficié de ce geste de bonne volonté, les Canadiens apprirent qu'ils allaient travailler à l'élargissement de la piste d'atterrissage sur l'aéroport de Kai Tak. Une vingtaine de grenadiers en relativement bonne forme physique, dont Howard, escortés par un gardien armé, prirent le ferry pour se rendre sur le continent en compagnie d'autres groupes sélectionnés pour cette tâche. De l'aube au crépuscule, les prisonniers de guerre trimèrent pour aplanir une petite hauteur. Ils transportaient la terre à l'autre bout de la piste dans des paniers suspendus à des tiges de bambou, style coolie.

Heureusement, le gardien responsable du groupe de Howard ne faisait pas partie des méchants.

La cruauté de la plupart de leurs geôliers, remarqua Howard, était en lien direct avec leur loyauté envers l'Empire japonais, avec leur arrogance ou avec un sentiment de supériorité très adolescent. Peu étaient aussi sadiques que Satan. Et peu étaient aussi bienveillants que leur propre gardien qui les traitait avec un semblant de respect, ne jouant les sévères qu'en présence de ses supérieurs. Il s'excusait souvent de « notre situation » et montrait des photos de sa famille chaque fois qu'il en avait l'occasion. À plusieurs reprises – ce qui était très risqué pour lui, Howard en était persuadé – il avait glissé une boîte de lait concentré à un prisonnier qui en avait impérativement besoin.

Alors qu'à l'aéroport les autres gardiens hurlaient continuellement des ordres, exigeant toujours plus de travail de leurs ouailles à bout de forces, il ne disait rien lorsque quelqu'un de son groupe faisait une pause. Avec lui, l'eau n'était pas rationnée, il les laissait boire à volonté. Et lorsqu'ils se rangeaient devant lui à l'heure des repas, il acceptait sans sourciller ceux qui revenaient chercher une deuxième portion.

Au coucher du soleil, il s'inclinait en remerciant les hommes de cette bonne journée de travail. Bizarre à quel point un peu de respect remontait le moral, même en pareilles circonstances, pensait Howard quand le groupe revenait vers le ferry, fatigué certes mais tout de même en forme. Sans parler des rations supplémentaires. Pour la dixième fois, il tâta le trésor de contrebande au fond de sa poche. Des sprats. Les minuscules poissons, qui ressemblaient à des sardines, étaient maintenant en bouillie mais ils fourniraient à Gordy un peu de ces protéines dont il manquait tellement. En approchant du quai, il se demanda comment son ami s'était débrouillé tout seul. Quelqu'un l'avait-il aidé à utiliser le bidon d'huile d'arachide ? Avait-il réussi à aller jusqu'à la clôture pour y monter la garde ? Y était-il toujours, attendant comme tous les jours, quelqu'un qu'ils espéraient bien, Howard et lui – même s'ils n'avaient jamais parlé d'elle depuis leur arrivée au camp –, ne jamais voir.

Et brusquement, il l'aperçut. Même de loin, il était persuadé que c'était Shun-ling. Elle était à côté du tourniquet du *Star ferry*, à l'endroit précis où elle les avait attendus ce premier soir, lorsqu'ils étaient allés au cinéma.

Howard se faufila dans le groupe compact des prisonniers, sans la quitter des yeux. Shun-ling le regardait, elle aussi, tout en observant le garde adossé à un réverbère en train de fumer une cigarette, l'arme à l'épaule, l'air désinvolte. Howard se retrouva enfin près d'elle, si près qu'ils n'étaient plus séparés que par le tourniquet de métal qui leur arrivait à la taille. D'abord, aucun des deux ne parla. Il chercha son regard. Quelque chose avait changé. Ce n'étaient pas les yeux d'une gamine. Mais elle n'avait jamais eu le regard d'une gamine. Elle n'avait que dix-huit ans mais, d'emblée, Howard s'était senti un vrai môme en sa présence. Un môme de vingt et un ans, marié, mais un môme tout de même. Son expérience de la vie était alors négligeable à côté de tout ce qu'on pouvait lire au fond des yeux de Shun-ling. La dernière fois qu'il l'avait vue, il endossait à peine le joug de sa virilité avec l'uniforme, le mariage précipité, le départ à la guerre alors qu'elle avait déjà vécu une vie entière d'atrocités. Mais ces cinq derniers mois avaient compté comme une vie entière. Howard avait perdu toute naïveté, il n'avait plus rien d'enfantin et leurs yeux se croisèrent, lourds de leurs expériences d'adultes.

Malgré lui, son regard se posa brièvement sur la manche de la jeune fille, attiré par le brassard blanc sur lequel on voyait un soleil rouge sang.

— Ah Sam dit qu'il faut absolument faire au moins semblant d'être de leur côté, déclara-t-elle.

— C'est un homme d'une grande sagesse, répondit Howard.

— Et un homme bon. Il s'occupe de notre famille. Nous sommes sous sa protection.

— Gordy sera heureux de l'apprendre.

— Où est-il ? J'ai entendu dire que les Canadiens travaillaient à l'aéroport. J'espérais le voir. Je…

Elle s'interrompit.

— Il va bien ? reprit-elle.

Fallait-il lui parler de la jambe de Gordy ? Lui révéler à quel point il avait maigri ? Lui raconter le sang et le pus qu'il voyait chaque fois qu'il vidait le bidon d'huile d'arachide ?

Il jeta un coup d'œil autour de lui pour voir qui pouvait les entendre.

— Il a besoin de médicaments, Shun-ling, chuchota-t-il. Des comprimés de soufre. Ah Sam peut-il nous en apporter ?

— Impossible de prendre pareil risque. Les Japonais le considèrent comme un de leurs alliés, dit-elle à voix si basse qu'il dut se pencher. J'en apporterai moi-même.

— Non. C'est dangereux. Ne t'approche pas du camp. Désormais, je travaille tous les jours à l'aéroport. Attends-moi là-bas.

— Très bien.

— Tu le vois, celui-là ? dit Howard en désignant discrètement le garde. Ne viens que si c'est ce garde. Ne prends pas ce risque si c'en est un autre.

La sirène du ferry retentit. Le garde écrasa sa cigarette sous son talon et d'un geste fit avancer ses troupes.

— Je suis content de voir que tu vas aussi bien, déclara Howard en s'éloignant à reculons.

Durant leur brève conversation, il avait remarqué que Shun-ling avait renoncé à tout faux-semblant de pidgin. Marque de confiance ou nécessité ?

Au moment où elle se retourna pour partir, il la vit de profil et, alors qu'elle protégeait à deux mains la rondeur révélatrice de son ventre, il comprit pourquoi elle était venue chercher Gordy.

Dès que Gordy fut au courant de ce qui s'était passé à l'embarcadère, il insista pour faire partie du groupe de ceux qui travaillaient à l'aéroport. Les gardes n'y virent aucun inconvénient. Ils avaient un quota de cinq cents hommes et, valides ou non, il leur fallait cinq cents prisonniers sur le ferry tous les matins.

Howard ignorait où il avait trouvé la force nécessaire mais le lendemain, Gordy, appuyé sur ses béquilles, mélangea une bassine de ciment dans l'espoir d'avoir quelques moments avec Shun-ling en fin de journée. Avant de partir, Howard avait fourré dans la doublure de son calot tout l'argent que Gordy et lui avaient réussi à conserver. Lorsqu'ils avaient été faits prisonniers, on leur avait confisqué les dollars de Hong Kong dont ils avaient bourré leurs poches d'uniforme mais on n'avait pas pensé à chercher au fond de leurs bottes. Au camp, l'argent ne servait à rien. Inutile de tenter de s'en servir pour corrompre les gardes, cela ne ferait que provoquer une fouille généralisée.

Lorsqu'ils reprirent le ferry en fin de journée, Shun-ling attendait près du tourniquet. Gordy, les yeux pleins de larmes, se pencha sur ses béquilles et Howard resta à distance. Lorsque le ferry arriva à quai, le garde entreprit de faire monter les prisonniers à bord et Howard en profita pour s'approcher. Tout en chuchotant quelques ultimes paroles à Gordy, elle glissa un petit paquet dans la main de Howard. En échange, il lui passa son calot. Ce fut un vrai soulagement d'être débarrassé de cet argent en sachant que Shun-ling et sa famille allaient en profiter.

Les jours suivants, quand il la vit au ferry, Howard préféra se tenir à distance. Il ne souhaitait nullement être témoin de leurs conversations pressées. Pas plus que d'entendre Shun-ling revenir au langage d'une servante appointée.

Que ce fût grâce au médicament de Shun-ling, ou simplement à sa présence, la santé de Gordy parut s'améliorer. Ravi à l'idée d'être père, il faisait des projets pour leur vie commune.

— On va se marier quand tout sera fini, raconta-t-il maintes fois à Howard, comme s'il ne parvenait pas à y croire. Tu te rends compte ! Elle va venir vivre au Canada avec ce pauvre Jambe-de-Bois.

Des semaines durant, Howard vécut par procuration, observant leurs brèves rencontres et écoutant Gordy prévoir leur avenir. De quoi certifier que la vie continuait.

« Ceux qui survivent sont ceux capables d'envisager la possibilité d'une autre vie », avait dit Ken Campbell à propos des patients du Mouroir.

Gordy en était bien la preuve.

De ses propres rêves, Howard avait de plus en plus de difficultés à se souvenir. Au Manitoba, il n'avait jamais prêté beaucoup d'attention à l'arrivée du courrier. Le facteur n'apportait que des catalogues et des factures. Maintenant, à l'instar des autres, il priait pour recevoir une lettre de chez lui. Mais il n'y en avait pas.

— Pas de courrier aujourd'hui, disaient les gardes en haussant les épaules.

Les plus cruels se moquaient d'eux.

— Vos familles vous ont oubliés. Elles ne se soucient plus de vous.

Personne ne croyait à ces affirmations, personne et surtout pas Howard. Il savait que Lucy devait lui écrire tous les jours, exactement comme elle le lui avait promis. N'empêche, il était difficile de garder confiance alors qu'il n'y avait plus qu'une photo toute cornée à laquelle se raccrocher.

29

Une fois convaincue que la fille du square avait quelque chose à voir avec ma famille, j'avais été obnubilée par cette idée. Ce soir-là, alors que Kipper et moi étions couchés, que Frankie était parti pour son service de nuit à la scierie, que papa avait éteint la télévision depuis longtemps, je restai éveillée à envisager un moyen d'aller en ville dès le lendemain. Au matin, j'attendis que Frankie soit monté se coucher pour expliquer à Kipper que nous allions vivre une aventure secrète. Lorsque papa entra dans la cuisine, je mis le doigt sur mes lèvres avec ce que j'espérais un air conspirateur. Mais c'était inutile. En le voyant se verser du café et s'asseoir, je compris que j'aurais pu lui raconter que Kipper et moi étions prêts à nous envoler sur la lune. Si tant est qu'il eût répondu, il aurait marmonné : « C'est une bonne idée », son regard vitreux fixé sur la fenêtre.

Au moment de quitter la maison, j'étais tellement préoccupée que je ne remarquai les nuages bas et chargés de pluie qu'en atteignant l'arrêt de bus sur Victoria Drive. Kipper, lui aussi, était surexcité. À peine installés dans le bus, je lui révélai notre destination ; dès lors, il ne parla plus de rien d'autre que de la petite maison rouge derrière le magasin. Aussi, lorsqu'il demanda si nous pouvions retourner la voir, je lui racontai que c'était une maison fantôme. Ce qui n'était pas tout à fait un mensonge. L'année dernière, en cours, on nous avait parlé des « maisons des esprits » qu'on trouve en Asie et il n'était pas impossible que c'en fût une. Sachant à quel point Kipper redoutait les fantômes, je me demande pourquoi je lui ai raconté une chose pareille si ce n'est, justement, que je souhaitais vraiment qu'il en oublie tout. Mais, si j'avais pu prévoir les répercussions qu'allaient avoir ces paroles imprudentes, je me serais abstenue.

Nous sommes descendus dans le centre-ville. Le ciel, au-dessus des immeubles, était d'un noir menaçant. Les premières grosses gouttes de pluie tombèrent au moment où nous traversions Hastings Street. Le temps d'arriver à Chinatown, nous étions trempés. La pluie débordait des flaques sur le trottoir et dégouttait des bords du chapeau de Kipper. L'eau ruisselait des auvents alors que nous marchions dans les rues grises, sautant d'un abri à l'autre jusqu'à nous retrouver enfin, tout frissonnants, entre les cageots de légumes, devant le magasin où nous avions vu la fille.

Mais, une fois là, je n'avais plus le cœur à entrer. J'avais atteint mon premier objectif mais je n'avais pas réfléchi à l'étape suivante. Et si elle n'était pas là, si elle ne travaillait pas aujourd'hui ? Qui allais-je demander ? Une Chinoise ?

Tandis que j'hésitais, une petite dame chinoise toute voûtée sortit du magasin, portant des sacs remplis de légumes. Je m'écartai pour la laisser passer mais elle s'arrêta pour dévisager Kipper.

— Quoi il a ? demanda-t-elle.

Cette question, je la détestais. Seuls les gens grossiers osaient la poser. Je répondis exactement comme maman m'avait toujours dit de le faire.

— Il est atteint de trisomie 21.

— Non, répondit la dame aux cheveux gris d'un ton irrité. C'est respiration. Lui comme pas respirer.

Je me tournai vers Kipper. Obsédée par l'idée de la fille, je n'avais pas remarqué à quel point son souffle était rauque. Il prit son inhalateur dans sa poche. Il appuya dessus et inspira par petits coups. Il le ressortit, l'examina. Le sifflement s'intensifia. Son visage avait pris une étrange teinte grise.

— Qu'est-ce qu'il y a ? demandai-je tandis qu'il secouait l'inhalateur.

— C'est… vide, réussit-il à dire.

Submergée de peur et de culpabilité, je me mis à le tapoter dans le dos.

— Détends-toi, bégayai-je tout en cherchant ce que maman disait pour le calmer. Concentre-toi pour respirer lentement.

Tandis qu'il se battait pour faire entrer l'air dans ses poumons sifflants, les clients entraient et sortaient du magasin. La plupart le regardaient mais sans s'arrêter. Même la vieille dame nous avait abandonnés. Alors que j'étais sur le point de céder à la panique, elle ressortit de la boutique, accompagnée de la fille en tablier.

Tandis que la dame ouvrait son parapluie et s'éloignait d'un pas traînant, la jeune fille se pencha vers Kipper jusqu'à ce que leurs yeux soient à la même hauteur.

— Re-bonjour, dit-elle.

— Sa-lut, réussit-il à haleter mais avec un sourire qui montrait qu'il la reconnaissait.

— Qu'est-ce qui t'arrive ? s'enquit-elle gentiment.

Je m'empressai de répondre à sa place.

— Une crise d'asthme. Kipper – mon frère – a de l'asthme. Son inhalateur est vide.

Je parlai à toute vitesse comme si, moi aussi, je risquais de manquer d'air.

— Venez avec moi.

La douceur de sa voix était apaisante, rassurante. Prenant Kipper par la main, je la suivis dans le magasin. Sans s'arrêter, elle dit quelques mots inintelligibles à un homme derrière le comptoir ; celui-ci acquiesça d'un hochement de tête en continuant à rendre la monnaie à un client.

L'odeur de terre qui régnait dans l'arrière-boutique me fit penser au camion de livraison du vieux M. Fong. Des piles de cageots remplis de fruits et de légumes se devinaient dans le clair-obscur.

Kipper s'immobilisa soudain. Il me lâcha la main et se mit à reculer.

— Et si... les... fantômes... les fantômes viennent ? lâcha-t-il.

— Les fantômes ? répéta la jeune fille en se tournant vers lui.

— Ceux... de...la... petite... la petite...

Il se battait avec son souffle, il se battait avec les mots.

— C'est ma faute, avouai-je. Je lui ai dit qu'il y avait des fantômes dans la... euh... dans la petite maison derrière le magasin.

La jeune fille me regarda d'un air perplexe.

— La petite maison ?

Elle comprit brusquement de quoi je parlais et ses yeux noirs brillèrent.

— Ah ! s'exclama-t-elle en se tournant vers Kipper. Il ne faut pas avoir peur. Ce n'est qu'un lieu de culte. Les précédents propriétaires de ce magasin l'avaient construit pour honorer leurs ancêtres.

— Leurs... ancêtres ? répéta-t-il.

— Les membres de leur famille qui n'étaient plus vivants.

— Les... morts ?

— Oui, mais les ancêtres sont des esprits bien-faisants, lui expliqua-t-elle. La famille se rendait dans cette petite maison pour discuter avec eux, pour leur demander conseil. C'est comme un temple. Un lieu favorable.

Kipper digéra cette information et moi, j'avais honte de ma responsabilité dans cette crise d'asthme. Il s'efforça d'inspirer profondément.

— C'est... bien, conclut-il et il laissa la fille le guider dans le labyrinthe de cageots.

Au fond de l'arrière-boutique, elle s'arrêta au pied d'un escalier. Sans un mot, comme s'ils communiquaient à un autre niveau, elle l'interrogea du regard pour savoir s'il parviendrait à monter. Kipper hocha la tête et elle le prit par le bras. Je les suivis tandis qu'ils progressaient lentement, une marche à la fois, le souffle laborieux de mon frère et le craquement des marches de bois résonnant dans ce clair-obscur.

Dans l'appartement au-dessus du magasin, ça sentait la naphtaline et l'encens. Une entrée étroite donnait sur une cuisine minuscule où une femme, vêtue d'un pantalon ample et d'une grande tunique grise, s'activait devant l'évier. Elle se retourna et en nous voyant, son visage – une version plus âgée de celui de la jeune fille – se rembrunit. Peu importe si je ne comprenais pas les mots étrangers. Le ton grondeur suffisait à exprimer qu'elle n'approuvait pas notre présence. Mais la contrariété se transforma en inquiétude lorsque la jeune fille, l'air déterminé, entoura d'un bras protecteur les épaules de Kipper haletant.

— Asseyez-vous, nous ordonna-t-elle à Kipper et moi avant de disparaître dans l'entrée.

Il ne restait qu'à obéir ; la fille remplit une casserole d'eau, la posa sur le fourneau et quitta la pièce, elle aussi. Dans la cuisine, on n'entendait que le sifflement du gaz et le souffle rauque de Kipper.

La fille revint rapidement avec des serviettes ; elle m'en tendit une. Posant l'autre sur les épaules de Kipper, elle lui

ôta son chapeau trempé. Je tressaillis, prête à l'entendre protester, mais à ma grande surprise – avec le regard qu'il réservait
habituellement à maman ou à moi –, il ne dit rien et la laissa
accrocher sa coiffure au-dessus du fourneau pour la faire
sécher.

La femme plus âgée revint quelques instants plus tard, portant un grand bocal en verre rempli de feuilles sèches. Elle le
posa sur le plan de travail et dévissa le couvercle. Elle en
mesura une bonne quantité qu'elle versa dans la casserole et
laissa infuser en remuant. Puis elle s'éloigna du fourneau et
prononça quelques paroles incisives en chinois. Elle prit
ensuite le tablier de la fille et, après nous avoir jeté un dernier
coup d'œil en coin, descendit au rez-de-chaussée.

— Elle dit qu'il doit inhaler la vapeur pendant dix minutes,
expliqua la fille.

Elle remua rapidement les feuilles sans éteindre le feu et
remplit une petite bouilloire pour préparer du thé.

Tout en la regardant s'activer, la question qui me brûlait
la langue bourdonnait dans ma tête. Pourquoi était-elle venue
parler à ma mère le jour de sa mort ? Pouvais-je le lui
demander ? Cherchant comment m'exprimer, j'examinais la
cuisine mal éclairée, si différente de la nôtre. Des casseroles
noires au fond arrondi étaient pendues au-dessus du fourneau.
Des bocaux en verre et des boîtes métalliques colorées étaient
alignés sur les plans de travail. De là où j'étais assise, je voyais
un petit salon où les accoudoirs et les dossiers d'un canapé et
d'un fauteuil bordeaux étaient recouverts de napperons en
dentelle. Sur une étagère murale, s'entassaient des bibelots de
porcelaine et des photographies. Des dragons de bois s'enrou-
laient autour du paravent pliant qui séparait les deux pièces.

On retrouvait les mêmes dragons sur le saladier dans lequel
la fille versa la décoction brûlante. Elle le déposa devant
Kipper.

— Cela va t'aider à respirer, dit-elle en s'asseyant à côté de lui.

Elle le fit se pencher en avant puis le recouvrit de la serviette pour empêcher la vapeur de se disperser.

Après s'être assurée qu'il inspirait comme il fallait, elle alla s'occuper du thé.

— Je n'ai encore jamais bu de thé dans un verre, déclarai-je quand elle posa la boisson fumante devant moi.

— À Hong Kong, c'est ainsi que nous le buvons.

— Hong Kong ! m'exclamai-je, le cœur battant.

— C'est là que j'ai grandi. Je vis ici maintenant.

Elle s'assit à côté de Kipper.

Les oreilles bourdonnantes, je l'entendis raconter qu'elle n'était à Vancouver que depuis un mois. Elle devait suivre des cours à l'université à partir de septembre. Lorsqu'elle annonça qu'elle s'appelait Lily, je bafouillai :

— Lily ? C'était comme ça que maman voulait m'appeler.

En m'entendant parler de ma mère, la fille releva la tête et ses yeux noirs cherchèrent les miens.

— Je suis désolée pour ta mère, dit-elle d'une voix douce.

L'espace d'un instant, je me demandai comment elle était au courant puis le jour de l'enterrement me revint en mémoire, ce jour où nous l'avions suivie jusqu'au centre-ville : Kipper lui avait raconté que maman était partie au « bradis ».

— Merci, murmurai-je, la gorge serrée.

Ces dernières semaines, je m'étais rendue compte que cette réponse suffisait amplement. En rajouter était inutile – pour moi et pour celui qui m'offrait sa compassion.

Elle souleva la serviette de Kipper pour lui demander si ça allait.

— Oui ! acquiesça-t-il en hochant la tête, la respiration déjà plus aisée.

— Tu connaissais ma mère ? ai-je demandé.

— Non, je ne lui ai parlé qu'une seule fois, répondit-elle en remettant la serviette. Elle avait l'air très gentille.

Il fallait saisir la perche qu'elle me tendait.

— De quoi aviez-vous discuté ? m'enquis-je en m'efforçant de garder une voix posée.

Elle hésita un moment.

— J'étais à la recherche de quelqu'un.

— Qui ? Qui cherchais-tu ?

Frankie ?

— C'est compliqué.

— Compliqué ?

— Tous les mois, toute ma vie durant, répondit-elle en s'affairant autour de Kipper, quelqu'un nous a envoyé de l'argent par l'intermédiaire d'un ami de notre famille à Hong Kong. Cet homme, qui était pour moi comme un oncle, a toujours refusé de nous révéler d'où venait cet argent. Malheureusement, il est mort. Son neveu, ignorant le côté secret de cette affaire, nous a remis le dernier mandat.

— Mais quel est le rapport avec ma mère ?

Elle s'appuya au dossier de sa chaise et posa les mains sur les genoux.

— Sur l'enveloppe, l'adresse de l'expéditeur était 6979 Barclay Street.

— 6979 ! répéta Kipper en relevant la tête. C'est chez nous.

Il souriait. Il avait le menton dégoulinant mais il respirait à nouveau normalement.

Lily rajusta la serviette et l'aida à se replacer au-dessus du saladier.

— Encore quelques minutes, l'encouragea-t-elle.

Elle prit la casserole sur le fourneau pour rajouter un peu de mixture brune et brûlante.

— Tu as parlé de ça à maman ? Comment a-t-elle réagi ? demandai-je, persuadée qu'il devait y avoir eu une erreur dans l'adresse.

Personne chez nous n'avait jamais envoyé d'argent à Hong Kong.

— Elle a dit que c'était une méprise. Puis elle m'a demandé de revenir la voir le lendemain. Mais ce matin-là, il y avait beaucoup de monde chez vous. Je n'ai pas voulu déranger. Je suis revenue tous les jours pour la guetter. Et puis j'ai rencontré Kipper dans le square et il m'a informé de la triste nouvelle, conclut-elle en baissant les yeux.

— C'est la raison pour laquelle tu as cessé de venir ?

— Oui. Je ne voulais pas perturber votre chagrin familial.

Elle récupéra le saladier qu'elle alla mettre dans l'évier, laissant Kipper se sécher la tête avec la serviette.

Je soufflai sur mon thé brûlant. Kipper avait raison. Lily était sympathique. Mais finalement, elle n'avait absolument rien à voir avec notre famille. Comme l'avait dit maman, il s'agissait d'une erreur. Une mauvaise adresse. Somme toute, j'étais assez déçue. En la regardant verser une tasse de thé à mon frère, je me prenais à regretter qu'elle ne soit pas une des admiratrices de Frankie. Puis, brusquement, je réagis : pourquoi maman lui avait-elle demandé de revenir le lendemain ? Était-ce parce qu'elle était pressée, prête à sortir retrouver son amie Marlene, au moment où Lily s'était présentée ? Avait-elle eu de la peine pour cette jeune fille qui ne frappait pas à la bonne porte ? Comme ces chats et ces chiens errants qui avaient trouvé le chemin de notre maison, maman avait-elle eu l'intention de l'adopter, elle aussi ? Ou, plus probablement, avait-elle eu envie de présenter Lily à Frankie ? L'idée de maman jouant les entremetteuses me fit sourire.

Soulagée, presque triste même, d'avoir résolu si facilement ce mystère, je bus un peu de thé. Par-dessus le bord du verre, quelque chose dans le bric-à-brac de l'étagère du salon m'attira l'œil. Je m'approchai pour regarder de plus près la photographie sans cadre qui trônait au milieu. Sans réfléchir, je tendis la main pour la prendre. À observer ces visages familiers, je me sentis gagnée par une intense brûlure. Comment était-ce possible ?

— C'est ma mère, annonça tranquillement Lily.

Surprise, je fis volte-face. Bien sûr, la fille de la photo, c'était sa mère. Je voyais bien à quel point elles se ressemblaient. Mais ce n'était pas elle qui avait attiré mon attention. C'étaient les deux soldats qui l'entouraient. Perplexe, je contemplai les visages souriants. Nous avions une photographie identique à la maison. Mais sur la nôtre, c'était le visage de ma mère qu'on retrouvait coincé entre les joues des deux mêmes soldats, dont l'un était mon père.

Pourquoi se retrouvait-il en photo avec la mère de Lily ? Quels liens y avait-il entre eux ? J'ouvris la bouche pour le lui demander mais, avant que je puisse formuler ma question, mes réflexions furent fracassées par la douce voix de Lily.

— Et mon père, je crois que c'est lui qui nous envoie de l'argent tous les mois.

Brusquement, il y eut un déclic dans ma tête. Mais tout en moi, cherchait à protester. « Non ! C'est impossible ! » Je jetai un œil à Kipper en train d'avaler sa dernière gorgée de thé et m'obligeai à garder le silence. Je reposai la photo sur l'étagère.

— Il faut qu'on s'en aille, annonçai-je.

Je me précipitai dans la cuisine récupérer le chapeau de Kipper au-dessus du fourneau.

— Merci d'avoir soigné mon frère, dis-je à Lily tout en le poussant à se lever.

— Je vais vous raccompagner jusqu'à l'arrêt de bus, proposa Lily.

— Non, on va se débrouiller.

— J'ai envie d'y aller avec vous, insista-t-elle.

Elle ouvrit un des tiroirs de la cuisine, en sortit un stylo et une feuille de papier ; elle griffonna quelque chose. En sortant, elle prit deux parapluies dans l'entrée.

Je traversai en courant le magasin, évitant le regard sombre de la femme qui ressemblait tellement à Lily et à la jeune fille de la photographie.

Kipper fit tout le trajet jusqu'à Hastings Street avec Lily, bien abrité sous son parapluie ; il la remercia encore trois fois de l'avoir si bien « remonté ». Il respirait d'une façon absolument normale.

— Tu viendras nous voir chez nous ? demanda-t-il une fois à l'arrêt de bus.

— Je ne sais pas, répondit-elle, son regard grave posé non sur lui mais sur moi.

Le bus vint se ranger le long du trottoir et les portes s'ouvrirent en chuintant. Je fermai le parapluie et voulus le rendre à Lily, mais elle refusa de le prendre. Elle sortit la feuille de papier de sa poche et tendit le bras sous la pluie battante pour me la fourrer dans la main.

— Tu vois, Ethie ? claironna Kipper en se penchant pour lui faire signe par la fenêtre tandis que le bus s'éloignait. Je t'avais dit qu'elle était gentille.

— Ouais.

C'était vrai, Lily était gentille.

— Elle va venir nous voir ?

Je lui fis la même réponse que Lily.

— Je ne sais pas.

D'ailleurs, là, je ne savais plus rien. J'étais incapable d'aligner deux idées. Je ne pensais qu'à une seule chose : à quel point maman s'inquiétait du manque d'argent toutes les fins de mois. Et dans ma tête se mélangeaient en permanence l'image de mon père assis à la table de la cuisine, penché sur ses enveloppes, et son visage souriant sur cette photographie.

Sur le siège devant nous, un adolescent tenait collé contre son oreille un minuscule transistor en plastique. L'antenne argentée était braquée sur moi tandis que la voix aiguë de Frankie Valli chantait que les grandes filles ne pleu-eu-eu-rent pas. Refoulant mes larmes brûlantes, je regardai le bout de papier froissé dans ma main. Je le lissai doucement sur mon genou pour pouvoir déchiffrer cette écriture bien nette. « Lily Feng. Fille de Feng Shun-ling ». Et en dessous, un numéro de téléphone.

Elle n'avait pas eu besoin de le préciser. Je l'avais lu dans son regard sombre. Le papier ne m'était pas destiné. Il était pour mon père.

30

24 août 1942 : Île de Hong Kong

Adams… Berzenski… Ellis… Payne… Dans la tête de Howard, ces noms se consumaient. Les quatre Winnipeg Grenadiers s'étaient enfuis le 20 août à la faveur de l'obscurité et avaient été repris trois jours plus tard. Ce jour-là, tout le monde – y compris les malades et les moribonds – avait été contraints d'assister, debout ou couchés, au rassemblement. Tête basse, Howard répétait silencieusement le mantra de ces quatre noms tandis que quatre gardes, leur épée de cérémonie posée sur leurs mains gantées de blanc, quittaient le camp.

Des heures plus tard, une voix stridente perça sa stupeur. Des cannes de bambou zébrèrent l'air pour obliger les prisonniers à se scinder par groupes de dix.

— Ichi.

— Ni.

— San.

À chaque homme on criait son numéro d'un ton provocant. Howard était numéro huit. « Hachi. »

— N'oubliez pas votre numéro, cria un garde japonais. Si l'un de vous s'enfuit, les neuf autres mourront.

Ce qui sonna la fin des projets d'évasion et des conciliabules secrets au milieu de la nuit.

En réalité, les mailles du filet étaient lâches et les occasions multiples. Il en avait toujours été ainsi. Les Japonais étaient tellement persuadés que leurs prisonniers ne chercheraient pas à s'évader qu'ils ne respectaient plus guère les règles de sécurité.

Howard n'avait aucun mal à comprendre pourquoi les grenadiers avaient risqué leur vie. Le petit espoir de liberté opposé à la certitude de la maladie et de la faim ? Le camp était ravagé par la dysenterie, le béribéri et la pellagre. Même la diphtérie avait pointé son vilain nez. Et il y avait maintenant des rumeurs de choléra.

Les quatre fuyards avaient accepté le risque ; ils avaient échoué mais, au moins, ils avaient eu un projet et étaient passés à l'acte. Voyant l'état de Gordy s'améliorer, Howard avait laissé son imagination s'embraser. Une étincelle désormais éteinte.

Douze heures plus tard, les prisonniers étaient toujours debout sous le soleil de plomb. Les chefs du camp considéraient cela comme un châtiment mais Howard, à l'instar des autres Canadiens, il en était certain, voyait cela comme un honneur rendu aux quatre braves.

Les officiers japonais avaient encore en réserve une torture bien pire. Au coucher du soleil, deux gardes apportèrent dans la cour un énorme sac de courrier qu'ils laissèrent tomber devant les hommes épuisés. Dans les rangs, on entendit des cris étouffés. Assoiffé, hébété, Howard baissa sa garde et se laissa aller à un moment d'espoir. Le sac de toile fut renversé et son contenu se répandit. L'espoir se transforma en horreur lorsqu'un garde répandit de l'essence sur la montagne de lettres tandis que l'autre jetait dessus une allumette enflammée. Ces flammes provoquèrent des crises de nerfs. Il fallut retenir des prisonniers déchaînés et leurs camarades se mirent à pleurer à chaudes larmes en voyant les lettres de leurs bien-aimés partir en fumée, les cendres dispersées par le vent.

À la fin de septembre, on ramena les Canadiens dans leurs anciens baraquements sur le continent. Durant le trajet en ferry, Howard repéra le *Lisbon Maru*, le cargo japonais qu'il avait vu à quai à Hawaï près d'un an plus tôt, ancré dans le port. La rumeur courait que le navire militaire, reconverti et prêt à partir avec la marée du matin, transportait deux mille prisonniers de guerre anglais, sortis de Sham Shui Po, vers les camps de travail au Japon. Howard ne fit pas part de ses soupçons à Gordy mais, d'après lui, leur retour signifiait qu'ils seraient les prochains sur la liste. Gordy était déjà suffisamment dans tous ses états. Depuis quinze jours, ils ne voyaient plus Shun-ling au tourniquet en revenant de leurs journées de travail.

Une fois de plus, côte à côte, Howard et Gordy remontèrent péniblement Nathan Road, désormais familière. Contrairement à leur première arrivée au camp, il n'y avait personne pour agiter des drapeaux anglais et saluer le défilé dépenaillé des grenadiers et des Royal Rifles. Au lieu de cela, tout le long du chemin, balcons et vitrines arboraient des Soleil levant. Des foules de Chinois, jadis amicaux, portaient l'emblème rouge sang sur des brassards blancs et conspuaient les prisonniers épuisés.

À huit cents mètres du camp, Howard saisit le bras de Gordy.

— Regarde ! chuchota-t-il en désignant de la tête un groupe de spectateurs agressifs sur le bord de la route.

Parmi eux, tenant contre elle un paquet gris, il y avait Shun-ling.

— Oh, Seigneur ! croassa Gordy, en faisant un brusque écart.

— N'attire pas l'attention sur elle, lui souffla Howard à l'oreille en le tirant en arrière.

Lorsque Shun-ling les vit, elle tourna le paquet vers eux. Howard, devant le minuscule visage rose et les cheveux noirs, sentit sa gorge se serrer de façon inattendue ; il lui fut aussi difficile qu'à Gordy de ne pas se précipiter – elle était à la fois si près et pourtant si loin.

Howard fut bouleversé de voir ce qu'était devenu Sham Shui Po. Il ne restait plus grand-chose de leur ancien camp. Comme North Point, il avait été pillé jusqu'à l'os. Les cabanes jadis impeccables étaient réduites à l'état de taudis. Les fenêtres sans vitres étaient masquées par de la tôle ondulée. Les murs n'étaient plus que stuc et papier goudronné. Mais les lits de camp avaient résisté. Leurs matelas pliants infestés de puces et de punaises valaient mieux que le sol de béton et les planchers nus.

Les rares prisonniers anglais qui restaient – les malades et les estropiés, ainsi que ceux qui les soignaient – vivaient dans l'hôpital, une réplique exacte du Mouroir de North Point. Howard passa le premier jour à chercher Peter Young et Dick Baxter. Mais nul ne put le renseigner sur le sort des deux artilleurs.

Trois jours plus tard, la radio de contrebande, réinstallée, leur apprit une nouvelle qui se répandit dans le camp à la vitesse de l'éclair. Le *Lisbon Maru* avait été coulé. Le bateau japonais, qui ne signalait d'aucune façon qu'il transportait des prisonniers de guerre, avait été torpillé par un sous-marin américain. On craignait que plus de mille prisonniers anglais aient ainsi trouvé la mort.

Abattu, Howard digéra la nouvelle, priant pour que les deux artilleurs du Middlesex soient quand même sains et saufs.

La vie s'organisa dans ce nouveau camp. Et la mort aussi.

La diphtérie ravageait les rangs. Trois hommes, en moyenne, mouraient par jour. Et Gordy s'affaiblissait. Avec ses habituelles manières de bulldog, il refusait de l'avouer et plaisantait en faisant des gammes sur sa cage thoracique décharnée. Un matin, alors que Howard suggérait qu'il restât se reposer plutôt que d'accompagner les équipes de travail, il aboya : « Tu te prends pour ma mère, peut-être ? » Effort qui provoqua une brutale quinte de toux. Après avoir maîtrisé cette crise, il releva la tête, les yeux pleins de larmes.

— Tu sais à quel point j'ai besoin de ces quelques moments, Howie. C'est ça qui me fait tenir.

Si le transfert sur le continent avait signifié qu'ils se rapprochaient de l'endroit où la famille de Shun-ling vivait avec Ah Sam, cela avait également signifié la fin de ces conversations volées au tourniquet. Désormais, ils pouvaient seulement espérer l'apercevoir sur le bord de la route avec son bébé pendant le trajet de l'aérodrome de Kai Tak à Sham Shui Po en fin de journée.

Et puis, comme si les dieux étaient déterminés à leur briser le moral, comme si les privations et la maladie ne suffisaient pas, le déplacement à Sham Shui Po amena un nouveau sujet de terreur.

Tout d'abord, le nouvel interprète du camp apparut comme un sauveur. Lorsque le bruit courut qu'il était nippo-canadien, qu'il était né et avait grandi en Colombie-Britannique, les prisonniers se prirent à espérer. À coup sûr, il se montrerait plein de compassion à l'égard de ses compatriotes. Le premier jour, lorsque le sergent, grand et maigre comme un clou, surgit sur le terre-plein, ses bottes marron foncé brillant dans le soleil, il fut accueilli par une vague de murmures.

— Mate les plis de son pantalon... On pourrait se raser avec.

— C'est bien d'un Canadien, ça.

Mais ces commentaires tournèrent court. Le sergent s'immobilisa devant eux. Raide comme un piquet, il posa une main gantée de blanc sur la garde de son épée. Ses yeux étroits, sévères sous les lourds sourcils, firent le tour de la cour, attendant le silence complet. Dans un anglais parfait, il expliqua alors sa tâche d'interprète. Puis il précisa aux prisonniers sa vision personnelle de la situation. Il leur raconta à quel point, pendant son enfance au Canada, il avait été humilié et traité en intrus par les Blancs. Les hommes comprirent rapidement qu'il était bien décidé à leur faire payer tout ce qu'il avait lui-même souffert.

Deuxième semaine d'octobre. Après bientôt dix mois de captivité, Howard, assis sur son lit de camp, regardait les hommes autour de lui ouvrir leur courrier. Des lettres de chez eux ! Lui tenait serré celle de Lucy. À côté, Gordy, allongé sur le dos, se cramponnait à une enveloppe identique. Howard la lui lirait plus tard. Cela ressemblait bien à Lucy d'écrire à Gordy, sachant qu'il n'avait pas de famille. Et, heureusement pour Howard, ainsi, il aurait deux lettres d'elle à savourer. Il souleva avec précaution le rabat de son enveloppe ouverte, souhaitant déguster chaque seconde de ce cadeau.

— Merde ! cria Ken Campbell.

Des jurons identiques résonnèrent d'un bout à l'autre du baraquement. Howard releva la tête pour voir Ken déplier sa lettre. Le papier fin était taché de grosses marques noires. Dans tout le camp, on se mettait à jurer en voyant le nombre de mots, de phrases, de paragraphes entièrement supprimés par le stylo de la censure. Pendant qu'ils s'efforçaient de déchiffrer ce qui restait, Howard revint à la sienne le cœur battant.

Il sortit doucement les minces feuilles de papier pelure bleu. Abasourdi, il les sépara, les vérifia l'une après l'autre, la première, la deuxième, la troisième… Les trois étaient intactes, pas un seul mot barré. Il tourna le dos aux autres, refusant de laisser quiconque être témoin de sa bonne fortune.

La lettre était datée du 12 mars 1942.

Mon Howard chéri,

Est-ce que tu es noyé sous toutes les lettres que je t'envoie ? Je n'ai aucun moyen de savoir si elles te parviennent. Je prie tous les jours pour en recevoir une de toi. Je ne sais rien. Mais je n'ai pas besoin d'Ottawa pour me le dire. Je sais que tu es vivant. Je sens ta présence chaque jour. N'empêche, je meurs d'envie d'avoir de tes nouvelles, mon chéri. Comment vas-tu ? Es-tu traité correctement ?

Tous les soirs, je descends jusqu'à Kitsilano Beach pour voir le soleil se coucher. Contempler les eaux de l'English Bay me donne tout de même le sentiment de me rapprocher un peu de toi…

À Vancouver, on a droit au couvre-feu quotidien. Comme cela paraît étrange de ne voir aucune lumière sur le North Shore. Mais chacun tient à apporter sa pierre dans l'effort de guerre.

Tout n'est pas rose. La jeune femme nippo-canadienne qui travaille dans le bureau de Sidney a disparu. Avec toute sa famille, ils ont été raflés et transférés dans un camp international quelque part à l'intérieur du pays. Sidney a tenté d'intervenir. Mais en vain. La façon dont ils ont été traités est honteuse. Ce sont des Canadiens. Le père, qui s'est battu pour le Canada au cours de la dernière guerre, est un héros et il a été décoré ; son nom est gravé sur le monument aux morts nippo-canadien de Stanley Park. Pourtant, on les a tous virés en ne les autorisant à prendre que ce qu'ils pouvaient porter. Sidney a rangé le reste de leurs biens dans le sous-sol en attendant que toute cette pagaille soit terminée…

Le reste de la lettre était moins grave, donnant de façon décousue des nouvelles de Mildred et Sidney ainsi que de la vie quotidienne dans un monde rationnel. Jusqu'à la dernière page.

Je me sens assez bien, maintenant que les nausées du matin ont disparu. J'ai perdu mon travail au drugstore, évidemment.

On pourrait croire que cette idée démodée selon laquelle les femmes enceintes doivent dissimuler leur état est dépassée. Surtout lorsqu'on est en pleine guerre. Mais Mildred est ravie de m'avoir sous la main tous les jours et elle me dorlote comme un enfant gâté.

Je ne dois pas accoucher avant la mi-juillet mais je suis déjà tellement grosse que les gens se demandent si je n'attends pas des jumeaux. Ce n'est pas le cas. Du moins, d'après Sidney. Même si le bébé donne de tels coups de pied que j'ai parfois l'impression qu'il y en a deux. Ce doit être un garçon. Je l'espère bien. Un beau grand garçon, exactement comme son père.

Reviens vite me voir, nous voir, mon chéri, tu me manques tellement.

Je t'aime pour toujours,
Lucy

Un bébé ? En juillet ? Il était déjà père ? Ces nouvelles lui donnèrent autant de force qu'un bon repas. Plus même. Il relut encore la lettre, lentement cette fois, savourant chaque mot. Ce ne fut qu'après l'avoir lue trois fois qu'il s'interrogea : pourquoi était-elle passée à travers les griffes de la censure, tant ici qu'au Canada ? La censure frappait-elle de façon aléatoire ? Ou les censeurs étaient-ils tellement débordés que certaines y échappaient ? Ça lui était bien égal. À cheval donné, on ne regarde pas les dents.

Brusquement, Howard sentit se dresser les petits cheveux sur sa nuque. Derrière lui, le bourdonnement des conversations s'interrompit. Un silence terrifiant s'installa dans la baraque – l'immobilité de la proie prise dans le regard du prédateur. Une sinistre odeur de haine satura l'air humide. Le bruit méprisant des semelles de cuir frappant les planches brutes fracassa le silence. Talon, pointe, talon, pointe. Les pas résonnèrent avant de s'arrêter dans un claquement final devant Howard. Le bourdonnement indifférent des mouches remplit le vide laissé par l'immobilité des bottes aux confins de la vision de Howard. Il s'obligea à les contempler fixement, en se répétant son mantra... Bacon, Baptiste, Barclay. Il laissa les noms se dérouler lentement sur le tableau noir de son esprit avant de relever la tête et de permettre à son regard de se poser sur le visage grimaçant. Avec une insolence calculée, il replia la lettre et la remit dans l'enveloppe.

Un geste vain. La censure faisait partie du travail de l'interprète. N'empêche, Howard ne put empêcher le dégoût de l'envahir à l'idée que le sergent avait lu ce qu'avait écrit Lucy.

Le regard reptilien ne lâchait pas Howard.

— Mon père, lui aussi, s'est battu pour le Canada pendant la dernière guerre, déclara-t-il. Un héros médaillé. Je jouais avec ses décorations lorsque j'étais enfant. Son nom se trouve également gravé sur le mémorial de Stanley Park. Et pourtant, nous n'étions rien d'autre que des salopards de petits jaunes.

Il savoura un instant le silence, l'air satisfait.

— Et maintenant, reprit-il, vous allez voir ce dont est capable ce salopard de petit jaune.

Trois jours plus tard, l'interprète tenait ses promesses, annonçant que les rations de nourriture seraient réduites pour ceux qui ne travaillaient pas ou de façon insuffisante. Il fallait mettre la pression pour achever la piste de l'aéroport de Kai Tak. On amena sur place ceux qui étaient trop faibles ou trop malades. S'ils ne se relevaient pas, leur ration était supprimée.

— C'est contre-productif, protesta Howard. Dites à vos supérieurs qu'on ne peut pas espérer faire travailler des hommes morts de faim. Il leur faut davantage à manger, pas moins.

Contrairement à ceux dont les plaintes étaient récompensées par un bon coup de canne de bambou, Howard ne fut pas châtié de son insolence.

— Pas de travail, pas de repas, répondit seulement le sergent en s'éloignant à grands pas.

À la mi-novembre, il devint évident que les Japonais réclamaient l'impossible. Le corps gonflé par le béribéri, la bouche et la face rongées par les plaies ouvertes de la pellagre, bien des hommes perdaient toute volonté de vivre. La malnutrition systématique provoquait un phénomène de « pieds électriques », empêchant nombre d'entre eux de marcher. Torturés par des picotements insupportables, ceux qui souffraient de ce symptôme ne pouvaient que se coucher et pleurer. Tant qu'ils tenaient assis, ils faisaient tremper leurs pieds dans des seaux d'eau, ignorant les avertissements suppliants de Ken Campbell qui leur disait que ce soulagement transitoire risquait de provoquer une infection mortelle ou, pire encore, une pneumonie.

La diphtérie et la dysenterie amibienne étaient désormais endémiques. Les efforts déployés par le personnel médical étaient réduits à néant par le manque de médicaments.

Les Japonais, inquiets pour eux-mêmes, commencèrent à porter des masques et réprimandèrent les malheureux médecins incapables de contrôler les épidémies. La nuit où sept prisonniers moururent, Ken Campbell revint en boitant jusqu'aux baraquements. Quand il ôta avec précaution sa chemise, Howard vit que son dos n'était qu'une plaie sanglante.

— L'interprète, grommela Ken en se couchant sur le ventre. Chaque toubib a eu droit à sa raclée parce qu'on donne une mauvaise image de lui.

Il arriva une petite quantité d'antitoxines et les médecins n'eurent plus qu'à jouer à Dieu avec ces maigres réserves. Les cas de diphtérie augmentèrent. Les hommes de la C Force avaient quitté Vancouver dans une telle urgence que la plupart n'avaient pas été vaccinés. Howard faisait partie des chanceux. Quand il était adolescent, il avait marché sur un clou rouillé. La piqûre antitétanique et antidiphtérique à laquelle il avait eu droit alors l'immunisait contre l'épidémie qui ravageait le camp.

Ce n'était pas le cas de Gordy. Il ne tenait plus qu'avec difficulté sur ses béquilles. Cependant, il ne supportait pas l'idée de rester au camp. Tant qu'il eut encore la force de se lever, il refusa d'avouer qu'il avait de la fièvre et mal à la gorge, ces symptômes redoutés.

Lorsque la piste de l'aéroport fut achevée, Howard se mit à observer les réfugiés qui venaient furtivement racler les laisses de vase tous les jours. Depuis le départ de Satan, les incidents entre les Chinois et les gardes étaient assez rares. Les supérieurs japonais avaient mis fin aux comportements sadiques à l'égard des civils. Cela faisait plus d'un mois que Howard n'avait pas aperçu Shun-ling, mais lorsqu'il la vit surgir au milieu d'un groupe de fouilleurs d'ordures dans la brume de l'aube – sa gorge se serra malgré lui –, il recula dans l'ombre. Mais elle l'avait vu.

Elle attendit que le reste du groupe ait disparu de l'autre côté. Une fois seule, elle s'accroupit dans les buissons à l'angle de la clôture de fil barbelé. Howard vérifia qu'il n'y avait pas de gardes dans les alentours.

— C'est dangereux, chuchota-t-il en s'accroupissant de l'autre côté.

Elle lui fit passer un petit paquet enveloppé de papier brun.

— Pour les intestins de Gordy.

Il le prit tout en sachant que ces plantes médicinales seraient impuissantes à guérir ce dont souffrait maintenant Gordy.

— Il a la diphtérie, Shun-ling, annonça-t-il en glissant le petit paquet dans sa poche. Ah Sam peut-il se procurer du sérum ?

— Je reviendrai demain.

Et sur ces mots, elle disparut dans la brume.

Le lendemain matin, elle lui rapporta d'autres plantes.

— Les Japonais ont confisqué les réserves de sérum. Voilà tout ce que Ah Sam peut vous offrir. Il dit que Gordy doit boire de grandes quantités d'eau bouillie.

Tous les matins, à l'aube, Howard la guettait. Elle réussissait à venir régulièrement pour lui transmettre des trésors. En plus des plantes, elle apportait de minuscules morceaux de nourriture, des nouvelles du monde extérieur et des anecdotes sur le bébé, une fille qu'elle avait appelée Lily en hommage à la mère de Gordy. Ces échanges hâtifs, ces conversations longuement commentées représentaient pour Howard comme pour Gordy, ravagé par la maladie, une véritable bouée de sauvetage.

Les potions de Ah Sam avaient bel et bien marché sur la dysenterie des deux amis, mais elles n'agissaient nullement sur la diphtérie, et l'état de Gordy empirait.

Finalement, il n'y eut plus le choix. Il fallut le transporter dans le hangar qui servait d'hôpital. Howard n'avait pas besoin des médecins ni de Ken Campbell pour comprendre : il reniflait la vérité dans le souffle de Gordy, il la voyait dans les ganglions gonflés de son cou, il l'entendait dans sa toux. Mais son ami résistait quand même, faisant un pied de nez à la mort alors même qu'elle l'avait rattrapé. Howard ne quittait plus son chevet, restant à ses côtés jour et nuit. Il humectait d'eau stérilisée, comme prescrit par Ah Sam, la langue parcheminée de Gordy. Il lui faisait boire à la cuillère le bouillon fait à partir des herbes fournies par Shun-ling, mais Gordy le régurgitait en crachant noir. Rien ne marchait et Gordy lâchait prise. Tous les soirs, Howard dormait par terre, à côté de son lit, ne sortant que pour utiliser les latrines ou surveiller la clôture au fond du camp le matin. Mais, tout en acceptant sans discuter les minuscules paquets d'espoir transmis par Shun-ling, il ne pouvait se résoudre à lui avouer à quel point la situation était tragique.

Un matin, Howard fut réveillé par le bruit d'une respiration haletante. Il se redressa puis s'agenouilla à côté de Gordy, observant sa poitrine creuse monter et descendre laborieusement. Son ami était réduit à une enveloppe de peau racornie tendue sur ses os. Howard remonta la mince couverture, remarquant au passage les taches violettes, le sang qui se rassemblait dans le pied restant de Gordy.

Les paupières de Gordy battirent.

— Howie ?

Howard chercha le regard embrumé.

— Je suis là, répondit-il en lissant ses cheveux en arrière.

Les lèvres craquelées bougèrent avec effort.

— En voilà un nom de tapette, quand même ! chuchota Gordy.

En un éclair, ressurgit le gamin provocant. Puis ses paupières battirent à nouveau. À force d'observer la respiration haletante, Howard se surprit à inspirer au rythme trop lent de Gordy, dont la poitrine se soulevait avec difficulté.

Inspire… expire… inspire… expire… inspire…

Et puis… plus rien.

Non ! Non ! Howard expira brutalement pour entraîner la poitrine immobile.

Brusquement, l'air s'échappa en sifflant de la bouche ouverte de Gordy. Howard se glissa sur le lit de camp pour s'allonger à ses côtés. Il le prit dans ses bras.

— Veille… sur les filles…, entendit-il.

La gorge serrée, Howard voulait nier la vérité alors même que s'effaçaient la vie et l'énergie qui avaient été Gordy. Il avala sa salive. Pas question de le rabaisser avec des mensonges sans valeur, pas question de prétendre que la mort n'allait pas gagner.

— Bien sûr, compte sur moi, souffla-t-il.

4 décembre 1942 : ... Gordon Veronick...

31

Kipper et moi sommes arrivés chez nous au beau milieu d'une nouvelle averse. Même le parapluie de Lily n'aurait pu nous protéger de la pluie battante qui tambourinait sur les trottoirs. Comme deux rats trempés nous sommes entrés par le sous-sol. Nous aurions pu nous en dispenser. Frankie dormait encore. Et papa n'était pas là. Il avait dû sortir se promener sous la pluie. Ce qui me fit plaisir. Je ne savais ce que j'aurais pu ou dû lui dire.

Pendant que Kipper prenait un bain, je me mis en pyjama. Une fois sorti de la baignoire, il monta à l'étage. Frankie descendit dans la cuisine alors que j'étais en train de mélanger du fromage râpé avec les pâtes Kraft Dinner toutes prêtes. Il bâilla en se grattant la poitrine.

— Alors, qu'est-ce que vous avez fait aujourd'hui, Kipper et toi ? demanda-t-il en attrapant la cafetière.

Je savais qu'il posait cette question simplement pour remplir le vide de la maison, de nos vies mais en le regardant rincer la cafetière, j'envisageai de tout lui raconter. Je l'envisageai vraiment. Mais qu'aurais-je pu dire ? « Nous sommes allés en ville et nous avons découvert que papa a une autre fille – une autre famille ».

Kipper entra dans la cuisine à son tour, en pyjama et coiffé de son chapeau détrempé.

— Rien, répondis-je avant d'ajouter, dans l'espoir de changer de sujet : Tu veux des macaronis ?

— Je ne crois pas, dit-il en m'ébouriffant les cheveux. C'est mon petit déjeuner, ne l'oublie pas. Et toi, mon bonhomme, reprit-il en s'adressant à Kipper, tu as envie de te coucher tôt ?

— Non, j'étais trempé, répondit Kipper. Exactement comme papa.

— Papa est sorti se promener ? demanda Frankie.

Il prit une boîte d'œufs dans le réfrigérateur et jeta un coup d'œil à la bouteille de whisky à moitié vide.

— Je suppose, répondis-je en haussant les épaules.

À la fin de notre repas, papa n'avait toujours pas réapparu.

— Je vais suivre un cours du soir avant de repartir au travail, annonça Frankie en se levant de table. Pas de problème pour rester seuls tous les deux ?

N'étions-nous pas toujours dans cette situation ?

Kipper et moi, on s'est installés sur le canapé pour regarder un épisode de la série *Leave It to Beaver*. Comme j'enviais la vie imaginaire de Beaver et Wally Cleaver. Leurs vêtements paraissaient toujours flambant neufs, leurs lits faits au carré et ils avaient même leur propre salle de bains dans leur chambre. Existait-il vraiment des gens aussi riches ? Le plus incroyable, c'était leur père qui pouvait leur consacrer tout son temps comme s'il n'avait rien d'autre à faire.

À la fin de l'épisode, laissant Kipper sur le canapé, les paupières bien lourdes, j'allai mettre de l'ordre dans la cuisine. Je débarrassai la table au rythme des sifflements qui venaient de la télévision alors que le shérif Andy et Opie se dirigeaient une fois de plus vers leur cabane dans la montagne. J'avais généralement de la peine pour le petit Opie Taylor qui n'avait pas de maman. Désormais, sa vie d'enfant unique, avec un père qui résolvait tous ses problèmes à l'aide de quelques sages paroles, me paraissait tout à fait enviable.

Je raclai les restes de nourriture collés sur mon assiette pour les jeter dans la poubelle sous l'évier. En refermant le placard, je remarquai deux sacs en papier brun derrière le tuyau d'évacuation. Inutile de les ouvrir pour savoir ce qu'il y avait dedans. Du whisky.

Brusquement folle de rage, je saisis les deux bouteilles et les posai sans douceur sur le plan de travail. Je les arrachai des sacs et dévissai les bouchons. Les mains tremblantes, je les renversai au-dessus de l'évier et regardai le liquide ambré gicler sur l'émail blanc. Tandis qu'il disparaissait par la bonde, ma détermination mollit. À quoi bon ? Il s'en procurerait d'autre, voilà tout. Je vidai tout de même les deux bouteilles puis j'allai récupérer celle qui était en haut du réfrigérateur. Une feuille de papier glissa et vint atterrir sur le sol. Je me penchai pour la ramasser.

Si seulement j'avais remis cette lettre à sa place, sans l'ouvrir, sans la lire, rien de ce qui a suivi ne serait arrivé. Mais ce n'est pas ce que je fis. Je la dépliai et je lus ce que ma mère avait écrit.

> *Dora,*
>
> *J'ai désespérément besoin de te parler. La petite que nous avons vue dans le square hier est venue frapper à ma porte ce matin – elle cherchait son père !*
>
> *J'ai de bonnes raisons de soupçonner Howard d'avoir envoyé de l'argent à sa famille, à Hong Kong, depuis dix-sept ans. Je me sens tellement perdue que je ne sais même plus quoi penser.*
>
> *Je lui ai demandé de revenir demain. J'ai besoin de temps pour mettre mes pensées au clair avant de pouvoir affronter la situation. L'affronter elle. Ou lui.*
>
> *Si j'ai jamais eu besoin d'une amie, c'est bien maintenant. Je t'en prie, appelle-moi dès que tu rentreras.*
>
> *Lucy*

Ma mère était au courant ! Voilà pourquoi elle était bouleversée et pourquoi elle était partie voir son amie Marlene. Abasourdie, je relus cette lettre puis je laissai la feuille me glisser des doigts et tomber par terre. Abandonnant la vaisselle sale sur le plan de travail et dans l'évier, les casseroles et la poêle collantes sur le fourneau, Kipper dans le salon, je saisis la bouteille de whisky à moitié pleine sur le haut du réfrigérateur et je me précipitai à l'étage.

Dans ma chambre, je me mis au lit avec les couvertures jusqu'aux genoux et entrepris de dévisser le bouchon. C'était peut-être comme un médicament. Une fois, Frankie en avait versé dans une dent douloureuse pour l'endormir. J'allais peut-être pouvoir endormir ma cervelle, arrêter le flot de mes pensées. Exactement comme papa.

Je jetai le bouchon par terre, attrapai la bouteille par le col, la renversai et avalai une énorme rasade. Le liquide brûlant m'arracha la gorge. Je m'étouffai, le whisky ressortit en jet par la bouche et les narines, provoquant un accès de toux qui me fit souffrir le martyre tandis que je me débattais pour tenter de récupérer mon souffle.

— Non, Ethie ! cria Kipper.

Malgré ma vue brouillée, je me rendis compte qu'il se précipitait vers le lit.

— C'est mal ! me gronda-t-il en voulant récupérer la bouteille.

Je m'y cramponnai alors qu'il s'efforçait de me la retirer des mains. Sans grande conviction, je résistai un petit moment puis je cédai. Kipper vacilla en arrière et lâcha la bouteille. Celle-ci vola en l'air, le liquide ambré décrivit un arc de cercle en éclaboussant le lit et le mur, puis elle tomba par terre et roula dans un angle.

— Oups ! s'écria Kipper.

— De toute façon, j'en voulais pas.

Je me couchai de tout mon long en rabattant les couvertures sur moi. Ce que je voulais, c'était que tout redevienne comme avant. Je voulais que maman revienne. Je voulais que mon père soit un père. Je voulais que ce que ma mère avait écrit dans sa lettre ne soit pas vrai.

— T'es triste, Ethie ? s'enquit Kipper, à mon chevet.

Un gros sanglot était en train de gonfler dans sa gorge. Mais je ne pouvais pas le réconforter. Je pouvais seulement me pousser et ouvrir les couvertures pour le laisser se coucher à côté de moi ; nous avons pleuré ensemble jusqu'à nous endormir, épuisés.

Le lendemain matin, je fus réveillée en sursaut par le cri de surprise de ma tante.

32

— Reste ici ! m'ordonna tante Mildred avant de tirer un Kipper en larmes hors de ma chambre.

Quelques secondes plus tard, le vacarme retentissant de sa porte qui claquait ricocha dans l'entrée, véritable accusation sonore. Lorsque j'entendis ma tante descendre lourdement l'escalier en hurlant le nom de mon père, je bondis hors de mon lit.

Je débarquai dans l'entrée juste à temps pour voir papa enfiler son pantalon en toute hâte.

— Mildred, dit-il en fermant sa braguette, que se passe-t-il ?

Elle fonça vers sa chambre, le souffle court.

— Je suis venue chercher Ethie qui a besoin de vêtements pour l'école et j'ai trouvé...

— Je suis désolé, l'interrompit papa d'un ton las tout en mettant sa chemise. J'ai oublié que tu devais venir.

— Oublié ? Tu n'as pas oublié... Tu as seulement une sacrée gueule de bois ! siffla-t-elle. Trop soûl pour savoir ce que tes enfants fabriquent.

Debout sur le seuil, les pieds écartés et les mains sur les hanches, elle continua à l'apostropher.

— Christopher était dans le lit d'Ethie ! Je l'ai pris sur le fait. Et ils avaient bu du whisky ! Ton whisky ! Ça pue la débauche dans sa chambre !

— Mais de quoi parles-tu ? rétorqua papa.

— On l'a pas bu, criai-je, derrière elle.

Ma tante fit volte-face pour me regarder.

— Je t'ai dit de rester dans ta chambre, Ethie !

Papa la bouscula pour sortir de la sienne.

Tante Mildred bondit à ce contact et ses yeux se plissèrent.

— Tu n'étais même pas là hier soir, Howard ! Regarde-toi, reprit-elle. Tes vêtements sont encore trempés. Tu as préféré céder au fameux démon de tes balades plutôt que de rester chez toi avec tes enfants.

Sans se soucier d'elle, papa me prit par l'épaule.

— Montons donc voir Kipper, dit-il en me faisant retraverser l'entrée.

— Je ne partirai pas, Howard, le prévint tante Mildred. Nous allons avoir une petite discussion, toi et moi.

— À ta guise, répliqua papa sans se retourner. Pour l'instant, je suis occupé avec mes enfants.

— C'est peut-être un peu tard...

— Ce n'était pas la faute de Kipper, intervins-je en reniflant. Il n'a rien fait de mal.

Il était assis par terre dans sa chambre, affalé contre le mur, encore en pyjama. Lorsque papa ouvrit la porte, il leva vers nous un visage maculé de larmes et de mucus.

— Tante... Mildred... dit... que... je... suis... méchant, sanglota-t-il. Je... suis... pas... méchant. Hein... papa ?

— Bien sûr que non.

Papa s'accroupit et l'aida à se relever.

— Ne te soucie pas d'elle, ajouta-t-il en s'asseyant sur le bord du lit et en prenant Kipper dans ses bras.

Il le tint serré contre lui jusqu'à ce que ses sanglots s'apaisent.

— Où est ton chapeau ? demanda-t-il alors.

Kipper s'essuya le nez sur la manche de son pyjama et renifla, en s'efforçant de sourire.

— Dans la chambre d'Ethie.

— Je vais le chercher, dit papa en repliant le couvre-lit. Toi, recouche-toi pendant que je descends discuter avec ta tante. D'accord ?

— D'accord, papa.

Dans ma chambre, papa haussa les sourcils en voyant le lit froissé qui n'avait pas été fait depuis des jours, les vêtements éparpillés par terre et la bouteille de whisky vide dans un coin. Ça puait encore l'alcool éventé. Mais cela lui échappa sans doute car lui-même dégageait la même odeur.

— Si on se met à la place de ta tante, on peut comprendre qu'elle ait été choquée, concéda-t-il.

— C'est ma faute, avouai-je. J'ai pris la bouteille. Mais je ne l'ai pas bue. Elle s'est renversée.

Me souvenant brusquement que j'étais en colère contre lui, je m'assis sur le lit.

— Une vilaine affaire, non ? déclara papa en s'asseyant à côté de moi.

Je repoussai sa main puis m'adossai à la tête du lit, les bras croisés, refusant de le regarder.

— Ce n'est ni ta faute ni celle de ton frère. C'est la mienne. Sur ce sujet, ta tante a raison. J'aurais dû être présent.

Il prit le chapeau de Kipper accroché au montant du lit.

— Bon, je vais essayer de la calmer, décida-t-il.

Il tendit la main pour me caresser les cheveux. Je reculai, refusant toujours de le regarder.

Il descendit dans la salle de bains. J'en profitai pour aller m'asseoir sur la marche juste avant le tournant de l'escalier. La marche où, quand j'étais petite, je me cachais quand on jouait à cache-cache, Kipper et moi. La marche où lui et moi, on s'endormait la veille de Noël en attendant l'arrivée du Père Noël. La même marche sur laquelle je m'étais assise la nuit où la police était venue chez nous, alors qu'il pleuvait et que le vent soufflait.

Dans la salle de bains, papa ferma les robinets ; il ouvrit la porte et se rendit dans la cuisine. Il régnait un tel silence que je l'entendis prendre la cafetière posée au-dessus du fourneau.

— Écoute, commença-t-il, je sais que cela paraît...

Il s'interrompit brusquement.

La voix de ma tante rompit le silence.

— Tu... tu...

— Où as-tu trouvé ça ? répliqua mon père, le souffle court.

— Une fille ? cria ma tante, sans lui répondre. Le jour où elle est morte, Lucy avait appris que tu avais un enfant illégitime ?

La lettre de maman ! Sans me soucier de rester discrète, je me précipitai dans le salon pour aller m'accroupir dans l'angle, près du canapé.

Dans la cuisine, papa n'avait pas bougé, la cafetière dans la main, l'air sidéré.

— Non, ce n'est pas...

— Mentir à Lucy durant toutes ces années ! cria tante Mildred. Envoyer de l'argent en Chine, à une autre famille, alors que ma sœur tirait le diable par la queue !

— Tu te trompes complètement.

— Ah oui ? Alors, explique-moi ça ! hurla-t-elle en brandissant la feuille de papier. Lucy s'est trompée elle aussi, alors ? Elle est donc morte en croyant ça... quoi ? Un mensonge ? Une erreur ?

— Oui, malheureusement, ça s'est passé ainsi.

— Malheureusement ? Sais-tu combien de fois j'ai donné de l'argent à ma sœur ? Elle ne m'en a jamais demandé. Oh non ! Demander lui aurait été trop difficile. Mais elle le prenait, cet argent. Et toujours, toujours, il fallait te le cacher. Elle ne voulait surtout pas heurter ton précieux orgueil. Et toi, pendant tout ce temps, tu envoyais de l'argent pour élever un enfant illégitime.

— Ce n'est pas du tout ça.

Elle dut alors remarquer les bouteilles de whisky vides car elle s'enquit d'un ton glacial :

— Deux bouteilles par jour, maintenant, Howard ? Ça fait des années que je mets Lucy en garde. Mais elle ne voulait rien savoir. Tu n'es qu'un alcoolique.

J'étais prête à me précipiter pour lui expliquer qu'il n'avait pas bu ces deux bouteilles, que je les avais vidées dans l'évier, mais papa dit :

— Tu as raison, je suis alcoolique. Mais je vais m'arrêter. Je…

— Parfait, l'interrompit tante Mildred. J'emmène Ethie vivre avec moi le temps que tu t'y mettes. Et je vais envoyer Christopher dans une bonne institution où il sera…

— Non, la coupa résolument papa.

— Que diraient les services sociaux s'ils étaient au courant de la situation, d'après toi ? le menaça tante Mildred. Un adolescent dans le même lit que sa petite sœur ? Une chambre d'enfant qui pue l'alcool ? L'état de cette maison ? Toi ? On te retirerait tes enfants à la minute.

— Si on se calmait un peu et qu'on discutait de tout cela rationnellement ? plaida papa.

— Non, rétorqua-t-elle. Assieds-toi et écoute-moi. Il est temps que quelqu'un prenne la situation en main. Pour l'instant, tu es incapable de prendre soin de cette famille.

— Nous… je vais changer. Je vais cesser de boire. On va se débrouiller.

— Et comment ? Qui va s'occuper du gamin pendant la journée ? Qui sera là pour Ethie après l'école ? Qui va leur faire à manger ? À moins que tu ne souhaites les voir se nourrir de macaronis en boîte ? railla-t-elle en saisissant une assiette maculée de fromage.

Elle balança l'assiette dans l'évier avec le reste de la vaisselle sale.

— On trouvera quelqu'un pour venir. La voisine d'à côté a promis de demander à la personne qui s'occupe de son fils après les cours. Dora pense qu'elle sera sans doute d'accord pour venir les jours où Frankie et moi nous sommes au travail.

— Dora !

Elle cracha ce nom comme s'il était venimeux.

— Ah. Elle doit rêver de te mettre le grappin dessus. Et sur ma nièce aussi.

— Il ne s'agit pas de ça. C'était… c'était l'amie de Lucy.

— Tu parles d'une amie !

Sa réaction brutale me fit frissonner. Mais je me rendis brusquement compte que, derrière, il y avait autre chose que de la colère. Bien sûr. Le mot destiné à Dora Fenwick. Lorsque maman avait cherché quelqu'un à qui parler, elle s'était tournée vers deux amies mais pas vers sa sœur. Comme si papa avait fait la même découverte, il déclara :

— Je regrette qu'elle ne t'ait pas appelée, toi.

— Ça suffit ! Je ne te permets pas de me faire des reproches !

Mais tante Mildred avait la gorge serrée, cela s'entendait dans sa voix.

— Je ne te fais aucun reproche. Je sais que tu l'aimais.

Il y eut un moment de silence.

— Écoute-moi, Howard, reprit tante Mildred, d'un ton plus calme. Soyons rationnels. As-tu vraiment le choix ? Crois-tu vraiment que tu agis au mieux de l'intérêt de tes enfants ? Je ne le crois pas. Et je ne resterai pas là à regarder souffrir les enfants de ma sœur parce que tu es trop aveugle pour t'en rendre compte. S'il le faut, j'irai au tribunal et je me battrai pour en obtenir la garde.

— Mildred, ne fais pas cela, implora papa mais d'une voix cassée, brisée.

— Je ne suis pas en train de te menacer. Je te dis simplement tes quatre vérités. Il faut bien que quelqu'un le fasse. Je te jure que si on se retrouve au tribunal, je gagnerai. Ou tu me laisses emmener Ethie à la maison immédiatement sans discuter. Laisse-moi m'occuper d'elle pendant que tu remets ta vie sur des rails. Laisse-moi placer le gamin dans un endroit prévu pour les gens comme lui. Un endroit où il sera en sécurité, où on prendra bien soin de lui.

Elle prit une profonde inspiration.

— Toi et moi, nous savons très bien que Lucy passait des heures chaque jour à lui apprendre des choses, à prendre soin de lui. Qui pourra la remplacer ? Il bénéficiera de ce genre d'attention dans une institution. Et si Ethie vit avec moi, insista-t-elle, tu pourras la voir aussi souvent que tu veux. Ensuite, si vraiment tu remets ta vie dans le droit chemin, alors, on verra.

Devant le silence de papa, elle continua :

— Il est temps de penser à d'autres que toi, pour changer. Pense à ce qui est bien pour Ethie... et pour Christopher. Et pour Frankie. Tu as pensé à lui ? N'est-il pas temps de le délivrer lui aussi de ce fardeau ? C'est à toi de décider, Howard. Si Lucy était là, je suis persuadée que, même elle, te dirait qu'il est temps de faire ce qui est le mieux pour ces enfants. Et, reprit-elle en ouvrant son sac, il n'y a aucune raison pour qu'ils soient jamais au courant de cette histoire.

Elle fit tomber le mot de maman dans son sac et le referma d'un coup sec.

— Ça n'a aucune importance, dit papa dans un murmure. La réalité est bien pire.

33

18 décembre 1942 : Camp de Sham Shui Po

Gordy était mort depuis quinze jours, mais Howard n'avait pas encore prévenu Shun-ling. Dans l'obscurité, il se glissa hors de sa couchette et se dirigea avec précaution vers la clôture au fond du camp. Il creusa autour du poteau d'angle dans le sable mou puis rampa sous les barbelés pour sauter sur le rebord en dessous. Enveloppé dans sa couverture mince, il prit une décision tandis qu'il attendait dans le noir. Cette fois, il allait le lui dire. Sans prévenir, elle surgit silencieusement de l'ombre et vint s'accroupir à côté de lui.

En la voyant, Howard perdit toute détermination. D'autant qu'elle était venue avec deux flacons de sérum.

— Antitoxines de la diphtérie, souffla-t-elle en les lui montrant avec fierté. De la part d'Ah Sam.

— Quel risque a pris ton ami ! s'exclama Howard en acceptant les deux petites bouteilles. Et toi aussi ! ajouta-t-il à voix très basse.

— Ça vaut la peine. Il promet qu'il y en aura d'autre la semaine prochaine. Je l'apporterai.

À plonger dans ces yeux sombres, si pleins d'espoir, Howard n'eut pas le courage de lui annoncer que tout était perdu. Il allait lui offrir encore quelques jours d'ignorance, quelques jours où elle croirait que les plantes, les potions et maintenant le sérum qu'elle avait apportés étaient très utiles à Gordy.

Donc, plutôt que de lui avouer la vérité, il l'interrogea à propos de l'argent.

— Ne t'inquiète pas, lui répondit-elle. Ah Sam tient les comptes. Il dit qu'il vous présentera la facture le jour où tout ceci sera terminé.

— Il croit que ça va finir un jour ?

— Il en est persuadé.

Avant qu'elle remonte sur la berge recouverte d'herbe, Howard lui toucha le bras.

— Feng Shun-ling, chuchota-t-il. Je…

Il se tut. Il ne savait pas très bien ce qu'il avait eu l'intention de dire. Peut-être avait-il simplement eu envie de prononcer son nom. Peut-être s'apprêtait-il à lui révéler la vérité au sujet de Gordy mais il avait laissé passer l'occasion. Le regardant droit dans les yeux, elle tendit le bras et lui effleura les lèvres du bout des doigts.

— Howard Coulter, murmura-t-elle avant de disparaître dans les ombres du petit matin.

— Bon sang, elle peut en avoir d'autres, mon pote ? demanda Ken Campbell lorsque Howard lui tendit les deux flacons.

— Elle pense que c'est pour Gordy, avoua Howard.

Ken insista pour qu'il continue à assurer les livraisons.

— Ce truc va permettre à beaucoup d'hommes de vivre.

Il était trop tard pour Gordy mais les antitoxines allaient sauver des vies humaines. Comment Howard aurait-il pu le leur refuser ?

Il accepta donc à contrecœur en prévenant que, en définitive, il serait bien obligé d'annoncer à Shun-ling que Gordy était mort. Qu'elle n'avait plus de raison de prendre le risque de venir jusque là.

Puisqu'ils continuaient à se retrouver, il étouffa sa conscience en se convainquant qu'au moins, certains profitaient de cette duperie. Mais il savait que derrière toutes ces excuses pour ne pas l'avertir – le besoin de sérum, les sachets de remèdes chinois, la souffrance qu'il ne voulait pas lui infliger – au-delà de toutes ces raisons, il y avait ses propres besoins. Il ne s'agissait pas de ces bribes de nourriture – destinées à Gordy, elles avaient un goût de sciure dans la bouche de Howard – mais de ces instants fugaces de bonne santé mentale. Ces moments volés où il s'enfuyait de l'autre côté de la clôture lui permettaient de tenir chaque fois quelques jours de plus. Lorsqu'il se retrouvait en compagnie d'un autre être humain qui avait de la lumière plein les yeux, lorsqu'il écoutait sa voix douce chuchoter dans l'ombre, il pouvait encore croire qu'un jour tout recommencerait.

Elle lui apportait des nouvelles du monde extérieur. S'ils avaient écouté l'interprète qui, tous les matins, pendant l'appel, se répandait sur les glorieuses victoires remportées par l'Empire japonais sur terre et sur mer, ils auraient complète-ment craqué. Quelque part dans le camp, une radio était dissimulée, c'était vrai, mais seuls quelques officiers avaient le privilège de pouvoir l'écouter. Le temps que les nouvelles parviennent aux oreilles de Howard, il était difficile de faire le tri entre la vérité et les rumeurs.

Et Shun-ling donnait également des nouvelles de Lily, les anecdotes d'une mère fière de son enfant qu'il était censé transmettre à Gordy. Blotti avec elle sous sa couverture, der-rière la clôture, il l'écoutait raconter les progrès de l'enfant et laissait ces images volées l'emporter de l'autre côté de l'océan.

Il attendait encore de recevoir une deuxième lettre de Lucy. Leur bébé – un garçon ? une fille ? – devait être né un ou deux mois avant Lily. Et donc, chaque fois qu'il écoutait les douces vantardises de Shun-ling, il imaginait Lucy rayonnante de fierté devant un premier sourire, un rire, une dent qui pointait sur la gencive minuscule. Des choses si simples qui paraissaient extraordinaires, impossibles. Tout comme Lucy. Un monde inaccessible. Un monde auquel il avait de plus en plus de mal à croire. Shun-ling l'aidait à maintenir la réalité de ce monde. Elle représentait la liberté, l'espoir, une vie après tout ce malheur. Donc, encore et encore, ces quelques instants chargés de promesses le réduisaient au silence.

Et, après chaque rendez-vous clandestin, comme un voleur qui décharge sa conscience à coups d'offrandes, il déposait les sachets d'espoir volé sur le lit de Ken Campbell.

Accordé au rythme de la nuit, Howard écoutait les bruits du camp, les inspirations et les expirations des damnés qui étaient devenues la nouvelle norme. Par-dessus les borborygmes et les ronflements de ceux qui avaient la chance de dormir, on entendait la toux déchirante, les gémissements involontaires et les plaintes étouffées de ceux que tourmentaient la faim, les pieds électriques, les intestins barattés, la fièvre et le délire. Il priait pour ne pas entendre ce soir un moribond appeler plaintivement sa femme, sa fiancée ou, plus banalement – à son dernier souffle –, sa mère.

Fixant l'obscurité, Howard attendait comme un aveugle, tous ses sens en alerte. De temps à autre, le clair de lune se faufilait entre les fentes des fenêtres barrées de planches. Cela projetait des ombres dans la cabane, trouées à intervalles réguliers par des silhouettes de fantômes émaciés qui se rendaient aux latrines.

Quelque macabre statisticien du camp avait estimé qu'un prisonnier lambda atteint de dysenterie vidait ses intestins un minimum de dix fois par heure durant la journée. La nuit n'apportait aucun répit. Et la veille, ce défilé de misère était devenu une torture pire encore avec la soudaine réapparition du garde surnommé Satan. Entre lui et l'interprète, avec sa haine incandescente de tout Canadien, de tout Blanc, personne n'était plus en sécurité.

Le sergent nippo-canadien tenait ses promesses. Toute excuse lui était bonne pour punir les prisonniers. Beaucoup avaient dû endurer ses tortures. Sa préférée, forcer la gorge de ses victimes pour les obliger à boire jusqu'à ce que leurs ventres soient distendus puis leur sauter dessus, faisait de lui l'homme le plus détesté du camp.

Au cours d'une inspection de la Croix-Rouge à la fin novembre, un officier canadien avait commis l'erreur presque fatale de s'avancer pour informer la délégation des conditions de détention dont ils étaient témoins. Après leur départ, l'interprète, fou de rage, l'avait frappé avec sa boucle de ceinturon, ses poings nus et ses bottes, jusqu'à lui faire perdre conscience. Depuis, l'officier s'accrochait à la vie dans le Mouroir.

Aussi dangereuse qu'elle pût être, la colère du sergent était réservée aux prisonniers. Il ne s'intéressait nullement aux civils chinois. Howard sentait qu'il ne représentait pas une vraie menace pour Shun-ling. Ni, pour quelque étrange raison, pour lui-même. Depuis la lettre de Lucy, l'interprète l'avait traité de façon presque amicale. Howard faisait de son mieux pour l'éviter, ce qui n'était pas toujours facile : l'homme, pris entre deux cultures, n'était accepté par aucune et, régulièrement, il ressentait le besoin de trouver quelqu'un avec qui discuter. Chaque fois qu'il se faisait ainsi coincer, Howard restait immobile, la tête baissée, répétant silencieusement son mantra. Mais ce n'était pas l'interprète qu'il craignait de croiser dans l'obscurité du petit matin.

Le brutal retour de Satan représentait un vrai péril pour Shun-ling. Étant donné ces nouvelles circonstances effrayantes, cette rencontre devait être la dernière. C'était crucial. Il devait la prévenir de la mort de Gordy, il devait s'assurer qu'elle ne reviendrait plus au camp. Il aurait aimé pouvoir l'avertir de ne plus s'approcher. Il avait espéré que commencent les pluies torrentielles – il avait prié pour qu'elles arrivent : elles l'auraient empêchée de venir. Mais la lune, qui réapparaissait régulièrement, lui faisait un pied de nez alors qu'il se levait.

Il s'enveloppa dans sa pauvre couverture et, se déplaçant avec précaution pour éviter les planches qui craquaient, traversa la cabane, ses godillots à la main. Dehors, il plongea sous les marches pour les enfiler, tout en prêtant l'oreille – une poignée de cailloux lancés contre un mur, un éternuement inattendu ou trois toux rauques, autant de signaux qu'un garde était tout près. N'entendant rien, il se faufila vers la clôture, en rasant les murs du baraquement.

Vague promesse de pluie, des nuages galopaient dans le ciel, lui permettant de se faufiler discrètement entre les bâtiments. Le couvre-feu régnait sur l'île et, lorsque la lune disparaissait, l'obscurité devenait totale. Au fond du camp, plié en deux, Howard longea le jardin des officiers japonais. Un rayon de lune révéla un mouvement au milieu des plants de pommes de terre. Il se figea. À quelques mètres, de l'autre côté de la première rangée de légumes, un dos courbé bougea, une tête se releva et des yeux exorbités apparurent dans un visage décharné. Rien qu'un autre prisonnier en train de chaparder. Howard laissa échapper son souffle. Il échangea un salut silencieux avec l'apparition. Il y avait quelque chose de familier dans le visage surpris du prisonnier. En voyant Howard, il sourit et leva un poing couvert de terre, le pouce dressé, signal que la voie était libre. Puis il recommença à creuser. Voler les minuscules pommes de terre par les racines sans arracher les plantes était une activité des plus dangereuses. Dangereuse et qui, finalement, lui coûterait très cher, mais ça, c'était le problème du soldat, pensa Howard. Brusquement, il relia ce visage souriant au jeune soldat qu'il avait vu à l'avant de l'*Awatea*, cet homme-enfant qui provoquait les Japonais à bord du *Lisbon Maru*, il y avait de cela toute une vie. C'était ou ce n'était pas le même garçon – non, pas un garçon : ici, il ne restait plus de garçons.

Le braconnier du potager releva la tête et tendit la main pour montrer son trésor puis il enfourna les vers dans sa bouche et les mâcha avec appétit. La faim poussait à manger à peu près n'importe quoi. Howard avait identifié des morceaux de rats, de serpents, de souris et d'insectes – même des asticots – mélangés avec le riz. Il avait appris à avaler ces protéines bienvenues. Il n'en avait pas encore été réduit à manger des vers crus. La culpabilité le frappa de plein fouet. Il toucha le carré de chocolat enveloppé au fond de sa poche. Le dernier bout qui restait de sa part des colis de la Croix-Rouge distribués pendant l'inspection humanitaire. Il avait conservé cet ultime morceau comme cadeau de Noël – désormais un cadeau d'adieu – pour Shun-ling.

Mais il ne parvenait pas à se détourner du jeune soldat dans le jardin, de ces yeux qui parlaient de mort et de la terre qui maculait sa bouche comme des miettes de gâteau. Howard sortit le carré de chocolat soigneusement gardé, se pencha et le lança à l'autre homme.

Quelques minutes plus tard, il s'accroupissait sur le rebord sablonneux de l'autre côté de la clôture pour attendre Shunling. Le tintement d'une bouée à cloche montait de la baie, accompagné du bruit des vagues qui venaient lécher les laisses de vase. Les mêmes bruits innocents que lors de son premier jour au camp, plus d'une année auparavant. Une année. Une année entière passée dans cet enfer. « Rentrés à Noël. » On n'entendait plus dire ça dans le camp. Plutôt : « Que le printemps nous ramène chez nous. »

La lune se refléta brusquement sur l'eau en contrebas, ses rayons éclairèrent le port, donnant une illusion de liberté. Une proximité tellement trompeuse. Une distance si infranchissable. Comme il était tentant de descendre dans la baie et de partir avec la marée. De s'en aller à la nage et de tenter sa chance avec les sampans et les bateaux de pêche qui dansaient sur les vagues. Mais les neuf autres hommes qui seraient punis, peut-être exécutés, s'il ne revenait pas, le faisaient se tenir tranquille. Et Shun-ling. Il devait rester là pour la prévenir.

Et soudain, elle fut là, accroupie, s'avançant sans bruit vers lui. Howard sentit le sang bourdonner dans ses oreilles en voyant la robe de coton qu'elle portait, avec son motif de fleurs bleu et blanc qui brillait – trop – dans le clair de lune. Il souleva la couverture pour la cacher et elle s'installa contre lui, si près qu'il sentait l'odeur douce et épicée de sa transpiration. Elle tira la robe sur ses genoux et, lentement, releva la tête pour croiser son regard. Elle le fixait intensément de ses yeux sombres dans lesquels brillait ce même clair de lune dangereux que reflétait son visage. Sans prévenir, elle posa la main sur la joue de Howard.

— Howard.

Ce n'était ni une question ni une affirmation. Une conversation entière contenue dans un seul mot.

Surpris par la douceur de sa paume tiède, il se sentit prêt à basculer. Mais il n'y avait pas le temps. Il devait lui parler à la seconde même. Il lui caressa la main, la pressa contre son visage et l'y maintint un court instant.

— Shun-ling, écoute-moi, murmura-t-il. C'est…

La dernière chose dont il se souvint avant que la crosse du fusil le frappe en pleine tempe, ce fut un sifflement, celui que faisait l'air aspiré entre des dents écartées.

Le gravier lui entamait les genoux. Le fil métallique lui coupait la nuque et les poignets. À l'extrémité de son champ de vision surgirent des bottes cavalières brun foncé, familières, l'extrémité bien cirée à quelques centimètres de sa tempe.

Par-dessus le bourdonnement aigu qui résonnait dans ses oreilles, il entendit des cris étouffés qui sortaient du corps de garde. Shun-ling. Il se débattit avec l'énergie du désespoir et le lien autour de son cou qui lui maintenait les mains attachées dans le dos s'enfonça plus profondément dans sa chair.

— Laissez-la partir, supplia-t-il en s'adressant aux bottes immobiles tout en luttant contre l'évanouissement qui le menaçait. Elle n'a rien fait. Ce n'est qu'une réfugiée qui fouille dans les ordures des laisses de vase.

Les bottes bougèrent, encerclant lentement leur proie.

— Je n'en ai rien à faire d'elle, répondit l'interprète. Elle représente sa récompense à lui pour avoir fait échouer ton évasion.

— Je ne...

Howard s'interrompit brutalement. Toute explication ne pouvait qu'impliquer Shun-ling. Dans le corps de garde, les cris de sa résistance frénétique et les représailles brutales de Satan s'intensifiaient.

— Espèces de porcs ! gronda Howard.

— La tentative d'évasion est punie de mort, dit l'interprète. Que vais-je faire de toi ?

La réponse ne se fit pas attendre ; la canne de bambou siffla sur le dos d'Howard. Encore et encore. Il lutta pour ne pas sombrer dans la fulgurance de la douleur mais il finit par être emporté dans le tourbillon des ténèbres.

Quand il revint à lui, quelque chose de lourd tombait sur le sol. Il ouvrit les yeux : Shun-ling était couchée face contre terre, étalée, son visage à portée de main.

— Une guerrière ! s'exclama Satan en gratifiant le corps inanimé d'un coup de pied. Elle s'est bien battue.

Elle releva la tête et ses cheveux emmêlés glissèrent au sol. Quand son regard croisa celui de Howard, elle écarta ses lèvres ensanglantées en un sourire de défi.

— Shun-ling, chuchota-t-il en cherchant ses yeux stoïques.

Au-dessus d'eux, il y eut le bruit glaçant de l'acier glissant hors de son fourreau.

— Une guerrière mérite une mort honorable, roucoula Satan.

— Laissez-la ! hurla Howard.

Il se tourna vers les bottes de l'interprète.

— Arrêtez-le. Pour l'amour du ciel ! Au nom de votre père – un héros canadien –, je vous en supplie ! S'il vous plaît. Épargnez-la.

Il baissa la tête vers le sol.

— Ici, ici, supplia-t-il en tendant le cou aussi loin que le fil métallique le lui permettait, offrant ainsi une cible facile. Je vous en prie !

Il ferma les yeux, implorant la mort de le prendre au fil d'une épée bien aiguisée. Ses muscles se crispèrent en entendant la lame trancher l'air. L'acier froid pénétra rudement dans la chair. Un jet de liquide chaud l'aspergea et ses narines furent submergées par une odeur métallique. Un cri silencieux monta du fond de sa gorge.

La canne de bambou lui fouetta le dos, l'obligeant à relever la tête. Il lutta pour ne pas ouvrir ses paupières alourdies. Un deuxième coup ne fit que renforcer sa détermination. Il refusait d'être témoin, il ne laisserait pas l'horreur qui l'attendait derrière le voile rouge prendre forme. Les coups continuèrent à pleuvoir jusqu'à ce qu'il ne puisse plus résister ; ses paupières se soulevèrent pour voir cette image inimaginable – le buste effondré, le cou déchiqueté d'où jaillissait le sang. Et, à terre, les yeux aveugles de Shun-ling qui fixaient l'espace entre ses bras tendus. Des bras tendus vers lui, presque à le toucher.

Les premières lourdes gouttes de pluie tombèrent en même temps que les gants blancs qui atterrirent par terre, près de la joue de Howard. Satan s'éloigna d'un pas insouciant en aspirant l'air entre ses dents et l'interprète jeta son bâton au loin.

— Tu ne mérites pas pareil honneur, déclara-t-il avant de faire volte-face et de laisser Howard seul à implorer le ciel en larmes de bien vouloir le faire mourir.

Tandis que l'averse torrentielle nettoyait la terre gorgée de sang, il sombra à intervalles réguliers dans l'inconscience. Il finit par se réveiller dans la lumière grise de l'aube et vit qu'on traînait les restes de Shun-ling à l'extérieur du camp et qu'on les abandonnait sur la route. Au bout d'un certain temps, un groupe de réfugiés surgit de la bruine et les emporta.

34

Mon père s'est débarrassé de moi. Il s'est débarrassé de moi ! Comme on se débarrasse d'un chiot ou d'un chaton dont on s'est lassé. Il ne voulait plus de moi. C'était aussi simple que cela. Il ne voulait plus de Kipper non plus. C'était seulement maman qui voulait de nous depuis toujours. À présent qu'elle était morte, nous devenions encombrants. Une source d'ennuis.

« Pour quelque temps », voilà ce que nous dit papa lorsqu'il vint s'asseoir sur le lit de mon frère pour nous prévenir. Kipper, plus Kipper que nature, accepta sa décision en toute confiance et n'émit aucun doute quand papa lui expliqua que l'endroit où il devait aller ressemblait à une école dans laquelle on dormait ; il y apprendrait beaucoup de nouvelles choses et il s'y ferait des nouveaux amis. Et il pourrait rentrer à la maison tous les week-ends s'il le souhaitait. Enfin, après le premier mois.

— Considère que tu pars en colonie de vacances, déclara papa quand la lèvre de Kipper commença à trembler. Tu as toujours eu envie d'aller en colonie. Et si ça ne te plaît pas, tu ne seras pas obligé de rester.

— D'accord, papa, répondit Kipper en se mordant la lèvre.

Papa leva la tête vers moi, debout sur le seuil de la porte, les bras croisés.

— Ça n'a rien de définitif, promit-il.

— Ah !

Je lui tournai le dos, traversai le palier à grands pas et claquai la porte de ma chambre.

J'attendis qu'il redescende et qu'il quitte la maison ; puis j'ouvris mon placard et je le vidai entièrement. Mes vêtements, mes jeux, mes cordes à sauter, mes trésors soigneusement rangés dans des boîtes à chaussures, je balançai tout par terre. J'attrapai mon précieux tas de bandes dessinées sur l'étagère et je les déchirai en petits morceaux, l'une après l'autre. Lorsque tante Mildred voulut entrer, le sol était jonché des morceaux irréductibles du puzzle de ma colère.

Elle haussa les sourcils mais ne fit aucun commentaire sur le désordre.

— J'ai trouvé une vieille valise que Christopher pourrait prendre, affirma-t-elle en me montrant celle qu'elle avait récupérée au sous-sol. Toi, emporte seulement ce qui tient dans ton sac, ma chérie, ajouta-t-elle comme s'il s'agissait de partir en vacances et non de quitter définitivement la maison.

Pendant qu'elle s'occupait de Kipper, je jetai dans le sac que je prenais généralement pour aller dormir chez elle du linge et quelques vêtements. Je laissai tout le reste derrière moi avec mon enfance. Mais j'emportai le secret de Lily. Je pliai et repliai le papier froissé sur lequel elle avait écrit son nom et son numéro de téléphone et quand je l'eus réduit à pas grand-chose, je le collai derrière la doublure de mon sac. Si mon père ne voulait plus de nous, il ne voudrait pas d'elle non plus, pensai-je. Ou bien je redoutais le contraire.

Je me remis au lit, rabattis les couvertures sur ma tête et attendis les instructions de tante Mildred. Je me réveillai en l'entendant m'appeler : il était temps de partir. Avant de quitter ma chambre, je pris le tableau de Kipper accroché au-dessus de mon lit. Je descendis avec le tableau sous le bras, prête à supporter les récriminations de ma tante. Mais elle m'emmena jusqu'à sa Volvo, ouvrit le coffre et mit mes affaires dedans sans prononcer un mot.

— Où est Kipper ? demandai-je devant la banquette arrière vide.

Il était parti. Ils étaient déjà venus le chercher.

— C'est mieux ainsi, expliqua tante Mildred.

Mieux ? Je ne lui avais même pas dit au revoir. Je ne pus me retenir, je me mis à pleurer.

— Je veux Frankie, réclamai-je en reniflant.

— Frankie viendra nous rendre visite, rétorqua-t-elle en m'ouvrant la portière du côté passager.

Durant le trajet jusqu'à chez elle, je me collai le plus possible contre la portière. Je n'avais rien à lui dire. Rien à dire à personne. Je me demandai s'il était possible de se taire pour l'éternité. De toute façon, il n'y avait plus rien à dire qui en vaille la peine. Et d'après moi, il n'y aurait plus jamais rien à dire.

Tenant le volant d'une main, tante Mildred voulut me caresser les cheveux.

— Ce soir, on te lavera les cheveux et je démêlerai cette tignasse. Et demain matin, je te ferai des nattes. Tu sais, je faisais ça pour ta mère. Quand elle était petite, je lui faisais des nattes tous les jours.

J'esquivai sa caresse.

La maison de mon oncle et ma tante était gigantesque. Une maison toujours silencieuse avec des relents d'antiseptique.

— Trop grande pour deux, répétait souvent oncle Sidney.

Même pour trois, elle était encore trop grande. L'entrée exhalait une odeur de vieux bois et d'encaustique. À peine arrivée, je grimpai le large escalier de chêne. Tante Mildred me cria que le repas serait servi dans une heure.

À l'étage, je balançai ma valise dans un coin de la chambre. Je posai le tableau de Kipper contre le mur et je me jetai sur le lit.

Aussi loin que remontent mes souvenirs, j'ai toujours eu ma chambre chez ma tante. Une chambre qu'elle a décorée exprès pour moi, tout en rose. Je l'adorais. J'adorais les rangées de poupées qui paradaient sur les étagères au-dessus du lit, des poupées qu'elle m'avait rapportées de ses voyages autour du monde. Je montai sur le lit pour les atteindre et dans un grand geste, je balayai tout par terre. Les poupées dégringolèrent en tas, reste de l'enfance, masse confuse de bras et de jambes en porcelaine. Je rassemblai ces débris pour les fourrer au fond du placard dont je claquai la porte. Puis je vins m'asseoir devant la coiffeuse. Tortillant une longue mèche de cheveux dans ma bouche, je contemplai mon reflet dans le miroir. Exactement les cheveux de ma mère. J'avais entendu ça toute ma vie. Je sortis de la chambre et de l'autre côté du palier, j'entrai dans la pièce que tante Mildred réservait à ses travaux de couture. Je fouillai dans tous les tiroirs jusqu'à trouver ce que je cherchais. Je revins m'installer devant le miroir. Saisissant une touffe de cheveux, je levai les ciseaux à cranter. Mes boucles tombèrent à terre et je souris méchamment en pensant à la tête que ferait ma tante lorsque je descendrais dans la salle à manger.

35

— Mais qu'est-ce qu'elle a fait ? voulut savoir Frankie. Qu'est-ce qu'elle a bien pu dire, ou faire, pour te convaincre de la laisser les emmener ?

Les épaules voûtées, Howard contemplait fixement le contenu de sa tasse.

— Ce n'est pas définitif, marmonna-t-il. Seulement le temps que je me remette un peu d'aplomb. C'est la bonne décision à prendre.

— La bonne décision ? La bonne décision pour qui ? Pour toi ? répliqua Frankie.

Howard ne l'aurait jamais cru capable de se montrer aussi sarcastique. Frankie traversa la cuisine et lui arracha sa tasse des mains pour la flairer, faisant ainsi gicler le café froid sur la table.

Ce n'était que du café mais Howard soupçonnait son souffle d'être encore chargé des preuves de son passage à la légion peu de temps auparavant. Rien qu'un verre – il lui avait fallu un verre, rien qu'un – pour l'aider à passer cette journée, à rester loin de la maison pendant qu'elle réglait le destin des deux enfants.

— Oui, pour moi, pour toi, pour tout le monde à vrai dire.

Frankie reposa brutalement la tasse sur la table et Howard sursauta.

— Ce n'est pas définitif, répéta-t-il.

De leur propre initiative, ses yeux vinrent errer sur le haut du réfrigérateur.

— Bon Dieu ! jura Frankie.

Il secoua la tête et se dirigea vers la porte. La main sur la poignée, il fit volte-face pour regarder son père qui tressaillit devant la colère – une colère avivée de douleur – qui consumait le visage de son fils.

— Je me suis toujours demandé pourquoi maman faisait tellement l'autruche devant ton problème d'alcool, dit-il à voix basse. Pourquoi elle ne t'avait jamais forcé à choisir entre elle et la bouteille.

Il cligna des paupières pour chasser ses larmes.

— Je crois que j'ai compris maintenant, reprit-il. Elle savait parfaitement ce que tu aurais choisi.

— Non, chuchota Howard. Jamais.

Frankie crispa les mâchoires. Une larme roula sur sa joue. Il se frappa pour s'en débarrasser. Puis, sans avertissement, il fonça sur Howard qu'il attrapa par la chemise ; leurs visages se rapprochèrent au point que Howard pouvait voir une veine violette battre sur le front de son fils.

— Tu veux que je te dise ? cria-t-il en postillonnant abondamment. J'aurais voulu que ce soit toi ! J'aurais voulu que ce soit toi plutôt qu'elle !

Il ravala un sanglot puis lâcha si brutalement la chemise de Howard que celui-ci tomba en arrière et se cogna la tête contre le rebord de la fenêtre.

— Moi aussi, murmura-t-il, s'adressant au dos de Frankie.

La porte claqua, et le bruit résonna dans la cuisine silencieuse et dans les oreilles bourdonnantes de Howard. Il se passa la main dans les cheveux. Il se tâta le crâne : il était sensible. Un marteau cognait à l'intérieur. Même ses globes oculaires étaient douloureux. Il avait la bouche comme un canyon asséché.

Il se leva et, les mains tremblantes, fouilla les placards sous l'évier. Ne trouvant rien, il se dirigea vers sa chambre et frénétiquement, chercha sous le lit et explora tous les tiroirs de la coiffeuse. Rien. Il ouvrit la porte du placard.

Le parfum qui s'en dégagea le frappa en plein cœur. Il tomba par terre, saisit une poignée de vêtements de Lucy dans le panier à linge et les colla contre son visage. Il s'imprégna de leur odeur, qui comblait un vide que l'alcool était incapable de combler. Au bout d'un moment, il prit conscience du rythme apaisant de la pluie qui tambourinait sur la vitre. Il s'essuya les yeux d'un revers de manche et regarda l'heure. Puis il se leva et traversa la maison silencieuse, affreusement vide. Il prit son blouson de cuir dans le placard de l'entrée et l'enfila. Dehors, il s'arrêta sur la première marche, pencha la tête en arrière et laissa la pluie ruisseler sur son visage. Puis il releva son col de mouton et partit.

Contrairement à ce qui s'était produit la veille – il s'était réveillé au milieu de la nuit, couché sur l'herbe détrempée au-dessus de la tombe de Lucy, ignorant comment il était arrivé là et depuis combien de temps –, il savait où il allait. Il dépassa le magasin de spiritueux de Victoria Drive et la Royal Canadian Legion de Fraser Street. Il continua à marcher jusqu'à l'adresse qu'il cherchait sur Oak Street. L'adresse qu'il n'avait pas réussi à faire sortir de son esprit. Celle que Ken Campbell lui avait donnée le jour de l'enterrement de Lucy. Il s'arrêta devant l'immeuble, prit une profonde inspiration puis fit le tour pour entrer par le sous-sol.

Lorsqu'il ouvrit la porte, toutes les têtes se tournèrent vers lui. Howard s'immobilisa, brusquement paralysé, incapable de franchir le seuil. Il entendit une chaise racler le sol de béton, une bouée lancée à un homme qui se noie. Il fit un pas en avant, tendit la main et se cramponna au dossier. Il était entouré de visages bienveillants. Il carra les épaules, ouvrit la bouche et dit :

— Je m'appelle Howard Coulter et je suis alcoolique.

36

17 janvier 1943 : Camp de Sham Shui Po

Howard attendait son tour. Ken Campbell était en train de finir d'écouvillonner la gorge du gars devant lui. Comme tous les autres prisonniers de guerre, toute trace de gras avait disparu du visage de Ken depuis belle lurette, ne laissant plus rien deviner des joues jadis rondes comme celles d'un chérubin. Sa silhouette massive s'était réduite à des membres dégingandés reliés entre eux par des articulations noueuses.

— Mais qu'est-ce que tu fiches ici ? demanda-t-il lorsque Howard ouvrit la bouche devant lui. Ne fais pas l'imbécile, mon pote. Tu ne pourras jamais résister au voyage. Tu es atteint de malaria. Tu tiens à peine debout.

— Ouais, mais je n'ai pas la diphtérie et c'est la seule chose qui leur importe. Fais-moi un prélèvement de gorge.

Ken jeta un coup d'œil par-dessus son épaule vers les gardes qui surveillaient l'opération de dépistage en portant des masques blancs.

— Écoute, avec eux, c'est une simple question d'arithmétique, chuchota-t-il. Il leur faut six cent cinquante corps, des esclaves pour leurs mines de charbon et leurs chantiers navals Ils savent qu'il y aura des pertes pendant le voyage. Tu feras partie de ceux-là.

Howard resserra les bras pour tenter de calmer une nouvelle crise de frissons. D'un signe de tête, il montra Jack Dell, appuyé contre le chambranle de la porte.

— Et lui alors ? demanda-t-il d'une voix rauque. Tu lui as fait un prélèvement. Manchot comme il est, il va partir ?

— Ce petit gus de Terre-Neuve est solide comme le roc, rétorqua Ken. Il résistera à tout. Pas toi.

— Fais-moi un prélèvement de gorge.

Ken ouvrit l'emballage du petit bâton à contrecœur.

— Je sais exactement à quoi tu joues.

Deux jours plus tard, Howard se réveilla baigné de sueur. Quand il voulut se lever, il sentit une main pesante lui écraser la poitrine.

— Faut que je me lève, marmonna-t-il.

— Personne t'en empêche, répliqua quelqu'un de loin.

Howard s'obligea à redresser la tête et scruta les ombres du petit matin. Il n'y avait pas de main, personne près de lui. Libéré de cette contrainte imaginaire, il réussit à s'asseoir et à poser les pieds par terre. Il devait absolument se lever. Mais pourquoi ? Son cerveau torturé par la fièvre ne lui offrit aucune réponse. De l'autre côté de la pièce, Ken Campbell, penché sur son lit de camp, pliait ses maigres biens dans sa couverture.

C'était donc ça ! Le bateau partait pour le Japon aujourd'hui même…

— Je pars avec vous, déclara Howard en se penchant pour attraper ses godillots.

— Désolé, mais tu ne pars pas, dit Ken en nouant les coins de sa couverture avec détermination.

— Mais bien sûr que si.

Balançant son baluchon sur son épaule, Ken s'avança vers lui.

— Ton test de diphtérie est positif, prétendit-il en dominant Howard de toute sa taille.

— N'importe quoi !

— Prouve-le.

Howard fut saisi d'une quinte de toux.

— Je suis vacciné, lâcha-t-il, hors d'haleine. Et tu le sais très bien.

— Monter à bord de ce bateau serait ton arrêt de mort. Et tu le sais très bien.

Mais Howard ne l'écoutait pas. Il tentait de se mettre debout.

— Tu as falsifié mon test ? Je vais…

— Tu vas quoi ? rétorqua Ken. Me dénoncer ?

Howard avait perdu.

Ken posa la main sur son épaule.

— Dans cet endroit, ce qui fait la différence entre la vie et la mort, lui rappela-t-il, c'est la capacité de voir au-delà de la survie immédiate, au-delà de cette existence de bête pour envisager un avenir d'être humain. Tu as perdu cette capacité. Je t'ai vu provoquer les gardes, les implorer pratiquement de te rosser pour ton insolence, prendre la corvée des chiottes quand ce n'était pas ton tour, te porter volontaire à l'hôpital, distribuer ta nourriture. Mais tout ça, tu ne le fais pas pour le bon motif, mon pote, et compte pas sur moi pour t'aider à mourir.

— Tout le monde doit mourir un jour, affirma Howard mais il lui fut impossible de croiser le regard de Ken.

— Oui, et finalement, un homme se définit par les raisons pour lesquelles il accepte de mourir. Pense à Gordy, à tous ces hommes que nous avons enterrés, même à la petite — aucun n'a risqué sa vie pour rien. Pour quoi ? L'amour de leur pays ? L'amour d'un autre être humain ? C'est pareil.

Même les Japonais sont prêts à mourir pour une cause qui les dépasse. Et toi, tu vaux moins que ça ?

Il lâcha l'épaule de Howard et recula d'un pas.

— Il faut que tu te ressaisisses, mon vieux. Je refuse de revenir du Japon quand tout cela sera terminé pour découvrir que tu es mort pour quelque chose d'aussi mesquin et égoïste que la culpabilité.

37

Barclay Street me manquait. Mon ancienne école, mes amis me manquaient. Mais surtout, surtout, ma famille me manquait. J'en accusais ma tante. Et mon père.

Pendant quinze jours, je refusai de le voir. La première fois qu'il vint nous rendre visite, je me précipitai au premier pour m'enfermer dans ma chambre. Couchée sur mon lit fait au carré, les oreilles enfouies sous les coussins roses et duveteux, je fis semblant de ne pas l'entendre m'appeler de l'autre côté de la porte.

Le lendemain soir, tante Mildred monta lorsque, à nouveau, je refusai de sortir.

— Ça suffit, Ethie, gronda-t-elle. Ouvre !

Son tambourinement insistant prit le pas sur les coups discrets de mon père.

— Ne la force pas, dit papa. Je reviendrai demain.

Je me laissai glisser le long du mur et assise près de la porte, j'écoutai diminuer le bruit de ses pas.

Après, cela devint un rituel nocturne ; il attendait en bas pendant que ma tante montait essayer de me convaincre de sortir de ma chambre. Une fois qu'elle était redescendue, je me dissimulais derrière les rideaux à ruchés de ma coquette nouvelle chambre, vêtue de mes somptueux habits neufs, pour regarder mon père retourner à sa voiture garée dans la rue.

Frankie vint lui aussi tenter de me raisonner.

— Papa fait des efforts, Ethie. Il fait vraiment des efforts.

Il me parla des Alcooliques anonymes et des réunions auxquelles il était allé avec lui.

— Moi aussi, j'étais en colère après lui, avoua-t-il, mais je sais qu'il se donne du mal.

J'avais envie de croire Frankie lorsqu'il affirmait que, bientôt, nous serions à nouveau réunis, que cette situation n'allait pas durer. Mais papa, lui aussi, avait prétendu cela.

Je faillis bien tout déballer à ce moment-là. Révéler à Frankie l'énorme secret de notre père, maintenant le mien. J'avais envie de demander : « Si papa a menti à maman, s'il ne lui a jamais parlé de Lily, pourquoi devrions-nous croire à ce qu'il raconte ? » Mais je tus ces réflexions, les enfouissant au plus profond de moi. Et je ne savais vraiment pas pourquoi.

Je ne comprenais plus qui j'étais. Lorsque je me regardais dans le miroir le matin, je ne reconnaissais plus la fille qui me faisait face. Ce n'était pas seulement à cause de la coupe de cheveux, que le coiffeur de tante Mildred avait arrangée de son mieux. Dans ma nouvelle école, je me sentais plus vieille que les autres élèves. Je les traitais par le mépris, je me cantonnais dans le silence. Je faisais de même avec le reste du monde. Particulièrement avec ma tante. J'obéissais à toutes ses demandes mais je ne parlais que pour lui répondre. Je ne lui offrais rien de plus. Et, le pire, je cessai de l'appeler « tante », savourant la peine que je lisais dans son regard chaque fois que je m'adressais à elle en disant « Mildred ».

Un dimanche matin, alors que je vivais chez eux depuis quinze jours, elle était sortie dans le jardin ramasser les prunes que le vent avait fait tomber. Moi, j'étais vautrée sur le canapé du salon et je contemplais un écran de télévision vide – exactement comme mon père. Soudain, oncle Sidney surgit devant

moi, portant un gros album photo sous le bras. Je n'avais
même pas remarqué qu'il était entré dans la pièce.

— Je peux m'asseoir à côté de toi, Ethie ?

Je me redressai pour lui laisser de la place.

Il s'installa près de moi et posa l'album sur ses genoux.

— J'ai pensé que ça te ferait plaisir de regarder des vieilles
photos de ton père et de ta mère, dit-il en souriant. Tu sais
que ta mère a vécu avec nous pendant que ton père était parti
à la guerre, non ?

J'acquiesçai d'un signe de tête. Il ouvrit l'album et lissa les
grosses pages noires du plat de la main. Je sentis ma gorge se
serrer en voyant une photo de ma mère, le menton dans les
mains, assise sur l'escalier devant chez mon oncle et ma tante.

Oncle Sidney enleva le cliché des coins qui le retenaient en
place.

— Je me souviens encore d'elle assise là à attendre le facteur, déclara-t-il en me le tendant. Pendant plus de deux ans,
tous les matins. Elle s'asseyait sur les marches ou, s'il pleuvait,
à l'intérieur, et elle espérait qu'une lettre allait tomber par la
fente pour lui annoncer que ton père était en vie. Il a fait la
guerre à Hong Kong. Tu le savais ?

Je me mordis la lèvre en haussant les épaules, sans cesser
d'examiner la photo de maman.

— Durant les deux années qui ont suivi les combats,
reprit-il, on n'a eu aucune nouvelle. J'ai essayé de faire jouer
des relations à Ottawa pour obtenir une liste des prisonniers
et des victimes. Mais ils n'avaient aucun relevé complet.
Cependant, ta mère, elle, savait. Elle n'a jamais eu le moindre
doute. Au bout d'un an, le premier janvier, elle est descendue
en nous annonçant qu'elle avait entendu la voix de ton papa
au milieu de la nuit. Aussi limpide que le son d'une cloche,
elle a juré qu'elle l'avait entendu lui dire qu'il allait bien.
Lorsqu'une lettre est enfin arrivée du War Office, le facteur

ne l'a pas glissée dans la fente. Il a préféré frapper à la porte pour la lui remettre en mains propres.

Il tourna la page.

— L'*Admiral Hughes*, continua-t-il en montrant la photo d'un navire approchant du quai. Le bateau militaire américain qui a ramené ton père ici. Nous sommes allés le chercher au port avec ta mère.

Je scrutai le visage des soldats qui faisaient des grands signes sur les ponts.

— Ton père ne figure sur aucune de ces photos. Je ne l'ai pas photographié ce jour-là. Après quatre ans dans un camp de prisonniers, il n'avait plus que la peau sur les os quand il est descendu de la passerelle. Ta mère et ta tante ont refusé de le laisser partir à l'hôpital des vétérans. Nous l'avons ramené à la maison, et, à elles deux, elles l'ont soigné et elles l'ont remis sur pied.

Il me regarda un petit moment.

— Je sais que ta tante peut parfois se montrer dure, poursuivit-il, mais elle était autrefois une infirmière extrêmement compétente et toujours pleine de compassion. Ton père serait le premier à le certifier.

Il se tut pour réfléchir.

— Peut-être eût-il mieux valu qu'elle continue à travailler. Mais nous espérions fonder une famille. Et puis ta mère est venue vivre avec nous. Après la guerre, eh bien, Mildred n'a pas eu le courage de tout recommencer à zéro.

Il tourna à nouveau son attention vers l'album et désigna une photo où on les voyait tous en train de dîner lors du premier Noël qui avait suivi le retour de mon père.

— Quand il est rentré, il était insatiable de sandwiches à la sardine. Tu le savais, ça ? Il n'en avait jamais assez. Ni de ça ni du reste, d'ailleurs, ajouta-t-il en riant. Un jour, sans réfléchir, ta tante a préparé du riz pour le dîner. Elle l'a posé sur la table et puis, brusquement, elle s'est rappelé d'où venait ton père et elle s'est excusée. « J'imagine que tu as dû avoir ta dose de riz là-bas », a-t-elle déclaré en reprenant le plat. Mais ton père lui a dit de le laisser là. « Le problème, c'était qu'on n'en avait jamais assez. »

Je savais qu'il me racontait tout cela à propos de ma tante et de mon père parce qu'il souhaitait que je les comprenne mieux, mais je l'écoutais à peine. J'étais littéralement abasourdie par ce que je venais d'apprendre de sa bouche : mon père avait passé quatre ans dans un camp de prisonniers.

38

16 août 1945 : Camp de Sham Shui Po

C'était fini. Vêtu seulement d'un pagne gris et de lambeaux de chemise, Howard, debout sur le seuil de la baraque sanitaire, regardait, dans la brume d'une pluie fine, les avions cargo américains voler au-dessus du camp. Une nuée de parachutes emplissait le ciel gris, fleurs insouciantes qui flottaient vers la terre. Des bidons et des caisses de toutes formes et de toutes tailles se balançaient en dessous et beaucoup s'éventraient en touchant terre, révélant leur précieux contenu. Des boîtes de conserve, des barres de chocolat, des cigarettes et du matériel médical jonchaient le sol du camp et alentour. Cet étalage d'abondance et de générosité des Yankees, après une éternité passée dans le dépouillement absolu, laissait Howard, comme nombre de prisonniers, dans un état de sidération momentané. D'autres couraient partout se jeter sur le butin et se bourraient de chocolat en essayant d'emporter le maximum de boîtes de pêches en conserve.

Une fois les avions cargo repartis, il y eut dans le ciel affluence d'appareils de chasse qui piquaient et plongeaient dans une démonstration de force victorieuse. Les aigles américains jouant sur les ailes du vent.

Howard ne pouvait s'empêcher de comparer cette démonstration aéronautique à celle de la flotte désuète qui avait accueilli à Hong Kong les deux mille jeunes soldats enthousiastes, Winnipeg Grenadiers et Royal Rifles, quatre ans plus tôt. Il restait aujourd'hui moins de quatre cents Canadiens à Sham Shui Po pour acclamer les libérateurs. Plus de mille de leurs camarades avaient été envoyés au Japon au cours des deux dernières années. Combien avaient survécu pour voir cette journée ?

Plusieurs mois auparavant, la radio clandestine avait annoncé la fin de la guerre en Europe et l'intensification des combats dans le Pacifique. La marine américaine avait pris le contrôle des mers. Les Japonais, soumis au blocus, mouraient de faim. Des bombardements à basse altitude sur Tokyo avaient réduit quarante kilomètres carrés en cendres et fait cent mille morts.

Ce n'est plus qu'une question de temps désormais. Tenez bon. Tenez bon.

Le 13 août, les gardes japonais avaient rendu les armes. Avant qu'ils disparaissent du camp, le petit garde sympathique qui avait emmené les groupes de prisonniers travailler sur l'aéroport de Kai Tak avait confié à Howard, le visage tordu par la souffrance, qu'une bombe, une seule bombe, avait détruit une ville japonaise entière. Deux jours plus tard, une seconde bombe en avait pulvérisé une autre.

Était-ce vraiment possible ? Sauvé par la mort de centaines de milliers de civils ? Peu importait de quel côté on se trouvait, pensa Howard, cette guerre avait tranché dans l'âme des hommes pour exposer leur cœur de bête. Mais c'était bel et bien terminé. Cette démonstration dans le ciel en était l'ultime preuve.

Il ignorait ce qu'il s'attendait à ressentir quand ce moment arriverait. S'il arrivait. Mais il se sentait étrangement vide. Aucune agitation, aucune joie. Une absence d'émotion.

Dans le sillage des avions chasseurs, il vit un nuage de papiers blancs. Comme des flocons de neige géants, ils envahirent le ciel avant de descendre se poser, tandis que les avions plongeaient en signe de victoire. Puis, un par un, les appareils américains repartirent vers la mer, certains volant à si basse altitude que, en dépit du rideau de pluie, Howard distinguait les pin-up peintes sur les fuselages et le visage souriant des pilotes. Brusquement, un paquet de couleur sombre vola hors d'un cockpit. Il tomba à pic et vint atterrir à moins de deux mètres de la baraque devant laquelle se tenait Howard. Il alla récupérer le blouson d'aviateur dans la boue. À genoux, il le posa sur ses épaules tremblantes. Tandis qu'il s'enfonçait dans cette chaleur, il sentit quelque chose dans la poche intérieure. Il en sortit une feuille de papier pliée.

« À l'intention des prisonniers de guerre alliés. » Le document, identique à ceux qui tombaient autour de lui, confirmait la reddition inconditionnelle du Japon. Il informait les internés d'attendre à l'intérieur du camp l'arrivée des personnels humanitaires et sanitaires. Le Pacific Fleet, les Anglais et les Américains, étaient en route. Il était signé A. C. Wedemeyer, lieutenant général, États-Unis.

Il examina le papier de plus près. Quelque chose était écrit au stylo de l'autre côté. Howard sentit sa gorge se nouer en lisant le message griffonné : « Avec les salutations du lieutenant-colonel Gregory Jonas, de Little Rock dans l'Arkansas. Profitez de cette liberté retrouvée et d'un monde meilleur. »

Un monde meilleur ? La liberté ? Était-ce possible ?

Howard toucha sa poche de chemise pour s'assurer de la présence de la lettre qu'il gardait près de son cœur. Une lettre reçue peu de temps après que le dernier groupe de Canadiens fut parti pour le Japon, presque deux ans auparavant.

Shun-ling morte, Howard avait refusé d'adresser la parole à l'interprète nippo-canadien. Il niait son existence. Il avait supporté, non, il avait souhaité les raclées que lui avait values cette insolence. Une fois Ken Campbell parti pour le Japon, Howard s'était traîné pendant des mois, quittant rarement son lit de camp. Et puis, un matin, au réveil, il avait trouvé l'interprète debout devant lui, une enveloppe bleue de courrier aérien dans la main. Quelque chose à l'intérieur de Howard avait cédé en voyant l'écriture familière. À ce moment-là, plus rien ne comptait en dehors de cette lettre. Ni la vie ni la mort, même pas la haine. Il avait tendu la main pour la prendre.

Le sergent s'était alors penché vers lui, aiguillonnant encore son désir de lire cette lettre.

— Prononce mon nom et je te la donne. Rien que mon nom.

Malgré le hurlement de son âme, malgré la torture de sa gorge desséchée, Howard s'efforça de prononcer ce nom à voix haute. Mais cela lui fut impossible.

Il se tourna sur le côté. Dans le silence qui suivit, il sentit l'énervement monter dans la respiration de l'autre. Il attendit le choc de la boucle de ceinturon sur son dos, le coup de pied l'envoyant valser hors de son lit. Rien ne vint. Un long moment s'écoula puis il entendit son bourreau sortir en trombe de la baraque. Howard ne le revit jamais.

En définitive, ce ne fut ni l'espoir de l'avenir ni les rêves de liberté qui maintinrent Howard en vie. Ce fut la lettre non censurée que l'interprète avait laissé tomber sur son lit de camp.

Il en avait retenu chaque mot.

15 décembre 1942

Mon Howard chéri,
Comme toujours, je prie pour que cette lettre te trouve sain et sauf. Je n'ai encore reçu aucune nouvelle de toi mais je te sens au

fond de mon cœur et j'espère que tu as reçu au moins quelques-unes de mes lettres…

Sidney et Mildred promettent de prendre des tas de photos du premier Noël de Frankie. Peux-tu imaginer que notre fils a presque six mois ? J'ai moi-même beaucoup de mal à y croire et je le vois grandir tous les jours. Il te ressemble tellement, mon chéri…

Promets-moi de faire tout ce que tu pourras pour traverser cette épreuve. Nous — comme c'est étrange et merveilleux de dire « nous » et plus seulement « je » — nous avons besoin de toi. Reviens vite dans notre maison.

Ta femme bien-aimée,
Lucy

39

— J'ai toujours soupçonné que l'amour de ton père pour Birch Bay est lié au comportement des Américains envers les survivants canadiens durant le trajet de retour, déclara oncle Sidney en tournant la page de l'album de photos. Ils avaient été traités comme du bétail, on les a traités ensuite comme des dieux.

Les deux pages suivantes étaient consacrées à Frankie bébé puis sur ses deux jambes, soit avec ma mère soit avec ma tante, ou avec les deux. J'en connaissais déjà une bonne partie mais je ne protestai pas, tentant de digérer cette nouvelle information concernant mon père pendant qu'oncle Sidney continuait ses commentaires.

— Frankie avait trois ans et demi quand ton père est rentré et, durant tout ce temps, ta mère et ta tante l'ont élevé ensemble. Je suis persuadé que pendant une certaine période, il ne faisait même pas la différence entre les deux. Il appelait ta mère Mommy et Mildred, c'était Mum-Mum. Ta tante l'adorait. Cela a été très dur pour elle quand ils sont partis. Pour moi aussi, je dois l'avouer.

Il sourit devant une photo de papa avec Frankie sur ses genoux osseux.

— Dès le moment où ton père est descendu du bateau, ce gamin n'a plus eu d'yeux que pour lui. Il est devenu son ombre, il ne le quittait pas d'une semelle. Après qu'ils ont quitté la maison, chaque fois qu'on allait leur rendre visite, Frankie s'affolait en voyant ta tante, effrayé à l'idée qu'elle était venue l'arracher à son père. Il a fallu longtemps pour qu'il cesse de courir se cacher chaque fois qu'elle apparaissait à la porte. Cela lui brisait le cœur.

J'émis un petit reniflement et me reculai dans le canapé, les bras croisés.

— Je sais que tu es en colère contre elle pour le moment, Ethie, déclara tranquillement oncle Sidney, mais je veux seulement te faire comprendre son point de vue. Elle adorait sa sœur — ta mère — et elle vous aime tout autant. Et, à tort ou à raison, elle estime faire ce qui lui semble le mieux pour toi, pour Frankie et…

— Et Kipper ? l'interrompis-je.

— Oui, à sa façon. Je ne suis peut-être pas d'accord avec elle mais je crois vraiment qu'elle a agi en pensant faire au mieux pour lui. À la naissance de Kipper, ta tante ne pouvait imaginer qu'une vie de souffrance et de chagrin pour ta mère. Elle a essayé dès le premier jour de la convaincre de le confier. Heureusement, pas plus ta mère que ton père n'ont jamais envisagé une chose pareille, ne serait-ce qu'un instant.

— Pourquoi ne peut-elle l'aimer, lui aussi ?

— Je crois qu'elle ne sait pas comment faire. La différence effraye certaines personnes. Dont ta tante. J'ai toujours espéré que, si on lui en laissait le temps, elle dépasserait ses réticences. Quand on connaît Kipper, peut-on faire autrement que de l'aimer ?

« Elle n'essaye même pas de le connaître », pensai-je.

Je n'eus pas le temps de prononcer ces mots à voix haute. On entendit des pas lourds devant la maison et ma tante cria le nom de mon père.

Je bondis du canapé et courus dans l'entrée. La porte s'ouvrit à la volée au moment où j'arrivais. Mon père se tenait sur le seuil, tante Mildred sur ses talons.

— Howard, je croyais qu'on s'était mis d'accord : tu devais téléphoner d'abord !

Sans lui répondre, il entra. Son regard se posa sur moi. Quelque chose dans ses yeux me figea sur place.

— C'est Kipper, dit-il.

40

Une fois de plus, les souvenirs de Frankie ont dû remplir les blancs à ma place. Après que tante Mildred nous avait embarqués, papa marquait tous les jours un X sur le calendrier près du téléphone. Un jour supplémentaire de sobriété. Un jour de plus sans sa famille. Des jours qui se traînaient avec une lenteur horrible et se terminaient presque tous de la même façon – avec la douleur cuisante de mon refus obstiné de le voir.

— Elle est aussi tenace et têtue que sa mère, disait-il à Frankie, mais le silence, c'est de moi qu'elle le tient.

— Laisse-lui du temps, répondait Frankie. Elle va s'y faire.

Au travail, papa se servait du taxiphone du réfectoire pour appeler Sunnywoods tous les jours. La nouvelle résidence de Kipper avait pour politique de ne pas autoriser les visites de la famille pendant trente jours, afin de laisser aux pensionnaires une chance de s'acclimater, à en croire tante Mildred.

— Comment ai-je pu accepter de ne pas le voir pendant un mois ?

Papa ne cessait de se faire ce reproche.

La réceptionniste de l'institution en vint à reconnaître sa voix et elle le transférait sans commentaire sur la ligne de la directrice. Au début, Mme Crossly répondit à ses questions avec une indifférence polie. Oui, Christopher s'adaptait très bien. Non, la maison ne lui manquait pas. Son asthme ? Je m'en occuperai. Non, on ne pouvait pas lui rendre visite tant que les trente jours n'étaient pas écoulés – les règles sont les règles, mieux vaut ne pas perturber cet enfant.

Au bout d'une semaine, ses réponses neutres aux questions de papa raccourcirent considérablement. Au bout de dix jours, elle suggéra avec beaucoup d'énergie que ces appels incessants étaient injustifiés. Puis, le vendredi, d'une voix crispée d'impatience, elle lui reprocha tous ces coups de téléphone parfaitement inutiles qui lui faisaient perdre son temps et elle lui demandait de ne plus embêter ainsi la terre entière. Elle lui raccrocha au nez en concluant très fermement qu'ils espéraient bien ne plus entendre parler de lui tant que le délai de trente jours ne serait pas écoulé. Jusque là, « s'il y a un problème, nous vous appellerons. »

Ils appelèrent à dix heures, le dimanche matin.

Papa répondit, son visage s'assombrit aussitôt et la peur serra le ventre de Frankie.

— Non, il n'est pas ici. Comment ça, il est parti se balader ? Quand ?... Il n'a pas réapparu de toute la nuit ? Nous arrivons tout de suite ! cria-t-il en raccrochant brutalement.

À Sunnywoods, l'employé trapu qui ouvrit les portes massives ressemblait plutôt à un videur dans quelque bar mal famé, d'après Frankie. La mine sinistre, un trousseau de clés accroché à la ceinture, il leur fit traverser le hall et prendre un couloir mal éclairé. L'écho métallique des portes qu'il refermait à clé derrière eux les suivait dans les corridors déserts.

Dans le bureau de la directrice, papa et Frankie demeurèrent debout tandis que Mme Crossly restait assise. La colère de Frankie fut immédiate, bizarrement provoquée par le fait que cette femme, au courant depuis la veille de la disparition de Kipper, avait pris le temps de se maquiller et de lisser à la perfection son chignon banane d'où pas un cheveu ne dépassait. Ébahi, il l'écouta décrire la situation comme un désagrément mineur.

— Mais, bon Dieu, pourquoi avez-vous mis tant de temps avant de m'appeler ? s'écria papa.

— Nous étions certains de le voir réapparaître incessamment. Nous étions persuadés qu'il était parti bouder quelque part dans le bâtiment.

— Bouder ?

— Eh bien, lâcha-t-elle, il avait été réprimandé, euh, entravé à vrai dire. Pour comportement agressif.

— Agressif ? l'interrompit Frankie. Kipper ?

Elle ignora l'interruption, ne s'adressant qu'à papa.

— Oui, le jeune homme a mordu un membre du personnel.

— Mon fils n'a jamais mordu personne de sa vie.

— Je vous assure, il l'a fait. De toute façon, continua-t-elle, le personnel a passé l'après-midi et la soirée à fouiller les chambres et la propriété. Comme je vous l'ai dit, nous étions convaincus qu'il allait réapparaître. À la nuit tombée, nous ne l'avions pas retrouvé et nous avons donc prévenu la police. Il était parfaitement inutile de vous alerter à pareille heure. Qu'auriez-vous pu faire de plus ?

— J'aurais pu trouver mon fils avant qu'il passe la nuit tout seul je ne sais où, rétorqua papa. Je veux interroger le personnel. Ainsi que tous ses amis ici.

— La police s'en est déjà chargée. Et je refuse de vous laisser déranger encore notre personnel. Votre fils a causé déjà assez d'ennuis. Il est trop dangereux que ce garçon soit si indépendant.

Elle se leva et se dirigea vers la porte, mettant fin à l'entretien.

— Je suis certaine qu'on va le retrouver, reprit-elle. Lorsqu'il aura trop faim, il réapparaîtra soit ici soit chez vous. Je vous suggère de rentrer et d'attendre. Si nous le voyons ici, nous vous appellerons.

— Eh bien, il y a une chose dont vous pouvez être vraiment certaine : il ne remettra plus les pieds ici, rétorqua papa.

Dehors, dans le parking, un jeune homme surgit d'une haie derrière la voiture de papa.

— Vous êtes la famille de Kipper ? demanda-t-il en s'approchant, l'air abattu.

— Oui, répondit Frankie. Et vous, qui êtes-vous ?

Le regard de l'homme sautait nerveusement de papa à Frankie.

— Je travaille ici, annonça-t-il en fixant papa. Enfin, pour le moment.

Il jeta un coup d'œil par-dessus son épaule et s'approcha davantage.

— Je voulais seulement vous dire que Kipper n'est pas parti se balader, leur glissa-t-il à voix basse. Il s'est enfui. Nous avons trouvé une fenêtre ouverte dans la buanderie au sous-sol. Il a dû filer par là.

— La directrice a dit qu'il avait été entravé. Qu'est-ce que cela signifie exactement ? s'enquit papa.

— Mettons que je ne vous ai rien dit. On lui attachait les poignets au montant du lit la nuit pour l'empêcher de sucer son pouce.

— Quoi ? s'exclama Frankie. Ça fait des années que Kipper ne suce plus son pouce.

La voix trop forte de Frankie fit tressaillir l'homme.

— Eh bien, ici, il suçait son pouce. Il y a quelques jours, alors qu'on faisait le tour des dortoirs avant l'extinction des feux, nous l'avons trouvé en train de ronger ses liens. Un des employés a voulu les resserrer et Kipper lui a mordu la main par erreur.

Son regard se braqua sur le bâtiment puis revint à papa.

— Avez-vous une idée de ce qu'ils font subir aux pensionnaires qui mordent ? demanda-t-il avant d'ajouter doucement : votre fils, lui, le sait.

Le jeune homme s'esquiva et papa contempla le bâtiment de trois étages, la façade blanchie qui brillait dans le soleil matinal comme un mensonge, les ombres qu'on devinait derrière les fenêtres à barreaux.

— Quand je pense au nombre de fois où je suis passé devant cet endroit, marmonna-t-il, comment moi, entre tous, je n'ai pas compris ce dont il s'agissait ?

Ce ne fut qu'à cet instant que Frankie remarqua les visages blêmes derrière les vitres. De si loin, il était impossible de déterminer s'ils étaient jeunes ou vieux, hommes ou femmes, s'ils étaient réels ou un jeu de lumière. Mais l'image du regard hanté tapi dans l'ombre l'obsédait.

Papa ouvrit la portière de la voiture.

— Kipper n'a pas fait une fugue, grommela-t-il. Il s'est évadé.

41

Tante Mildred ne protesta pas lorsque papa annonça qu'il m'emmenait avec eux pour rechercher Kipper.

— Si quelqu'un peut deviner où il a pu aller, c'est bien toi, Ethie, dit-il tandis que je laçais mes tennis avec des doigts tremblants. J'ai toujours pensé que tu avais un sixième sens en ce qui concerne ton frère.

Plus je les écoutais, Frankie et lui, expliquer ce qui s'était passé à oncle Sidney et tante Mildred, plus j'avais peur. Qu'avait bien pu faire Kipper, tout seul en pleine nuit ? Le pire de tout, c'était qu'il n'avait pas son inhalateur sur lui.

Frankie le sortit de sa poche.

— Un gars qui travaille là-bas nous l'a donné dans le parking. Il a dit que la directrice refusait que Kipper le garde sur lui. Elle estimait que c'était une « béquille ». Que ses crises d'asthme étaient psychologiques.

— Nom de Dieu ! jura oncle Sidney.

Il prit l'inhalateur, l'examina puis le rendit à Frankie.

— J'aurais volontiers tordu le cou de cette femme, pesta Frankie en l'empochant.

— Cette idée m'a traversé l'esprit, marmonna papa.

Je bondis sur mes pieds, mes lacets enfin noués.

— Prends une veste ou un pull, me recommanda papa. Personne ne sait combien de temps ça va durer.

Je saisis ma veste accrochée au porte-manteau.

Tante Mildred paraissait totalement affolée.

— Nous allons venir avec vous, proposa-t-elle d'une petite voix très rauque.

— Non, ce ne sera pas nécessaire, répondit papa en ouvrant la porte.

— Mais...

— Mildred ! intervint oncle Sidney sans douceur. Dis-nous ce que nous pouvons faire pour aider, Howard, ajouta-t-il en lui serrant brièvement le bras.

— Allez donc chez nous. Il faut que quelqu'un soit là. Au cas où.

Je m'assis sur la banquette avant entre papa et Frankie. On suivit Marine Drive en direction de Sunnywoods. L'institution se trouvait à la frontière de Burnaby et de New Westminster, à quelques kilomètres seulement de la maison. Papa pensait qu'en voyant précisément d'où Kipper était parti, on pourrait en déduire où il avait pu aller.

Frankie contemplait par la vitre les eaux boueuses de la Fraser qui coulait en contrebas.

— Crois-tu qu'il aurait pu aller au bord de la rivière, Ethie ?

Mon ventre se noua. J'avais du mal à réfléchir. Non. Non. Pourquoi y serait-il allé ?

— Je ne crois pas, chuchotai-je, refusant même d'envisager cette hypothèse. Nous n'y allons jamais.

Au-delà de Victoria Drive, la route sinueuse devenait familière. Je m'agitai sur mon siège, me tortillant pour scruter la végétation dense sur notre gauche.

— Nous avons vu Danny Fenwick au moment de partir, expliqua papa. Il va rassembler quelques-uns de ses amis pour aider à fouiller les alentours. Penses-tu à d'autres endroits où Kipper aurait pu aller ?

— Le terrain de golf, lâchai-je. Nous sommes allés y chercher des balles. Danny a construit une cabane là-bas.

Dans mon énervement, je me mis à bafouiller.

— Il est peut-être allé là-bas. Il a peut-être dormi dans la cabane la nuit dernière.

Au carrefour suivant, je guidai papa dans le dédale des nouvelles rues, des maisons à moitié construites et des terrains vagues au-dessus de Marine Drive. Je désignai un chemin qui menait dans la forêt entourant le terrain de golf.

— La cabane de Danny est par là-bas.

Papa fit une embardée et des cailloux volèrent sous les pneus quand il redressa. La route montait un peu et au sommet un brutal éclat de lumière se reflétant dans un rétroviseur m'aveugla pendant une seconde. L'Hudson ralentit avant de s'arrêter sur une ultime secousse. Devant nous la clairière ressemblait à un vrai parking. Le soleil de l'après-midi brillait sur les pare-brise, les calandres et les capots de tous les véhicules garés là. Frankie se pencha pour regarder dehors.

— Ce sont nos voisins, constata papa.

Il ouvrit la portière et nous nous précipitâmes vers la foule rassemblée derrière un camion. Papa ne s'était pas trompé : Mme Fenwick, les Manson, les Jackson, les Black, tout Barclay Street, tous ceux qui avaient assisté à l'enterrement de maman étaient là. Même le garçon avec qui je m'étais disputée à propos des bouteilles était en train de poser son vélo dans l'herbe pour se joindre à nous.

Dora Fenwick nous aperçut et vint à notre rencontre. Danny avait fait circuler l'histoire de Kipper dans tout le voisinage, nous expliqua-t-elle. Le père d'Ardith, qui était pompier, organisait le ratissage de cette zone. La foule s'écarta en silence pour nous laisser atteindre l'endroit où M. Price étalait une carte sur le hayon du camion. Il échangea une poignée de main silencieuse avec papa.

Danny surgit soudain à côté de moi. Il remonta ses lunettes sur son nez.

— J'ai pensé qu'il avait pu venir à la cabane, mais je viens de vérifier, dit-il d'un air déçu, et apparemment personne n'est venu ici.

Durant tout l'après-midi, on ratissa la forêt, les clairières, les ruisseaux et les fossés. Des groupes battirent minutieusement les hautes herbes, les chardons et l'enchevêtrement des taillis. On explora systématiquement toutes les maisons en construction. Plus la rumeur se propageait, plus on voyait de gens arriver pour donner un coup de main. La scierie où papa et Frankie travaillaient ferma pour la journée et les employés vinrent aider. Beaucoup de golfeurs délaissèrent les fairways pour se joindre à nous, se frayant un chemin dans les broussailles avec leurs cannes. On dénicha grenouilles et écureuils, on trouva des pneus éclatés et un chien errant, mais pas Kipper.

À la fin de l'après-midi, notre groupe parvint à l'entrée d'un des tunnels des égouts.

— Où mènent-ils ? demanda papa.

— À la rivière, répondit M. Price.

— Ethie ? m'interrogea papa.

— Non. Il n'entrerait pas là-dedans.

J'étais peut-être trop affirmative car il s'accroupit pour me regarder au fond des yeux.

— Tu en es sûre ? insista-t-il doucement. Ou tu l'espères ? Vous n'avez jamais joué là-dedans ?

— Moi, oui. Mais pas Kipper.

Maman soutenait toujours que, laissé à lui-même, Kipper ferait toujours le bon choix. Je savais par ma propre expérience que c'était vrai.

— Non, affirmai-je, en regardant mon père qui paraissait tellement inquiet. Je suis certaine qu'il n'est pas entré là-dedans. Il n'a jamais voulu y aller, même avec moi. Quand on a joué dedans, Danny et moi, Kipper est resté à l'extérieur.

Il est resté à l'extérieur et il a pris un bâton pour dessiner des maisons dans la boue.

— Le magasin de fournitures artistiques ! m'écriai-je, le cœur soudain battant. Il est peut-être allé en ville au magasin de Marlene !

Évidemment ! C'était parfaitement plausible. Il y était allé tant de fois avec maman qu'à coup sûr il connaissait le chemin.

Papa s'arrêta à la première cabine téléphonique de Marine Drive. Par la vitre ouverte, je l'écoutai discuter avec M. Telford, insistant pour qu'il nous retrouve immédiatement à la boutique.

— Non, ça n'a strictement rien à voir avec ses peintures, s'énerva papa. Kipper a disparu et il peut très bien être allé là-bas.

Sa mâchoire se crispa, ses muscles se gonflèrent alors qu'il était à nouveau interrompu.

— Écoutez-moi, dit-il à voix plus basse, prononçant chaque mot distinctement. Nous serons là-bas d'ici vingt minutes. Si vous n'y êtes pas, je vous jure que je défonce cette putain de porte.

En arrivant dans la ruelle qui passait derrière le magasin, nous vîmes M. Telford debout à côté de sa voiture. Papa ouvrit la portière à la volée et sauta dehors avant même que le moteur de la Hudson se fût tu. Il montra du doigt une fenêtre en hauteur, ouverte, sur le côté du bâtiment et deux poubelles métalliques retournées juste en dessous.

— Ah bon sang ! s'exclama M. Telford.

Il sortit une clé de sa poche et se dirigea vers la porte.

— Vite ! cria papa.

À la seconde où la clé tourna dans la serrure, il le bouscula pour entrer, Frankie et moi sur ses talons ; M. Telford alluma les lumières derrière nous. On visita le bâtiment au pas de course, fouillant frénétiquement chaque pièce, le magasin, les placards, les toilettes, en criant le nom de Kipper.

Je m'arrêtai avec Frankie au seuil de la salle d'exposition.

— Qu'est-ce que c'est que ça ? hurla Frankie en se précipitant dans la pièce mal éclairée.

M. Telford alluma le plafonnier.

— Eh bien, eh bien, on dirait que quelqu'un est venu ici, conclut-il.

Frankie s'accroupit pour examiner un tas de chiffons à peinture sous la table au fond de la salle.

— On dirait que quelqu'un s'en est servi pour dormir, constata-t-il.

Il en souleva un et un grand carnet à esquisses tomba du tissu et glissa à terre, à l'envers.

M. Telford le ramassa.

— C'est à Marlene, dit-il. Les esquisses dont je vous avais déjà parlé, ajouta-t-il en tendant le carnet à papa.

La poitrine et les épaules de papa s'affaissèrent aussitôt, comme si on avait aspiré l'air hors de ses poumons. Il referma lentement le carnet mais j'avais eu le temps de voir un dessin au crayon du visage de ma mère. Un déclic se fit alors dans ma tête.

— Papa, appelai-je en l'attrapant par le bras. Papa, je sais où il est.

42

Les rayons du soleil couchant tapaient sur les immeubles de béton et les fenêtres du centre-ville qui s'obscurcissaient déjà. L'embrasement du ciel à l'ouest promettait un beau temps pour demain. La nuit à venir n'était pas aussi enthousiasmante. Je n'avais besoin ni de papa ni de Frankie pour savoir que le temps ne jouait pas en notre faveur. Si nous ne le trouvions pas rapidement, Kipper risquait de passer une autre nuit interminable tout seul, sans rien à manger et – j'en frissonnais rien que d'y penser – sans son inhalateur.

Frankie était au volant. Il ne ralentissait pas aux feux oranges ni même aux rouges, fonçant dans Granville Street.

— Si la police nous poursuit, lui avait dit papa quand nous nous étions entassés dans l'Hudson, continue sans t'arrêter. On leur expliquera plus tard.

Il était maintenant assis à côté de moi sur la banquette avant et m'encourageait à continuer ma confession : pourquoi croyais-je qu'on allait trouver Kipper dans Chinatown, derrière une épicerie ?

— Je crois qu'il est allé là-bas pour parler à maman. Je lui ai dit – nous lui avons dit – que c'était un endroit où on venait pour parler aux morts de sa famille.

— Nous ?

Et je déballai toute l'histoire – la fille dans le square de l'autre côté de la rue, quand on l'avait suivie dans le centre-ville le jour de l'enterrement de maman, et la petite maison rouge dans la cour derrière le magasin.

— Kipper n'arrêtait pas d'en parler. Il voulait revenir la voir. Il a même commencé à la peindre. Alors, quand on est retournés en ville, je lui ai affirmé qu'il y avait des fantômes dedans.

— Vous êtes retournés en ville ? demanda papa d'une voix clairement étonnée.

Frankie, lui aussi, écarquilla les yeux mais se concentra à nouveau rapidement sur la conduite.

— Je suis désolée…, bégayai-je. Je sais…

— Pas de problème, me calma papa en me tapotant le genou. Donc, vous êtes retournés en ville et alors… ?

La tête basse, j'expliquai d'un ton hésitant comment Kipper avait eu une crise d'asthme au moment où nous arrivions au magasin.

— Mais son inhalateur était vide. La fille nous a emmenés à l'étage dans l'appartement où elle a fait bouillir des feuilles qui l'ont aidé à respirer.

J'éclatai en sanglots sans le regarder.

— Je n'aurais jamais dû raconter ça à propos des fantômes, me lamentai-je. Je n'aurais jamais dû l'emmener là-bas.

Papa m'attira dans ses bras et je me mis à pleurer contre sa poitrine.

— Tout va s'arranger, murmura-t-il en me serrant contre lui. Nous allons le retrouver.

Le silence s'installa un moment.

— Comment s'appelle la fille ? demanda-t-il d'un ton posé, au bout de quelques instants.

Je me redressai et m'essuyai les yeux.

— J'ai oublié son nom de famille, déclarai-je en reniflant. Elle l'a écrit ainsi que son numéro de téléphone sur un bout de papier. Mais je l'ai laissé dans ma valise chez tante Mildred. Quand même, je me souviens de son prénom. Lily.

Je sentis papa se raidir, comme s'il avait cessé de respirer.

— Je suis désolée de ne pas t'avoir parlé d'elle.

— Pour l'instant, ça n'a pas d'importance, dit-il d'une voix couverte. La seule chose qui compte, c'est de retrouver Kipper.

Quelques pâtés de maisons plus loin, je marmonnai :

— Elle a une photo de toi, avec sa mère. Je l'ai vue. Lily pense... elle pense...

À nouveau, je baissai la tête.

— Elle pense quoi ? insista papa. Tout va bien, Ethie. Tu peux me le dire.

— Elle pense que tu es... tu es son père, chuchotai-je.

La voiture fit une embardée.

— Quoi ? s'exclama Frankie en reprenant le contrôle du véhicule.

Papa me releva le menton.

— Ethie, regarde-moi, ordonna-t-il en essuyant avec son pouce les larmes qui roulaient sur mes joues.

Je relevai la tête pour croiser son regard. Et l'espace qui nous séparait s'anéantit.

Toute ma vie, je me souviendrai du bleu de ses yeux ce jour-là. Et la lumière que je vis dedans. La tristesse y était toujours, la douleur à cause de maman, la peur pour Kipper, mais, tandis que nous nous regardions au fond des yeux, mon père et moi, je compris que j'étais partie intégrante de cette lumière.

— J'ai une seule fille, déclara-t-il doucement, et c'est toi, Ethie. Je ne suis pas le père de Lily.

— Mais... alors... à propos de... l'argent que tu lui envoyais tous les mois ?

Une fois encore, Frankie nous jeta un coup d'œil mais il n'intervint pas.

— C'est une longue histoire, soupira papa, et je vous promets de la raconter – un jour. Mais pour le moment, il faut se concentrer sur Kipper.

Nous l'avons entendu avant de le voir. Au moment où nous poussions la barrière en bois derrière le magasin, nous avons entendu le bruit rauque de ses respirations courtes et déchirantes.

Papa a traversé la cour jusqu'à la petite maison en trois longues enjambées, Frankie et moi sur ses talons. Nous avons trouvé Kipper pelotonné dans un coin du minuscule porche, les yeux clos, en train de se battre avec ses poumons sifflants pour laisser passer l'air malgré sa langue gonflée. Papa s'est agenouillé pour le prendre dans ses bras. Les paupières de Kipper se sont entrouvertes. Un pâle sourire a relevé les commissures de ses lèvres desséchées.

— Salut, papa, a-t-il murmuré d'une voix enrouée, à peine audible. Maman a bien dit que tu viendrais.

Papa appuya ses lèvres sur le visage gris de Kipper.

— Tu as rêvé, mon fils, chuchota-t-il.

Sans cesser de le bercer, il se recula pour laisser Frankie lui glisser l'inhalateur dans la bouche ; puis ils se mirent à respirer profondément, en rythme avec l'appareil, comme si cela pouvait aider le médicament à pénétrer dans les poumons congestionnés de Kipper.

— Je vais chercher Lily, annonçai-je.

43

Le souffle douloureux de Kipper vint brouiller la rencontre – la collision brutale – de papa avec son passé.

— Montez-le à l'étage, les invita Lily dès qu'elle vit Kipper.

Dans la cuisine au-dessus du magasin, la même femme qui s'activait déjà la dernière fois devant le fourneau jeta à nouveau une poignée de feuilles dans une casserole d'eau bouillante. De la tête, elle nous fit signe de passer au salon.

Tandis que papa et moi nous nous asseyions sur le canapé avec Kipper calé entre nous, Frankie demanda la permission d'utiliser le téléphone. Lily l'emmena dans l'entrée. Pendant qu'il appelait la police et oncle Sidney pour les prévenir que nous avions retrouvé Kipper, j'observais mon frère affalé contre notre père, mou comme une poupée de chiffon.

Comment avait-il pu parcourir à pied pareille distance sans attirer l'attention de personne ? Vêtu d'une ample salopette de mécano et d'une chemise grise, sa tête rasée tout entaillée et croûteuse, il ressemblait aux hommes qui travaillaient dans les champs des fermes-prisons de la vallée de la Fraser.

Lily revint avec des serviettes qu'elle posa sur la table basse. Elle en prit une et Kipper releva la tête pour qu'elle puisse lui en envelopper les épaules. Pendant qu'elle faisait cela, papa lui adressa un sourire mélancolique.

— Tu ressembles tout à fait à ta mère, constata-t-il.

Brusquement timide, Lily baissa ses yeux noirs. La femme dans la cuisine leur jeta un coup d'œil tout en versant le liquide fumant dans un bol. Ses yeux croisèrent ceux de papa.

— Shun-qin ? demanda-t-il.

Elle acquiesça d'un signe de tête, sans dire un mot, puis reprit sa tâche. Elle reposa la casserole sur le fourneau, apporta le bol dans le salon et retourna dans la cuisine.

Lily remonta la serviette pour en entourer la tête de Kipper. Il lui sourit puis il se pencha pour respirer la vapeur d'eau.

— Je vois que tu connais ça par cœur, remarqua papa en riant.

— Oui, papa, ça va me faire du bien, répondit Kipper dont la voix étouffée sortait de sous la serviette.

— Dans un quart d'heure, il sera comme neuf, dit la femme dans la cuisine en disposant des verres de thé sur la table.

— Shun-qin, s'exclama papa, surpris, mais vous parlez !

— On élève enfant, on apprend à parler.

Tandis que la respiration de Kipper s'allégeait, je sirotais mon thé en examinant la pièce, Frankie assis raide comme un bâton, complètement éberlué, Lily à genoux par terre près de la table basse, veillant sur Kipper, soulevant la serviette à intervalles réguliers pour vérifier ses progrès.

— Merci de l'aider ainsi, Lily, déclara papa, brisant soudain le silence. Cette fois et l'autre.

Leurs regards se croisèrent et elle lui répondit par un sourire timide.

— Ta mère apportait des plantes médicinales à ton père dans le camp de prisonniers, à Hong Kong.

Il prit une profonde inspiration comme s'il mesurait la gravité de ce qu'il s'apprêtait à dire.

— Malheureusement, continua-t-il, elles sont arrivées trop tard pour lui. Mais beaucoup d'autres soldats, moi compris, doivent leur vie à ces remèdes volés.

Il jeta un œil vers Shun-qin, debout sur le seuil de la cuisine.

— Comment va votre ami, Ah Sam ? se risqua-t-il à demander.

— Mort, répondit-elle. Depuis beaucoup mois maintenant.

— Je suis navré de l'apprendre. C'était un homme de cœur. Je t'ai vue dans le square, dit-il alors à Lily. Et puis je me suis convaincu que c'était un effet de mon imagination, que j'avais des visions. Pendant des années après la fin de la guerre, j'ai cru reconnaître ta mère dans toutes les femmes asiatiques que je voyais.

Il garda le silence un long moment.

— Est-ce lui qui t'a donné mon adresse ? s'enquit-il finalement.

— Non. Son neveu. Il ignorait que c'était un secret.

Elle regarda ses mains puis de nouveau papa, ses yeux noirs noyés de larmes.

— Je suis désolée d'être allée chez vous ce jour-là. J'ai apporté la malchance à votre porte. Peut-être si je n'avais pas parlé à votre femme. Si…

Papa devint tout pâle.

— Non.

Il leva la main comme pour endiguer le flot des paroles de Lily.

— Non, répéta-t-il.

La douleur contenue dans ce seul et unique mot emplit toute la pièce plongée dans le silence.

44

Devant l'expression de Lily, la gorge de Howard se serra. Tous les matins, depuis dix-sept ans, il se réveillait avec le même regard dans la tête. Dix-sept ans, qui s'étaient écoulés dans une fugue de regrets. Si. Si seulement.

Si seulement il avait prévenu Shun-ling de la mort de Gordy avant ce soir-là. Si seulement il l'avait empêchée de continuer à venir au camp. Et désormais l'angoisse supplémentaire de savoir que, s'il avait raconté la vérité à Lucy bien des années plus tôt, elle ne serait jamais allée sur ce bateau.

Regardant droit dans les yeux la fille de Shun-ling et de Gordy, il comprit qu'il devait à ces deux-là de s'assurer qu'elle ne portait pas un fardeau similaire de culpabilité, fondée sur l'idée superstitieuse que c'était sa présence qui avait provoqué la tragédie dans leur foyer.

— Non, affirma-t-il en secouant la tête. La mort de Lucy était un accident, un terrible accident. Ce n'est pas toi qui l'as provoqué et tu n'aurais rien pu faire pour l'empêcher. Si elle le pouvait, elle serait la première à te dire que c'était le Destin – la constance du ciel, comme elle l'appelait.

Il se rendit compte que ces paroles prononcées à l'improviste valaient également pour lui. Répéter les mots d'une prière apprise par cœur ne suffirait pas et il devait trouver le moyen d'accepter ce qu'il ne pouvait pas changer.

À ce moment-là, il remarqua une photographie sans cadre posée sur l'étagère d'angle couverte de bibelots. Il se leva du canapé pour aller la regarder de plus près.

— Tu permets ? demanda-t-il.

Du coin de l'œil, il vit Lily acquiescer.

Sentant son regard sur lui, il prit la vieille photographie sépia. Il l'examina attentivement, laissant les souvenirs remonter, tandis que, quelque part, une horloge tictaquait dans le silence. Il se tourna vers Lily, la photo à la main.

— Cet homme, déclara-t-il en désignant Gordy, cet homme était ton père. Vous le saviez ? demanda-t-il à Shun-qin.

— Non, répondit-elle. Je sais seulement un homme père de Lily – un homme ami de Shun-ling.

Howard se tourna à nouveau vers Lily.

— Ton père s'appelait Gordy Veronick. C'était mon meilleur ami. Nous avons grandi ensemble. Il aimait ta mère, et toi. Il vous aimait beaucoup.

Les yeux sombres de Lily se remplirent de larmes.

— Il est mort ?

— Oui et j'en suis désolé.

— Mais c'était vous qui envoyiez de l'argent tous les mois ? voulut-elle savoir en essuyant une larme de la main.

— Oui. J'en avais fait la promesse à ton père. Et je le devais à ta mère, ajouta-t-il au bout d'un moment.

— Dette soldée, déclara Shun-qin du seuil de la cuisine.

— Impossible.

— Ce que veut dire ma tante, expliqua Lily, c'est que nous n'avons plus besoin d'aucun soutien financier. Ah Sam l'a aidée à faire d'excellents investissements. Nous avons eu de quoi venir ici, acheter ce magasin avec notre deuxième oncle et me permettre de suivre les cours à l'université. Voilà pourquoi je suis venue chez vous. Pour vous remercier.

— Moi aussi je veux aller chez nous, gémit Kipper de sous sa serviette.

Frankie se secoua comme s'il émergeait d'un rêve. Il se pencha vers Kipper et lui serra le bras.

— Ah ça oui ! La maison est trop triste sans toi.

— Je crois que ça suffit, déclara Lily en se tournant vers Kipper.

Elle troqua la serviette mouillée contre une sèche et lui épongea les cheveux.

— Mon chapeau ! cria-t-il en touchant son crâne rasé. Ils m'ont pris mon chapeau.

— Désolé, fiston, dit Howard en le prenant par les épaules. Demain matin, à la première heure, on ira t'en acheter un autre.

Lily se leva et disparut dans l'entrée. Elle réapparut quelques instants plus tard, un calot à la main.

— Tiens, Kipper. Tu peux prendre celui-là. C'est un chapeau tout à fait spécial. C'était celui de mon père.

Surpris de voir son vieux calot militaire – celui dont il s'était servi pour passer l'argent à Shun-ling au ferry – Howard ouvrit la bouche pour la corriger. Mais il se ravisa. Pourquoi la priver de ce souvenir et de ce geste généreux ?

Souriant à travers ses larmes, Kipper enfonça le calot en biais sur son crâne rasé.

— Un chapeau spécial ? demanda-t-il.

— Oui, confirma Shun-qin, les yeux fixés non sur Kipper mais sur Howard. Ma sœur a dit que chapeau appartenait à l'homme à qui elle donnait son cœur.

45

Kipper et moi, nous sommes montés derrière avec papa pour rentrer à la maison.

— Ils avaient l'intention de m'arracher toutes les dents, rapporta Kipper d'une voix endormie. C'est méchant, hein, papa ?

— Absolument, répondit papa en nous entourant de ses bras et en nous serrant contre lui.

Kipper bâilla.

— Tu as dit que je pouvais partir si je voulais, expliqua-t-il en s'appuyant contre son père. C'est ce que j'ai fait.

— Ça, tu l'as fait ! s'exclama papa en riant.

Nous serrant encore plus fort, il promit à Kipper qu'il ne retournerait plus jamais à Sunnywoods.

— À partir d'aujourd'hui, ajouta-t-il, les membres de cette famille ne se quittent plus.

Mais Kipper dormait déjà.

Je me fondis contre papa, pensant à ce qu'il avait raconté à Lily : Gordy Veronick n'avait plus du tout de famille au Canada.

— Ton père et moi, nous étions comme des frères, et je lui ai promis de prendre soin de toi. Donc, même si tu n'as plus besoin d'aide financière, je serai quand même là pour toi, je serai ton oncle canadien, si tu m'y autorises.

— Papa, chuchotai-je dans l'obscurité de la banquette arrière, j'aime vraiment beaucoup Lily.

Il m'embrassa le sommet du crâne.

— J'en suis heureux, mon trésor.

Dans le rétroviseur, les yeux de Frankie se plissèrent dans un sourire. Quelques pâtés de maisons plus loin, il brisa le silence bourdonnant qui régnait dans la voiture.

— Tu n'as jamais rien dit à maman.

C'était plus une constatation qu'une question, mais j'attendis néanmoins la réponse.

— Non, reconnut papa à voix basse.

— Pourquoi ?

Après un silence qui parut durer une éternité, papa répondit :

— Je ne sais pas exactement. Au début, quand je suis rentré, il m'était carrément impossible d'en parler. Et après, plus le temps passait, plus ça paraissait difficile.

Au feu suivant, Frankie se retourna vers nous.

— Je crois qu'elle aurait compris, déclara-t-il.

— Oui, elle aurait compris.

Il était tard en arrivant dans Barclay Street, presque minuit. Nous passâmes lentement devant les maisons de nos voisins. Tous les porches étaient encore éclairés.

Kipper se réveilla. Il se redressa et se frotta les yeux.

— Me revoilà maison, me revoilà maison, et ding et ding et dong !!

— Oui, fiston, te voilà revenu chez toi.

La voiture ralentit et je me raidis en voyant celle qui était garée devant chez nous.

— Oncle Sidney veut examiner Kipper, dit Frankie en se rangeant le long du trottoir derrière la Volvo de tante Mildred.

De l'autre côté de la rue, les rideaux bougèrent à la fenêtre de Mme Manson. Elle surgit hors de chez elle au moment où papa aidait Kipper à sortir de la voiture.

— Je suis contente de savoir que vous l'avez retrouvé !
cria-t-elle. Tout va bien, Howard ?

— Oui, répondit papa par-dessus son épaule. Il est seulement fatigué. On vous verra demain.

Au milieu du trottoir, il s'arrêta et cria :

— Et merci, Irene.

Dans le salon, Kipper s'assit sur le canapé pour qu'oncle
Sidney ausculte son cœur et ses poumons ; il vérifia ensuite
sa gorge, ses yeux et ses oreilles. Je restais collée contre papa,
accrochée à son bras et j'évitais le regard de tante Mildred.
Lorsqu'il eut terminé son examen, oncle Sid tapota le genou
de Kipper.

— Il a juste besoin d'une bonne nuit de sommeil, annonça-
t-il en se levant. Comme nous tous d'ailleurs. On va vous
laisser maintenant.

Tante Mildred fit un pas en avant.

— Viens donc, Ethie, m'appela-t-elle.

Je m'accrochai encore plus fort à papa. Frankie aida Kipper
à se relever et on fit front.

— Elle reste, déclara papa en me serrant contre lui. Ce soir
et pour toujours. Ainsi que Kipper. Ici, c'est leur foyer.

Tante Mildred ouvrit la bouche mais, sans lui laisser le
temps de parler, papa leva la main.

— Écoute, je sais que tu as de bonnes intentions et je sais
que j'ai envers toi une dette de reconnaissance que je ne serai
sans doute jamais capable de régler, mais ce n'est pas avec ma
famille que je vais le faire. Si tu veux te battre avec moi sur
ce terrain, vas-y, fonce, mais je ne reculerai pas. Pas cette fois.

— Mais comment vas-tu réussir à te débrouiller ? s'enquit-
elle. Que vas-tu faire ?

— Qu'allons-nous faire ? corrigea papa. C'est bien de cela
qu'il s'agit. Nous formons une famille et nous ferons ce
qu'il faut à dater d'aujourd'hui pour que cela continue ainsi.

Maintenant, tu peux choisir de faire partie de ce nous ou pas.
À ta guise.

— Mais...

— Mildred, l'interrompit oncle Sidney, ça suffit maintenant ! (Il regarda papa.) Elle ne se battra pas contre toi,
Howard. Je te le promets. Et nous vous aiderons par tous les
moyens à votre convenance.

— Merci, Sid.

Brusquement, tante Mildred s'écroula dans le fauteuil de
papa.

— Oh mon Dieu, sanglota-t-elle, le visage dans les mains,
maintenant je vous ai tous perdus.

Kipper s'avança vers elle et posa la main sur son épaule
tremblante.

— On n'est pas perdus, tante Mildred, dit-il en la tapotant
gentiment. On est tous là et c'est bien.

46

Dans les années qui suivirent, il y eut des bons et des mauvais moments, le yin et le yang. Au début, les périodes de tristesse dépassaient nettement les périodes heureuses. Bien des matins, et c'était vrai pour chacun de nous, l'idée de se lever pour affronter une nouvelle journée sans maman paraissait vraiment trop douloureuse à supporter. Ces jours-là, nous apprenions à nous concentrer sur le fait de poser un pied devant l'autre, nous méfiant de ces trous secrets de sombre désespoir dans lesquels nous glissions parfois. C'était Kipper qui nous sauvait, qui nous aidait à remonter du fond de ces trous pour repartir et avancer. Si jamais trop de temps s'écoulait sans que nul ne mentionnât notre mère – parce que, parfois, rien que prononcer son nom était une souffrance intolérable –, lui, il brisait ce silence tacite en évoquant quelque moment particulier vécu avec elle ou en répétant une de ses innombrables citations préférées ; il nous rappelait ainsi, de façon très concrète, qu'elle était toujours à nos côtés.

Il y eut des moments où mon père mena de rudes batailles, probablement plus intenses que tout ce que nous pouvions imaginer. Mais, au bout d'un certain temps, je finis par cesser de m'inquiéter chaque fois que je le voyais enfiler son blouson d'aviateur et j'en vins à penser qu'il continuait à faire ses longues promenades sous la pluie plus par habitude que par nécessité.

Ce ne fut pas toujours facile, j'en suis persuadée, mais il tint parole. De ce que j'en sais, il n'a plus jamais bu le moindre verre. Et, avec le temps, il nous a bel et bien fait partager son passé, comme promis ; ce qui m'a permis de raconter son histoire toutes ces années après.

Après la guerre, au printemps 1947, on lui demanda de revenir à Hong Kong pour témoigner dans les enquêtes sur les crimes de guerre. Il refusa.

Au terme de ces enquêtes, le capitaine du *Lisbon Maru*, ce navire qui transportait des prisonniers de guerre, fut reconnu coupable d'avoir donné l'ordre de fermer les écoutilles et d'ôter les chutes de ventilation pendant le naufrage. Il fut condamné à sept ans d'emprisonnement pour avoir contribué à tuer huit cent quarante-six prisonniers britanniques délibérément coincés au fond de la cale. Les artilleurs du Middlesex, Peter Young et Dick Baxter, faisaient partie des victimes.

Même sans le témoignage de mon père, le commandant et l'officier sanitaire des camps de prisonniers à Hong Kong furent déclarés coupables d'« atteinte grave à la vie humaine ». Ils furent tous deux condamnés à la pendaison. Condamnation ultérieurement commuée en une peine de vingt ans d'emprisonnement.

L'interprète du camp de Sham Shui Po, ce citoyen canadien né et élevé à Kamloops en Colombie-Britannique, ne bénéficia pas de pareille indulgence. Le sergent – le nom de son père est gravé sur le monument aux morts du Stanley Park à Vancouver qui rend hommage aux milliers de nippo-canadiens qui se sont battus pour le Canada durant les deux guerres mondiales – fut reconnu coupable de haute trahison le 21 avril 1947. Il fut pendu trois jours plus tard.

Le garde du camp connu sous le nom de Satan ne fut jamais traduit en justice. Le lendemain de la reddition du Japon, son corps, roué de coups et tout boursouflé, fut rejeté sur les laisses de vase en dessous du camp. « La guerre ne laisse aucune âme sans tache », aurait commenté mon père.

Papa ne s'est jamais remarié. Kipper et lui vivent toujours dans notre vieille maison de Barclay Street. Il y a bien longtemps, ils ont construit à l'arrière un atelier. Ils y passent des heures ensemble, Kipper avec ses tableaux et papa qui s'occupe des cadres.

Mon frère Frankie m'a souvent accusée de raffoler des fins heureuses. Et je dois avouer qu'il fut un temps où je fantasmais sur l'idée de mon père tombant amoureux de l'amie de ma mère, Dora Fenwick. Mais, quand j'avais quinze ans, Mme Fenwick a épousé un homme qui travaillait à la compagnie des téléphones.

Ensuite, je me suis imaginé qu'un jour il épouserait Shun-qin qu'il voyait régulièrement. Mais ils n'ont jamais été autre chose que de bons amis. Comme Danny Fenwick et moi. Après les événements de l'été, Danny est redevenu mon meilleur copain. Il fut aussi le premier garçon que j'aie jamais embrassé. Mais, au lycée, nous nous sommes rendu, compte que nous n'avions nulle envie de gâcher une amitié parfaite en sortant ensemble. Danny est parti vivre à Calgary, dans l'Alberta, peu de temps après que nous avons obtenu nos diplômes. Tous les ans, à Noël, je reçois une carte signée de sa femme et lui.

Frankie a fini par entrer à l'université, il est devenu professeur et il s'est marié. Mieux vaut tard que jamais, d'après tante Mildred.

Il y a bien des années de cela, notre père a fait la paix avec elle. Comme nous tous, d'ailleurs. Les événements de l'été l'ont changée. Elle a pris papa au mot : elle est devenue partie intégrante de ce « nous » qui constitue la famille. C'est elle qui a trouvé les gouvernantes indispensables tant que nous étions encore enfants et elle proposait souvent de venir elle-même s'occuper de nous lorsque papa était obligé de faire des heures supplémentaires. La première fois qu'elle nous a invités à dormir chez elle, Kipper et moi, j'étais mal à l'aise et j'ai accepté à contrecœur. Mais, en entrant dans le salon, quand j'ai vu le tableau que Kipper leur avait donné, à oncle Sidney et à elle, accroché au-dessus de la cheminée, j'ai compris que tout se passerait comme sur des roulettes. La peinture représentant la petite maison rouge – où Kipper affirmait qu'il avait parlé à maman – était tellement décalée dans cette pièce à la décoration formelle que, même à moi, il paraissait bizarre. Aujourd'hui, il est toujours au même endroit.

Quand tante Mildred s'est mise à passer du temps avec Kipper, elle s'est acharnée à apprendre tout ce qu'elle pouvait sur la trisomie 21, exactement comme l'avait fait maman. Lentement, elle a pris conscience que, loin d'être une calamité, c'était tout un pan de la personnalité de Kipper. Je jure que le visage de ma tante s'adoucit quand elle le voit. Et, de temps à autre, en un éclair, je reconnais le regard de maman dans ses yeux verts.

Depuis des années maintenant, à chaque week-end ensoleillé, papa et Kipper installent les dernières toiles de mon frère sur le marché en plein air du Stanley Park.

C'est là où je suis aujourd'hui. Assise en tailleur sur ma couverture, à quelques pas du monument aux morts nippo-canadien, je referme mon carnet. Un peu plus haut, Lily s'allonge dans les bras de Frankie pour regarder leur fils aux cheveux d'ébène jouer au ballon avec son oncle Kipper. Oui, c'est bien cela, Frankie et Lily sont tombés amoureux l'un de l'autre et se sont mariés. Il ne peut pas me reprocher cette fin romanesque. Ou peut-être que si. Ça m'est bien égal. Depuis qu'ils se connaissent, Frankie affirme que c'était une rencontre inévitable. Finalement, Lily, qui est maintenant pharmacienne, est entrée dans notre famille. Rien n'aurait pu rendre mon père plus heureux.

Installé dans une chaise longue, il bavarde avec mon mari et oncle Sidney tout en surveillant les éventuels acheteurs qui s'intéressent aux tableaux de Kipper. Je jette un coup d'œil à mon frère.

Kipper ne tient plus le rythme. Son cœur le trahit. Le souffle court, il tend la balle à son neveu.

— Il faut que je repose mon cœur maintenant, dit-il au petit Gordy en se dirigeant vers ma couverture.

Perchée sur les genoux de tante Mildred, ma fille l'observe tandis que, lentement, il se laisse tomber à côté de moi. Elle fronce les sourcils, inquiète.

— Pourquoi oncle Kipper doit-il reposer son cœur ? demande-t-elle.

— Eh bien, mon trésor, répond tante Mildred en lissant une boucle cuivrée sur le front sérieux de Lucille, c'est parce que son cœur est plus gros que celui des autres gens.

Kipper lui fait un grand sourire.

— Tante Mildred, s'exclame-t-il, ça, c'est pure vantardise !

En octobre 1945, les survivants de la C Force du Canada finirent par rentrer chez eux. Quatre ans plus tôt, neuf mille neuf cent soixante-dix-neuf Royal Rifles et Winnipeg Grenadiers, jeunes et enthousiastes, avaient quitté le port de Vancouver pour répondre à la requête de la Grande-Bretagne qui souhaitait renforcer la garnison de Hong Kong. Sur les cinq cent cinquante-sept qui n'en revinrent pas, deux cent quatre-vingt-neuf moururent durant les dix-huit jours que dura la bataille de Hong Kong. Les deux cent soixante-huit autres périrent dans les camps de prisonniers, à Hong Kong et au Japon.

Manquant de matériel et peut-être d'entraînement – mais pas de courage –, ces fantassins, tous volontaires, furent les premiers Canadiens à s'engager dans les combats de la Seconde Guerre mondiale.

Et ils furent les derniers à rentrer chez eux.

Remerciements

Je remercie mon agent, Jane Gregory, mon éditeur, Stephanie Glencross, de Gregory and Company, et Jane Wood de Quercus, pour leurs encouragements, leurs conseils et leur patience durant les relectures de ce texte ainsi que de leur confiance sans faille dans ce projet.

Je tiens à exprimer ma reconnaissance à la Hong Kong Veterans Commemorative Association qui se consacre à maintenir et partager informations et memorabilia de la C Force. Toutes les erreurs sont de mon fait et si j'ai pris des libertés dans le déroulement du temps, des situations ou des dialogues attribués à des personnages historiques, c'est seulement dans l'intérêt du roman.

Cette histoire est une œuvre de fiction. À l'exception des figures historiques, les personnages – y compris le brigadier J. K. Lawson et le lieutenant J. L. R. Sutcliffe – sont également le fruit de mon imagination. Malheureusement, la bataille de Hong Kong de 1941 avec, pour conséquence, l'internement des alliés survivants, n'est pas un effet de mon imagination.

Je souhaite manifester aussi ma profonde reconnaissance à ces vétérans de Hong Kong qui ont, avec tant de générosité, pris le temps de partager leurs souvenirs avec moi : Aubrey Flegg, Dick Wilson, Robert (Flash) Clayton et Jan Solecki. Tous d'authentiques gentlemen, dans les yeux desquels j'ai compris à quel point Dwight D. Eisenhower disait vrai : « Personne ne déteste la guerre plus que le soldat qui l'a vécue, qui a vu sa brutalité, son inutilité, sa bêtise. »

COMPOSITION PCA – 44400 REZÉ

CET OUVRAGE A ÉTÉ IMPRIMÉ EN FRANCE
PAR CPI BUSSIÈRE
À SAINT-AMAND-MONTROND (CHER)
EN JANVIER 2013

JC Lattès s'engage pour
l'environnement en réduisant
l'empreinte carbone de ses livres.
Celle de cet exemplaire est de :
1 kg éq. CO_2
PAPIER À BASE DE   Rendez-vous sur
FIBRES CERTIFIÉES   www.jclattes-durable.fr

N° d'édition : 01. – N° d'impression : 124706/4.
Dépôt légal : février 2013.